THIRD CANADIAN EDITION

basic statistics
for business & economics

Douglas A. Lind
Coastal Carolina University and The University of Toledo

William G. Marchal
The University of Toledo

Samuel A. Wathen
Coastal Carolina University

Carol Ann Waite
Sheridan Institute of Technology and Advanced Learning

McGraw-Hill Ryerson

Toronto Montréal Boston Burr Ridge, IL Dubuque, IA Madison, WI New York
San Francisco St. Louis Bangkok Bogotá Caracas Kuala Lumpur Lisbon London
Madrid Mexico City Milan New Delhi Santiago Seoul Singapore Sydney Taipei

The McGraw·Hill Companies

McGraw-Hill Ryerson

Basic Statistics for Business & Economics
Third Canadian Edition

ISBN-13: 978-0-07-098035-8
ISBN-10: 0-07-098035-7

5 6 7 8 9 DOW 1 9 8 7 6 5 4 3 2 1

Printed and bound in the United States of America.

Vice President and Editor-in-Chief: Joanna Cotton
Sponsoring Editor: Kimberley Redhead
Executive Marketing Manager: Joy Armitage Taylor
Managing Editor, Development: Kelly Dickson
Developmental Editors: Sarah Fulton, Kara Stahl, Arlene Bautista
Editorial Associate: Stephanie Hess
Senior Supervising Editor: Joanne Limebeer
Copy Editor: Joe D'Agostino
Production Coordinator: Lena Mastromarco
Cover Design: Liz Harasymczuk
Cover Image: © Corbis Premium RF/Alamy
Interior Design: Liz Harasymczuk
Composition: SR Nova Pvt Ltd, Bangalore, India
Printer: RR Donnelley

Library and Archives Canada Cataloguing in Publication Data

Basic statistics for business & economics / Douglas A. Lind ... [et al.]. – 3rd Canadian ed.
Includes index.

ISBN 978-0-07-098035-8

1. Industrial management–Statistical methods–Textbooks. 2. Commercial statistics–Textbooks.
I. Lind, Douglas A. II. Title: Basic statistics for business and economics.

HA29.B38 2009 519.502'465 C2008-905427-X

Brief Contents

Available in PDF format on the Student CD-ROM:

Contents

Available in PDF format on the Student CD-ROM:

Preface

Welcome to the Third Canadian Edition of *Basic Statistics for Business and Economics*! As the name implies, the objective of this textbook is to provide Canadian business students majoring in economics, finance, marketing, accounting, management, and other fields of business administration with an introductory survey of the many business applications of descriptive and inferential statistics.

Today's business environment requires people skilled to deal with numerical information from an increasingly wide variety of sources. We need to be critical consumers of the information presented by others, and we need to be able to reduce large amounts of data into meaningful formats, so that we can make effective interpretations, judgments, and decisions. *Basic Statistics for Business and Economics* introduces students to these business applications, while maintaining a student-oriented learning environment. Examples and problems are designed to teach the basics while remaining relevant to the real world.

FEATURES OF THE THIRD CANADIAN EDITION

The Third Canadian Edition makes every effort to support student learning. We present the concepts clearly for students, and we support these concepts immediately with examples and exercises.

A Canadian Perspective

Feedback from reviewers had one common theme—that more Canadian content was needed. You will notice a change almost immediately in that the example used throughout chapters two and three (and referred to in later chapters) has been changed to real estate data from Edmonton and the surrounding areas. We have also added and updated several Canadian data sets, such as:

- house prices in major cities across Canada
- salaries of Canadian men and women
- the Consumer Price Index (CPI)

Furthermore, many explanations have been edited for clarity, and more examples and end of chapter exercises have been added to this new edition.

Emphasis on Interpretation of Statistical Results

In response to market feedback, we have placed more emphasis on the interpretation of the statistical results.

Emphasis on Microsoft® Excel®/MegaStat®

Microsoft Excel is widely used in business settings and we have thoroughly integrated the usage of this package throughout the text. Input, intermediate, and output steps are presented visually and are accompanied by step-by-step instructions for students to facilitate use. This will enable instructors to focus on teaching concepts and techniques rather than spending time explaining the usage of the computer software to students. **Microsoft Excel** does contain a number of statistical techniques, but is enhanced by a separately written software package called MegaStat®. Created by J. B. Orriss of Butler University, MegaStat® adds to the functionality of Excel for statistical techniques not covered by Excel. MegaStat® Version 10.2

is available on the CD-ROM packaged with this book. Help files are built in and an introductory manual is also included on the Student CD-ROM that accompanies the text.

Learning Goals and Introduction

Each chapter begins with a set of learning goals designed to provide a focus for the chapter and motivate learning. These goals indicate what students should be able to do after completing the chapter. Students can locate learning goals in the margin where they occur in the text. In addition, each chapter opens with an introduction that reviews the important concepts of the previous chapter(s) and describes how these concepts will apply to those of the current chapter.

Statistics in Action

Each chapter contains a number of Statistics in Action articles. These articles provide unique and interesting applications and historical insights into the field of statistics.

Statistics in Action

The heights of adults approximate a normal distribution, but those individuals who are very tall can cause design problems. For example, Shaquille O'Neal, a professional basketball player with the Los Angeles Lakers, is 216 cm tall. The height of the standard doorway is 203 cm, so Shaquille and many other NBA players duck to get into most rooms.

As another example, the driver's seat in most vehicles is set to comfortably fit a person who is at least 159 cm tall. The distribution of heights of adult women is approximately a normal distribution with a mean of 161.5 cm and a standard deviation of 6.3 cm. Thus about 35 percent of adult women will not fit comfortably in the driver's seat.

Example and Solution

After important concepts are introduced, we provide a straightforward, student-oriented example, including a full solution. Examples with solutions are a key learning tool as they serve two purposes. First, they provide a "how to" illustration. Second, they show a relevant business or economics application that helps answer the question—"what will I use this for?" All examples attempt to strike the appropriate balance, providing a realistic scenario or application, but also making the size and scale of the math reasonable for introductory students.

example

The weekly incomes of shift supervisors in the glass industry are normally distributed with a mean of \$1000 and a standard deviation of \$100. What is the z-value for the income X of a supervisor who earns \$1100 per week? For a supervisor who earns \$900 per week?

solution

Using formula (6–1), the z-values for the two X values (\$1100 and \$900) are:

For $X = \$1100$:

$$z = \frac{X - \mu}{\sigma} = \frac{\$1100 - \$1000}{\$100} = 1.00$$

For $X = \$900$:

$$z = \frac{X - \mu}{\sigma} = \frac{\$900 - \$1000}{\$100} = -1.00$$

The z of 1.00 indicates that a weekly income of \$1100 is 1 standard deviation above the mean, and a z of -1.00 shows that a \$900 income is 1 standard deviation below the mean. Note that both incomes (\$1100 and \$900) are the same distance (\$100) from the mean.

Microsoft® Excel® Screen Captures

Computer examples and commands using **Excel** spreadsheets, including the use of MegaStat®, can be found throughout the text in a clear, readable format. Over 70 screen captures are highlighted with an **Excel** icon in the margin, and provide immediate visuals of the concepts being presented, as well as instructions on how to achieve the results. Computer examples using MINITAB are available on the CD-ROM that accompanies the text, and correspond to the MINITAB icons found in the chapters.

MegaStat was used to develop the following chart. The commands follow.

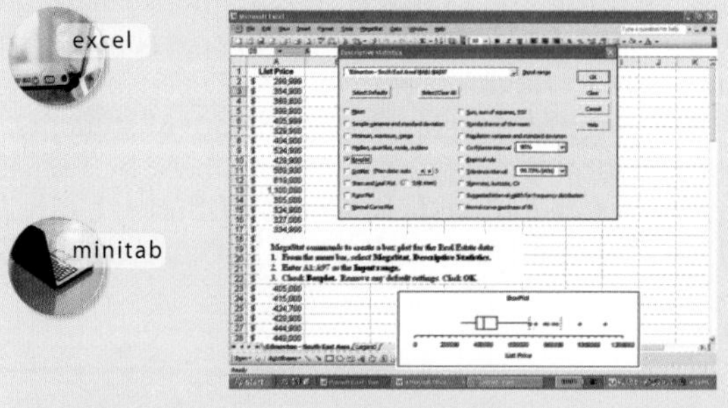

Self-Review

Self-Reviews are interspersed throughout the chapter and are closely patterned after the preceding examples. These reviews help students monitor their progress, and provide immediate reinforcement for the particular techniques illustrated in the examples. The worked-out solutions are provided at the end of each chapter.

self-review 2–2

The commissions earned, in dollars, for the first quarter of last year by the 11 members of the sales staff at Master Chemical Company are:

\$1650	1475	1510	1670	1595	1760	1540	1495	1590	1625	1510

(a) What are the values such as \$1650 and \$1475 called?
(b) Using \$1400 up to \$1500 as the first class, \$1500 up to \$1600 as the second class, and so forth, organize the quarterly commissions into a frequency distribution.
(c) What are the numbers in the right column of your frequency distribution called?
(d) Describe the distribution of quarterly commissions, based on the frequency distribution. What is the largest amount of commission earned? What is the smallest? What is the typical amount earned?

Exercises

Exercises can be found within the chapter and in the end-of-chapter material. Generally, the end-of-chapter exercises are the most challenging and integrative of the chapter concepts. The answers for all odd-numbered exercises appear at the end of the text. For exercises with more than 10 observations, the data can be found on the CD-ROM included with the text. These files are in two formats: **Excel** and MINITAB.

Exercises

65. Determine the median and the values corresponding to the first and third quartiles in the following data.

46	47	49	49	51	53	54	54	55	55	59

66. Determine the median and the values corresponding to the first and third quartiles in the following data.

5.24	6.02	6.67	7.30	7.59	7.99	8.03	8.35	8.81	9.45
9.61	10.37	10.39	11.86	12.22	12.71	13.07	13.59	13.89	15.42

The Standard Normal Distribution

The number of normal distributions is unlimited, each having a different mean (μ), standard deviation (σ), or both. While it is possible to provide probability tables for discrete distributions such as the binomial and the Poisson, providing tables for the infinite number of normal distributions is impossible. Fortunately, one member of the family can be used to determine the probabilities for all normal distributions. It is called the **standard normal distribution**, and it is unique because it has a mean of 0 and a standard deviation of 1.

Any normal distribution can be converted into a *standard normal distribution* by subtracting the mean from each observation and dividing this difference by the standard deviation. The results are called z-values or z scores.

2 **Define and calculate z-values.**

z-value The signed distance between a selected value, designated X, and the mean, μ, divided by the standard deviation, σ.

So, a z-value is the distance from the mean, measured in units of the standard deviation. In terms of a formula:

STANDARD NORMAL VALUE $$z = \frac{X - \mu}{\sigma} \quad [6\text{–}1]$$

where:

X is the value of any particular observation or measurement.
μ is the mean of the distribution.
σ is the standard deviation of the distribution.

Definitions

Definitions of new terms or terms unique to the study of statistics are set apart from the text and highlighted for easy reference and review.

Margin Notes

There are more than 200 concise notes in the margin. Each is aimed at re-emphasizing the key concepts presented immediately adjacent to it.

Formulas

Formulas used for the first time are boxed and numbered for reference. New to the third edition is a formula tearout sheet—a great learning aid for students. In addition, these key formulas are listed on the text's accompanying CD-ROM and on the Online Learning Centre.

Chapter Summary

As a summary, each chapter concludes with a Chapter Summary. This learning aid provides the opportunity to review material, and summarizes the learning goals.

Chapter Summary

I. The normal distribution is a continuous probability distribution with the following characteristics.
   A. It is bell-shaped and the mean, median, and mode are equal.
   B. It is symmetrical.
   C. It is asymptotic, meaning the curve approaches but never touches the X-axis.
   D. It is completely described by the mean and standard deviation.
   E. There is a family of normal distributions. Each time the mean or standard deviation changes, a new distribution is created.
   F. The area under a normal curve expresses the probability of an outcome.

II. The standard normal distribution is a particular normal distribution.
   A. It has a mean of 0 and a standard deviation of 1.
   B. Any normal distribution can be converted to the standard normal distribution by the following formula.

$$z = \frac{X - \mu}{\sigma} \quad [6\text{–}1]$$

   C. By standardizing a normal distribution, we can report the distance from the mean in units of the standard deviation.

Pronunciation Key

This tool lists mathematical symbols, their meanings, and how to pronounce them. This learning tool helps students retain the meanings of the symbols and generally enhance course communications.

Pronunciation Key

SYMBOL	MEANING	PRONUNCIATION
$P(A)$	Probability of A	P of A
$P(\sim A)$	Probability of not A	P of not A
$P(A$ and $B)$	Probability of A and B	P of A and B
$P(A$ or $B)$	Probability of A or B	P of A or B
$P(A \mid B)$	Probability of A given B has happened	P of A given B
${}_nP_r$	Permutation of n items selected r at a time	Pnr
${}_nC_r$	Combination of n items selected r at a time	Cnr
$n!$	Product of all positive integers $\leq n$	n factorial
$r!$	Product of all objects selected $\leq r$	r factorial

Data Set Exercises

The last several exercises at the end of each chapter are based on four large data sets. A complete listing of all the data sets used is available on the inside front cover of this text.

These data sets are included in Appendices I through Y on the CD-ROM packaged with the text. They present real-world applications of statistics and more complex applications of the concepts.

Data Set Exercises

14. Refer to the Home Listings Edmonton South-East Area, on the CD-ROM, which reports information on listed homes for January 2008. Consider the variables list price, style, number of rooms, number of bedrooms, full baths, half baths, and total square feet.
    a. Which of the variables are qualitative and which are quantitative?
    b. Determine the level of measurement for each of the variables.
15. Refer to the Employment Insurance Benefits data, which report the average weekly amount received by type of benefit. Consider the variables type and dollars (amount).
    a. Which of these variables are quantitative and which are qualitative?
    b. Determine the level of measurement for each of the variables.
16. Refer to the Average Earnings by Sex and Work Pattern data, which reports information on the average salary earned by men and women in Canada. The variables are year, women, men, and earnings ratio (%).
    a. Which of the four variables are qualitative and which are quantitative?
    b. Determine the level of measurement for each variable.

LYRYX INTERACTIVE BUSINESS STATISTICS (LABS)

LYRYX LEARNING INC
Online Learning and Assessment
lyryx.com

Based on *Basic Statistics for Business and Economics by Lind, Marchal, Wathen and Waite*, Lyryx Interactive *Business Statistics* is a leading-edge online assessment system, designed to support both students and instructors. The assessment takes the form of a homework assignment called a *lab*. The assessments are algorithmically generated and automatically graded so that students get instant grades and feedback. New labs are randomly generated each time, providing the student with unlimited opportunities to try each type of question. After they submit a lab for marking, students receive extensive feedback on their work, thus promoting their learning experience.

For the Instructors: The goal of the product is for instructors to use these labs for course marks instead of creating and marking their own labs, saving instructors and teaching assistants valuable time to instead help students directly. After registering their courses with us, instructors can create labs of their choice by selecting problems from our bank of questions and setting a deadline for each one of these labs. The content, marking, and feedback of the problems has been developed and implemented with the help of experienced instructors in business statistics. Instructors have access to all their students' marks and can view their best labs. At any time, the instructors can download the class grades for their own programs.

For the Student: LABS offers algorithmically generated and automatically graded assignments. Students get instant grades and instant feedback—no need to wait until the next class to find out how well they did! Grades are instantly recorded in a grade book that the students can view.

Students are motivated to do their labs for two reasons: first, because the labs can be tied to assessment, and second, because they can try the labs as many times as they wish prior to the due date with only their best grade being recorded.

Instructors know from experience that if students are doing their business statistics homework, they will be successful in the course. Recent research regarding the use of Lyryx has shown that when labs are tied to assessment, even if worth only a small percentage of the total grade for the course, students WILL do their homework—and MORE THAN ONCE!!

Visit http://www.lyryx.com

INSTRUCTOR SUPPLEMENTS

Instructor's Online Learning Centre

Online LearningCentre

The Online Learning Centre at http://www.mcgrawhill.ca/olc/lind includes a password-protected Web site for instructors. The site offers downloadable supplements and customizable teaching aids.

Content cartridges are also available for course management systems, such as WebCT and Blackboard, to expand the reach of your course and open up distance-learning options.

WebCT

Instructor Resources Include:

Instructor's Solutions Manual
This manual contains the complete solutions to all exercises.

Downloadable Computerized Test Bank
This electronic test-generating engine is stocked with true/false, multiple choice, and short answer questions; generating quizzes and tests is as easy as clicking a mouse. The Computerized Test Bank, prepared by Colleen Quinn of Seneca College, contains the answers to all questions, along with a difficulty rating and the learning goal each question supports. For secure online testing, exams can be exported to WebCT

Wimba
people teach people

or Blackboard. This test bank is available on the Lind Online Learning Centre at www.mcgrawhill.ca/olc/lind.

Microsoft® PowerPoint® Lecture Slides
Prepared by Jean-Paul Olivier of Red River College, these full-colour slides include chapter objectives, definitions of key terms, graphics, and additional examples. Instructors can use them to enhance their lectures or add additional material of their own.

*i*Learning Sales Specialist

Your *Integrated*-Learning Sales Specialist is a McGraw-Hill Ryerson representative who has the experience, product knowledge, training, and support to help you assess and integrate any of the below-noted products, technology and services into your course for optimum teaching and learning performance. Whether it's how to use our test bank software, helping your students improve their grades, or how to put your entire course online, your *i*Learning Sales Specialist is there to help. Contact your local *i*Learning Sales Specialist today to learn how to maximize all McGraw-Hill Ryerson resources!

*i*Learning Services Program

McGraw-Hill Ryerson offers a unique services package designed for Canadian faculty. This includes technical support, access to our educational technology conferences, and custom e-courses to name just a few. Please speak to your local *i*Learning Sales Specialist for details.

STUDENT SUPPLEMENTS

Student Online Learning Centre

The Student Online Learning Centre, prepared by Joe Ilsever, Ph.D., of Douglas College, is available at www.mcgrawhill.ca/olc/lind and offers the following materials:

Additional content including additional chapters, Chapter Summaries, Multiple Choice Quizzes, Key Terms and Formulas and a User's Guide for MegaStat®.

*i*Study

In partnership with Youthography, a Canadian youth research company, and hundreds of students from across Canada, McGraw-Hill Ryerson conducted extensive student research on student study habits, behaviours, and attitudes—we asked questions and listened . . . and we heard some things we didn't expect. We had two goals: to help faculty be more efficient in and out of the classroom by providing a study tool that would help them improve student engagement and to help students learn their course material and get better grades. Through this research, we gained a better understanding of how students study—and how we could make vast improvements to our current online study tools. The result is a study tool that students overwhelming said is *better* and there's *nothing else like it out there*. *i*Study really is the first study tool built by students for students. Getting better grades really is only a click away!

***i*Study Business Statistics:** www.mcgrawhill.ca/olc/lind. This innovative online study space helps students master the concepts with all of the learning tools they've come to expect, including multiple-choice and true/false quizzes and chapter-by-chapter learning goals, plus statistics interactivities and pre- and post-diagnostic assessments that point them to the concepts they need to focus on to improve their grades. Students can choose from all of these features to create their own personalized study plan—*i*Study offers the best, most convenient way to Learn, Interact, and Succeed!

Study Plan
An innovative tool that helps students customize their own learning experience. Students can diagnose their knowledge with pre and post test, identify the areas where they

are weak, search contents of the entire learning package for content specific to the topic they're studying and add these resources to their study plan. Students told us the act of creating a study plan is how they actually study and that having the opportunity to have everything in one place, with the ability to search, customize, and prioritize the class resources, was critical. No other publisher provides this type of tool and students told us without a doubt, the "Study Plan" feature is the most valuable tool they have used to help them study.

eText

Now students can search the textbook online, too! When struggling with a concept or reviewing for an exam, students can conduct key word searches to quickly find the content they need.

Homework Assessment

*i*Study assessment activities don't stop with students. There is material for instructors to leverage as well. For Business Statistics, this includes quizzes you can use in class, assign as homework, or add to exams.

Student CD-ROM

Every new copy of *Basic Statistics for Business and Economics*, Third Canadian Edition, includes a CD-ROM that features three additional chapters on Index Numbers, Time Series and Forecasting, and An Introduction to Decision Theory. Also included are data files (in Excel and MINITAB formats) for the large data sets and exercises, electronic tutorials, Web exercises, MINITAB examples and computer commands, and answers to odd-numbered exercises for Data Set Exercises.

MegaStat for Excel® by J. B. Orriss of Butler University is also included on the CD-ROM. **MegaStat® Version 10.2**, an Excel add-in, includes new routines for nonparametrics, time series, regression modeling, control charts, and box plots. Help files are built in and an introductory manual is also included on the CD.

Also included free on the student CD-ROM is **Visual Statistics 2.23**, by Doane, Mathieson, and Tracy. This package of 21 software programs and hundreds of data files and examples is designed for teaching and learning basic statistics. The modules of Visual Statistics provide an interactive, highly graphical, experimental format in which to explore statistics. The software and worktext promote active learning through competency building exercises, individual and team projects, and built-in databases. Over 400 data sets from business setting are included within the package, and the Visual Statistics CD includes the worktext in electronic files.

Primis Online

Primis Online gives you access to our resources in the best medium for your students: printed textbooks or electronic e-books. There are more than 350,000 pages of content available from which you can create customized learning tools from our online database at www.mhhe.com/primis.

CourseSmart

CourseSmart brings together thousands of textbooks across hundreds of courses in an eTextbook format, providing unique benefits to students and faculty. By purchasing an eTextbook, students can save up to 50 percent off the cost of a print textbook; reduce their impact on the environment; and gain access to powerful Web tools for learning, including full text search, notes and highlighting, and e-mail tools for sharing notes between classmates. For faculty, CourseSmart provides instant access to review and compare textbooks and course materials in their discipline area without the time, cost, and environmental impact of mailing print examination copies. For further details contact your *i*Learning Sales Specialist or go to www.coursesmart.com.

ACKNOWLEDGEMENTS

Comments and suggestions have been invaluable to the development of the Third Canadian Edition were provided by a variety of reviewers, and a debt of gratitude is owed to the following educators:

Joe Campeau	*Canadore College*
Eva Dabrowski	*Seneca College*
Ajit Dayanandan	*University of Northern British Columbia*
Bruno Fullone	*George Brown College*
Paul Hobson	*Acadia University*
Muhammed Nurul Islam	*Concordia University*
Dennis Kira	*Concordia University*
Gerry Kowalchuk	*Lethbridge College*
Rick Law	*Humber College*
Carol Leppinen	*Conestoga College*
Lisa MacKay	*Southern Alberta Institute of Technology*
Don St. Jean	*George Brown College*
George Stroppa	*Douglas College*
Lourdes Zubieta	*Bishops University*
Edmund Zuke	*Red River College*

Thanks also to those who reviewed the Second Canadian Edition:

Aphy Artopoulo	*Seneca College*
Felix Ernst	*Camosun College*
Bruno Fullone	*George Brown College*
Paul Hobson	*Acadia University*
Harriette Huang	*Algonquin College*
Chris Kellman	*British Columbia Institute of Technology*
Anshuman Khare	*Athabasca University*
Thambyrajah Kugathasan	*Seneca College*
Carol Leppinen	*Conestoga College*
Susan Vallery	*Sir Sanford Fleming College*
Victor Yu	*University of Toronto*
Edmund Zuke	*Red River College*

A special thank you must be given to Bruno Fullone of George Brown College for his meticulous and thorough work as the Technical Reviewer for the text and the solutions.

I also wish to thank the staff at McGraw-Hill Ryerson. This includes: Joanna Cotton, Vice President and Editor-in-Chief; Kimberley Redhead, Sponsoring Editor; Kelly Dickson, Managing Editor, Development; Sarah Fulton, Kara Stahl, Arlene Bautista, Developmental Editors; Joy Armitage Taylor, Senior Marketing Manager; Liz Harasymczuk, Interior Design; Joe D'Agostino, Copy Editor; and others who I do not know personally, but who made important contributions.

Carol Ann Waite

chapter 1

What Is Statistics?

LEARNING GOALS

When you have completed this chapter, you will be able to:

1. Understand why we study statistics.
2. Explain what is meant by *descriptive statistics* and *inferential statistics.*
3. Distinguish between a *qualitative variable* and a *quantitative variable.*
4. Distinguish between a *discrete variable* and a *continuous variable.*
5. Distinguish among the *nominal, ordinal, interval,* and *ratio* levels of measurement.
6. Define the terms *mutually exclusive* and *exhaustive.*

Introduction

More than 100 years ago H. G. Wells, an English author and historian, suggested that one day quantitative reasoning will be as necessary for effective citizenship as the ability to read. He made no mention of business because the Industrial Revolution was just beginning.

Mr. Wells could not have been more correct. While "business experience," some "thoughtful guesswork," and "intuition" are key attributes of successful managers, today's business problems tend to be too complex for this type of decision making alone. One of the tools used to make decisions is statistics. Statistics is used not only by businesspeople, but we also apply statistical concepts in our lives. For example, to start the day you turn on the shower and let it run for a few moments. Then you put your hand in the shower to sample the temperature and decide if you need to add more hot or cold water before you enter the shower. Then, later in the day, you are at the grocery store and want to buy a frozen pizza. One of the pizza makers has a stand, and has samples of his or her product for you to try. After sampling the pizza, you decide whether to buy that pizza or not. In both the shower and the pizza examples, you make a decision and select a course of action based on a sample.

Businesses face similar situations. The Kellogg Company must ensure that the mean amount of Raisin Bran in the 375g box meets label specifications. To do so, it might set a "target" weight somewhat higher than the amount specified on the label. Each box is then weighed after it is filled. The weighing machine reports a distribution of the content weights for each hour as well as the number "kicked-out" for being under the label specification during the hour. The Quality Control Department also randomly selects samples from the production line and checks the quality of the product and the weight of the product in the box. If the mean product weight differs significantly from the target weight or the percent of kick-outs is too large, the process is adjusted.

As a student of business or economics, you will need basic knowledge and skills to organize, analyze, and edit data in order to present the information. In this text, we will show you basic statistical techniques and methods that will develop your ability to make informed personal and business decisions.

1 Understand why we study statistics.

Why Study Statistics?

Examples of why we study statistics

If you look through any college or university catalogue, you will find that statistics is required for many programs. Why is this so? What are the differences in the statistics courses taught for engineering, psychology, sociology, or the arts and that taught for business? The biggest difference is the examples used. The course content is basically the same. In business we are interested in such things as profits, hours worked, and wages. In psychology they are interested in test scores, and in engineering they may be interested in how many units are manufactured on a particular machine. However, all three are interested in what is a typical value and how much variation there is in the data. There may also be a difference in the level of mathematics required. An engineering statistics course usually requires calculus. Statistics courses for business usually teach the course at a more applied level.

So why is statistics required in so many majors? The first reason is that numerical information is everywhere. Look in the newspapers (*National Post*), news magazines (*Time*, *Newsweek*, *Maclean's*), business magazines (*BusinessWeek*, *Forbes*), or general interest magazines (*People*), women's magazines (*Chatelaine*) or sports magazines (*Sports Illustrated*, *ESPN The Magazine*), or the Internet, and you will be bombarded with numerical information.

Here are some examples:

- In 2006, the average Canadian woman earned \$27 700 and the average Canadian man earned \$42 900.

Average Earnings by Sex and Work Pattern

Year	Women	Men	Earnings Ratio (%)
1993	\$22 300	\$34 700	64.3%
1994	22 500	36 200	62.2
1995	23 000	35 400	65.0
1996	22 700	35 300	64.3
1997	24 300	39 300	61.9
1998	25 400	40 400	62.8
1999	25 800	41 200	62.6
2000	26 300	42 500	61.7
2001	26 400	42 400	62.1
2002	26 700	42 500	62.8
2003	26 400	41 900	62.9
2004	26 700	42 100	63.4
2005	27 300	42 700	64.0
2006	27 700	42 900	64.7

Source: Statistics Canada, http://www40.statcan.ca/l01/cst01/labor01.htm, August 5, 2008.

- Based on information collected by Statistics Canada, the most popular sport in Canada is golf (7.4 percent) and the least popular sport is racquetball (0.2 percent); the most popular sport for Canadian men is hockey (ice) at 12 percent and the most popular sport for Canadian women is swimming at 5.6 percent. (Adapted from the Statistics Canada Web site http://www.statcan.ca/english/pgdb/arts16.htm, March 21, 2005.)

Statistics in Action

We want to call your attention to a feature we call *Statistics in Action*. Read each one carefully to get an appreciation of the wide application of statistics in management, economics, nursing, law enforcement, sports, and other disciplines.

- *Canadian Business* publishes an annual list of the richest Canadians. According to the November 30, 2007 issue, the Thomson family, with assets of \$25.35 billion, tops the 2006 list. (www.canadianbusiness.com)
- Canadian companies are ranked according to their after-tax profits in their most recent fiscal year, excluding extraordinary gains or losses, by *The Globe and Mail* (www.globeinvestor.com). The companies listed are the 1000 largest publicly traded corporations measured by assets. At the top of the list for 2007 is Royal Bank of Canada, ranked 2nd last year, followed by Manulife Financial ranked 4th last year.

- The percentage of Canadian smokers aged 15–19 years is 10.3 percent and aged 20–34 is 19.9 percent. Adapted from Statistics Canada, CANSIM Table 105-0427, April 30, 2007.
- In Canada, people drink an average of 1.15 cups of coffee per person per day. People in the United States drink more coffee than in any other country, an average of 1.75 cups per person per day.
- The Fox TV network is considering replacing one of its prime-time crime investigation shows with a new family-oriented comedy show. Before a final decision is made, network executives ask a group of their viewers to watch a pilot of the new show. After viewing the comedy, 63 percent of the group indicated they would watch the new show and suggested replacing the crime investigation show.
- A manufacturing company tests its final product before shipping to customers.Two thousand units were produced last Monday. A sample of 300 of the units was tested and 15 were found to be defective. Given this information, should the company test the entire production line from last Monday before shipping the product to customers?

How are we to determine if the conclusions reported are reasonable? Was the sample large enough? How were the sampled units selected? To be an educated consumer of this information, we need to be able to read the charts and graphs and understand the discussion of the numerical information. An understanding of the concepts of basic statistics will be a big help.

The second reason for taking a statistics course is that statistical techniques are used to make decisions that affect our daily lives. That is, they affect our personal welfare. Here are two examples:

- Insurance companies use statistical analysis to set rates for home, automobile, life, and health insurance. For example, the median age, which divides the population into two groups of equal size, has risen steadily since 1966, reaching 39.5 years in 2006. It is expected that the median age will rise in the future and could exceed 44 years by the year 2031. Also, nearly two out of three persons aged 80 years and over were women, as women have a higher life expectancy than men (82.5 years compared with 77.7 years, in 2004). (Statistics Canada, Census, 2006, Portrait of the Canadian Population in 2006, by Age and Sex: Highlights.) Life insurance premiums are established based on these and other estimates of life expectancy.
- Medical researchers study the cure rates for diseases, based on the use of different drugs and different forms of treatment. For example, what is the effect of treating a certain type of knee injury surgically or with physical therapy? If you take an aspirin each day, does that reduce your risk of a heart attack?

A third reason for taking a statistics course is that the knowledge of statistical methods will help you understand why decisions are made and give you a better understanding of how they affect you.

No matter what line of work you select, you will find yourself faced with decisions where an understanding of data analysis is helpful. In order to make an informed decision, you will need to be able to:

1. Determine whether the existing information is adequate or additional information is required.
2. Gather additional information, if it is needed, in such a way that it does not provide misleading results.
3. Summarize the information in a useful and informative manner.
4. Analyze the available information.
5. Draw conclusions and make inferences while assessing the risk of an incorrect conclusion.

The statistical methods presented in the text will provide you with a framework for the decision-making process.

In summary, there are at least three reasons for studying statistics: (1) data are everywhere, (2) statistical techniques are used to make many decisions that affect our lives, and (3) no matter what your future career, you will make decisions that involve data. An understanding of statistical methods will help you make these decisions more effectively.

What Is Meant by Statistics?

How do we define the word *statistics*? We encounter it frequently in our everyday language. It really has two meanings. In the more common usage, statistics refers to numerical information. Examples include the average starting salary of college graduates, the average number of Fords sold per month at Kistler Ford over the last year, the percentage of undergraduates attending McMaster University who will attend graduate school, the number of deaths due to alcoholism last year, the change in the S&P/TSX Composite Index from yesterday to today, or the number of home runs hit by the Blue Jays during the 2009 season. In these examples statistics are values or percentages. Other examples include:

- Statistics Canada projects the population of Canada to reach 36 to 42 million people by 2031. Canadians of working age (aged 15 to 64) currently represent 70 percent of the population, but this is expected to drop and level off to about 60 percent within the next 20 years. (Statistics Canada, Canada's Population Future, http://www41.statcan.ca/2007/3867/ceb3867_001_e.htm)
- The mean time waiting for technical support is 17 minutes.
- The mean length of the business cycle since 1945 is 61 months.

statistics The science of collecting, organizing, presenting, analyzing, and interpreting data to assist in making more effective decisions.

The above are all examples of **statistics**. A collection of numerical information is called **statistics** (plural).

We often present statistical information in a graphical form. A graph is a visual way to convey information and is often useful for capturing reader attention. For example, Chart 1–1 shows the average house prices in five Canadian cities in July 2007 as compared to the national average (The Canadian Real Estate Association, January 2008; www.crea.ca). It requires only a quick glance to see the differences, the magnitudes of which are emphasized when displayed in a bar graph.

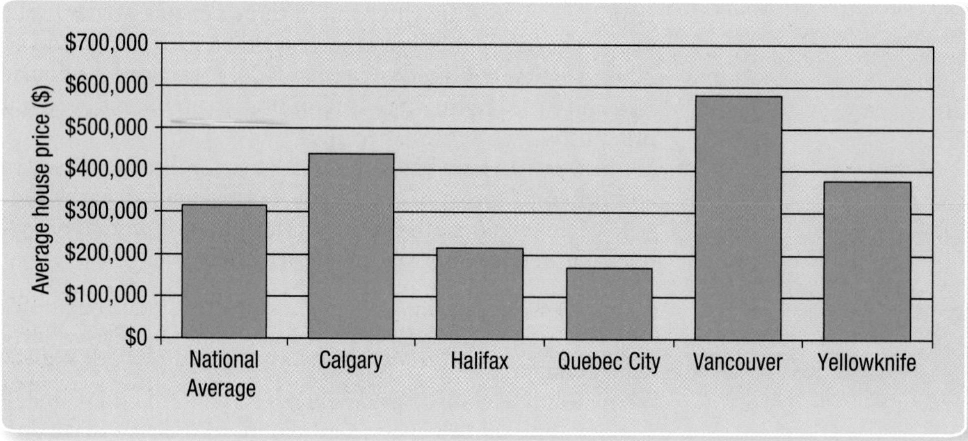

CHART 1–1 Average Canadian House Prices, July 2007

The subject of statistics, as we will explore it in this text, has a much broader meaning than just collecting and publishing numerical information.

As the definition in the margin suggests, the first step in investigating a problem is to collect relevant data. It must be organized in some way and perhaps presented in a chart, such as Chart 1–1. Only after the data have been organized are we then able to analyze and interpret it. Here are some examples of the need for data collection.

- Financial analysts evaluate many facets of a particular stock before making a "buy" or "sell" recommendation. They collect the past sales data of the company and estimate future earnings. Other factors, such as the projected worldwide demand for the company's products, the strength of the competition, and the effect of the new union-management contract, are also considered before making a recommendation.

- The marketing department at Lever Brothers, a manufacturer of soap products, has the responsibility of making recommendations regarding the potential profitability of a newly developed group of face soaps having fruit smells, such as grape, orange, and pineapple. Before making a final decision, the company will test it in several markets. That is, it may advertise and sell it in Vancouver, British Columbia, and Montreal, Quebec. Based on the test marketing in these two regions, Lever Brothers will make a decision whether to market the soaps in the entire country.
- The Canadian government is concerned with the present condition of our economy and with predicting future economic trends. The government conducts a large number of surveys to determine consumer confidence and the outlook of management regarding sales and production for the next 12 months. Indexes, such as the Consumer Price Index, are constructed each month to assess inflation. Information on department store sales, housing starts, money turnover, and industrial production are just a few of the hundreds of items used to form the basis of the projections. These evaluations are used by banks to decide their prime lending rate and by the Bank of Canada to decide the level of control to place on the money supply.
- Management must make decisions on the quality of production. For example, automatic drill presses do not produce a perfect hole that is always 3.3 cm in diameter each time the hole is drilled (because of drill wear, vibration of the machine, and other factors). Slight tolerances are permitted, but when the hole is too small or too large, these products are defective and cannot be used. The Quality Control Department is charged with continually monitoring production by using sampling techniques to ensure that outgoing production meets standards.

2 Explain what is meant by *descriptive statistics* and *inferential statistics.*

Types of Statistics

Descriptive Statistics

descriptive statistics Methods of organizing, summarizing, and presenting data in an informative way.

The study of statistics is usually divided into two categories: descriptive statistics and inferential statistics. The definition of statistics given earlier referred to "organizing, presenting, analyzing . . . data." This facet of statistics is usually referred to as **descriptive statistics**.

For instance, the Canadian government reports the population of Canada was 18 238 000 in 1961, 21 568 000 in 1971, 24 820 000 in 1981, 28 031 000 in 1991, 31 050 700 in 2001 and 31 612 895 in 2006. This information is descriptive statistics. It is descriptive statistics if we calculate the percentage growth from one decade to the next. However, it would **not** be descriptive statistics if we used the data to forecast the population of Canada in the year 2015 or the percentage growth from 2000 to 2015. Why? Because these statistics are not being used to summarize past populations but to estimate future populations.

Masses of unorganized data—such as the census of population, the weekly earnings of hospitality workers, and the individual responses of 2340 registered voters regarding their choice for Prime Minister of Canada—are of little value as is. However, statistical techniques are available to organize this type of data into a meaningful form. Some data can be organized into a **frequency distribution**. (The procedure for doing this is covered in Chapter 2.) Various **charts** may be used to describe data; several basic chart forms are also presented in Chapter 2.

Specific measures of central tendency, such as the mean, describe the central value of a group of numerical data. A number of statistical measures are used to describe how closely the data cluster about an average. These measures of central location and dispersion are discussed in Chapter 3.

Inferential Statistics

inferential statistics The methods used to determine something about a population, based on a sample.

Another aspect of statistics is **inferential statistics**—also called **statistical inference**. Our main concern regarding inferential statistics is finding something about a population based on a sample taken from that population. For example, a recent survey showed only 46 percent of high school students can solve problems involving fractions, decimals, and percentages, and that only 77 percent of high school students could correctly total the cost of a salad, a burger, fries, and a cola on a restaurant menu. Since these are inferences about the population (all high school students) based on sample data, we refer to them as inferential statistics.

You might think of inferential statistics as a "best guess" of a population value based on sample information.

population The entire set of individuals or objects of interest or the measurements obtained from all individuals or objects of interest.

Note the words **population** and *sample* in the definition of inferential statistics. We often make reference to the population living in Canada or the 1.31 billion population of China. However, in statistics the word *population* has a broader meaning. A *population* may consist of *individuals*—such as all the students enrolled at the University of Toronto, all the students in Accounting 201, or all the inmates of Millhaven penitentiary. A population may also consist of *objects*, such as all the Cobra G/T tires produced at Cooper Tire and Rubber Company, the accounts receivable at the end of October for Lorrange Plastics Inc., or auto claims filed in the first quarter of 2009 at the Northeast Regional Office of State Farm Insurance. The *measurement* of interest might be the scores on the first examination of all students in Accounting 201, the tread wear of the Cooper tires, the dollar amount of Lorrange Plastics accounts receivable, or the amount of auto insurance claims at State Farm. Thus, a population in the statistical sense does not always refer to people.

sample A portion, or part, of the population of interest.

To infer something about a population, we usually take a **sample** from the population.

Reasons for sampling

Why take a sample instead of studying every member of the population? A sample of registered voters is necessary because of the prohibitive cost of contacting millions of voters before an election. Testing wheat for moisture content destroys the wheat, thus making a sample imperative. If the wine tasters tested all the wine, none would be available for sale. It would be physically impossible for a few marine biologists to capture and tag all the seals in the ocean. (These and other reasons for sampling are discussed in Chapter 7.)

As noted, taking a sample to learn something about a population is done extensively in business, agriculture, politics, and government, as cited in the following examples:

- Television networks constantly monitor the popularity of their programs by hiring Nielsen and other organizations to sample the preferences of TV viewers. For example, in a sample of 800 prime-time viewers, 560 or 70 percent indicated they watched "*CSI* (*Crime Scene Investigation*)" on CTV last week. These program ratings are used to set advertising rates or to cancel programs.
- An accounting firm is conducting an audit of M Studios. To begin, the accounting firm selects a random sample of 100 invoices (from a population of 2000 invoices), and checks each for accuracy. There is at least one error on five of the invoices; hence the accounting firm estimates that 5 percent of the population of invoices contain at least one error.
- A random sample of 1260 marketing graduates showed their mean starting salary was \$42 694. We therefore estimate the mean starting salary for all marketing graduates to be \$42 694.

The relationship between a sample and a population is portrayed below. For example, we wish to estimate the mean fuel efficiency of SUVs. Six SUVs are selected from the population. The mean fuel efficiency of the six is used to estimate fuel efficiency for the population.

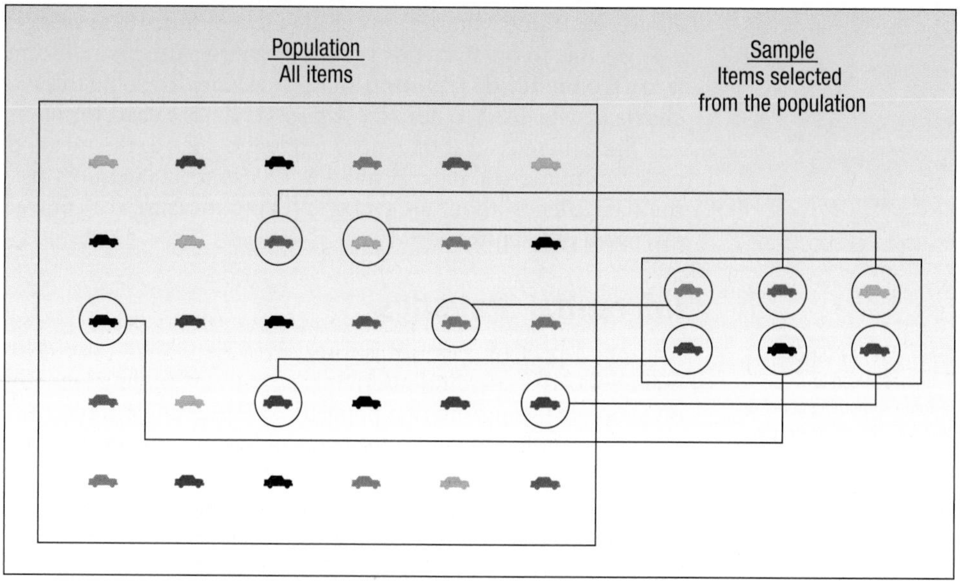

We strongly suggest you do the self-review exercises.

The following is a self-review problem. There are a number of them interspersed throughout each chapter. They test your comprehension of the preceding material. The answer and method of solution are given at the end of the chapter. You can find the answer to the following self-review at the end of the chapter. We recommend that you solve each one and then check your answer.

self-review 1–1

The answers are at the end of the chapter.

Brandon Foods asked a sample of 1960 consumers to try a newly developed frozen fish dinner called Fish Delight. Of the 1960 sampled, 1176 said they would purchase the dinner if it were marketed.

(a) What would Brandon Foods report to its Board of Directors regarding the percentage of acceptance of Fish Delight in the population?
(b) Is this an example of descriptive statistics or inferential statistics? Explain.

3 Distinguish between a *qualitative variable* and a *quantitative variable.*

Types of Variables

There are two basic types of variables: (1) qualitative and (2) quantitative (see Chart 1–2). When the characteristic being studied is non-numeric, it is called a **qualitative variable** or an **attribute**. Examples of qualitative variables are gender, religious affiliation, type of automobile owned, country of birth, and eye colour. When the data are qualitative, we are usually interested in how many or what proportion fall in each category. For example, what percent of the population has blue eyes? How many Catholics and how many Protestants are there in Canada? What percent of the total number of cars sold last month were SUVs? Qualitative data are often summarized in charts and bar graphs (Chapter 2).

Statistics in Action

Where did statistics get its start? In 1662 John Graunt published an article called "Natural and Political Observations Made upon Bills of Mortality." The author's "observations" were the result of his study and analysis of a weekly church publication called "Bill of Mortality," which listed births, christenings, and deaths and their causes. Graunt realized that the Bills of Mortality represented only a fraction of all births and deaths in London. However, he used the data to reach broad conclusions about the impact of disease, such as the plague, on the general population. His logic is an example of statistical inference. His analysis and interpretation of the data are thought to mark the start of statistics.

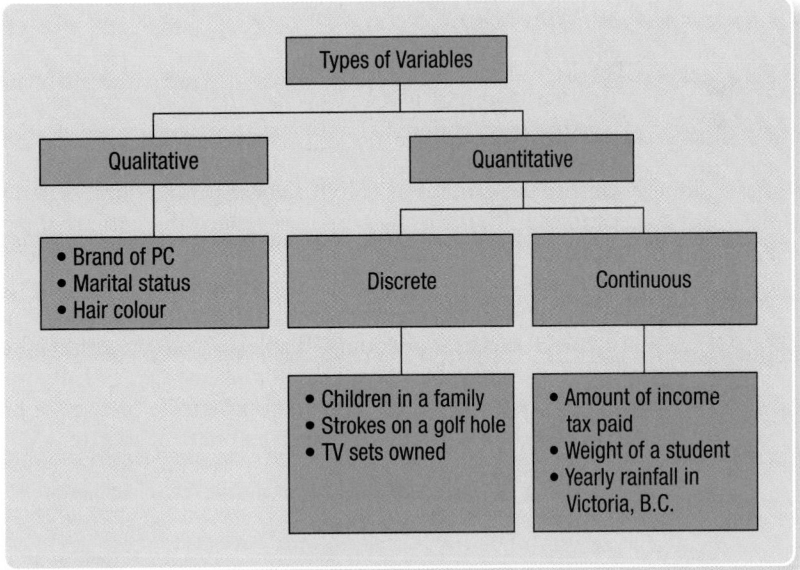

CHART 1–2 Summary of the Types of Variables

When the variable studied can be reported numerically, the variable is called a **quantitative variable.** Examples of quantitative variables are the balance in your chequing account, the ages of company CEOs, the life of a battery (such as 42 months), and the number of children in a family.

4 Distinguish between a *discrete variable* and a *continuous variable.*

Quantitative variables are either discrete or continuous. **Discrete variables** can assume only certain values, and there are "gaps" between the values. Examples of discrete variables are the number of bedrooms in a house (1, 2, 3, 4, etc.), the number of cars arriving at a shopping centre in an hour (326, 421, etc.), and the number of students in each section of a statistics course (25 in section A, 42 in section B, and 18 in section C). We count, for example, the number of cars arriving at a shopping centre, and the number of statistics students in each section. Notice that a home can have 3 or 4 bedrooms, but it cannot have 3.56 bedrooms. Thus, there is a "gap" between possible values. Typically, discrete variables result from counting.

Observations of a **continuous variable** can assume any value within a specific range. Typically, continuous variables result from measuring something. Examples of continuous variables are the air pressure in a tire, and the weight of a shipment of grain. Other examples are the amount of raisin bran in a box, and the duration of flights from Vancouver to Calgary.

Grade point average (GPA) is also a continuous variable. We could report the GPA of a student as 3.2576952. The usual practice is to round up to 3 decimal places, such as 3.258 in this example.

5 Distinguish among the *nominal, ordinal, interval,* and *ratio* levels of measurement.

Levels of Measurement

Data can be classified according to levels of measurement. The level of measurement of the data often dictates the calculations that can be done to summarize and present the data. It will also determine the statistical tests that should be performed. For example, there are six colours of candies in a bag of M&M's candies. Suppose we assign brown a value of 1, yellow 2, blue 3, orange 4, green 5, and red 6. From a bag of candies, we add the assigned colour values and divide by the number of candies and report that the mean colour is 3.56. Does this mean that the average colour is blue or orange? Of course not! As a second example, in a high school 400 m track meet there are eight competitors. We report the order of finish and that the mean finish is 4.5. What does the mean finish tell us? In both of these instances, we have not properly used the level of measurement.

There are actually four levels of measurement: nominal, ordinal, interval, and ratio. The lowest, or the most primitive, measurement is the nominal level. The highest, or the level that gives us the most information about the observation, is the ratio level of measurement.

Nominal Level Data

For the **nominal level** of measurement observations of a qualitative variable can only be classified and counted. There is no particular order to the labels. The classification of the six colours of M&M's candies is an example of the nominal level of measurement. We simply classify the candies by colour. There is no natural order. That is, we could report the brown candies first, the orange first, or any of the colours first. Gender is another example of the nominal level of measurement. Suppose we count the number of students entering a football game with a student ID and report how many are men and how many are women. We could report either the men or the women first. For the nominal level the only measurement involved consists of counts. Table 1–1 shows a breakdown of the style of homes listed by The Edmonton Weekly in the south-east area of Edmonton. This is a nominal level variable because we record the information by style or type of house and there is no natural order. We could have listed the styles in alphabetical order.

TABLE 1–1 Home Listings in the South-East Area of Edmonton

Style	Number of Listings	Code
Bungalow	45	1
Two Storey	46	2
Bi-Level	3	3
Four-Level Split	1	4
2½ Storey	1	5
Total	96	

Homes listed on the Multiple Listing Service® of the REALTORS® Association of Edmonton and advertised in the *Edmonton Real Estate Weekly*. Data retrieved January 18, 2008. *(http://www.rewedmonton.ca/RECENT_NEW_LISTINGS/Index_html).*

Table 1–1 shows the essential feature of the nominal level of measurement: there is no particular order to the categories.

6 **Define the terms *mutually exclusive* and *exhaustive.***

mutually exclusive A property of a set of categories such that an individual or object is included in only one category.

exhaustive A property of a set of categories such that each individual or object must appear in at least one category.

These categories are **mutually exclusive**, meaning, for example, that a home is listed as a particular style and will appear in only one category.

The categories in Table 1–1 are also **exhaustive**, meaning that every member of the population or sample must appear in one of the categories. So the categories include all of the homes listed in the south-east area of Edmonton by The *Edmonton Real Estate Weekly* on that day.

To process nominal data, such as the information regarding company benefits, the gender of a student, the program of study, or the area that the house is located in, we often numerically code the information. That is, we assign homes that are a bungalow style a code of 1, the two-storeys a code of 2, and so on. This coding facilitates counting by a computer. However, because we have assigned numbers to the various styles, this does not give us license to manipulate the numbers. To explain, 1 + 2 does not equal 3 in this case, that is a bungalow + a two-storey does not equal a bi-level.

To summarize, nominal level data have the following properties:

1. The variable of interest is divided into mutually exclusive categories or outcomes.
2. There is no natural order to the outcomes.

Ordinal Level Data

The next higher level of data is the **ordinal level**. Objects are placed in order. Table 1–2 lists the student ratings of Professor James Brunner in an Introduction to Finance course. Each student in the class answered the question "Overall how did you rate the instructor in this class?" The variable rating illustrates the use of the ordinal scale of measurement. One classification is "higher" or "better" than the next one. That is, "Superior" is better than "Good," "Good" is better than "Average," and so on. However, we are not able to distinguish the magnitude of the differences between groups. Is the difference between "Superior" and "Good" the same as the difference between "Poor" and "Inferior"? We cannot tell. If we substitute a 5 for "Superior" and a 4 for "Good," we can conclude that the rating of "Superior" is better than the rating of "Good," but we cannot add a ranking of "Superior" and a ranking of "Good," with the result being meaningful. Further we cannot conclude that a rating of "Good" (rating is 4) is necessarily twice as high as a "Poor" (rating is 2). We can only conclude that a rating of "Good" is better than a rating of "Poor." We cannot conclude how much better the rating is.

TABLE 1–2 Rating of a Finance Professor

Rating	Frequency
Superior	6
Good	28
Average	25
Poor	12
Inferior	3

Another example of ordinal level data is found in the levels of risk of a terrorist attack to the United States. We often hear of these risks on television or read of them in newspapers. The five risk levels from lowest to highest including a description and colour codes are:

Risk Level	Description	Colour
Low	Low risk of terrorist attack	Green
Guarded	General risk of terrorist attack	Blue
Elevated	Significant risk of terrorist attack	Yellow
High	High risk of terrorist attack	Orange
Severe	Severe risk of terrorist attack	Red

This is an example of the ordinal scale data because we know the order or ranks of the risk levels—that is, orange is higher than yellow—but the amount of the difference between each of the levels is not necessarily the same. To put it another way, the difference in the risk level between yellow and orange is not necessarily the same between green and blue. You can check the current risk level and read more about the various levels by going to www.whitehouse.gov/homeland.

In summary, the properties of ordinal level data are:

1. Data classifications are represented by labels or names (high, medium, low) that are mutually exclusive.
2. Data classifications are ranked or ordered according to the particular trait they possess.

Interval Level Data

The **interval level** of measurement is the next highest level. It includes all the characteristics of the ordinal level, but in addition, the difference between values is a constant size. An example of the interval level of measurement is temperature. Suppose the high temperatures on three consecutive winter days are 0, −2, and −3 degrees Celsius. These temperatures can be easily ranked, but we can also determine the difference between temperatures. This is possible because 1 degree Celsius represents a constant unit of measurement. Equal differences between two temperatures are the same, regardless of their position on the scale. That is, the difference between 10 degrees Celsius and 15 degrees is 5, the difference between 50 and 55 degrees is also 5 degrees. It is also important to note that 0 is just a point on the scale. It does not represent the absence of the condition. Zero degrees Celsius does not represent the absence of heat, just that it is cold! In fact, 0 degrees Celsius is 32 degrees Fahrenheit, and 0 degrees Fahrenheit is about –18 degrees on the Celsius scale.

The properties of interval level data are:

1. Data classifications are mutually exclusive and exhaustive.
2. Data classifications are ordered according to the amount of the characteristic they possess.
3. Equal differences in the characteristic are represented by equal differences in the measurements.

There are few examples of the interval scale of measurement. Temperature, which was just cited, is one example. Others are shoe size and IQ scores.

Ratio Level Data

Practically all quantitative data are at the ratio level of measurement. The **ratio level** is the "highest" level of measurement. It has all the characteristics of the interval level, but in addition, the 0 point is meaningful and the ratio between two numbers is meaningful. Examples of the ratio scale of measurement include: wages, units of production, weight, changes in stock prices, distance between branch offices, and height. Money is a good illustration. If you have $0, then you have no money. Weight is another example. If the dial on the scale is at zero, then there is a complete absence of weight. The ratio of two numbers is also meaningful. If Jim earns $30 000 per year selling insurance and Rob earns $60 000 per year selling cars, then Rob earns twice as much as Jim.

The difference between interval and ratio measurements can be confusing. The fundamental difference involves the definition of a true zero and the ratio between two values. If you have $50 and your friend has $100, then your friend has twice as much money as you. You may convert this money to Japanese yen or English pounds, but your friend will still have twice as much money as you. If you spend your $50, then you have no money. This is an example of a true zero. As another example, a sales representative travels 150 km on Monday and 300 km on Tuesday. The ratio of the distances traveled on the two days is 2/1; converting the distances to metres or miles will not change the ratio. It is still 2/1. Suppose on Wednesday the sales representative works at home and does not travel. The distance traveled on Wednesday is zero, and this is a meaningful value. Hence, the variable distance has a true zero point.

In summary, the properties of ratio level data are:

1. Data classifications are mutually exclusive and exhaustive.
2. Data classifications are ordered according to the amount of the characteristics they possess.
3. Equal differences in the characteristic are represented by equal differences in the numbers assigned to the classifications.
4. The zero point is the absence of the characteristic and the ratio between two numbers is meaningful.

Table 1–3 illustrates the use of the ratio scale of measurement. It shows the incomes of four father and son combinations.

TABLE 1–3 Father–Son Income Combinations

Name	Father	Son
Lahey	$80 000	$40 000
Nale	90 000	30 000
Rho	60 000	120 000
Steele	75 000	130 000

Observe that the senior Lahey earns twice as much as his son. In the Rho family the son makes twice as much as the father.

Chart 1–3 summarizes the major characteristics of the various levels of measurement.

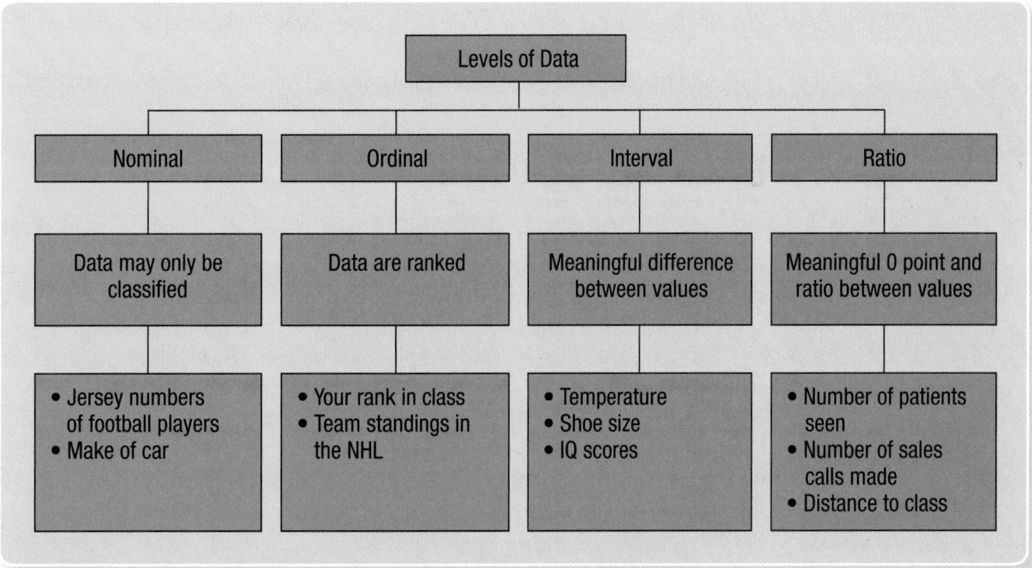

CHART 1–3 Summary of the Characteristics for Levels of Measurement

self-review 1–2

What is the level of measurement reflected by the following data?

(a) The ages for a sample of 50 adults who listen to the Oldies radio stations in Canada are:

35	29	41	34	44	46	42	42	37	47
30	36	41	39	44	39	43	43	44	40
47	37	41	27	33	33	39	38	43	22
44	39	35	35	41	42	37	42	38	43
35	37	38	43	40	48	42	31	51	34

(b) In a survey of 200 luxury-car owners, 100 were from Victoria, 50 from Halifax, 30 from Calgary, and 20 from Winnipeg.

Exercises

The answers to the odd-numbered exercises are at the end of the book.

1. What is the level of measurement for each of the following variables?
   a. Student IQ ratings.
   b. Distances students travel to class.
   c. Student scores on the first statistics test.
   d. A classification of students by province of birth.
   e. A ranking of students by letter grades.
   f. Number of hours students study per week.
   g. The political parties in Canada.
   h. Team standings in the NHL.
   i. Jersey numbers in basketball.
   j. The number of car sales in the last six months.
2. What is the level of measurement for these items related to the newspaper business?
   a. The number of papers sold each Sunday during 2008.
   b. The number of employees in each of the departments, such as editorial, advertising, sports, etc.
   c. A summary of the number of papers sold by county.
   d. The number of years with the paper for each employee.
   e. The number of male and female employees.
   f. The height of each employee.
3. Look in the latest edition of your local newspaper and find examples of each level of measurement. Write a brief memo summarizing your findings.
4. For each of the following, determine whether the group is a sample or a population.
   a. The participants in a study of a new diabetes drug.
   b. The drivers who received a speeding ticket in Halifax last month.
   c. Those on welfare in Victoria, B.C.
   d. The 30 stocks reported as a part of the Dow Jones Industrial Average.

Ethics and Statistics

You have probably heard the old saying that there are three kinds of lies: lies, damn lies, and statistics. This saying is attributable to Benjamin Disraeli and is over a century old. It has also been said that "figures don't lie: liars figure." Both of these statements refer to the misuse of statistics in which data are presented in ways that are misleading.

For example, charts and graphs can be used to visually mislead. Suppose that the price of a townhouse in Collingwood increased from $50 000 in 1998 to $300 000 in 2008 (see Chart 1–4). That is, the price doubled during the 10-year period. To show this change, the dollar sign on the right is twice as tall as the one on the left. However, it is also twice as wide! Therefore the area of the dollar sign on the right is four times (not twice) that on the left. Chart 1–4 is misleading because visually the increase is much larger than it really is.

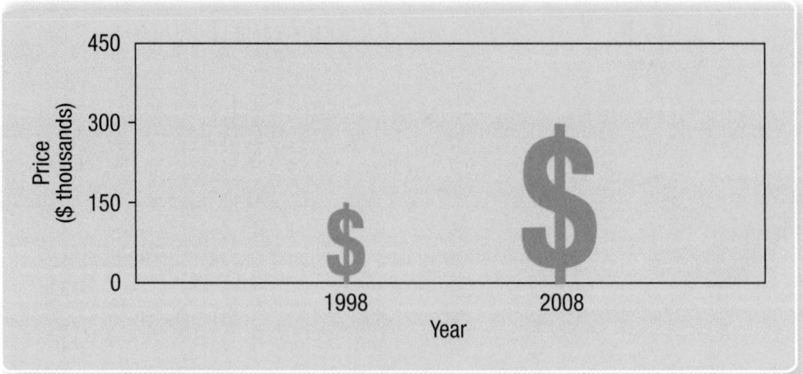

CHART 1–4 The Price of a Townhouse in Collingwood

There are many graphing techniques, but there are no hard and fast rules about drawing a graph. It is therefore both a science and an art. Your aim should always be a truthful representation of the data. The objectives and the assumptions underlying the data must be kept in mind and mentioned briefly along with graphs. The visual impressions conveyed by the graphs must correspond to the underlying data. The graphs should reveal as much information as possible with the greatest precision and accuracy. *Graphical excellence is achieved when a viewer can get the most accurate and comprehensive picture of the situation underlying the data set in the shortest possible time.* In brief, a graph should act like a mirror between the numerical data and the viewer. According to a popular saying, *"Numbers speak for themselves."* This is true for small data sets. For large data sets, it may be difficult to discern any patterns by looking at numbers alone. We therefore *need accurate portrayal of data through graphs that can speak for numbers*, and can give a quick overview of the data. We discuss graphic techniques in chapter 2 and subsequent chapters.

Several years ago, a series of TV advertisements reported that "two out of three dentists surveyed indicated they would recommend Brand X toothpaste to their patients." The implication is that 67 percent of all dentists would recommend the product to their patients. The trick is that the manufacturer of the toothpaste could take *many* surveys of three dentists and report *only* the survey of three dentists that had two indicating they would recommend Brand X. Undoubtedly, a survey of more than three is needed, and it must be unbiased and representative of the population of all dentists. We discuss sampling methods in Chapter 7.

Another area where there can be a misrepresentation of data is the association between variables. In statistical analysis often we find there is a strong *association* between variables. We find there is a strong association between the number of hours a student studies for an exam and the score he or she receives. Does this mean that studying causes the higher score? No. It means the two variables are related, that is, they tend to act together in a predictable fashion. We study the association between variables in Chapters 12 and 13.

Sometimes numbers themselves can be deceptive. The mean price of homes sold last month in Winnipeg, Manitoba is \$167 800. This sounds like a very precise value and may instill a high degree of confidence in its accuracy. To report that the mean selling price is \$175 000 doesn't convey the same precision and accuracy. However, a statistic that is very precise and carries 5 or even 10 decimal places is not necessarily accurate.

Throughout this text, we highlight ethical issues in the collection, analysis, presentation, and interpretation of statistical information. We also hope that, as you learn about using statistics, you will become a more informed consumer of information. For example, you will question a report based on data that do not fairly represent the population, a report that does not include all relevant statistics, one that includes an incorrect choice of statistical measures, or a presentation that introduces the writer's bias in a deliberate attempt to mislead or misrepresent.

Computer Applications

Computers are now available to students at most colleges and universities. Spreadsheets, such as **Microsoft Excel**, and statistical software packages, such as MINITAB, are available in most computer labs. In this text we use both **Excel** and MINITAB for the applications. We also use an **Excel** add-in called MegaStat. This add-in gives **Excel** the capability to produce additional statistical reports. MINITAB examples and solutions can be found on the CD-ROM.

The following example shows the application of computers in statistical analysis. In Chapters 2 and 3 we illustrate methods for summarizing and describing data. An exercise used in those chapters refers to the list price of homes in the south-east area of Edmonton. The following MegaStat output reveals, among other things, that (1) 96 homes were listed, that (2) the average (mean) list price was \$447 403.14, and (3) the list prices ranged from \$269 900 to \$1 100 000.

excel

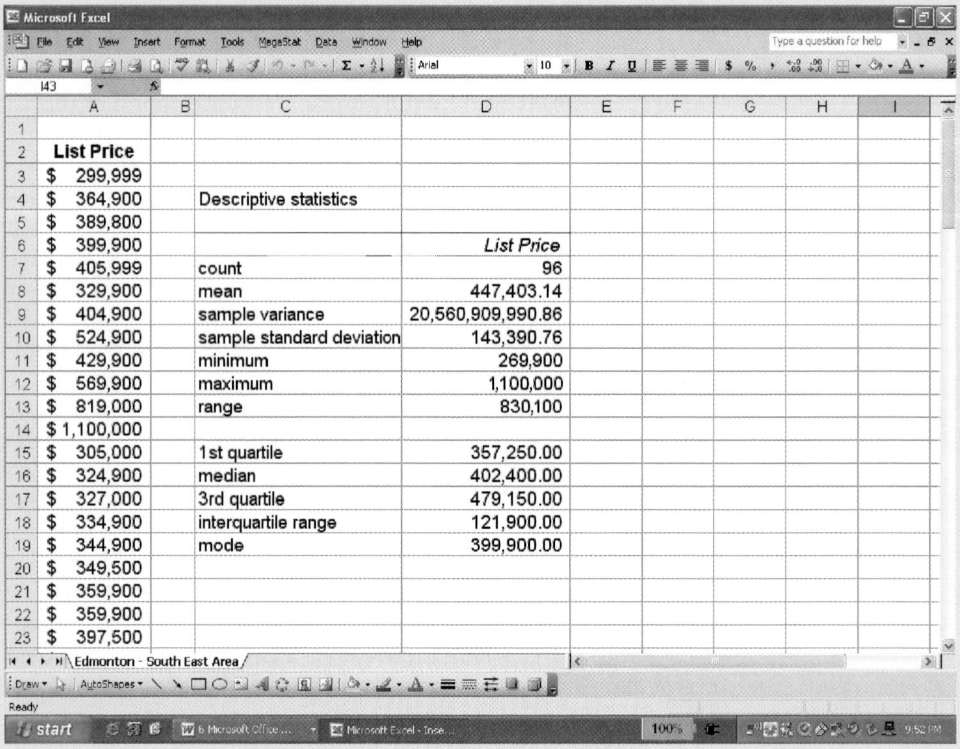

	A	B	C	D
1				
2	List Price			
3	$ 299,999			
4	$ 364,900		Descriptive statistics	
5	$ 389,800			
6	$ 399,900			*List Price*
7	$ 405,999		count	96
8	$ 329,900		mean	447,403.14
9	$ 404,900		sample variance	20,560,909,990.86
10	$ 524,900		sample standard deviation	143,390.76
11	$ 429,900		minimum	269,900
12	$ 569,900		maximum	1,100,000
13	$ 819,000		range	830,100
14	$ 1,100,000			
15	$ 305,000		1st quartile	357,250.00
16	$ 324,900		median	402,400.00
17	$ 327,000		3rd quartile	479,150.00
18	$ 334,900		interquartile range	121,900.00
19	$ 344,900		mode	399,900.00
20	$ 349,500			
21	$ 359,900			
22	$ 359,900			
23	$ 397,500			

Had we used a calculator to arrive at these measures and others needed to fully analyze the list prices, hours of calculations would have been required. The likelihood of an error in arithmetic is high when a large number of values are concerned. On the other hand, statistical software packages and spreadsheets can provide accurate information in seconds. We will see more of this data in subsequent chapters.

Chapter Summary

I. Statistics is the science of collecting, organizing, presenting, analyzing, and interpreting data to assist in making more effective decisions.

II. There are two types of statistics.

- **A.** Descriptive statistics are procedures used to organize and summarize data.
- **B.** Inferential statistics involve taking a sample from a population and making estimates about a population based on the sample results.
  - **1.** A population is an entire set of individuals or objects of interest or the measurements obtained from all individuals or objects of interest.
  - **2.** A sample is a part of the population.

III. There are two types of variables.

- **A.** A qualitative variable is non-numeric.
  - **1.** Usually we are interested in the number or percent of the observations in each category.
  - **2.** Qualitative data are usually summarized in graphs and bar charts.

B. There are two types of quantitative variables and they are usually reported numerically.
   1. Discrete variables can assume only certain values, and there are gaps between values.
   2. A continuous variable can assume any value within a specified range.

IV. There are four levels of measurement.

A. With the nominal level, the data are sorted into categories with no particular order to the categories.
   1. The categories are mutually exclusive. An individual or object appears in only one category.
   2. The categories are exhaustive. An individual or object appears in at least one of the categories.

B. The ordinal level of measurement presumes that one classification is ranked higher than another.

C. The interval level of measurement has the ranking characteristic of the ordinal level of measurement plus the characteristic that the distance between values is a constant size.

D. The ratio level of measurement has all the characteristics of the interval level, plus there is a meaningful zero point and the ratio of two values is meaningful.

Chapter Exercises

5. Explain the difference between *qualitative* and *quantitative* data. Give an example of qualitative and quantitative data.

6. Explain the difference between a sample and a population.

7. List the four levels of measurement and give an example (different from those used in the book) of each level of measurement.

8. For the following questions, would you collect information using a sample or a population? Why?
   a. Statistics 201 is a course taught at a college. Professor K. Khan has taught nearly 1500 students in the course over the past five years. You would like to know the average grade for the course.
   b. As part of a research project, you need to report the average profitability of the number one corporation as reported by *BusinessWeek* for the past 10 years.
   c. You are looking forward to graduation and your first job is as a salesperson for a pharmaceutical company. Planning for your interviews, you will need to know about each company's mission statement, profitability, products, and markets.
   d. You are shopping for a new MP3 player such as the Apple iPod. The manufacturers advertise the number of music tracks that can be stored in the memory. Usually, the advertisers assume relatively short, popular music to estimate the number of tracks that can be stored. You, however, like Broadway musicals tunes and they are much longer. You would like to estimate how many Broadway tunes will fit on your MP3 player.

9. For the following variables, classify each as discrete or continuous, qualitative or quantitative, and determine the level of measurement.
   a. Salary.
   b. Gender.
   c. Sales volume of MP3 players.
   d. Soft drink preference.
   e. Temperature.
   f. GPA score.
   g. Student rank in class.
   h. Rating of a new movie.
   i. Number of home computers.

10. Using data from magazines, or your local newspaper, give examples of the nominal, ordinal, interval, and ratio levels of measurement.

11. A random sample of 300 executives out of 2500 employed by a large firm showed that 270 would move to another location if it meant a substantial promotion. Based on these findings, write a brief note to management regarding all executives in the firm.

12. A random sample of 500 customers was asked to test a new toothpaste. Of the 500, 400 said it was excellent, 32 thought it was fair, and the remaining customers had no opinion. Based on these sample findings, make an inference about the reaction of all customers to the new toothpaste.

13. The table below reports the number of cars and light duty trucks sold by the six largest automakers for the months of January 2006 and January 2007.

	Units	
Company	**2007**	**2006**
General Motors	244 614	293 302
Toyota	175 850	160 594
DaimlerChrysler	173 407	168 030
Ford Motor	165 668	204 528
Honda	100 790	98 428
Nissan	82 644	75 890

a. Compare the total sales in the two years. What would you conclude? Has there been an increase or decrease in sales?
b. Compare the percent change in sales for the six companies. Has there been a change in the size of the market or did one company steal sales from the other?

Data Set Exercises

14. Refer to the Home Listings Edmonton South-East Area, on the CD-ROM, which reports information on listed homes for January 2008. Consider the variables list price, style, number of rooms, number of bedrooms, full baths, half baths, and total square feet.
a. Which of the variables are qualitative and which are quantitative?
b. Determine the level of measurement for each of the variables.

15. Refer to the Employment Insurance Benefits data, which report the average weekly amount received by type of benefit. Consider the variables type and dollars (amount).
a. Which of these variables are quantitative and which are qualitative?
b. Determine the level of measurement for each of the variables.

16. Refer to the Average Earnings by Sex and Work Pattern data, which reports information on the average salary earned by men and women in Canada. The variables are year, women, men, and earnings ratio (%).
a. Which of the four variables are qualitative and which are quantitative?
b. Determine the level of measurement for each variable.

17. Refer to the International data, which reports demographic and economic information on 46 countries.
a. Which of the variables are quantitative and which are qualitative?
b. Determine the level of measurement for each of the variables.

18. Refer to the CREA (Canadian Real Estate Association) data on the CD-ROM, which reports information on average house prices nationally and in a selection of cities across Canada. Consider the variables region and average house prices.
a. Which of the variables are quantitative and which are qualitative?
b. Determine the level of measurement for each of the variables.

exercises.com

Additional exercises that require you to access information at related Internet sites are available on the CD-ROM included with this text.

Answers to Self-Reviews

1–1 **(a)** Based on the sample of 1960 consumers, we estimate that, if it is marketed, 60 percent of all consumers will purchase Fish Delight $(1176/1960) \times 100 = 60$ percent.

(b) Inferential statistics, because a sample was used to draw a conclusion about how all consumers in the population would react if Fish Delight were marketed.

1–2 **(a)** Age is a ratio scale variable. A 40-year-old is twice as old as someone 20 years old.

(c) Nominal scale. We could arrange the cities in any order.

chapter 2

Describing Data:

Frequency Distributions and Graphic Presentation

LEARNING GOALS

When you have completed this chapter, you will be able to:

1. Organize data into a *frequency distribution*.
2. Present data using such graphical techniques as *line charts, bar charts,* and *pie charts*.
3. Portray a frequency distribution in a *histogram, frequency polygon*, and *cumulative frequency polygon*.
4. Develop and interpret a *stem-and-leaf display*.

Introduction

In this chapter we will use data from *The Edmonton Real Estate Weekly*—published by the Realtors Association of Edmonton (www.rewedmonton.ca) to present techniques that organize and show the variability of house prices in the south-east area of Edmonton. The listings provide information such as the list price, the neighbourhood (area), the house type (bungalow, two-storey, bi-level, four-level split, 2½ storey), the number of rooms, bedrooms and bathrooms, and the square footage. We will use these listings to develop some tables and charts that can be reviewed to see where the list prices tend to cluster, to see the variation in the list prices, and to note any trends. These techniques will be useful to anyone in managing a business.

1 Organize data into a *frequency distribution*.

frequency distribution A grouping of data into mutually exclusive classes showing the number of observations in each class.

Constructing a Frequency Distribution

Recall from Chapter 1 that we refer to techniques used to describe a set of data as *descriptive statistics*. Descriptive statistics organize data to show the general shape of the data and where values tend to concentrate, and to highlight unusual or extreme data values. The first procedure we use to describe a set of data is a **frequency distribution**.

How do we develop a frequency distribution? The first step is to tally the data into a table that shows the classes and the number of observations in each class. The steps in constructing a frequency distribution are best described using an example. Remember, our goal is to make a table that will quickly reveal the shape of the data. In Chapter 1, we distinguished between qualitative and quantitative data. To review, a qualitative variable is non-numeric; that is, it can only be classified into distinct categories. There is no particular order to these categories. On the other hand, quantitative variables are numeric in nature.

In the data from *The Edmonton Real Estate Weekly*, the list price, the number of rooms, bedrooms and bathrooms, and the square footage are quantitative variables. There are two qualitative variables, the neighbourhood (area) and the house style. (The complete data set is on the CD-ROM.) We will start by summarizing the house style.

To summarize this qualitative data, we classify the homes listed as a bungalow (coded as 1), a two-storey (coded as 2), a bi-level (coded as 3), a four-level split (coded as 4), and a 2½ storey (coded as 5). Then , we will count the number in each class. We have five distinct types, and therefore, five mutually exclusive (distinct) classes. This means that a home can belong to only one class. The frequency table is shown in Table 2–1. The number of observations in each class is called the **class frequency**.

TABLE 2–1 Home Listings in the South-East Area of Edmonton

Style	Number of Listings	Code
Bungalow	45	1
Two Storey	46	2
Bi-Level	3	3
Four-level Split	1	4
2½ Storey	1	5
Total	96	

Relative Class Frequencies

You can convert class frequencies (number of listings) to **relative class frequencies** to show the fraction of the total number of observations in each class. So, a relative frequency captures the relationship between a class total and the total number of observations. We may also want to know the percentage of total homes that are bungalows.

To convert a frequency distribution to a **relative frequency distribution**, each of the class frequencies is divided by the total number of observations. For example, 45/96 (the fraction of bungalows listed) is 0.47. The relative frequency distribution is shown in Table 2–2.

TABLE 2–2 Relative Frequency Table of Home Listings in the South-East Area of Edmonton

Style	Class Frequencies	Relative Frequencies
Bungalow	45	0.47
Two Storey	46	0.48
Bi-Level	3	0.03
Four-level Split	1	0.01
2½ Storey	1	0.01
Total	96	1.00

When rounding, the total of the relative frequencies may not be exactly 1.00

Present data using such graphical techniques as *line charts, bar charts,* and *pie charts.*

Graphic Presentation of Data

Bar Charts

A common way to present a qualitative variable in graphic form is a **bar chart**. In most cases the horizontal axis shows the variable of interest and the vertical axis the amount, number or fraction of each of the possible outcomes. A distinguishing characteristic of a bar chart is that there is a distance or gap between the bars. That is, because the variable of interest is qualitative, the bars are not adjacent to each other. Thus, a bar chart graphically describes a frequency table using a series of uniformly wide rectangles (bars), where the height of each bar is the class frequency.

We use the data from Table 2–1 to create the bar chart (Chart 2–1). The variable of interest is the style of home listed (the horizontal axis) and the number of each type listed is the class frequency (the vertical axis). The height of the bars corresponds to the number of homes listed in each category. So, for the style of bungalow, the height of the bar is 45.

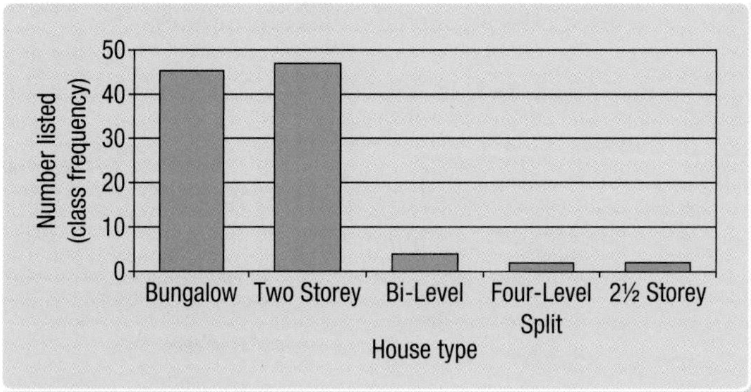

CHART 2–1 Homes Listed by Style in the South-East Area of Edmonton

A bar chart can also be used to depict any of the levels of measurement—nominal, ordinal, interval, or ratio. Recall we discussed the levels of data in Chapter 1. Suppose we wish to show the difference in income based on highest level of education. For example, the average income for someone over the age of 15 is \$21 230 if less than a high school

excel

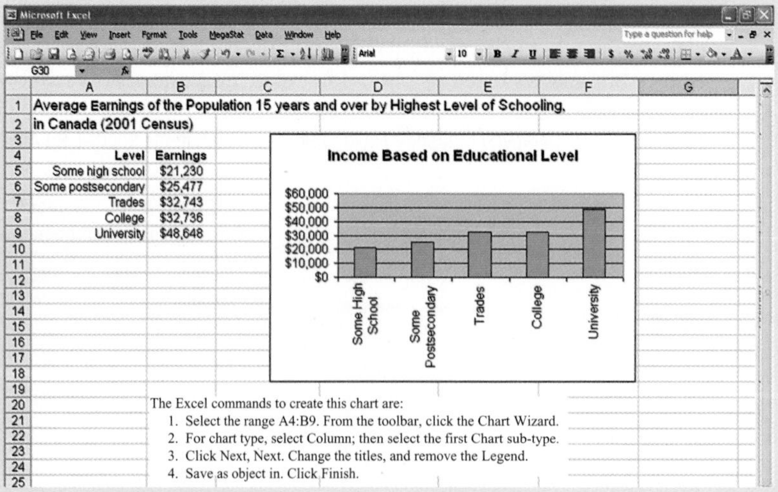

Source: Adapted from Statistics Canada, Census of Population (2001) http://www.statcan.ca/english/Pgdb/labor50a.htm, March 29, 2005 Data Set on the CDROM: Earnings (average) by level of schooling.

CHART 2–2 Income Based on Educational Level

graduation certificate is achieved. With a high school certificate and/or some postsecondary, the income increases to $25 477. This information is summarized in Chart 2–2. (Note: The data is from Statistics Canada, Census 2001. Full details and a breakdown of income by educational level by province can be found on the CD-ROM, Data Sets.) With this chart it is easy to see that a person with a university certificate, diploma or degree can expect to earn more than twice as much as someone with less than a high school graduation certificate. In **Excel**, this chart type is column.

Excel will also produce a horizontal bar chart. Then the chart type is Bar. Chart 2–3 displays the same information in a bar chart.

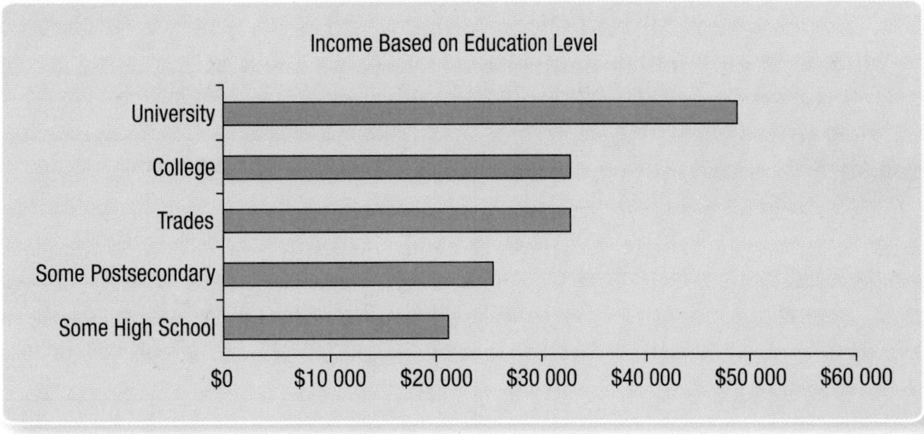

CHART 2–3 Income Based on Educational Level

Line Charts

The following graph is an example of a **line chart**.

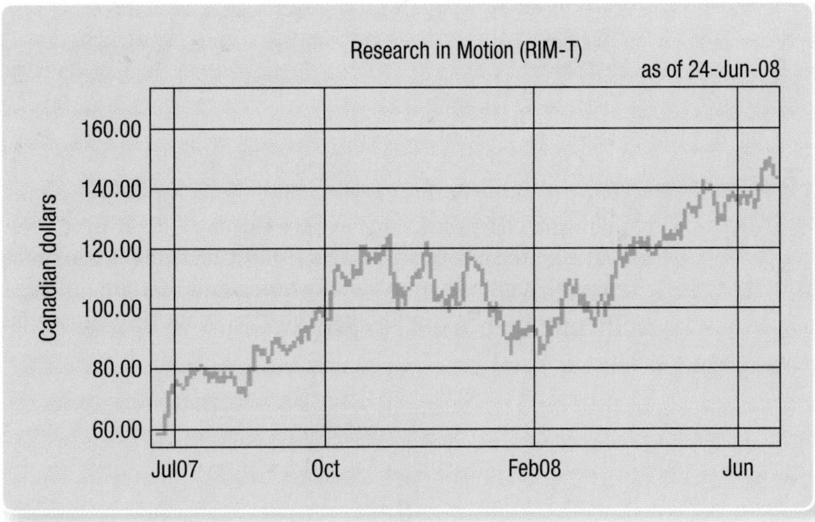

Courtesy *The Globe and Mail*

Line charts are particularly effective for business data because we can show the change in a variable over time. The variable, such as the number of units sold or the total value of sales is scaled along the vertical axis and time along the horizontal axis. The above chart depicts the stock value of RIM (Research In Motion Limited), trading at $141.20, as of June 24, 2008. Updates are available at www.globeinvestor.com.

To create a line chart we will use the data shown below of Apple's revenue (in billions of dollars) for the last six quarters (www.apple.com/investor).

Date	Revenue ($B)
Apr-08	$7.51
Jan-08	9.6
Oct-07	6.22
Jul-07	5.41
Apr-07	5.26
Jan-07	7.1

excel

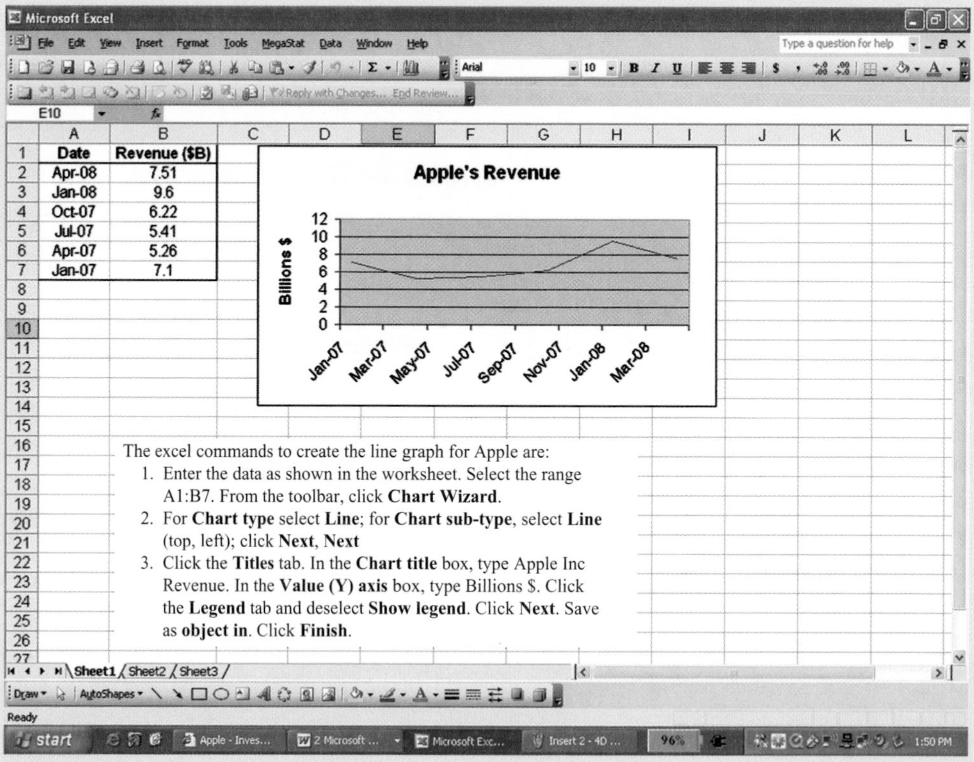

Quite often two or more series of data are plotted on the same chart. Thus, one chart can show the trend of those series. This allows for a comparison of several series over a period. The following chart shows the average earnings by sex for men and women from 1993 to 2006. The source of the information is Statistics Canada. We can quickly see that the average earnings for men are higher than those of women and that the difference in earnings fluctuates somewhat from year to year, but the gap remains about the same. Note: this data set is on the CD-ROM.

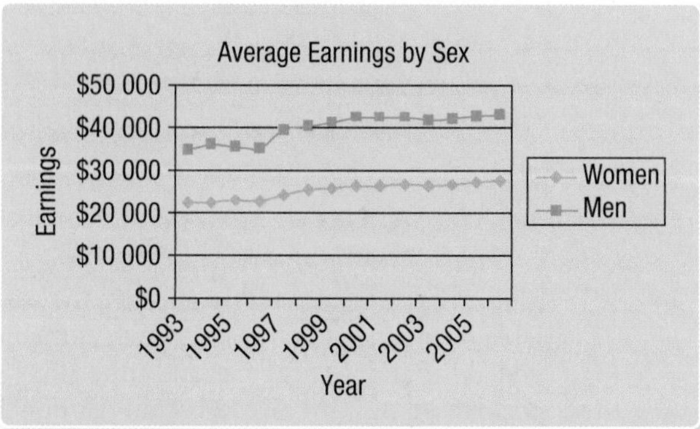

Source: Statistics Canada. (http://www40.statcan.ca/101/cst01/labor01a.htm?sdi=earnings), August 5, 2008.)

This chart is created in **Excel** following the same steps as the one-series set of data.

Pie Charts

Another useful type of chart for depicting qualitative information is a **pie chart**. A pie chart shows the percent or proportion that each class represents of the total number of frequencies. We will use the information in Table 2–3, which shows a breakdown of lottery proceeds from the OLG (Ontario Lottery and Gaming Corporation: www.olg.ca) to show how to construct a pie chart in **Excel**. Note that the values used in the pie chart need to be percents or proportions.

TABLE 2–3 OLG Lottery Proceeds (2005–2006)

Use of Profits	Percent Share (%)
Prizes	51.8%
Province of Ontario	30.0
Retailers	7.1
Operating Expenses	8.4
Government of Canada	2.4
	100.0%

excel

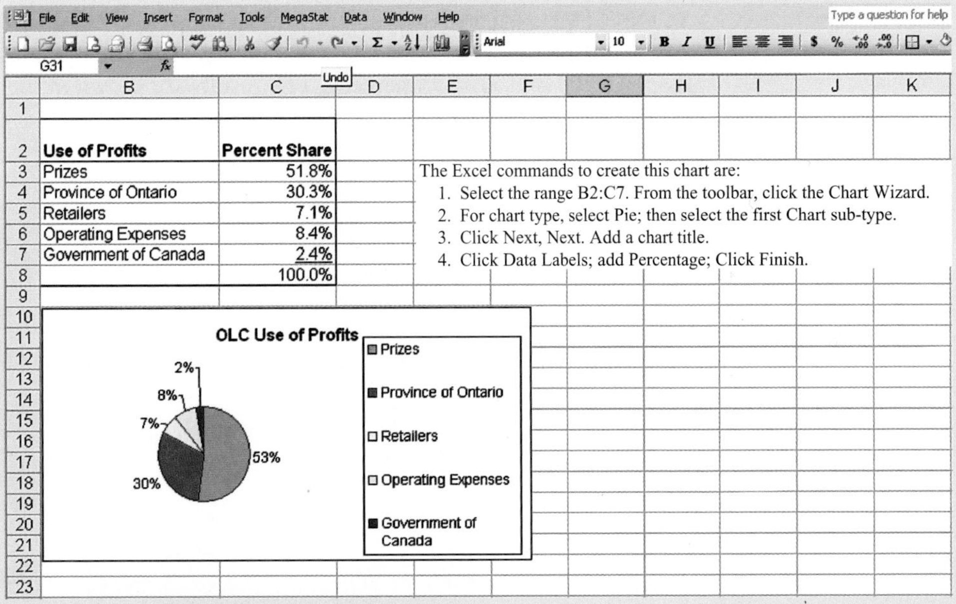

Each slice of the pie represents the relative share of each component, which makes it easy to compare them:

1. The largest expense of the OLG is for prizes.
2. Approximately 30 percent is transferred to the province of Ontario.
3. Operating expenses account for about 8 percent of the proceeds.

example

SkiLodges.com is test marketing its new website and is interested in how easy its web page design is to navigate. It randomly selected 200 regular internet users and asked them to perform a search task on the web page. Each person was asked to rate the ease of navigation as poor, good, excellent, or awesome. The results are shown in the following table:

Awesome	102
Excellent	58
Good	30
Poor	10

1. What level of measurement is used for ease of navigation?
2. Draw a bar chart for the survey results.
3. Draw a pie chart for the survey results.

solution

The data are measured on an ordinal scale. That is, the scale ranks the ease of navigation from a low of "poor" to a high of "awesome." Also, the interval between each rating is unknown so it is impossible, for example, to conclude that a rating of good is twice the value of a poor rating. For the bar chart, the vertical axis shows the number of frequencies in each class, and the horizontal axis shows the values of the ease of navigation.

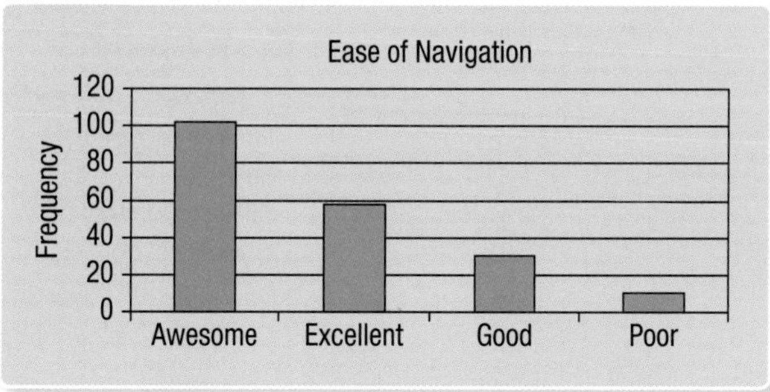

For the pie chart, we will need the proportion or percents in each category. For this we first total the Frequency column, and then calculate the percents. For example, in the first class, 102/200 = 0.51 = 51 percent. The results are shown in the following table:

	Frequency	Percent (%)
Awesome	102	51%
Excellent	58	29
Good	30	15
Poor	10	5
Total	200	100%

For the following pie chart, the second Chart sub-type was used in **Excel**.

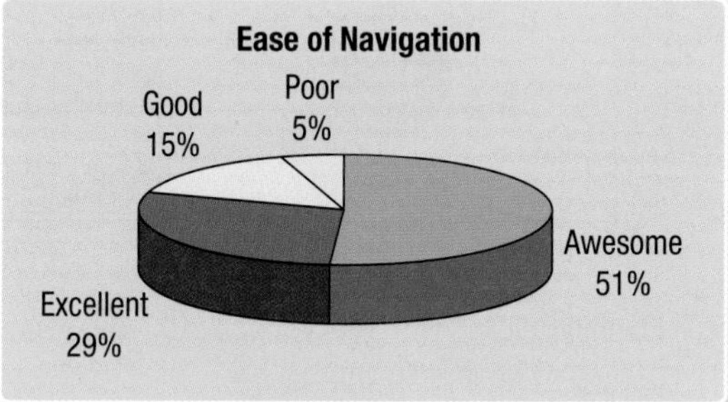

self-review 2–1

The answers are at the end of the chapter.

DiCarlo's Café has been serving an Italian soda drink with a vanilla flavouring that is very popular with its customers. Joe DiCarlo is interested in customer preferences for some new flavours. He asks 100 of his regular customers to take a taste test and pick the one they like the best. The results are shown in the following table.

Flavour	Number
Vanilla	40
Cherry	25
Lemon	20
Orange	15
Total	100

(a) Is the data quantitative or qualitative? Why?
(b) Develop a bar chart to depict the information.
(c) Develop a pie chart using the relative frequencies.
(d) Develop a line chart to depict the information.
(e) Which chart best portrays the information? Why?

Exercises

The answers to the odd-numbered exercises are at the end of the book.

1. A small business consultant is investigating the performance of several companies. The sales in 2008 (in thousands of dollars) for the selected companies were:

Corporation	Fourth-Quarter Sales ($ thousands)
Hoden Building Products	$1645.2
J & R Printing Inc.	4757.0
Long Bay Concrete Construction	8913.0
Mancell Electric and Plumbing	627.1
Maxwell Heating and Air Conditioning	24 612.0
Mizelle Roofing & Sheet Metals	191.9

The consultant wants to include a chart in his report comparing the sales of the six companies. Use a bar chart to compare the fourth quarter sales of these corporations and write a brief report summarizing the bar chart. Now, use a line chart to compare the fourth quarter sales of these corporations. Which chart is better suited to depict the information? Why?

2. The Blair Corporation sells fashion apparel for men and women plus a broad range of home products. Listed below are the net sales for Blair from 2003 through 2008. Draw a line chart depicting the net sales over the time period and write a brief report. Now, use a bar chart to depicting the net sales over the time period. Which chart is better suited to depict the information? Why?

Year	Net Sales ($ millions)
2003	$500.0
2004	519.2
2005	526.5
2006	550.7
2007	562.9
2008	619.4

3. A total of 1000 residents in Manitoba were asked which season they preferred. The results were 100 liked winters best, 300 liked spring, 400 liked summer, and 200 liked fall. If the data were summarized in a frequency distribution, how many classes would be used? What would be the relative frequencies for each class?

4. Statistics Canada reports that the average weekly employment insurance benefits for 2007 are as follows:

Type	Amount ($)
Regular	$315.93
Sickness	294.55
Maternity	330.47
Fishing	378.88
Work sharing	103.22
Adopton	379.41
All benefits	317.65

   a. Construct a bar chart for the data.
   b. Add relative frequencies to the table.
   c. Construct a pie chart for the data.

5. Wellstone Inc. produces and markets replacement covers for cell phones in a variety of colours. The company would like to allocate its production plans to five different colours: bright white, metallic black, magnetic lime, tangerine orange, and fusion red. The company set up a kiosk in the

Qwanlin Mall for several hours and asked randomly selected shoppers which colour they preferred for a cell phone cover. The results follow:

Bright white	130
Metallic black	104
Magnetic lime	325
Tangerine orange	455
Fusion red	286

a. Construct a bar chart for the data.
b. Add relative frequencies to the table.
c. Construct a pie chart for the data.

6. Shown below are the student loan amounts for 2008 for eight students in the business administration program. Develop a bar chart for the data and summarize the results in a brief report.

Name	Amount ($)	Name	Amount ($)
Susan Chan	$6087	Daniel Ng	$3228
Sam Simone	4747	Erin Brooks	2828
Mary Suhanic	3272	Jasmine Smith	2492
Danielle Brothers	3284	Enrique Lopes	2347

Constructing Frequency Distributions: Quantitative Data

In Chapter 1 and earlier in the chapter, we distinguished between qualitative and quantitative data. In the previous section, using the home listings from *The Edmonton Real Estate Weekly*, we summarized the qualitative variable, style, using a frequency table, a relative frequency table, and a bar chart.

The Edmonton Real Estate Weekly also includes quantitative data, such as the list price, the number of rooms, bedrooms and bathrooms, and the square footage. We will now use these listings to develop some tables and charts to show the typical list price.

example

How do we develop this frequency distribution? How do we determine the number of classes and the number of observations in each class? Once again, the steps to follow are best described using an example. Table 2–4 reports the list price of 96 of the homes listed by *The Edmonton Real Estate Weekly* in the south-east area of Edmonton. What is the typical list price? What is the highest list price? What is the lowest list price? Around what values do the list prices tend to group?

TABLE 2–4 Home Listings in the South-East Area of Edmonton

					lowest ↑	
	299 999	344 900	554 900	369 900	269 900	429 899
	364 900	349 500	589 000	435 000	397 900	429 900
	389 800	359 900	639 000	289 000	398 000	434 000
	399 900	359 900	374 900	324 828	398 888	434 900
	405 999	397 500	419 900	329 900	399 900	439 900
	329 900	405 000	950 000	345 000	449 000	495 000
	404 900	415 000	379 800	380 000	505 000	539 900
	524 900	424 700	359 500	329 900	446 000	548 900
	429 900	429 900	399 900	355 000	750 000	579 000
	569 900	444 900	430 000	358 800	323 900	656 800
	819 000	449 000	449 900	399 900	324 800	659 900
highest ←	1 100 000	459 900	529 000	419 900	339 900	664 500
	305 000	469 300	339 900	309 900	347 888	699 900
	324 900	477 700	344 900	349 900	358 000	797 700
	327 000	483 500	399 900	374 900	383 900	518 900
	334 900	519 000	334 900	378 900	394 000	768 000

solution

The steps for organizing data into a frequency distribution.

We refer to the unorganized information in Table 2–4 as **raw data** or **ungrouped data**. With a little searching, we can find the lowest list price ($269 900) and the highest list price ($1 100 000), but that is about all. It is difficult to determine a typical list price. It is also difficult to visualize where the list prices tend to cluster. The raw data are more easily interpreted if organized into a frequency distribution.

Step 1: Decide on the number of classes. The goal is to use just enough groupings or **classes** to reveal the shape of the distribution. Some judgment is needed here. Too many classes or too few classes might not reveal the basic shape of the set of data. In the real estate problem, for example, three classes would not give much insight into the pattern of the data (see Table 2–5).

TABLE 2–5 An Example of Too Few Classes

List Price ($ thousands)	Number of Homes
$0 to under $500	74
500 to under 1000	21
1000 to under 1500	1
Total	96

As a guideline, a useful recipe to determine the number of classes is the "2 to the k rule." This guide suggests you select the smallest number (k) for the number of classes such that 2^k (in words, 2 raised to the power of k) is greater than the number of observations (n).

In the real estate example, there were 96 listings. So $n = 96$. If we try $k = 6$, which means we would use 6 classes, then $2^6 = 64$, somewhat less than 96. Hence, 6 is not enough classes. If we let $k = 7$, then $2^7 = 128$, which is greater than 96. So the suggested number of classes is 7.

Step 2: Determine the class interval or width. Generally the **class interval** or width should be the same for all classes. The classes all taken together must cover at least the distance from the lowest value in the raw data up to the highest value. Expressing these words in a formula:

$$i \geq \frac{H - L}{k}$$

where i is the class interval, H is the highest observed value, L is the lowest observed value, and k is the number of classes.

In the real estate example, the lowest value is $269 900 and the highest value is $1 100 000. If we need seven classes, the interval should be at least ($1 100 000 − $269 900)/7 = $118 586. In practice this interval size is usually rounded up to some convenient number, such as a multiple of 10 or 100, and so, the value of $120 000 might readily be used but would give us eight classes. The intervals would be $250 000 to $370 000, $370 000 to $490 000 etc. However, common sense tells us that an interval width of $125 000 would more readily be understood by anyone trying to interpret the data, and using that interval would give us seven classes.

Unequal class intervals present problems in graphically portraying the distribution and in doing some of the computations that we will see in later chapters. Unequal class intervals, however, may be necessary in certain situations to avoid a large number of empty, or almost empty, classes. Such is the case in Table 2–6. Real estate companies in the greater Vancouver region would likely use unequal-sized class intervals to report the list price on individual homes in their area. Using an equal-sized interval of, say, $250 000, about 100 classes would be required to describe all the listings. A frequency distribution with 100 classes would be difficult to interpret. In this case the distribution is easier to understand in spite of the unequal classes. Note that the price of the homes reported is combined into larger intervals as the price increases to avoid empty classes. This also makes the information easier to understand.

TABLE 2–6 House Listings in the Greater Vancouver Area

List Price ($)
Under $1 000 000
1 000 000 to under 1 500 000
1 500 000 to under 2 000 000
2 000 000 to under 2 500 000
2 500 000 to under 3 000 000
3 000 000 to under 3 500 000
3 500 000 to under 4 000 000
4 000 000 to under 5 000 000
5 000 000 to under 7 000 000
7 000 000 to under 10 000 000
10 000 000 and over

Step 3: Set the individual class limits. State clear class limits so you can put each observation into only one category. This means you must avoid overlapping or unclear class limits. For example, classes such as $250 000 to $375 000 and $375 000 to $500 000 should not be used because it is not clear whether the value of $375 000 is in the first or second class. Classes stated as $250 000 to $374 000 and $375 000 to $499 000 are frequently used, but may also be confusing without the additional common convention of rounding all data at or above $374 500 up to the second class and data below $374 500 down to the first class. In this text we will generally use the format $250 000 to under $375 000, $375 000 to under $500 000 and so on. With this format it is clear that $374 500 goes into the first class and $375 000 in the second class.

Because we round the class interval to get a convenient class size, we cover a larger than necessary range. For example, seven classes of width $125 000 in the real estate example result in a range 7($125 000) = $875 000. The actual range is $1 100 000 − $269 900 = $830 100. Comparing that value to $875 000, we have an excess of $44 900. Because we need to cover only the distance (H−L), it is natural to put approximately equal amounts of the excess in each of the two tails. Of course, we should also select convenient class limits. A guideline is to make the lower limit of the first class a multiple of the class interval. Sometimes this is not possible, but the lower limit should at least be rounded. So here are the classes we could use for this data.

Statistics in Action

In 1788, James Madison, John Jay, and Alexander Hamilton anonymously published a series of essays entitled *The Federalist*. These Federalist papers were an attempt to convince the people of New York that they should ratify the Constitution. In the course of history, the authorship of most of these papers became known, but 12 remained contested. Through the use of statistical analysis, and particularly the study of the frequency of the use of various words, we can now conclude that James Madison is the likely author of the 12 papers. In fact, the statistical evidence that Madison is the author is overwhelming.

$250 000 to under $375 000
375 000 to under 500 000
500 000 to under 625 000
625 000 to under 750 000
750 000 to under 875 000
875 000 to under 1 000 000
1000 000 to under 1 125 000

The first class is $250 000 to under $375 000. The lower class limit of the first class is $250 000 and the upper class limit of the first class is $374 999.99. The second class is $375 000 to under $500 000; the lower class limit is exactly $375 000 and the upper class limit is $499 999.99, and so on.

Step 4: Tally the list prices into the classes. To begin, the first list price in Table 2–4 is $299 999. It is tallied in the $250 000 to under $375 000 class. The second list price in the first column of Table 2–4 is $364 900. It is also tallied in the

$250 000 to under $375 000 class. The other list prices are tallied in a similar manner. When all list prices are tallied, that table would appear as:

Class ($)	Tallies
$250 000 to under $375 000	𝍸 𝍸 𝍸 𝍸 𝍸 𝍸 III
375 000 to under 500 000	𝍸 𝍸 𝍸 𝍸 𝍸 𝍸 𝍸 𝍸 I
500 000 to under 625 000	𝍸 𝍸 I
625 000 to under 750 000	𝍸
750 000 to under 875 000	IIII
875 000 to under 1 000 000	I
1 000 000 to under 1 125 000	I

Step 5: Count the number of items in each class. The number of observations in each class is called the **class frequency**. In the $375 000 to under $500 000 class there are 41 observations, and in the $750 000 to under $875 000 class, there are 4 observations. Therefore, the class frequency is 41 in the second class and 4 in the fifth class. There are a total of 96 observations or frequencies in the set of data.

Often it is useful to express the data in thousands, or some convenient units, rather than the actual data. Table 2–7, for example, reports the list prices in thousands of dollars, rather than dollars.

TABLE 2–7 Frequency Distribution of Home Listings in the South-East Area of Edmonton

List Price ($ thousands)	Frequency
$250 to under $375	33
375 to under 500	41
500 to under 625	11
625 to under 750	5
750 to under 875	4
875 to under 1000	1
1000 to under 1125	1
Total	96

Now that we have organized the data into a frequency distribution, we can summarize the pattern in the list prices of the real estate example. Observe the following:

1. The list prices ranged from about $250 000 to under $1 125 000.
2. The list prices are concentrated between $250 000 and $500 000. A total of 74 list prices, or 77.1 percent of list prices, are within this range.
3. The largest concentration is in the $375 000 to under $500 000 range. The middle of this class is $437 500, so half the houses are listed at or below this price, the other half at or above this price.
4. Two of the list prices were more than $875 000.

By presenting this information, we can see a clearer picture of the distribution of list prices.

We admit that arranging the information on list prices into a frequency distribution does result in the loss of some detailed information. That is, by organizing the data into a frequency distribution, we cannot pinpoint the exact list price, such as $475 000 or $725 000. Or, we cannot tell that the actual list price for the least expensive home was $269 900 and for the most expensive $1 100 000. However, the lower limit of the first class and the upper limit of the largest class convey essentially the same meaning. For example, we can tell that the highest list price is more than $1 000 000 but less than $1 125 000. The advantages of condensing the data into a more understandable form more than offset this disadvantage.

self-review 2–2

The commissions earned, in dollars, for the first quarter of last year by the 11 members of the sales staff at Master Chemical Company are:

$1650	1475	1510	1670	1595	1760	1540	1495	1590	1625	1510

(a) What are the values such as $1650 and $1475 called?
(b) Using $1400 up to $1500 as the first class, $1500 up to $1600 as the second class, and so forth, organize the quarterly commissions into a frequency distribution.
(c) What are the numbers in the right column of your frequency distribution called?
(d) Describe the distribution of quarterly commissions, based on the frequency distribution. What is the largest amount of commission earned? What is the smallest? What is the typical amount earned?

Class Intervals and Class Midpoints

We will use two other terms frequently: **class midpoint** and **class interval**. The midpoint is halfway between the lower limits of two consecutive classes. It is computed by adding the lower limits of consecutive classes and dividing the result by two. Referring to Table 2–7, for the first class the lower class limit is $250 000 and the next limit is $375 000. The class midpoint is $312 500, found by ($250 000 + $375 000)/2. The midpoint of $312 500 best represents, or is typical of, the list price of the homes in that class.

To determine the class interval, subtract the lower limit of the class from the lower limit of the next class. The class interval of the list price data is $125 000, which we find by subtracting the lower limit of the first class, $250 000, from the lower limit of the next class; that is, $375 000 − $250 000 = $125 000. You can also determine the class interval by finding the difference between consecutive midpoints. The midpoint of the first class is $312 500 and the midpoint of the second class is $437 500. The difference is $125 000.

A Software Example

As we mentioned in Chapter 1, there are many software packages that perform statistical calculations and output the results. Throughout this text we will show the output from **Microsoft Excel** and from MegaStat, which is an add-in to **Microsoft Excel**. MINITAB output is on the CD-ROM.

The following is a frequency distribution, produced by MegaStat, showing the list prices of the real estate data. The form of the output is somewhat different than the frequency distribution of Table 2–7, but the overall conclusions are the same.

excel

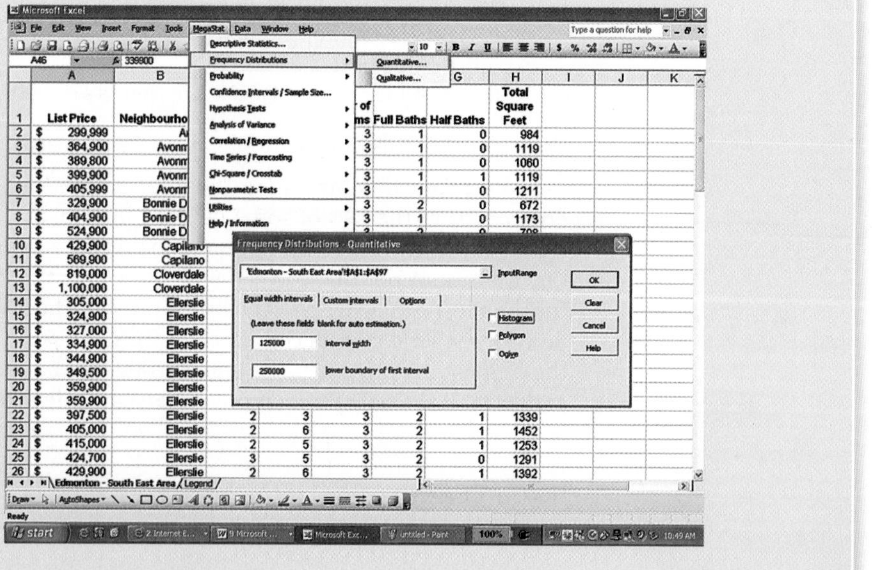

Frequency Distribution-Quantitative

List Price ($)							Cumulative	
Lower		Upper	Midpoint	Width	Frequency	Percent (%)	Frequency	Percent (%)
$250,000	<	$375,000	$312,500	$125,000	33	34.4%	33	34.4%
375,000	<	500,000	437,500	125,000	41	42.7	74	77.1
500,000	<	625,000	562,500	125,000	11	11.5	85	88.5
625,000	<	750,000	687,500	125,000	5	5.2	90	93.8
750,000	<	875,000	812,500	125,000	4	4.2	94	97.9
875,000	<	1,000,000	937,500	125,000	1	1.0	95	99.0
1,000,000	<	1,125,000	1,062,500	125,000	1	1.0	96	100.0
					96	100.0%		

The MegaStat commands to create the frequency distribution shown above are:

1. Open **Excel** and the **Excel** file Table 2–1 from the Data Files on the CD provided. From the menu bar, click MegaStat, Frequency Distributions, Quantitative.
2. In the dialogue box, input the range A1:A97; select the Equal width intervals tab; enter 125000 as the interval width and 250000 as the lower boundary of the first interval; click OK.

self-review 2–3

Kristina had 73 customers in her retail bicycle store, Kristina's Bikes, last Sunday. The customers spent between $48.50 and $300. Kristina wants to construct a frequency distribution of the amount spent by her customers for that day.

(a) How many classes would you use?
(b) What class interval would you suggest?
(c) What actual classes would you suggest?

A relative frequency distribution converts the frequency to a percent.

Relative Frequency Distribution

It may be desirable to convert class frequencies to **relative class frequencies** to show the fraction of the total number of observations in each class. In our real estate example, we may want to know what percent of the list prices are in the $375 000 to under $500 000 class. In another study, we may want to know what percent of the employees are absent between one and three days per year due to illness.

To convert a frequency distribution to a *relative* frequency distribution, each of the class frequencies is divided by the total number of observations. Using the distribution of list prices again (Table 2–7, where the list price is reported in thousands of dollars), the relative frequency for the $375 to under $500 class is 0.427, found by dividing 41 by 96. That is, 42.7 percent of the list prices are between $375 000 to under $500 000. The relative frequencies for the remaining classes are shown in Table 2–8.

TABLE 2–8 Relative Frequency Distribution of List Prices in the South-East Area of Edmonton

List Price ($ thousands)	Frequency	Relative Frequency	Found by
$250 to under $375	33	0.3438	33/96
375 to under 500	41	0.4271	41/96
500 to under 625	11	0.1146	11/96
625 to under 750	5	0.0521	5/96
750 to under 875	4	0.0417	4/96
875 to under 1000	1	0.0104	1/96
1000 to under 1125	1	0.0104	1/96
Total	96	1.00	

self-review 2–4

Refer to Table 2–8, which shows the relative frequency for the list prices of homes in the south-east area of Edmonton.

(a) How many homes were listed for $500 000 to under $625 000?
(b) What percent of homes were listed for $500 000 to under $625 000?
(c) What percent of the homes were listed at $750 000 or more?

Exercises

7. A set of data consists of 38 observations. How many classes would you recommend for the frequency distribution?
8. A set of data consists of 45 observations between $0 and $29. What size would you recommend for the class interval?
9. A set of data consists of 230 observations between $235 and $567. What class interval would you recommend?
10. A set of data contains 53 observations. The lowest value is 42 and the largest is 129. The data are to be organized into a frequency distribution.
    a. How many classes would you suggest?
    b. What would you suggest as the lower limit of the first class?
11. The Wachesaw Outpatient Center, designed for same-day minor surgery, opened last month. Following is the number of patients served for the first 16 days.

27	27	27	28	27	25	25	28
26	28	26	28	31	30	26	26

The information is to be organized into a frequency distribution.
    a. How many classes would you recommend?
    b. What class interval would you suggest?
    c. What lower limit would you recommend for the first class?
    d. Organize the information into a frequency distribution and determine the relative frequency distribution.
    e. Comment on the distribution of the values.
12. The Quick Change Oil Company has a number of outlets. The numbers of oil changes at the Oak Street outlet in the past 20 days are:

65	98	55	62	79	59	51	90	72	56
70	62	66	80	94	79	63	73	71	85

The data are to be organized into a frequency distribution.
    a. How many classes would you recommend?
    b. What class interval would you suggest?
    c. What lower limit would you recommend for the first class?
    d. Organize the number of oil changes into a frequency distribution.
    e. Comment on the distribution of the values. Also determine the relative frequency distribution.
13. The manager of the BiLo Supermarket gathered the following information on the number of times a customer visits the store during a month. The responses of 51 customers were:

5	3	3	1	4	4	5	6	4	2	6	6	6	7	1
1	14	1	2	4	4	4	5	6	3	5	3	4	5	6
8	4	7	6	5	9	11	3	12	4	7	6	5	15	1
1	10	8	9	2	12									

    a. Starting with 0 as the lower limit of the first class and using a class interval of 3, organize the data into a frequency distribution.
    b. Describe the distribution. Where do the data tend to cluster?
    c. Convert the distribution to a relative frequency distribution.

14. Moore Travel Agency, a nationwide travel agency, offers special rates on certain Caribbean cruises to senior citizens. The president of Moore Travel wants additional information on the ages of those people taking cruises. A random sample of 40 customers taking a cruise last year revealed these ages.

77	18	63	84	38	54	50	59	54	56	36	26	50	34	44
41	58	58	53	51	62	43	52	53	63	62	62	65	61	52
60	60	45	66	83	71	63	58	61	71					

a. Organize the data into a frequency distribution, using seven classes and 15 as the lower limit of the first class. What class interval did you select?
b. Where do the data tend to cluster?
c. Describe the distribution.
d. Determine the relative frequency distribution.

3 Portray a frequency distribution in a *histogram, frequency polygon*, and *cumulative frequency polygon*.

Graphic Presentation of a Frequency Distribution

Sales managers, stock analysts, hospital administrators, and other busy executives often need a quick picture of the trends in sales, stock prices, or hospital costs. These trends can often be depicted by the use of charts and graphs. Three charts that will help portray a frequency distribution graphically are the histogram, the frequency polygon, and the cumulative frequency polygon.

Histogram

histogram A bar graph where the classes are marked on the horizontal axis and the class frequencies on the vertical axis. The width of the bar is the class width and the height of the bar is the frequency of the class. The bars are drawn adjacent to each other.

A **histogram** for a frequency distribution based on quantitative data is very similar to the bar chart showing the distribution of qualitative data. The classes are marked on the horizontal axis and the class frequencies on the vertical axis. However, there is one important difference based on the nature of the data. Quantitative data is usually measured using scales that are continuous, not discrete. Therefore, the horizontal axis represents all possible values, and the bars are drawn adjacent to each other to show the continuous nature of the data.

We summarize the list price—a continuous variable—of the 96 homes listed in the southeast area of Edmonton. We construct a histogram to illustrate this frequency distribution.

example

Below is the frequency distribution.

List Price ($ thousands)	Midpoint	Frequency
$250 to under $375	$312.5	33
375 to under 500	437.5	41
500 to under 625	562.5	11
625 to under 750	687.5	5
750 to under 875	812.5	4
875 to under 1000	937.5	1
1000 to under 1125	1062.5	1
Total		96

Construct a histogram. What conclusions can you reach based on the information presented in the histogram?

solution

The class frequencies are scaled along the vertical axis (Y-axis) and either the class limits or the class midpoints along the horizontal axis (X-axis).

From Chart 2–4 we note that there are 33 homes listed in the \$250 000 to under \$375 000 class. Therefore, the height of the column for that class is 33. There are 41 listings in the \$375 000 to under \$500 000 class, so, logically, the height of that column is 41. The height of the bar represents the number of observations in the class.

This procedure is continued for all classes. The complete histogram is shown in Chart 2–4. Note that there is no space between the bars. This is a feature of the histogram. Why is this so? Because the variable plotted on the horizontal axis is quantitative and of the interval, or in this case, the ratio scale of measurement.

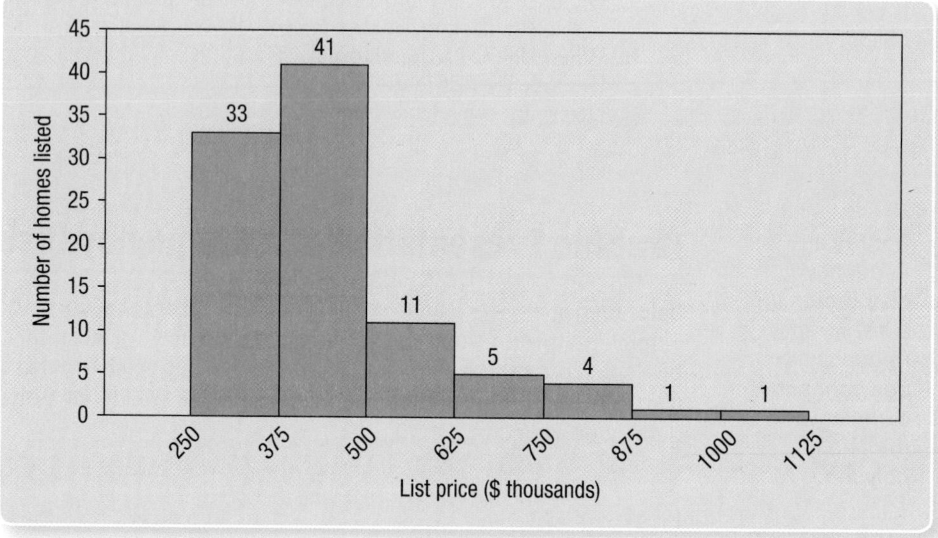

CHART 2–4 Histogram of List Prices, South-East Area of Edmonton

Based on the histogram in Chart 2–4, we conclude:

1. The lowest list price is greater than \$250 000 and the highest is between \$1 000 000 and \$1 125 000.
2. The largest class frequency is the \$375 000 to under \$500 000 class. A total of 41 of the 96 listings are within this price range.
3. Seventy-four of the list prices, or 77.1 percent, had a list price between \$375 000 and to under \$500 000.

Thus, the histogram provides an easily interpreted visual representation of a frequency distribution. We should also point out that we would have reached the same conclusions and the shape of the histogram would have been the same had we used a relative frequency distribution instead of the actual frequencies. That is, if we had used the relative frequencies of Table 2–8, we would have had a histogram of the same shape as Chart 2–4. The only difference is that the vertical axis would have been reported in percent of listings instead of the number of listings.

We used MegaStat to produce the histogram for the real estate data. Follow the commands to create the frequency distribution. A check automatically appears in the box to the left of the word Histogram. This will produce a histogram with percents on the *Y*-axis. To change this default to frequencies:

1. Right click inside the plot area of the histogram. Choose Source Data.
2. Click the Series tab. You need to change the range in the Values: box.
3. In the Values: box, change the range from the Percent column to the Frequency column. Click OK. Edit the chart titles.

In a frequency polygon the class midpoints are connected with a line segment.

Frequency Polygon

A **frequency polygon** shows the shape of a distribution and is similar to a histogram. It consists of line segments connecting the points formed by the intersections of the class midpoints and the class frequencies. The construction of a frequency polygon is illustrated in Chart 2–5. We use the list prices for homes in the south-east area of Edmonton. The midpoint of each class is scaled on the X-axis and the class frequencies on the Y-axis. Recall that the class midpoint is the value at the centre of a class and represents the values in that class. The class frequency is the number of observations in a particular class. The list prices for the real estate example are:

Statistics in Action

Florence Nightingale is known as the founder of the nursing profession. However, she also saved many lives by using statistical analysis. When she encountered an unsanitary condition or an undersupplied hospital, she improved the conditions and then used statistical data to document the improvement. Thus, she was able to convince others of the need for medical reform, particularly in the area of sanitation. She developed original graphs to demonstrate that, during the Crimean War, more soldiers died from unsanitary conditions than were killed in combat.

List Price ($ thousands)	Midpoint	Frequency
$250 to under $375	$312.5	33
375 to under 500	437.5	41
500 to under 625	562.5	11
625 to under 750	687.5	5
750 to under 875	812.5	4
875 to under 1000	937.5	1
1000 to under 1125	1062.5	1
Total		96

As noted previously, the $250 000 up to $375 000 class is represented by the midpoint $312 500. To construct a frequency polygon, move horizontally on the graph to the midpoint $312.5, and then vertically up to 33, the class frequency, and place a dot. The X and the Y values of this point are called the *coordinates*. The coordinates of the next point are $X = \$437.5$ and $Y = 41$. The process is continued for all classes. Then the points are connected in order. That is, the point representing the lowest class is joined to the one representing the second class and so on.

Note in Chart 2–5 that, to complete the frequency polygon, midpoints of $187.5 and $1187.5 are added to the X-axis to "anchor" the polygon at zero frequencies. These two values, $187.5 and $1187.5, were derived by subtracting the class interval of $125 from the lowest midpoint ($312.5) and by adding $125 to the highest midpoint ($1062.5) in the frequency distribution.

To produce a frequency polygon using MegaStat, follow the commands for the histogram, but select Polygon.

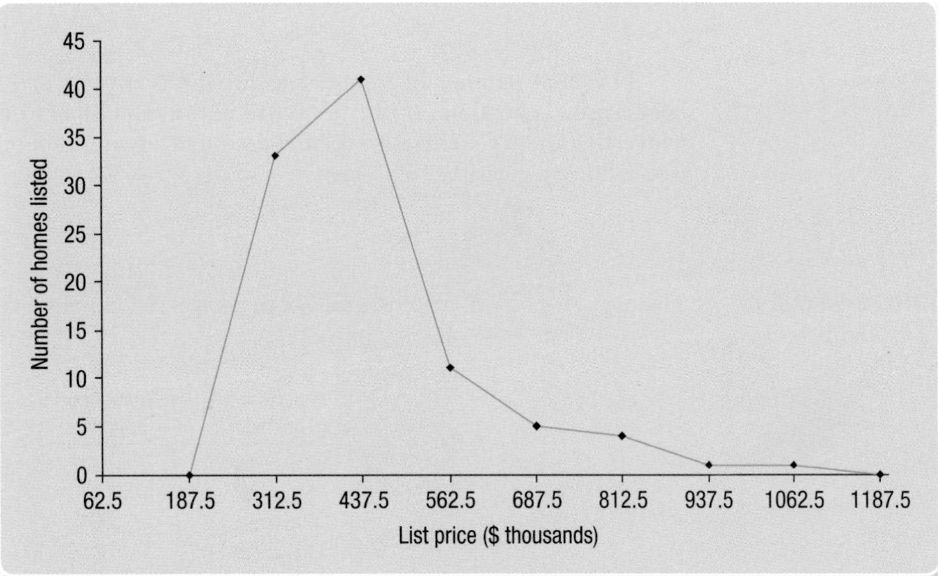

CHART 2–5 Frequency Polygon of List Prices, South-East Area of Edmonton

Both the histogram and the frequency polygon allow us to get a quick picture of the main characteristics of the data (highs, lows, points of concentration, etc.). Although the two representations are similar in purpose, the histogram has the advantage of depicting each class as a rectangle, with the height of the rectangular bar representing the number in each class. The frequency polygon, in turn, has an advantage over the histogram. It allows us to compare directly two or more frequency distributions. Suppose that the office manager at the real estate company wanted to compare the number of home listings in the same month last year. To do this, two frequency polygons are constructed, one on top of the other, as in Chart 2–6. As expected, for the most part, the typical list price is lower for the same month last year.

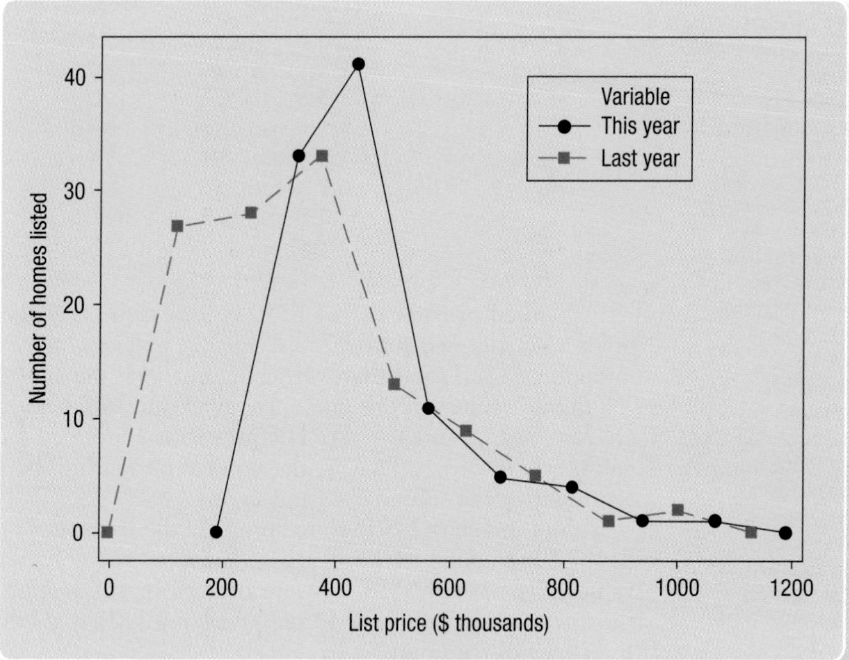

CHART 2–6 Distribution of List Prices, South-East Area of Edmonton

The total number of frequencies for the two years are about the same, so a direct comparison is possible. If the difference in the total number of frequencies is quite large, converting the frequencies to relative frequencies and then plotting the two distributions would allow a clearer comparison.

self-review 2–5

The annual imports of a selected group of electronics suppliers are shown in the following frequency distribution.

Imports ($ millions)	Number of Suppliers
$2 to under $5	6
5 to under 8	13
8 to under 11	20
11 to under 14	10
14 to under 17	1

(a) Portray the imports as a histogram.
(b) Portray the imports as a relative frequency polygon.
(c) Summarize the important facets of the distribution (such as low and high, concentration, etc.)

Exercises

15. Molly's Candle Shop has several retail stores in coastal areas. Many of Molly's customers ask her to ship their purchases. The following chart shows the number of packages shipped per day for the last 100 days.

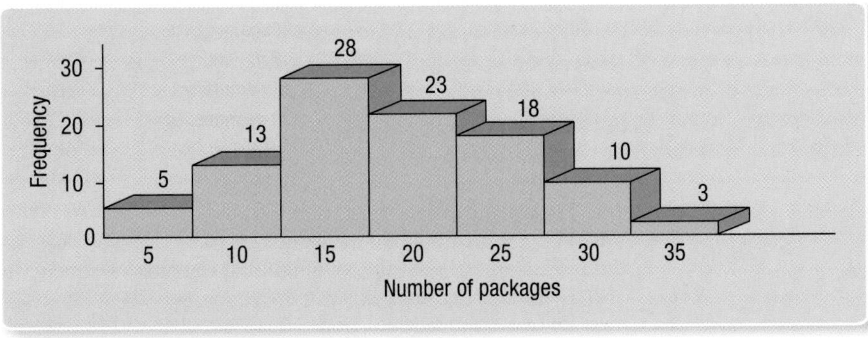

a. What is this chart called?
b. What is the total number of frequencies?
c. What is the class interval?
d. What is the class frequency for the 10 up to 15 class?
e. What is the relative frequency of the 10 up to 15 class?
f. What is the midpoint of the 10 up to 15 class?
g. On how many days were there 25 or more packages shipped?

16. The following chart shows the number of patients admitted daily to Memorial Hospital through the emergency room.

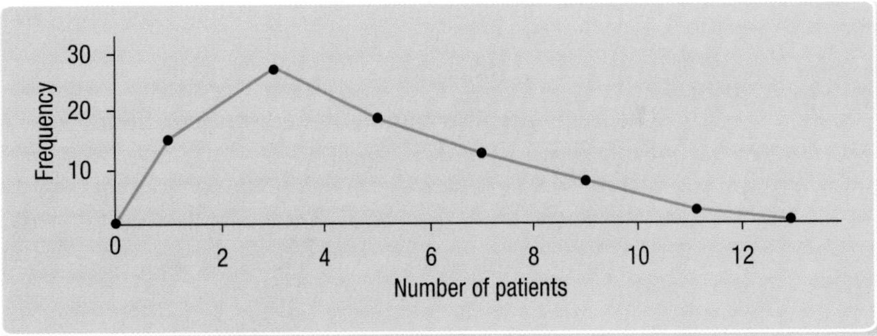

a. What is the midpoint of the 2 up to 4 class?
b. How many days were 2 up to 4 patients admitted?
c. Approximately how many days were studied?
d. What is the class interval?
e. What is this chart called?

17. The following frequency distribution reports the number of frequent flier miles, reported in thousands, for employees of Brumley Statistical Consulting Inc. during the first quarter of 2008.

Frequent Flier Miles (thousands)	Number of Employees
0 to under 3	5
3 to under 6	12
6 to under 9	23
9 to under 12	8
12 to under 15	2
Total	50

a. How many employees were studied?
b. What is the midpoint of the first class?
c. Construct a histogram.
d. A frequency polygon is to be drawn. What are the coordinates of the plot for the first class?
e. Construct a frequency polygon.
f. Interpret the frequent flier miles accumulated using the two charts.

18. Stop-One.com, a large Internet retailer, is studying the lead time (elapsed time between when an order is placed and when it is filled) for a sample of recent orders. The lead times are reported in days.

Lead Time (days)	Frequency
0 to under 5	6
5 to under 10	7
10 to under 15	12
15 to under 20	8
20 to under 25	7
Total	40

a. How many orders were studied?
b. What is the midpoint of the first class?
c. What are the coordinates of the first class for a frequency polygon?
d. Draw a histogram.
e. Draw a frequency polygon.
f. Interpret the lead times using the two charts.

Cumulative Frequency Distribution

Consider once again the distribution of list prices of the real estate example. Suppose we were interested in the number of homes listed for less than $400 000, or the value below which 40 percent of the homes were listed. These numbers can be approximated by developing a **cumulative frequency distribution**, and portraying it graphically in a **cumulative frequency polygon**, or **ogive**. There are two types: the less-than cumulative frequency distribution and the more-than cumulative frequency distribution.

example

The frequency distribution of the list prices, South-East Area of Edmonton is repeated from Table 2–7.

List Price ($ thousands)	Frequency
$250 to under $375	33
375 to under 500	41
500 to under 625	11
625 to under 750	5
750 to under 875	4
875 to under 1000	1
1000 to under 1125	1
Total	96

Construct a less-than cumulative frequency polygon. Fifty percent of the houses were listed for less than what amount? Twenty-five of the list prices were less than what amount?

solution

As the name implies, a cumulative frequency distribution and a cumulative frequency polygon require *cumulative frequencies*. To construct a cumulative frequency distribution, refer to the preceding table and note that there were 33 homes listed for less than $375 000. Those 33 list prices, plus the 41 in the next higher class, for a total of 74, were listed for less than $500 000. The cumulative frequency for the next higher class is 85, found by 3 + 41 + 11. This process is continued for all the classes. All the homes were listed for less than $1 125 000. (See Table 2–9.)

To plot a less-than cumulative frequency distribution, scale the upper limit of each class along the *X*-axis and the corresponding cumulative frequencies along the *Y*-axis. To provide additional information, you can label the vertical axis on the left in units and the vertical axis on the right in percent. In the real estate example, the vertical axis on the left is labelled from 0 to 96 and on the right from 0 to 100 percent. The value of 50 percent corresponds to 48 listings.

TABLE 2–9 Cumulative Frequency Distribution for List Price in the South-East Area of Edmonton

List Price ($ thousands)	Frequency	Cumulative Frequency	Found by
$250 to under $375	33	33	
375 to under 500	41	74	33 + 41
500 to under 625	11	85	33 + 41 + 11
625 to under 750	5	90	33 + 41 + 11 + 5
750 to under 875	4	94	
875 to under 1000	1	95	
1000 to under 1125	1	96	
Total	96		

To begin the plotting, 33 listings were less than $375 000, so the first point is $X = 375$ and $Y = 33$. The coordinates for the next point are $X = 500$ and $Y = 74$. The rest of the points are plotted as follows.

Less than 375:	33
Less than 500:	74
Less than 625:	85
Less than 750:	90
Less than 875:	94
Less than 1000:	95
Less than 1125:	96

Then the points are connected to form the chart (see Chart 2–7). To find the list price above which half the homes are listed, we draw a horizontal line from the 50 percent mark on the right-hand vertical axis over to the polygon, then drop down to the X-axis and read the list price. The value on the X-axis is about 400, so we estimate that 50 percent of the listings are less than $400 000.

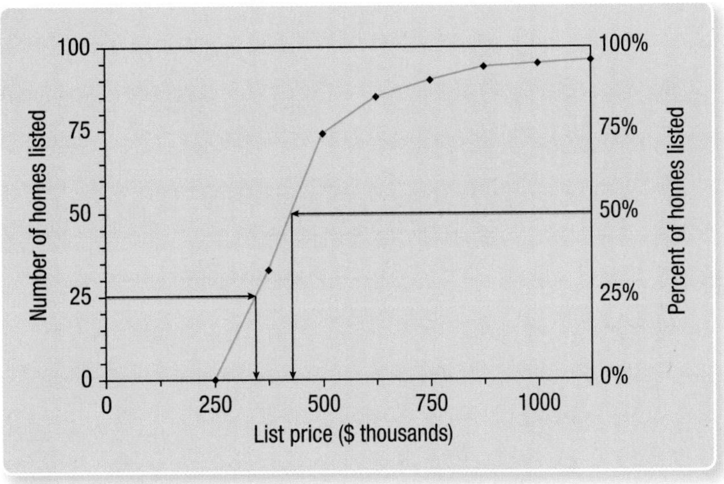

CHART 2–7 Cumulative Frequency Distribution for List Price in the South-East Area of Edmonton

To find the price below which 25 of the homes are listed, we locate the value of 25 on the left-hand vertical axis. Next, we draw a horizontal line from the value of 25 to the polygon, and then drop down to the X-axis and read the price. It is about 350, so we estimate that 25 of the homes were listed for less than \$350 000. We can also make estimates of the percent of homes that were listed less than a particular amount. To explain, suppose we want to estimate the percent of homes that were listed for less than \$600 000. We begin by locating the value of 600 on the X-axis, move vertically to the polygon, and then horizontally to the vertical axis on the right. The value is about 90 percent, so we conclude that 90 percent of the homes were listed for less than \$600 000.

To produce a less-than cumulative frequency polygon (Ogive) using MegaStat, follow the commands for the histogram, but select Ogive.

TABLE 2–10 More-than Cumulative Frequency Distribution for the List Price in the South-East Area of Edmonton

List Price (\$ thousands)	Cumulative Frequency
\$250 or more:	96
375 or more:	63
500 or more:	22
625 or more:	11
750 or more:	6
875 or more:	2
1000 or more:	1
1125 or more:	0

To construct a more-than cumulative frequency distribution, refer to the preceding table and note that there were 96 homes listed for \$250 000 or more, 63 homes listed for \$375 000 or more, and so on. To plot the distribution we can use the same axes as the less-than cumulative frequency distribution. To begin the plotting, 96 listings were \$250 000 or more, so the first point is $X = 250$ and $Y = 96$. The coordinates for the next point are $X = 350$ and $Y = 63$. The rest of the points are plotted and then they are connected to form the chart (see Chart 2–8).

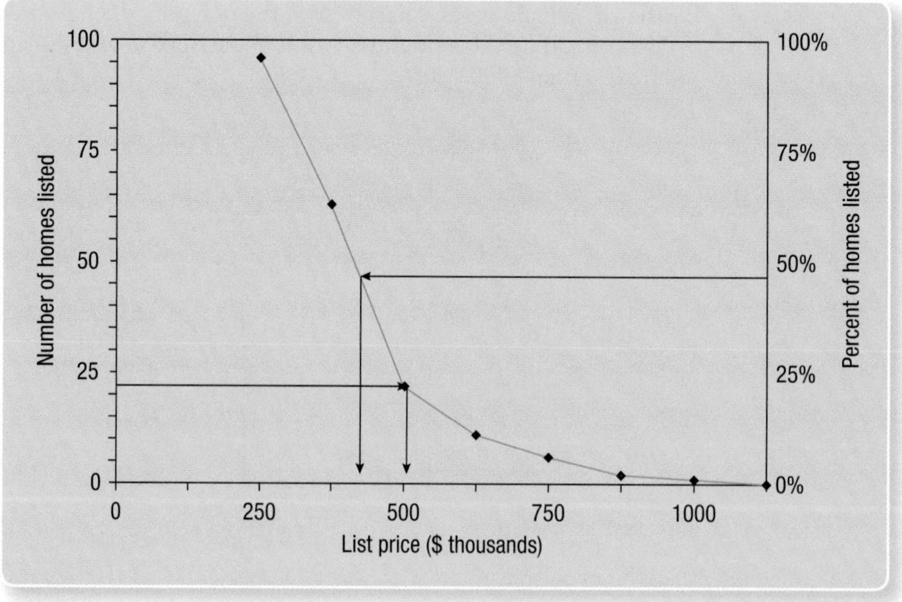

CHART 2–8 More-than Cumulative Frequency Distribution for List Price in the South-East Area of Edmonton

To find the list price above which half the homes are listed, we draw a horizontal line from the 50 percent mark on the right-hand vertical axis over to the polygon, then drop down to the X-axis and read the list price. The value on the X-axis is about 400, so we estimate that 50 percent of the listings are for \$400 000 or more. (This point is the same as for the less-than cumulative frequency distribution. To find the price above which 20 of the homes are listed, we locate the value of 20 on the left-hand vertical axis. Next, we draw a horizontal line from the value of 20 to the polygon, and then drop down to the X-axis and read the price. It is about 500, so we estimate that 20 of the houses were listed for \$500 000 or more.

self-review 2–6

A sample of the hourly wages of 15 employees at Food City Supermarkets was organized into the following table.

Hourly Wages (\$)	Number of Employees
\$6 to under \$8	3
8 to under 10	7
10 to under 12	4
12 to under 14	1

(a) What is the table called?
(b) Develop a less-than and more-than cumulative frequency distribution and portray the distribution in cumulative frequency polygons.
(c) Based on the cumulative frequency polygon, how many employees earn \$9 per hour or less? Half of the employees earn an hourly wage of how much or more? Four employees earn how much or less?

Exercises

19. The following chart shows the hourly wages of a sample of certified welders.

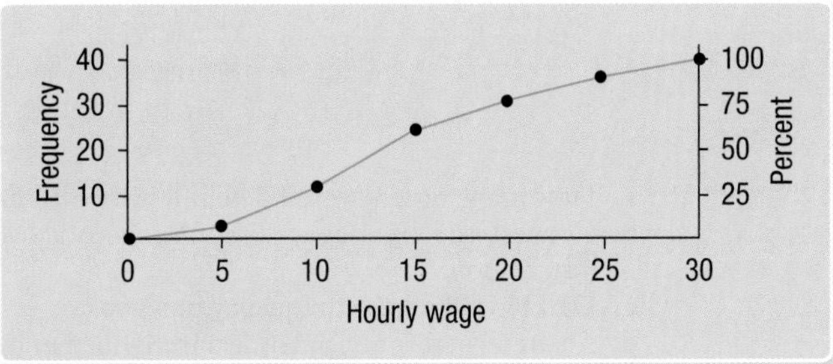

a. How many welders were studied?
b. What is the class interval?
c. About how many welders earn less than \$10.00 per hour?
d. About 75 percent of the welders make less than what amount?
e. Ten of the welders studied made less than what amount?
f. What percent of the welders make less than \$20.00 per hour?

20. The following chart shows the selling price, in thousands of dollars, of houses sold last month in Corner Brook, Nfld.

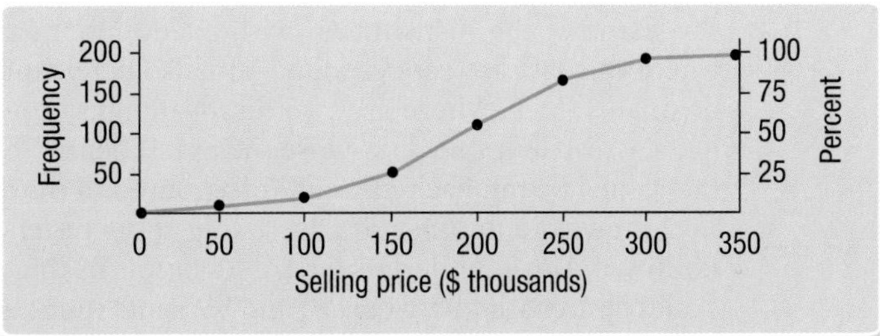

a. How many homes were studied?
b. What is the class interval?
c. One hundred homes sold for less than what amount?
d. About 75 percent of the homes sold for less than what amount?
e. Estimate the number of homes in the \$150 000 up to \$200 000 class.
f. About how many homes sold for less than \$225 000?

21. The frequency distribution representing the number of frequent flier miles accumulated by employees at Brumley Statistical Consulting Company is repeated from Exercise 17.

Frequent Flier Miles (thousands)	Frequency
0 to under 3	5
3 to under 6	12
6 to under 9	23
9 to under 12	8
12 to under 15	2
Total	50

a. How many employees accumulated less than 3000 miles?
b. Convert the frequency distribution to a less-than and more-than cumulative frequency distribution.
c. Portray the cumulative distributions in the form of cumulative frequency polygons.
d. Based on the cumulative frequency polygons, about 75 percent of the employees accumulated how many miles or less?
e. About 40 percent of the employees accumulated more than how many miles?

22. The frequency distribution of order lead time at Stop-One.com from Exercise 18 is repeated below.

Lead Time (days)	Frequency
0 to under 5	6
5 to under 10	7
10 to under 15	12
15 to under 20	8
20 to under 25	7
Total	40

a. How many orders were filled in less than 10 days? In less than 15 days?
b. Convert the frequency distribution to a less-than and more-than cumulative frequency distribution.
c. Develop cumulative frequency polygons.
d. About 60 percent of the orders were filled in less than how many days?
e. How many orders were filled in 10 or more days? In 15 or more days?
f. About 25 percent of the orders were filled in how many days or more?

4 Develop and interpret a *stem-and-leaf display.*

Stem-and-Leaf Displays

In the previous section, we showed how to organize data into a frequency distribution so we could summarize the raw data into a meaningful form. The major advantage to organizing the data into a frequency distribution is that we get a quick visual picture of the shape of the distribution without doing any further calculation. That is, we can see where the data are concentrated and also determine whether there are any extremely large or small values. There are two disadvantages, however, to organizing the data into a frequency distribution: (1) we lose the exact identity of each value and (2) we are not sure how the values within each class are distributed. To explain, the following frequency distribution shows the number of advertising spots purchased by the 45 members of the Greater Hilltown Automobile Dealers Association in the year 2008. We observe that 7 of the 45 dealers purchased between 90 and 99 spots (but less than 100). However, is the number of spots purchased within this class clustered about 90, spread evenly throughout the class, or clustered near 99? We cannot tell.

Number of Spots Purchased	Frequency
80 to under 90	2
90 to under 100	7
100 to under 110	6
110 to under 120	9
120 to under 130	8
130 to under 140	7
140 to under 150	3
150 to under 160	3
Total	45

stem-and-leaf display A statistical technique to present a set of data. Each numerical value is divided into two parts. The leading digit(s) becomes the stem and the trailing digit the leaf. The stems are located along the vertical axis, and the leaf values are stacked against each other along the horizontal axis.

One technique that is used to display quantitative information in a condensed form is the **stem-and-leaf display**. An advantage of the stem-and-leaf display over a frequency distribution is that we do not lose the identity of each observation. In the above example, we would not know the identity of the values in the 90 up to 100 class. To illustrate the construction of a stem-and-leaf display using the number of advertising spots purchased, suppose the seven observations in the 90 up to 100 class are: 96, 94, 93, 94, 95, 96, and 97. The **stem** value is the leading digit or digits, in this case 9. The **leaves** are the trailing digits. The stem is placed to the left of a vertical line and the leaf values to the right.

The values in the 90 up to 100 class would appear as follows:

9 | 6 4 3 4 5 6 7

Finally, we sort the values within each stem from smallest to largest. Thus, the second row of the stem-and-leaf display would appear as follows:

9 | 3 4 4 5 6 6 7

With the stem-and-leaf display, we can quickly observe that there were two dealers who purchased 94 spots and that the number of spots purchased ranged from 93 to 97. A stem-and-leaf display is similar to a frequency distribution with more information, that is, data values instead of tallies.

The following example will explain the details of developing a stem-and-leaf display.

example

Listed in Table 2–11 is the number of 30-second radio advertising spots purchased by each of the 45 members of the Greater Hilltown Automobile Dealers Association last year. Organize the data into a stem-and-leaf display. Around what values do the number of advertising spots tend to cluster? What is the fewest number of spots purchased by a dealer? The largest number purchased?

TABLE 2–11 Number of Advertising Spots Purchased by Members of the Greater Hilltown Automobile Dealers Association

96	93	88	117	127	95	113	96	108	94	148	156
139	142	94	107	125	155	155	103	112	127	117	120
112	135	132	111	125	104	106	139	134	119	97	89
118	136	125	143	120	103	113	124	138			

solution

From the data in Table 2–11 we note that the smallest number of spots purchased is 88. So we will make the first stem value 8. The largest number is 156, so we will have the stem values begin at 8 and continue to 15. The first number in Table 2–11 is 96, which will have a stem value of 9 and a leaf value of 6. Moving across the top row, the second value is 93 and the third is 88. After the first 3 data values are considered, your chart is as follows.

Stem	Leaf
8	8
9	6 3
10	
11	
12	
13	
14	
15	

Organizing all the data, the stem-and-leaf chart looks as follows.

Stem	Leaf
8	8 9
9	6 3 5 6 4 4 7
10	8 7 3 4 6 3
11	7 3 2 7 2 1 9 8 3
12	7 5 7 0 5 5 0 4
13	9 5 2 9 4 6 8
14	8 2 3
15	6 5 5

The usual procedure is to sort the leaf values from the smallest to largest. The last line, the row referring to the values in the 150s, would appear as:

15	5 5 6

The final table would appear as follows, where we have sorted all of the leaf values.

Stem	Leaf
8	8 9
9	3 4 4 5 6 6 7
10	3 3 4 6 7 8
11	1 2 2 3 3 7 7 8 9
12	0 0 4 5 5 5 7 7
13	2 4 5 6 8 9 9
14	2 3 8
15	5 5 6

You can draw several conclusions from the stem-and-leaf display. First, the lowest number of spots purchased is 88 and the largest is 156. Two dealers purchased less than 90 spots, and three purchased 150 or more. You can observe, for example, that the three dealers who purchased 150 spots or more actually purchased 155, 155, and 156 spots. The concentration of the number of spots is between 110 and 130. There were nine dealers who purchased between 110 and 119 spots and eight who purchased between 120 and 129 spots. We can also tell that within the 120 to 129 group the actual number of spots purchased was spread evenly throughout. That is, two dealers purchased 120 spots, one dealer purchased 124 spots, three dealers purchased 125 spots, and two purchased 127 spots.

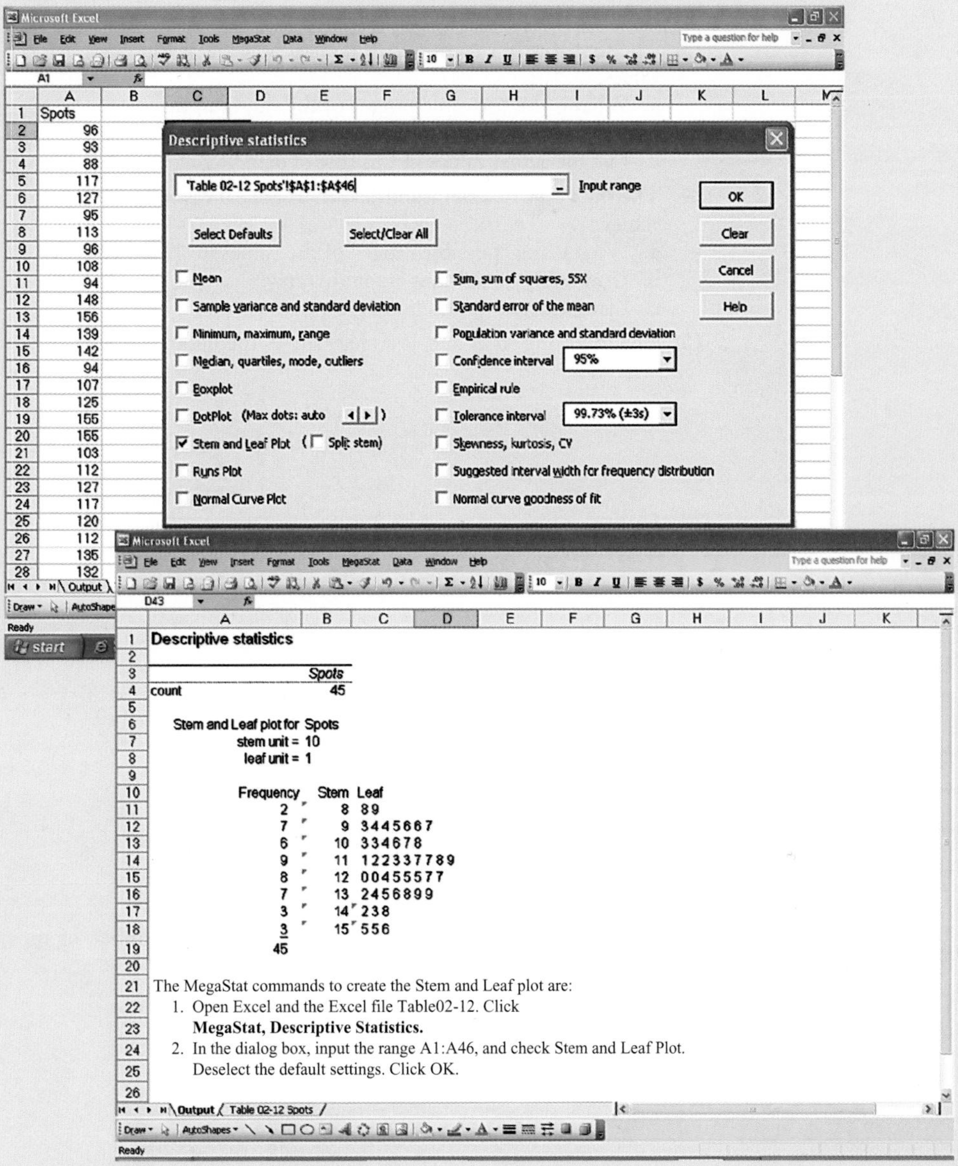

self-review 2–7

The price-earnings ratios for 21 stocks in the retail trade category are:

8.3	9.6	9.5	9.1	8.8	11.2	7.7	10.1	9.9	10.8	
10.2	8.0	8.4	8.1	11.6	9.6	8.8	8.0	10.4	9.8	9.2

Organize this information into a stem-and-leaf display.

(a) How many values are less than 9.0?
(b) List the values in the 10.0 up to 11.0 category.
(c) What is the middle value?
(d) What are the largest and the smallest price-earnings ratios?

Exercises

23. The first row of a stem-and-leaf chart appears as follows: 62 | 1 3 3 7 9. Assume whole number values.
   a. What is the "possible range" of the values in this row?
   b. How many data values are in this row?
   c. List the actual values in this row of data.

24. The third row of a stem-and-leaf chart appears as follows: 21 | 0 1 3 5 7 9. Assume whole number values.
   a. What is the "possible range" of the values in this row?
   b. How many data values are in this row?
   c. List the actual values in this row of data.

25. The following stem-and-leaf chart shows the number of units produced per day in a factory.

3	8
4	
5	6
6	0133559
7	0236778
8	59
9	00156
10	36

   a. How many days were studied?
   b. How many observations are in the first class?
   c. What are the smallest and the largest values?
   d. List the actual values in the fourth row.
   e. List the actual values in the second row.
   f. How many values are less than 70?
   g. How many values are 80 or more?
   h. What is the middle value?
   i. How many values are between 60 and 89, inclusive?

26. The following stem-and-leaf chart reports the number of movies rented per day at Video Connection.

12	689
13	123
14	6889
15	589
16	35
17	24568
18	268
19	13456
20	034679
21	2239
22	789
23	00179
24	8
25	13
26	
27	0

   a. How many days were studied?
   b. How many observations are in the last class?
   c. What are the largest and the smallest values in the entire set of data?
   d. List the actual values in the fourth row.
   e. List the actual values in the next to the last row.
   f. On how many days were less than 160 movies rented?
   g. On how many days were 220 or more movies rented?
   h. What is the middle value?
   i. On how many days were between 170 and 210 movies rented?

27. A survey of the number of calls received by a sample of Southern Phone Company subscribers last week revealed the following information. Develop a stem-and-leaf chart. How many calls did a typical subscriber receive? What were the largest and the smallest number of calls received?

52	43	30	38	30	42	12	46	39
37	34	46	32	18	41	5		

28. Altair Banking Co. is studying the number of times its automatic teller, located in a Loblaws Supermarket, is used each day. The following is the number of times it was used during each of the last 30 days. Develop a stem-and-leaf chart. Summarize the data on the number of times the automatic teller was used: How many times was the teller used on a typical day? What were the largest and the smallest number of times the teller was used? Around what values did the number of times the teller was used tend to cluster?

83	64	84	76	84	54	75	59	70	61
63	80	84	73	68	52	65	90	52	77
95	36	78	61	59	84	95	47	87	60

Chapter Summary

I. A frequency distribution is a grouping of data into mutually exclusive classes showing the number of observations in each class.

- **A.** The steps in constructing a frequency distribution are:
  1. Decide how many classes you wish.
  2. Determine the class interval or width.
  3. Set the individual class limits.
  4. Tally the raw data into the classes.
  5. Count the number of tallies in each class.
- **B.** The class frequency is the number of observations in each class.
- **C.** The class interval is the difference between the limits of two consecutive classes.
- **D.** The class midpoint is halfway between the limits of two consecutive classes.

II. A relative frequency distribution shows the percent of the observations in each class.

III. There are three methods for graphically portraying a frequency distribution.

- **A.** A histogram portrays the number of frequencies in each class in the form of rectangles.
- **B.** A frequency polygon consists of line segments connecting the points formed by the intersections of the class midpoints and the class frequencies.
- **C.** A cumulative frequency polygon shows the number of observations below a certain value.

IV. A stem-and-leaf display is an alternative to a frequency distribution.

- **A.** The leading digits are the stem and the trailing digit, the leaf.
- **B.** The advantages of the stem-and-leaf chart over a frequency distribution include:
  1. The identity of each observation is not lost.
  2. The digits themselves give a picture of the distribution.
  3. The cumulative frequencies are also reported

V. There are many charts used in business.

- **A.** A line chart is ideal for showing the trend or sales of income over time.
- **B.** Bar charts are similar to line charts and are useful for showing changes in nominal scale data.
- **C.** Pie charts are useful for showing the percent that various components compose of the total.

Chapter Exercises

29. Describe the similarities and differences of quantitative and qualitative variables. Be sure to include:
- **a.** What level of measurement is required for each variable type?
- **b.** Can both types be used to describe both samples and populations?

www.mcgrawhill.ca/olc/lind

30. Alexandra Dawn will be building a new resort in Cape Breton. She must decide how to design the resort based on the type of activities that the resort will offer to its customers. A recent poll of 300 potential customers showed that 63 liked planned activities, 135 did not like planned activities, 78 were not sure, and 24 did not respond.

a. Construct a bar chart to portray the survey results.
b. Construct a pie chart for the survey results.
c. If you were preparing a presentation, which graph would you prefer to show? Why?

31. A data set consists of 83 observations. How many classes would you recommend for a frequency distribution?

32. A data set consists of 145 observations that range from 56 to 490. What size class interval would you recommend?

33. There are 25 employees in the accounting department of East Penn Manufacturing, the world's largest and most modern battery manufacturing facility. The following is the time, in minutes, these employees spent commuting to work this morning.

28	25	48	37	41	19	32	26	16	23	23	29	36
31	26	21	32	25	31	43	35	42	38	33	28	

a. How many classes would you recommend?
b. What class interval would you suggest?
c. What would you recommend as the lower limit of the first class?
d. Organize the data into a frequency distribution.
e. Comment on the distribution of the values.

34. The following data give the weekly amounts spent on food for a sample of customers at The Green Wave Grocers newest location.

$271	363	159	76	227	337	295	319	250
279	205	279	266	199	177	162	232	303
192	181	321	309	246	278	50	41	335
116	100	151	240	474	297	170	188	320
429	294	570	342	279	235	434	123	325

a. How many classes would you recommend?
b. What class interval would you suggest?
c. What would you recommend as the lower limit of the first class?
d. Organize the data into a frequency distribution.

35. The following stem-and-leaf display shows the number of minutes of daytime TV viewing for a sample of college students.

0	05
1	0
2	137
3	0029
4	499
5	00155667799
6	023468
7	1366789
8	01558
9	1122379
10	022367899
11	2457
12	4668
13	249
14	5

a. How many college students were studied?
b. How many observations are in the second class?
c. What are the smallest and the largest values?
d. List the actual values in the fourth row.
e. How many students watched less than 60 minutes of TV?

f. How many students watched 100 minutes or more of TV?
g. What is the middle value?
h. How many students watched at least 60 minutes but less than 100 minutes?

36. The following stem-and-leaf display reports the number of orders received per day by a mail-order firm.

9	1
10	2
11	235
12	69
13	2
14	135
15	1229
16	2266778
17	01599
18	00013346799
19	03346
20	4679
21	0177
22	45
23	17

a. How many days were studied?
b. How many observations are in the fourth class?
c. What are the smallest and the largest values?
d. List the actual values in the sixth class.
e. How many days did the firm receive less than 140 orders?
f. How many days did the firm receive 200 or more orders?
g. On how many days did the firm receive 180 orders?
h. What is the middle value?

37. The following histogram shows the scores on the first statistics exam.

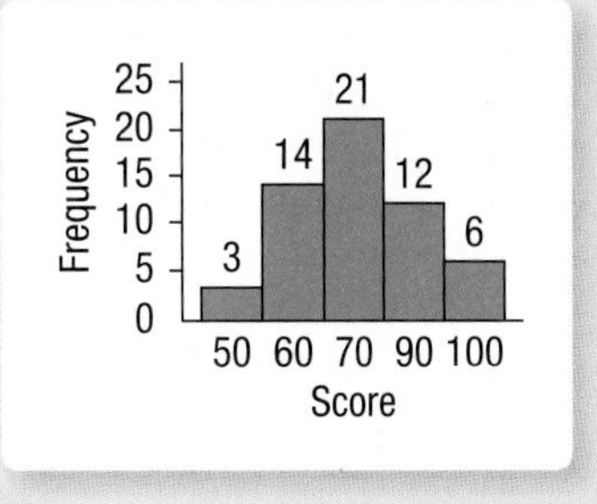

a. How many students took the exam?
b. What is the class interval?
c. What is the class midpoint for the first class?
d. How many students earned a score of less than 70?

38. The following chart summarizes the selling price of homes sold last month.

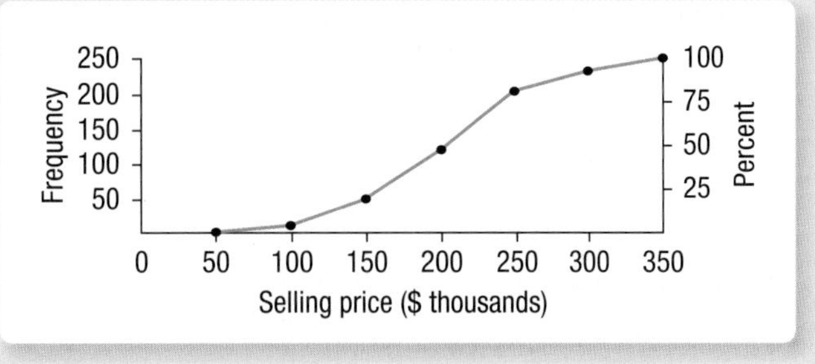

a. What is the chart called?
b. How many homes were sold during the last month?
c. What is the class interval?

d. About 75 percent of the houses sold for less than what amount?
e. One hundred seventy-five of the homes sold for less than what amount?

39. A chain of sport shops catering to beginning skiers, headquartered in Whistler, B.C., plans to conduct a study of how much a beginning skier spends on his or her initial purchase of equipment and supplies. Based on these figures, they want to explore the possibility of offerng combinations, such as a pair of boots and a pair of skis, to induce customers to buy more. A sample of their cash register receipts revealed these initial purchases:

$140	82	265	168	90	114	172	230	142
86	125	235	212	171	149	156	162	118
139	149	132	105	162	126	216	195	127
161	135	172	220	229	129	87	128	126
175	127	149	126	121	118	172	126	

a. Determine a suggested class interval. Use five classes, and let the lower limit of the first class be $80.
b. What would be a better class interval?
c. Organize the data into a frequency distribution using a lower limit of $80.
d. Interpret your findings.

40. The Saskatoon Credit Union selected a sample of 40 student chequing accounts. Below are their end-of-the-month balances, in dollars.

$404	74	234	149	279	215	123	55	43	321
87	234	68	489	57	185	141	758	72	863
703	125	350	440	37	252	27	521	302	127
968	712	503	489	327	608	358	425	303	203

a. Tally the data into a frequency distribution using $100 as a class interval and $0 as the starting point.
b. Draw a cumulative frequency polygon.
c. The bank considers any student with an ending balance of $400 or more a "preferred customer." Estimate the percentage of preferred customers.
d. The bank is also considering a service charge to the lowest 10 percent of the ending balances. What would you recommend as the cutoff point between those who have to pay a service charge and those who do not?

41. A recent survey showed that a typical car owner spends $3487 per year on operating expenses. Below is a breakdown of the various expenditure items. Construct an appropriate chart to portray the data and summarize your findings in a report.

Expenditures	Amount ($)
Fuel	$603
Interest on Car Loan	279
Repairs	930
Insurance and License	1400
Depreciation	275
Total	$3487

42. A recent study of home technologies reported the number of hours of personal computer usage per week for a sample of 60 persons. Excluded from the study were people who worked out of their home and used the computer as a part of their work.

9.3	5.3	6.3	8.8	6.5	0.6	5.2	6.6	9.3	4.3
6.3	2.1	2.7	0.4	3.7	3.3	1.1	2.7	6.7	6.5
4.3	9.7	7.7	5.2	1.7	8.5	4.2	5.5	5.1	5.6
5.4	4.8	2.1	10.1	1.3	5.6	2.4	2.4	4.7	1.7
2.0	6.7	1.1	6.7	2.2	2.6	9.8	6.4	4.9	5.2
4.5	9.3	7.9	4.6	4.3	4.5	9.2	8.5	6.0	8.1

a. Organize the data into a frequency distribution. How many classes would you suggest? What value would you suggest for a class interval?
b. Draw a histogram. Interpret your result.

43. Merrill Lynch recently completed a study regarding the size of investment portfolios (stocks, bonds, mutual funds, and certificates of deposit) for a sample of clients in the 40 to 50 age group. Listed below is the value of all the investments in thousands of dollars for the 70 participants in the study.

$669.9	7.5	77.2	7.5	125.7	516.9	219.9	645.2
301.9	235.4	716.4	145.3	26.6	187.2	315.5	89.2
136.4	616.9	440.6	408.2	34.4	296.1	185.4	526.3
380.7	3.3	363.2	51.9	52.2	107.5	82.9	63.0
228.6	308.7	126.7	430.3	82.0	227.0	321.1	403.4
39.5	124.3	118.1	23.9	352.8	156.7	276.3	23.5
31.3	301.2	35.7	154.9	174.3	100.6	236.7	171.9
221.1	43.4	212.3	243.3	315.4	5.9	1002.2	171.7
295.7	437.0	87.8	302.1	268.1	899.5		

a. Organize the data into a frequency distribution. How many classes would you suggest? What value would you suggest for a class interval?
b. Draw a histogram. Interpret your result.

44. The following table displays the average retail price of gasoline in June, in cents per litre, in St. John's, Newfoundland and Labrador over the last five years. Develop a bar chart depicting this information. (http://www40.statcan.ca/l01/cst01/econ154a.htm?sdi=gasoline)

Year	2008	2007	2006	2005	2004
Cents per litre	142.0	118.6	115.4	99.8	97.9

45. The business school at the local college reported the following percentage breakdown of expenses. Draw a pie chart showing the information.

Category	Percent (%)
Professional development	32.3%
Equipment	23.5
Mileage	12.6
PAC meetings	12.1
Office supplies	10.9
Other	8.6

46. The Consumer Price Index increases from 2003 to 2007 (base year 2002 = 100) is shown in the following table. Construct a line graph to depict the information. (http://www40.statcan.ca/l01/cst01/econ150a.htm?sdi=consumer%20price%20index)

Year	CPI
2007	111.5
2006	109.1
2005	107.0
2004	104.7
2003	102.8

47. The following table shows the average weekly earnings of workers in Canada. Develop an appropriate chart to summarize the findings. (http://www40.statcan.ca/l01/cst01/labr79.htm?sdi=earnings)

Year	Average Earnings ($)
2002	$679.32
2003	688.11
2004	702.61
2005	725.26
2006	746.89
2007	770.82

48. Annual imports from selected Canadian trading partners are listed below for the year 2003. Develop an appropriate chart or graph and write a brief report summarizing the information.

Partner	Annual Imports ($ millions)
Japan	$9550
United Kingdom	4556
South Korea	2441
China	1182
Australia	618

49. A large pharmaceutical company with distribution centres in Canada and the United States has its call centre located in Mississauga, Ontario. There are 20 customer service representatives answering calls from 8 a.m. to 9 p.m. through the week, and from 9 a.m. to 5 p.m. on Saturdays. The call centre reported the number of calls waiting to be answered between the hours of 9 a.m. and 10 a.m. over a 50-day period as shown below. Summarize the data in a chart and interpret.

47	1	8	46	76	26	4	3	39	45
4	21	80	63	100	65	91	29	7	15
7	52	87	39	106	25	55	2	3	8
14	38	59	33	76	71	37	51	1	24
35	86	185	13	7	43	36	20	79	9

50. One of the most popular candies in North America is M&M's, which is produced by the Mars Company. For many years the M&M's plain candies were produced in six colours: red, green, orange, tan, brown, and yellow. Recently, tan was replaced by blue. Did you ever wonder how many candies were in a bag, or how many of each colour? Are there about the same number of each colour, or are there more of some colours than others? Here is some information for a 500 g bag of M&M's plain candies. It contained a total of 544 candies. There were 135 brown, 156 yellow, 128 red, 22 green, 50 blue, and 53 orange. Develop a chart depicting this information and a brief report summarizing the information.

51. The following graph compares the average earnings of men and women in Canada from 1993–2006. Write a brief report summarizing the information in the graph. Be sure to include the changes that you see each period and the direction of the change over the 12-year period.

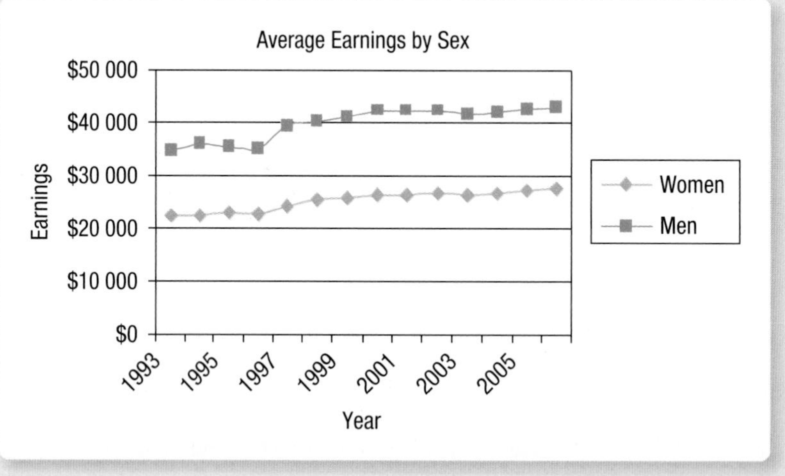

Source: Statistics Canada. (http://www40.statcan.ca/l01/cst01/labor01a.htm?sdi=earnings, August 5, 2008.)

Data Set Exercises

52. Refer to the Real Estate data, from the central area of Edmonton, on the CD-ROM, which reports information on listed homes.
   a. Select an appropriate class interval and organize the list prices into a frequency distribution.
      1. Around what values do the data tend to cluster?
      2. What is the largest list price? What is the smallest list price?
   b. Draw a less-than and more-than cumulative frequency polygon based on the frequency distribution developed in part (a).
      1. How many homes listed for less than $450 000?
      2. Estimate the percent of the homes that listed for more than $450 000?
      3. What percent of the homes listed for less than $550 000?
   c. Organize the information on the size (sq. ft.) into a frequency distribution. Select an appropriate class interval.
      1. What is a typical size? What is the range of sizes?
      2. Comment on the distribution of the values. Does it appear that any of the sizes are out of line with the others?
   d. Draw cumulative frequency distributions based on the frequency distributions developed in part (c).
      1. Forty percent of the sizes are less than what size?
      2. About how many houses have a total area of less than 1200 square feet?
      3. What percent of homes are greater than 1500 square feet?
   e. Develop a stem-and-leaf chart for the list price.
      1. Around what value are the list prices clustered?
      2. Are there any outliers?
      3. Summarize the results in a brief report.
   f. Develop a stem-and-leaf chart for the size (sq.ft.).
      1. Around what value are the number of square feet clustered?
      2. Are there any outliers?
      3. Summarize the results in a brief report.

53. Refer to the International data, which reports demographic and economic information on 46 countries.
   a. Develop a frequency distribution for the variable GNP per capita. Summarize your findings. Comment on the distribution of the values.
   b. Develop a stem-and-leaf chart for the variable referring to the number of cell phones. Summarize your findings.

Case

Rob Whitner is the owner of Whitner Pontiac. Rob's father founded the dealership in 1964, and for more than 30 years they sold exclusively Pontiacs. In the early 1990s Rob's father's health began to fail, and Rob took over more of the day-to-day operation of the dealership. At this same time, the automobile business began to change—dealers began to sell vehicles from several manufacturers—and Rob was faced with some major decisions. The first came when another local dealer, who handles Volvos, Saabs, and Volkswagens, approached Rob about purchasing his dealership. More recently, the local Chrysler dealership got into difficulty and Rob bought them out. So now, on the same lot, Rob sells the complete line of Pontiacs, the expensive Volvos, Saabs, Volkswagens, and the Chrysler products, including the popular Jeep line. Whitner Pontiac employs 83, including 23 full-time salespeople. Because of the diverse product line, there is considerable variation in the selling price of the vehicles. A top-of-the-line Volvo sells for more than twice the price of a Pontiac Grand Am. Rob would like you to develop some tables and charts that he could review monthly and would like you to report where the selling prices tend to cluster, where the variation is in the selling prices, and to note any trends. The data is on the CD-ROM, Data Files, Whitner-2007.

exercises.com

Additional exercises that require you to access information at related internet sites are available on the CD-ROM included with this text.

Answers to Self-Reviews

2–1

Flavour	Number	Relative Frequencies
Vanilla	40	0.40
Cherry	25	0.25
Lemon	20	0.20
Orange	15	0.15
Total	100	1.00

(a) Qualitative data, because the customers' response to the taste test is the flavour that they prefer.

(b)

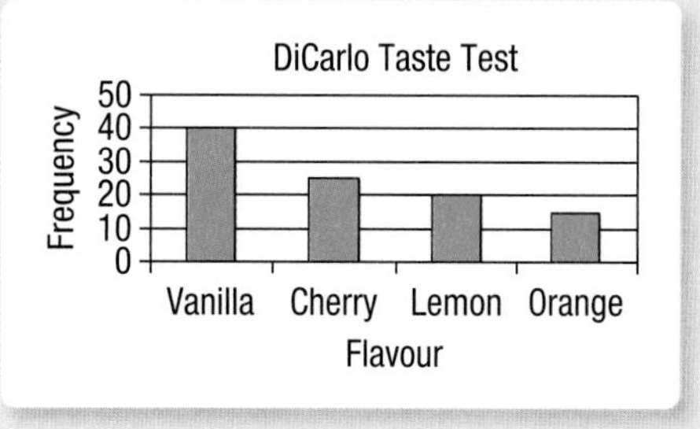

(c)

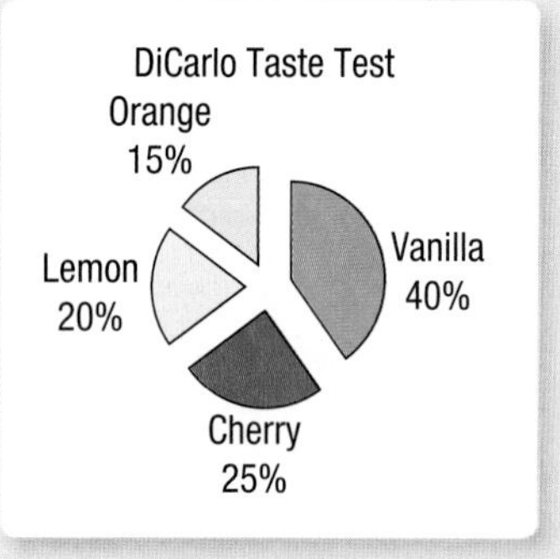

(d)

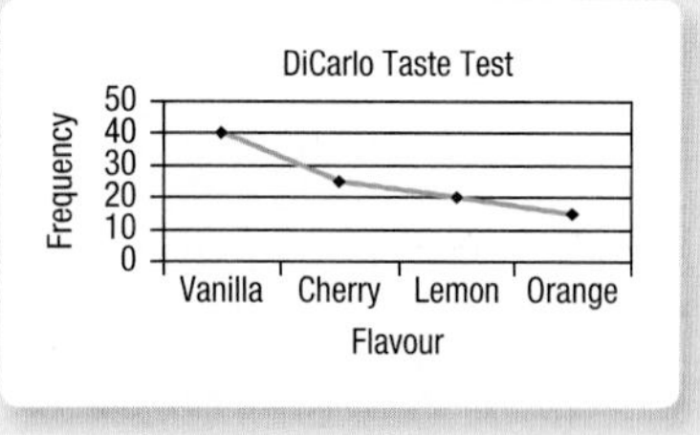

(e) The bar chart is better as there is no continuity between flavours.

2–2 **(a)** The raw data.

(b)

Commission ($)	Number of Salespeople
$1400 up to $1500	2
1500 up to 1600	5
1600 up to 1700	3
1700 up to 1800	1
Total	11

(c) Class frequencies.

(d) The largest concentration of commissions is $1500 up to $1600. The smallest commission is about $1400 and the largest is about $1800.

2–3 **(a)** $2^6 = 64 < 73 < 128 = 2^7$. So 7 classes are recommended.

(b) The interval width should be at least $(300 - 48.50)/7 = 35.93$. Class intervals of 30, 35, or 40 are reasonable.

(c) If we use a class interval of 30, and begin with $40, 9 classes would be required. A class interval of 40, starting with $40, would require 7 classes.

2–4 **(a)** 11

(b) 11.46 percent, found by $(11/96) \times 100$

(c) 6.25 percent, found by $(6/96) \times 100$

2–5 **(a)**

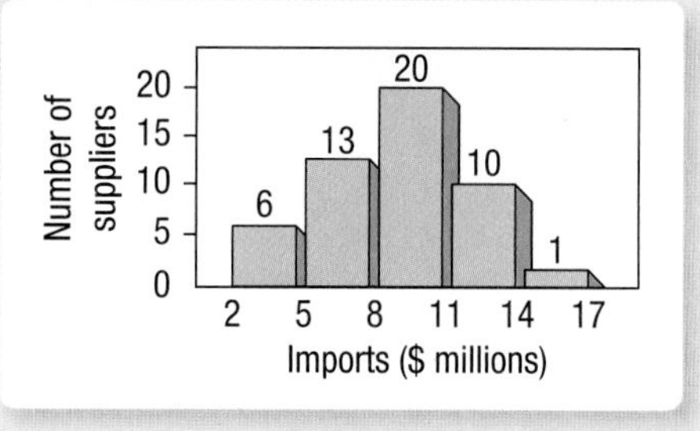

(b)

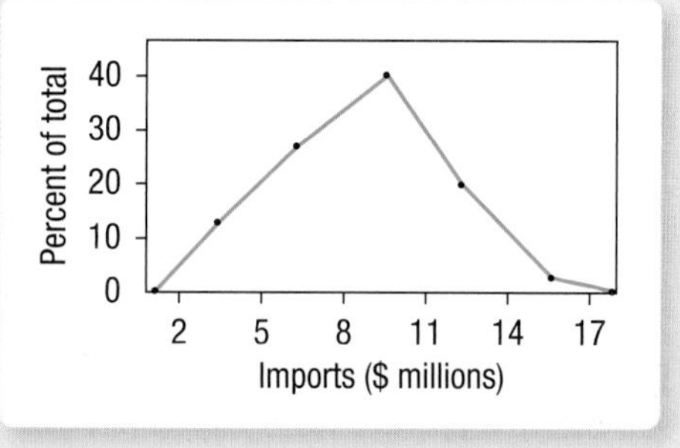

The points are: (3.5, 12), (6.5, 26), (9.5, 40), (12.5, 20), and (15.5, 2).

(c) The smallest annual sales volume of imports by a supplier is about $2 million, the highest about $17 million. The concentration is between $8 million and $11 million.

2–6 **(a)** A frequency distribution.

(b)

Hourly Wages ($)	Less-than Cumulative Number	More-than Cumulative Number
$6 to under $8	3	15
8 to under 10	10	12
10 to under 12	14	5
12 to under 14	15	1

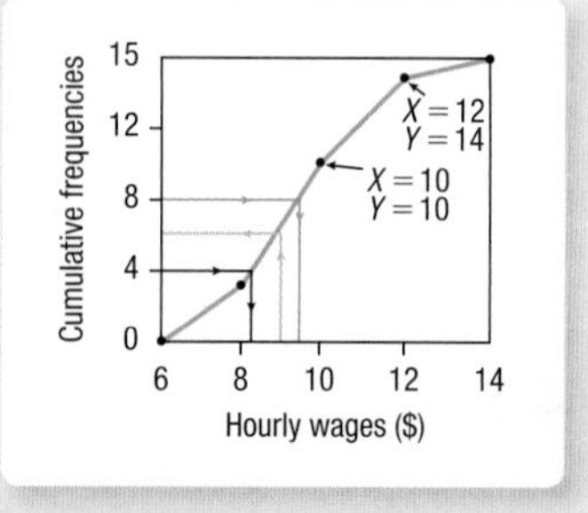

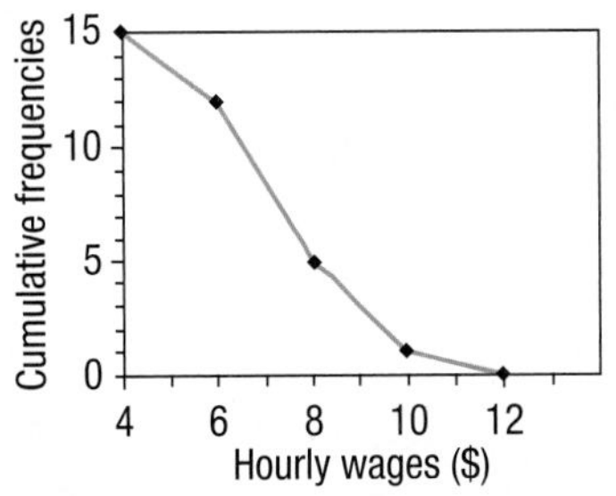

(c) About seven employees earn \$9.00 or less. About half the employees earn \$7.25 or more. About four employees earn \$8.25 or less.

2–7

7	7
8	0013488
9	1256689
10	1248
11	26

(a) 8
(b) 10.1, 10.2, 10.4, 10.8
(c) 9.5
(d) 7.7, 11.6

chapter 3

Describing Data:

Numerical Measures

LEARNING GOALS

When you have completed this chapter, you will be able to:

1. Calculate the *arithmetic mean*, *median*, *mode*, *weighted mean*, and *geometric mean*.
2. Explain the characteristics, uses, advantages, and disadvantages of each *measure of location*.
3. Identify the position of the *arithmetic mean*, *median*, and *mode* for both symmetric and skewed distributions.
4. Compute and interpret the *range*, *mean deviation*, *variance*, and *standard deviation*.
5. Explain the characteristics, uses, advantages, and disadvantages of each *measure of dispersion*.
6. Understand *Chebyshev's theorem* and the *Empirical Rule* as they relate to a set of observations.
7. Compute and interpret the *coefficient of skewness* and the *coefficient of variation*.
8. Compute and interpret *quartiles*, *interquartile range*, and *percentiles*.

Introduction

Chapter 2 began our study of descriptive statistics. To transform a mass of raw data into a meaningful form, we organized it into a frequency distribution and portrayed it graphically in a histogram or a frequency polygon. We also looked at other graphical techniques such as pie charts to portray qualitative data and frequency polygons to portray quantitative data.

This chapter is concerned with two numerical ways of describing data, namely, **measures of location** and **measures of dispersion**. Measures of location are often referred to as **averages**. The purpose of a measure of location is to pinpoint the centre of a set of values.

You are familiar with the concept of an average. An average is a measure of location that shows the central value of the data. Averages appear daily on TV, in the newspaper and other journals, and on the Internet. Here are some examples:

- The average amount of television watched by college-aged students.
- The average GPA required to be accepted at a college or university in Alberta.
- The average house price in Canada was \$317 825 in December 2007 and \$278 573 in December 2006 (http://www.crea.ca).
- As of June 2008, the average Canadian is worth \$171 000—on paper, at least. (Adapted from Statistics Canada, National Balance Sheet, http://www.statcan.ca/Daily/English/080624/d080624a.htm, June 24, 2008.)

1 Calculate the *arithmetic mean*, *median*, *mode*, *weighted mean*, and *geometric mean*.

If we consider only the measures of location in a set of data, or if we compare several sets of data using central values, we may draw an erroneous conclusion. In addition to the measures of location we should consider the **dispersion**—often called the *variation* or the *spread*—in the data. As an illustration, suppose the average annual income of marketing executives for Internet-related companies is \$80 000, and the average income for executives in pharmaceutical firms is also \$80 000. If we looked only at the average incomes, we might wrongly conclude that the two salary distributions are identical or nearly identical. A look at the salary ranges indicates that this conclusion is not correct. The salaries for the marketing executives in the Internet firms range from \$70 000 to \$90 000, but salaries for the marketing executives in pharmaceuticals range from \$40 000 to \$120 000. Thus, we conclude that although the average salaries are the same for the two industries, there is much more spread or dispersion in salaries for the pharmaceutical executives. To describe the dispersion we will consider the range, the mean deviation, the variance, and the standard deviation.

We begin by discussing measures of location. There is not just one measure of location; in fact, there are many. We will consider five: the arithmetic mean, the weighted mean, the median, the mode, and the geometric mean. The arithmetic mean is the most widely used and widely reported measure of location. We study the mean as both a population parameter and a sample statistic.

Statistics in Action

The average Canadian woman is 163 cm tall and weighs 65.8 kg. The average Canadian man is 178 cm, and weighs 83.2 kg. The average age at which Canadian women marry for the first time is 28, and for a Canadian man, it is 30. Canadian families need an average of 16.1 weeks to pay for income tax and 9.6 weeks to pay for food. The average Canadian couple will have 1.7 children. The average life expectancy of a Canadian boy in 1951 was 66 years, while that of a girl was 71 years. For those born in 2002, the average life expectancy for both males and females has increased by 11 years. On average, Canadian households have 19.6 cents of debt for every dollar of net worth. (Adapted from Statistics Canada, National Balance Sheet, http://www.statcan.ca/Daily/English/080624/d080624a.htm, June 24, 2008.)

The Population Mean

Many studies involve all the values in a population. For example, there are 12 sales associates employed at the Reynolds Road Carpet outlet. The mean amount of commission they earned last month was \$1345. This is a population value because we consider the commissions of *all* the sales associates. Other examples of a population mean would be: the average house prices in Canada in December 2007; the mean annual rate of return for the last 10 years for Berger Funds is 8.67 percent; and the mean number of hours of overtime worked last week by the six welders in the welding department of Butts Welding Inc. is 6.45 hours.

For raw data, that is, data that has not been grouped in a frequency distribution, the population mean is the sum of all the values in the population divided by the number of values in the population. To find the population mean, we use the following formula.

$$\textbf{Population mean} = \frac{\textbf{Sum of all the values in the population}}{\textbf{Number of values in the population}}$$

Instead of writing out in words the full directions for computing the population mean (or any other measure), it is more convenient to use the shorthand symbols of mathematics. The mean of a population using mathematical symbols is:

POPULATION MEAN $$\mu = \frac{\Sigma X}{N}$$ **[3–1]**

where:

μ represents the population mean. It is the Greek lowercase letter "mu."
N is the number of items in the population.
X represents any particular value.
Σ is the Greek capital letter "sigma" and indicates the operation of adding.
ΣX is the sum of the X values.

parameter A characteristic of a population.

Any measurable characteristic of a population is called a **parameter**. The mean of a population is a parameter.

example

There are 15 teams in the Eastern Conference of the NHL. Listed below is the number of goals scored by each team in the 2006–2007 season (www.nhl.com).

Team	Goals Scored	Team	Goals Scored
Buffalo Sabres	308	Montreal Canadiens	245
Ottawa Senators	288	New York Rangers	242
Pittsburgh Penguins	277	Carolina Hurricanes	241
Toronto Maple Leafs	258	Washington Capitals	235
Tampa Bay Lightning	253	Boston Bruins	219
New York Islanders	248	New Jersey Devils	216
Florida Panthers	247	Philadelphia Flyers	214
Atlanta Thrashers	246		

Is this a sample or a population? What is the arithmetic mean number of goals scored?

solution

This is a population if the researcher is considering only the teams in the Eastern Conference; otherwise, it is a sample. We add the number of goals scored for each of the 15 teams. The total number of goals scored for the 15 teams is 3737. To find the arithmetic mean, we divide this total by 15. Therefore, the arithmetic mean is 249, found by 3737/15. Using formula (3–1):

$$\mu = \frac{308 + 288 + \cdots + 214}{15} = \frac{3737}{15} = 249$$

How do we interpret the value of 249? The typical number of goals scored by a team in the Eastern Conference in the 2006–2007 season is 249.

The Sample Mean

As explained in Chapter 1, we often select a sample from a population to find something about a specific characteristic of the population. The quality control department, for example, needs to be assured that the ball bearings being produced have an acceptable outside diameter. It would be very expensive and time consuming to check the outside diameter of all the bearings produced. Therefore, we select a sample of five bearings and the mean outside diameter of the five bearings is calculated to estimate the mean diameter of all the bearings.

For raw data, that is, ungrouped data, *the mean is the sum of all the sampled values divided by the total number of sampled values*. To find the mean for a sample:

Mean of ungrouped sample data

$$\text{Sample mean} = \frac{\textbf{Sum of all the values in the sample}}{\textbf{Number of values in the sample}}$$

The mean of a sample and the mean of a population are computed in the same way, but the shorthand notation used is different. The formula for the mean of a *sample* is:

SAMPLE MEAN

$$\bar{X} = \frac{\Sigma X}{n} \quad \textbf{[3–2]}$$

where:

$\bar{X}$ is the sample mean. It is read "X bar."
n is the number in the sample.

statistic A characteristic of a sample.

The mean of a sample, or any other measure based on sample data, is called a **statistic**. If the mean outside diameter of a sample of five ball bearings is 0.625 centimetres, this is an example of a statistic.

example

SunCom is studying the number of minutes used by clients in a particular cell phone rate plan. A random sample of 12 clients showed the following number of minutes used last month.

90	77	94	89	119	112
91	110	92	100	113	83

What is the arithmetic mean number of minutes used?

solution

Using formula (3–2), the sample mean is:

$$\textbf{Sample mean} = \frac{\textbf{Sum of all the values in the sample}}{\textbf{Number of values in the sample}}$$

$$\bar{X} = \frac{\Sigma X}{n} = \frac{90 + 77 + \cdots + 83}{12} = \frac{1170}{12} = 97.5$$

The arithmetic mean of the number of minutes used last month by the sample of cell phone users is 97.5 minutes.

excel

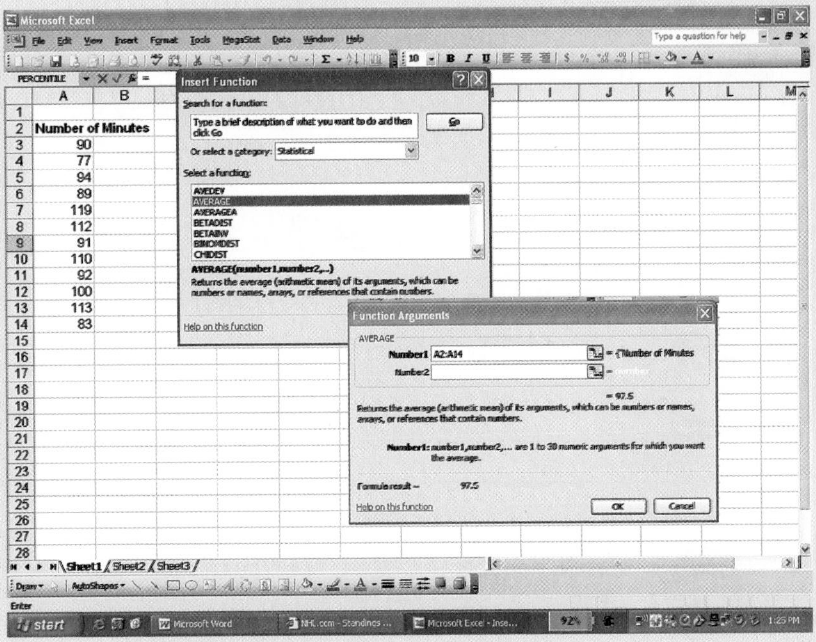

The Excel commands to find the mean are:

1. From the tool bar, select the **Paste Function, or use Insert, Function**.
2. From the **Function category** list, select **Statistical**. In the **Function name** list, select **AVERAGE**. Click **OK**. A dialog box opens.
3. Enter the range A2:A14 in the **Number1** box. The answer appears in the dialog box. Click **OK**.

2 Explain the characteristics, uses, advantages, and disadvantages of each *measure of location*.

The Properties of the Arithmetic Mean

The arithmetic mean is a widely used measure of central tendency. It has several important properties:

1. **Every set of interval-level or ratio-level data has a mean.** (Recall from Chapter 1 that ratio-level data include such data as ages, incomes, and weights, with the distance between numbers being constant.)
2. **All the values are included in computing the mean.**
3. **The mean is unique.** That is, there is only one mean in a set of data. Later in the chapter we will discover an average that might appear twice, or more than twice in a set of data.
4. **The sum of the deviations of each value from the mean is zero.** Expressed symbolically:

$$\Sigma(X - \bar{X}) = 0$$

As an example, the mean of 3, 8, and 4 is 5. Then:

$$\begin{aligned}\Sigma(X - \bar{X}) &= (3 - 5) + (8 - 5) + (4 - 5)\\ &= -2 + 3 - 1\\ &= 0\end{aligned}$$

Statistics in Action

Most colleges report the "average class size." This information can be misleading because average class size can be found several ways. If we find the number of students *in each class* at a particular school, the result is the mean number of students per class. If we compiled a list of the class sizes for each student and find the mean class size, we might find the mean to be quite different. One school found the mean number of students in each of its 747 classes to be 40. But when it found the mean from a list of the class sizes of each student it was 47. Why the disparity? Because there are fewer students in the small classes and a larger number of students in the larger class, which has the effect of increasing the mean class size when it is calculated this way.

Mean as a balance point

Thus, we can consider the mean as a balance point for a set of data. To illustrate, we have a long board with the numbers 1, 2, 3, . . . , 9 evenly spaced on it. Suppose three bars of equal weight were placed on the board at numbers 3, 4, and 8, and the balance point was set at 5, the mean of the three numbers. We would find that the board balanced perfectly! The deviations below the mean (−3) are equal to the deviations above the mean (+3). Shown schematically:

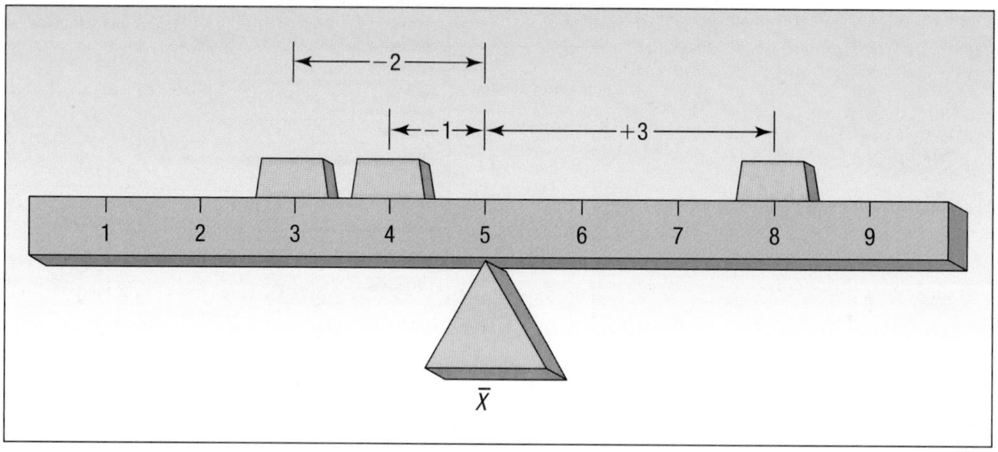

Mean unduly affected by unusually large or small values

The mean does have a weakness. Recall that the mean uses the value of every item in a sample, or population, in its computation. If one or two of these values are either extremely large or extremely small, compared to the majority of the data, the mean might not be an appropriate average to represent the data. For example, suppose the annual incomes of a small group of stockbrokers at Merrill Lynch are \$62 900, \$61 600, \$62 500, \$60 800, and \$1 200 000. The mean income is \$289 560. Obviously, it is not representative of this group, because all but one broker has an income in the \$60 000 to \$63 000 range. One income (\$1.2 million) unduly affects the mean.

self-review 3–1

1. The annual incomes of a sample of middle-management employees at Westinghouse are: \$62 900, \$69 100, \$58 300, and \$76 800.
   (a) Find the sample mean.
   (b) Is the mean you computed in (a) a statistic or a parameter? Why?
   (c) What is your best estimate of the population mean?
2. All the students in advanced Computer Science 411 are considered the population. Their course grades are 92, 96, 61, 86, 79, and 84.
   (a) Compute the mean course grade.
   (b) Is the mean you computed in (a) a statistic or a parameter? Why?

Exercises

The answers to the odd-numbered exercises are at the end of the book.

1. Compute the mean of the following population values: 6, 3, 5, 7, 6.

2. Compute the mean of the following population values: 7, 5, 7, 3, 7, 4.

3. **a.** Compute the mean of the following sample values: 5, 9, 4, 10.
b. Show that $\Sigma(X - \bar{X}) = 0$.

4. **a.** Compute the mean of the following sample values: 1.3, 7.0, 3.6, 4.1, 5.0.
b. Show that $\Sigma(X - \bar{X}) = 0$.

5. Compute the mean of the following sample values: 16.25, 12.91, 14.58.

6. Compute the mean hourly wage paid to carpenters who earned the following wages: \$15.40, \$20.10, \$18.75, \$22.76, \$30.67, \$18.00.

For Exercises 7–10, (a) compute the arithmetic mean and (b) indicate whether it is a statistic or a parameter.

7. There are 10 salespeople employed by Midtown Ford. The number of new cars sold last month by the respective salespeople were: 15, 23, 4, 19, 18, 10, 10, 8, 28, 19.

8. The accounting department at a mail-order company counted the following number of incoming calls per day to the company's toll-free number during the first seven days in May 2001: 14, 24, 19, 31, 36, 26, 17.

9. The Cambridge Power and Light Company selected 20 residential customers at random. Following are the amounts, to the nearest dollar, the customers were charged for electrical service last month:

\$54	48	58	50	25	47	75	46	60	70
67	68	39	35	56	66	33	62	65	67

10. The Human Resources Director at Ford began a study of the overtime hours in the Inspection Department. A sample of 15 workers was selected at random and records showed they worked the following number of overtime hours last month.

13	13	12	15	7	15	5	12
6	7	12	10	9	13	12	

11. AAA Heating and Air Conditioning completed 30 jobs last month with a mean revenue of \$5430 per job. The president wants to know the total revenue for the month. Based on the limited information, can you compute the total revenue? What is it?

12. A pharmaceutical company hires business administration graduates to sell its products. The company is growing rapidly and dedicates only one day of sales training for new salespeople. The company's goal for new salespeople is \$10 000 per month. The goal is based on the current mean sales for the entire company, which is \$10 000 per month. After reviewing the retention rates of new employees, the company finds that only 1 in 10 new employees stays longer than three months. Comment on using the current mean sales per month as a sales goal for new employees. Why do new employees leave the company?

The Weighted Mean

The weighted mean is a special case of the arithmetic mean. It occurs when there are several observations of the same value. To explain, suppose the nearby Wendy's Restaurant sold medium, large, and Biggie-sized soft drinks for \$1.19, \$1.39, and \$1.59, respectively. Of the last 10 drinks sold, 3 were medium, 4 were large, and 3 were Biggie-sized. To find the mean price of the last 10 drinks sold, we could use formula (3–2).

$$\bar{X} = \frac{\$1.19 + \$1.19 + \$1.19 + \$1.39 + \$1.39 + \$1.39 + \$1.39 + \$1.59 + \$1.59 + \$1.59}{10}$$

$$= \frac{\$13.90}{10} = \$1.39$$

The mean selling price of the last 10 drinks is \$1.39.

An easier way to find the mean selling price is to determine the weighted mean. That is, we multiply each observation by the number of times it happens. We will refer to the weighted mean as $\bar{X}_w$. This is read "X bar sub w."

$$\bar{X}_w = \frac{3(\$1.19) + 4(\$1.39) + 3(\$1.59)}{10} = \frac{\$13.90}{10} = \$1.39$$

In this case the weights are frequency counts. However, any measure of importance could be used as a weight.

In general the weighted mean of a set of numbers designated $X_1, X_2, X_3, \ldots, X_n$ with the corresponding weights $w_1, w_2, w_3, \ldots, w_n$ is computed by:

WEIGHTED MEAN

$$\bar{X}_w = \frac{w_1X_1 + w_2X_2 + w_3X_3 + \cdots + w_nX_n}{w_1 + w_2 + w_3 + \cdots + w_n} \quad \textbf{[3–3]}$$

This may be shortened to:

$$\bar{X}_w = \frac{\Sigma(wX)}{\Sigma w}$$

Note that the denominator of a weighted mean is always the sum of the weights.

example

Professor Hunking just marked a quiz for his finance class. The grades follow. What is the mean grade on the quiz?

Grade on Quiz	4	5	6	7	8	9	10
Number of Students	3	3	7	12	9	5	2

solution

To find the mean grade, we multiply each of the grades by the number of students earning that grade. Using formula (3–3), the mean grade is

$$\bar{X}_w = \frac{3(4) + 3(5) + 7(6) + 12(7) + 9(8) + 5(9) + 2(10)}{3 + 3 + 7 + 12 + 9 + 5 + 2} = \frac{290}{41} = 7.073$$

The weighted mean grade is rounded to 7.1.

self-review 3–2

Springers sold 95 Antonelli men's suits for the regular price of \$400. For the spring sale the suits were reduced to \$200 and 126 were sold. At the final clearance, the price was reduced to \$100 and the remaining 79 suits were sold.

(a) What was the weighted mean price of an Antonelli suit?
(b) Springers paid \$200 a suit for the 300 suits. Comment on the store's profit per suit if a sales-person receives a \$25 commission for each one sold.

Exercises

13. In June an investor purchased 300 shares of Oracle stock (an information technology company) at $20 per share. In August she purchased an additional 400 shares at $25 per share. In November she purchased an additional 400 shares, but the stock declined to $23 per share. What is the weighted mean price per share?
14. The Bookstall Inc. is a specialty bookstore concentrating on used books sold via the Internet. Paperbacks are $1.00 each, and hardcover books are $3.50. Of the 50 books sold last Tuesday morning, 40 were paperback and the rest were hardcover. What was the weighted mean price of a book?
15. The Loris Healthcare System employs 200 persons on the nursing staff. Fifty are nurse's aides, 50 are practical nurses, and 100 are registered nurses. Nurse's aides receive $16 per hour, practical nurses $20 per hour, and registered nurses $28 per hour. What is the weighted mean hourly wage?
16. Andrews and Associates specialize in corporate law. They charge $100 per hour for researching a case, $75 per hour for consultations, and $200 per hour for writing a brief. Last week one of the associates spent 10 hours consulting with her client, 10 hours researching the case, and 20 hours writing the brief. What was the weighted mean hourly charge for her legal services?

Statistics in Action

One way to measure a goalie's success is his or her GAA (goals-against average). For example, in the 2006–2007 regular hockey season, Roberto Luongo of the Vancouver Canucks had a GAA of 2.29. The goals against average is calculated by taking the number of goals against, dividing it by the number of minutes played, and then multiplying the result by 60 (60 minutes is the length of three periods played in a hockey game). What this average does not consider is the team playing against the goalie and how many shots the opposition takes. So, perhaps a better measure of a goalie's success is the save percentage. Roberto Luongo's save percentage in the same season was .921. This means that if he faced 1000 shots, he would save 921 of them. (www.nhl.com)

The Median

1 Calculate the *arithmetic mean*, *median*, *mode*, *weighted mean*, and *geometric mean*.

We have stressed that for data containing one or two very large or very small values, the arithmetic mean may not be representative. The centre for such data can be better described using a measure of location called the **median**.

median The midpoint of the values after they have been ordered from the smallest to the largest, or the largest to the smallest.

To illustrate the need for a measure of central location other than the arithmetic mean, suppose you are seeking to buy a condominium in St. John's, Newfoundland. Your real estate agent says that the typical price of the units currently available is $210 000. Would you still want to look? If you had budgeted your maximum purchase price at $190 000, you might think they are out of your price range. However, checking the individual prices of the units might change your mind. They are $160 000, $165 000, $170 000, $180 000, and a deluxe penthouse costs $375 000. The arithmetic mean price is $210 000, as the real estate agent reported, but one price ($375 000) is pulling the arithmetic mean upward, causing it to be an unrepresentative average. It does seem that a price around $170 000 is a more typical or representative average, and it is. In cases such as this, the median provides a more valid measure of location.

The median price of the units available is $170 000. To determine this, we order the prices from low ($160 000) to high ($375 000) and select the middle value ($170 000). For the median, the data must be at least an ordinal level of measurement.

Prices Ordered from Low to High ($)		Prices Ordered from High to Low ($)
$160 000		$375 000
165 000		180 000
170 000	← Median →	170 000
180 000		165 000
375 000		160 000

Median unaffected by extreme values

Note that there are the same number of prices below the median of $170 000 as above it. The median is, therefore, unaffected by extremely low or high prices. Had the highest price been $190 000, or $300 000, or even $1 million, the median price would still be $170 000. Likewise, had the lowest price been $20 000 or $50 000, the median price would still be $170 000.

In the previous illustration there is an *odd* number of observations (five). How is the median determined for an *even* number of observations? As before, the observations are ordered. Then we calculate the mean of the two middle observations. Note that for an even number of observations, the median may not be one of the given values.

example

The average list house price for a selection of Canadian cities, July 2007, is listed in the following table. Find the median list price.

City	Price
Yellowknife	$372 127
Vancouver	$581 108
Calgary	$436 739
Saskatoon	$182 920
Ottawa	$269 793
Montreal	$233 424
Halifax	$219 032
Saint John	$136 995

solution

Note that the number of list prices is even (8). As before, the list prices are first ordered from low to high. Then the two middle list prices are identified. The arithmetic mean of the two middle observations gives us the median list price. Arranging from low to high:

City	Price
Saint John	$136 995
Saskatoon	$182 920
Halifax	$219 032
Montreal	$233 424
Ottawa	$269 793
Yellowknife	$372 127
Calgary	$436 739
Vancouver	$581 108

$$\frac{\$233\,424 + \$269\,793}{2} = \$251\,608.50$$

Note that the median is not one of the values. Also, half of the list prices are below the median and half are above it.

2 **Explain the characteristics, uses, advantages, and disadvantages of each *measure of location*.**

The major properties of the median are:

1. **It is not affected by extremely large or small values.** Therefore the median is a valuable measure of location when such values do occur.
2. **It can be computed for ordinal-level data or higher.** Recall from Chapter 1 that ordinal-level data can be ranked from low to high—such as the response "excellent", "very good", "good", "fair", and "poor" to a question on a marketing survey.

Median can be determined for all levels of data except nominal

To use a simple illustration, suppose five people rated a new fudge bar. One person thought it was excellent, one rated it very good, one called it good, one rated it fair, and one considered it poor. The median response is "good." Half of the responses are above "good"; the other half are below it.

The **Excel** commands to find the median are:

1. From the tool bar, select the Paste Function, or use Insert, Function.
2. From the Function category list, select Statistical. In the Function name list, select MEDIAN. Click OK. A dialogue box opens.
3. Enter the range in the Number1 box. The answer appears in the dialogue box. Click OK.

1 Calculate the *arithmetic mean*, *median*, *mode*, *weighted mean*, and *geometric mean*.

mode The value of the observation that appears most frequently.

The Mode

The **mode** is another measure of location.

The mode is especially useful in summarizing nominal-level data. As an example of its use for nominal-level data, a company has developed five bath oils. The bar chart in Chart 3–1 shows the results of a marketing survey designed to find which bath oil consumers prefer. The largest number of respondents favoured Lamoure, as evidenced by the highest bar. Thus, Lamoure is the mode.

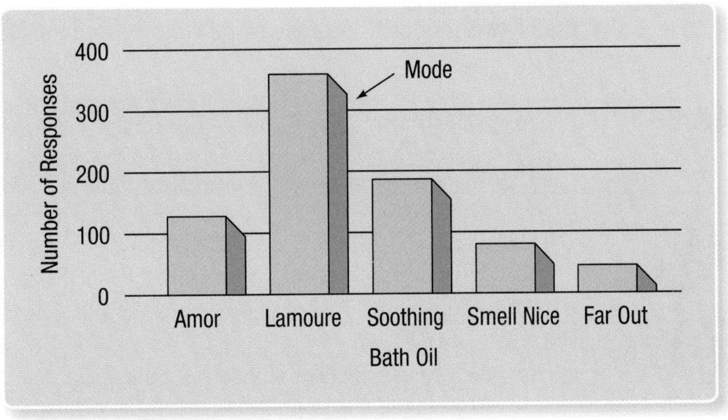

CHART 3–1 Number of Respondents Favouring Various Bath Oils

example

Average earnings of Canadians 15 years and older with university degrees in selected cities are shown below. (Statistics Canada, Census of Population, 2001)

City	Salary ($)	City	Salary ($)
Calgary	$58 000	Regina	$46 000
Edmonton	45 000	Saint John	46 000
Halifax	43 000	Greater Sudbury	50 000
Hamilton	52 000	Toronto	56 000
London	48 000	Winnipeg	43 000
Montreal	47 000	Vancouver	46 000
Ottawa-Gatineau	55 000	Victoria	42 000

Source: Adapted from the Statistics Canada website http://www.statcan.ca/english/Pgdb/labor50a.htm; March 29, 2005.

solution

A perusal of the earnings reveals that $46 000 appears more often (three times) than any other amount. Therefore, the mode is $46 000.

The **Excel** commands to find the mode are similar to those of the mean and median.

1. Select the Paste Function.
2. In the Function name list, select MODE. Click OK. A dialogue box opens.
3. Enter the range in the Number1 box. The answer appears in the dialogue box. Click OK.

2 Explain the characteristics, uses, advantages, and disadvantages of each *measure of location*.

In summary, we can determine the mode for all levels of data—nominal, ordinal, interval, and ratio. The mode also has the advantage of not being affected by extremely high or low values.

Disadvantages of the mode

The mode does have a number of disadvantages, however, that cause it to be used less frequently than the mean or median. For many sets of data, there is no mode because no value appears more than once. For example, there is no mode for this set of price data: \$19, \$21, \$23, \$20, and \$18. Since every value is different, however, it could be argued that every value is the mode. Conversely, for some data sets there is more than one mode. Suppose the ages of a group are 22, 26, 27, 27, 31, 35, and 35. Both the ages 27 and 35 are modes. Thus, this grouping of ages is referred to as *bimodal* (having two modes). One would question the use of two modes to represent the central tendency of this set of age data.

self-review 3–3

1. According to Statistics Canada, the average weekly employment insurance benefits for 2007, by category, are: \$316, \$295, \$330, \$379, \$103, and \$379. (Source: Adapted from Statistics Canada, http://www40.statcan.ca/l01/cst01/labor17.htm, September 23, 2008—*the complete file is on the CD-ROM*)
   (a) What is the median monthly benefit?
   (b) How many observations are below the median? Above it?
2. The numbers of work stoppages in the automobile industry for selected months are 6, 0, 10, 14, 8, and 0.
   (a) What is the median number of stoppages?
   (b) How many observations are below the median? Above it?
   (c) What is the modal number of work stoppages?

Exercises

17. What would you report as the modal value for a set of observations if there were a total of:
   a. 10 observations and no two values were the same?
   b. 6 observations and they were all the same?
   c. 6 observations and the values were 1, 2, 3, 3, 4, and 4?

For Exercises 18–20, (a) determine the median and (b) the mode.

18. The following is the number of oil changes for the last seven days at the Jiffy Lube located at the corner of Elm Street and Fortson Avenue.

41	15	39	54	31	15	33

19. The following is the percent change in net income from 2004 to 2005 for a sample of 12 construction companies in Benton.

5	1	−10	−6	5	12	7	8	2	5	−1	11

20. The following are the ages of the 10 people in the video arcade at the Southwyck Shopping Mall at 10 a.m. this morning.

12	8	17	6	11	14	8	17	10	8

21. Listed below is the average earnings ratio by sex for full-year, full-time workers from 1993 to 2006. (Source: Adapted from statistics Canada-the complete file is on the CD-ROM).

Year	Women	Men	Ratio (%)	Year	Women	Men	Ratio (%)
1993	\$22 300	\$34 700	64.3%	2000	\$26 300	\$42 500	61.7%
1994	22 500	36 200	62.2	2001	26 400	42 400	62.1
1995	23 000	35 400	65.0	2002	26 700	42 500	62.8
1996	22 700	35 300	64.3	2003	26 400	41 900	62.9
1997	24 300	39 300	61.9	2004	26 700	42 100	63.4
1998	25 400	40 400	62.8	2005	27 300	42 700	64.0
1999	25 800	41 200	62.6	2006	27 700	42 900	64.7

a. What is the median earnings ratio?
b. What is the modal earnings ratio?

22. Listed below are the total automobile sales (in millions) for the last 14 years. During this period, what was the median number of automobiles sold? What is the mode?

9.0	8.5	8.0	9.1	10.3	11.0	11.5	10.3	10.5	9.8	9.3	8.2	8.2	8.5

23. An accounting firm specializes in income tax returns for self-employed professionals, such as doctors, dentists, architects, and lawyers. The firm employs 11 accountants who prepare the returns. For last year, the number of returns prepared by each accountant was:

58	75	31	58	46	65	60	71	45	58	80

Find the mean, median and mode for the number of returns prepared by each accountant. If you could report only one, which measure of location would you recommend reporting?

24. The demand for video games has exploded in the last several years. So, the owner of Matt Videos needs to hire several new technical people in order to keep up with the demand. Matt Videos gives each applicant a special test, designed by Dr. McGraw, who believes that the result of the test is closely related to the ability to create video games. For the general population, the mean on this test is 100. The applicant's scores are listed below.

95	105	120	81	90	115	99	100	130	10

The president, Matt Schauer, is interested in the overall quality of the job applicants based on this test. Compute the mean and the median score for the 10 applicants. What would you report to the president? Does it seem that the applicants are better than the general population?

Software Solution

We can use a software package to find many measures of location.

example

Table 2–1 shows the list prices of 96 homes listed in the south-east area of Edmonton. Determine the mean, median and modal list price.

solution

The mean, median and modal list prices are reported in the following **Excel** output. There are 96 list prices, so calculations with a calculator would be tedious and prone to error.

Descriptive Statistics

	List Price
Count	96
Mean	447,403.14
1st quartile	357,250.00
Median	402,400.00
3rd quartile	479,150.00
Interquartile range	121,900.00
Mode	399,900.00

The mean list price is \$447 403, the median is \$402 400 and the mode is \$399 900. The mean is somewhat distorted by several listings that are over \$625 000 of which 2 are over \$875 000. The mode is much lower than both the mean and median, and so, the median value is most representative of the data. We can then conclude that the typical home was listed at about \$402 400. We can also see from the output that the count is 96, indicating that the sample consisted of 96 list prices.

The **Excel** commands to create the descriptive statistics for the list prices follow.

1. Open **Excel** and the **Excel** file Table 02-1 from the DataSets on the CD provided.
2. From the menu bar, select Tools, Data Analysis, and Descriptive Statistics; then click OK. In **Excel** 2007, select Data in place of Tools.
3. Enter A1:A97 as the Input Range. For Grouped By, select Columns to indicate that your data is in a column; select Labels in First Row to indicate that you have the label List Price in the first cell of the input range. Place the output in the same worksheet by entering C3 in the Output Range.
4. Select the Summary statistics box; click OK.

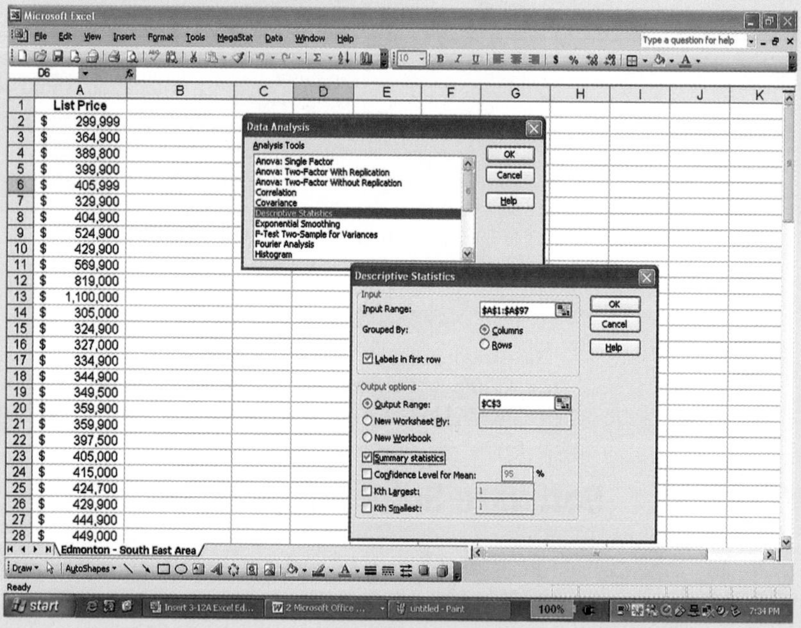

The MegaStat commands to create the descriptive statistics for the list prices follow.

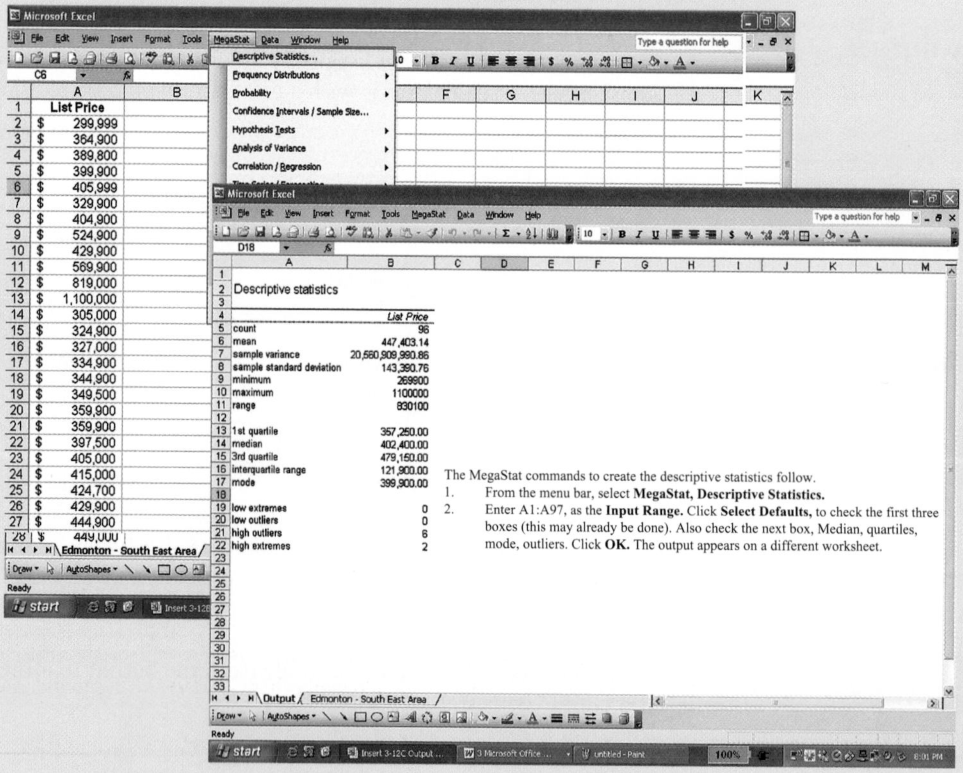

The MegaStat commands to create the descriptive statistics follow.

1. From the menu bar, select **MegaStat, Descriptive Statistics.**
2. Enter A1:A97, as the **Input Range.** Click **Select Defaults,** to check the first three boxes (this may already be done). Also check the next box, Median, quartiles, mode, outliers. Click **OK.** The output appears on a different worksheet.

3 **Identify the position of the *arithmetic mean, median,* and *mode* for both symmetric and skewed distributions.**

The Relative Positions of the Mean, Median, and Mode

Refer to the histogram in Chart 3–2. It is a symmetric distribution, which is also mound-shaped. This distribution *has the same shape on either side of the centre*. If the histogram were folded in half, the two halves would be identical. For any symmetric distribution, the mode, median, and mean are located at the centre and are always equal. They are all equal to 20 years in Chart 3–2. We should point out that there are symmetric distributions that are not mound-shaped.

For a symmetric, mound-shaped distribution, mean, median, and mode are equal.

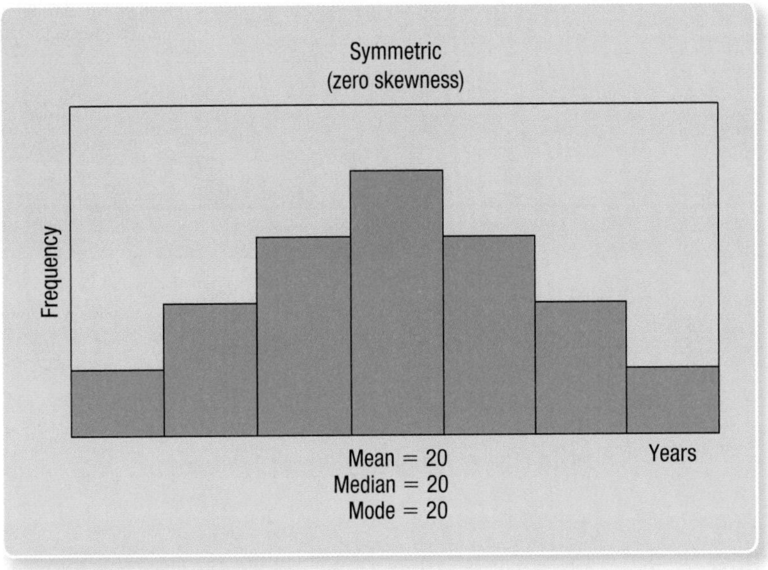

CHART 3–2 A Symmetric Distribution

A skewed distribution is not symmetrical.

The number of years corresponding to the highest point of the curve is the *mode* (20 years). Because the distribution is symmetrical, the *median* corresponds to the point where the distribution is cut in half (20 years). The total number of frequencies representing many years is offset by the total number representing few years, resulting in an *arithmetic mean* of 20 years. Logically, any of the three measures would be appropriate to represent this distribution.

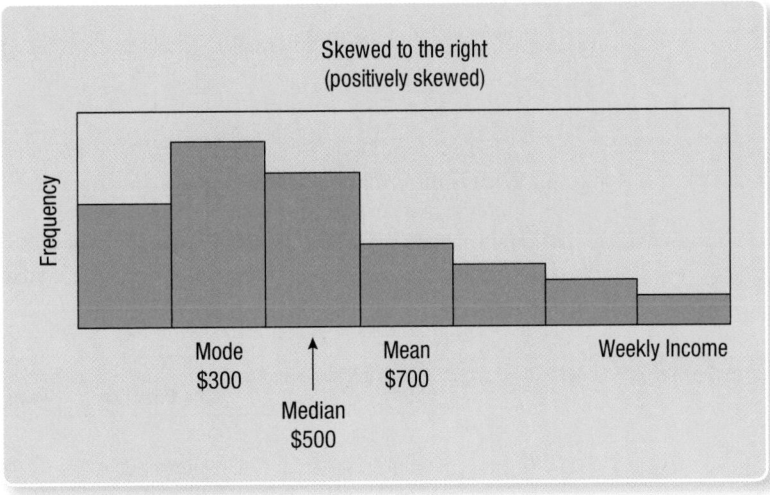

CHART 3–3 A Positively Skewed Distribution

If a distribution is nonsymmetrical, or **skewed**, the relationship among the three measures changes. In a **positively skewed distribution**, the arithmetic mean is the largest of the three measures. Why? Because the mean is influenced more than the median or mode by a few extremely high values. The median is generally the next largest measure in a positively skewed frequency distribution. The mode is the smallest of the three measures.

If the distribution is highly skewed, such as the weekly incomes in Chart 3–3, the mean would not be a good measure to use. The median and mode would be more representative.

Conversely, in a distribution that is **negatively skewed**, the mean is the lowest of the three measures. The mean is, of course, influenced by a few extremely low observations. The median is greater than the arithmetic mean, and the modal value is the largest of the three measures. Again, if the distribution is highly skewed, such as the distribution of tensile strengths shown in Chart 3–4, the mean should not be used to represent the data.

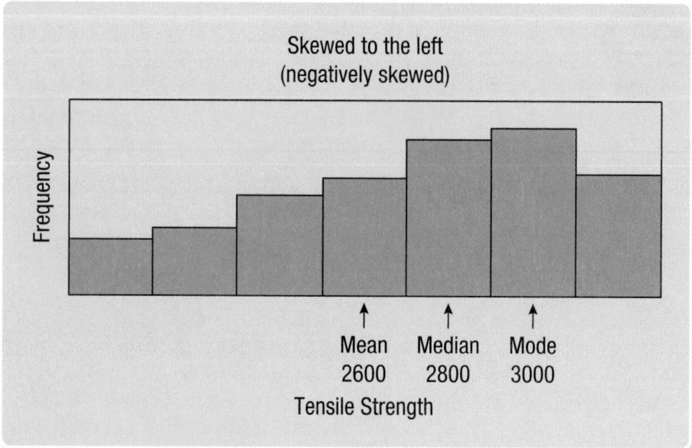

CHART 3–4 A Negatively Skewed Distribution

self-review 3–4

The weekly sales from a sample of Hi-Tec electronic supply stores were organized into a frequency distribution. The mean of weekly sales was computed to be $105 900, the median $105 000, and the mode $104 500.

(a) Sketch the sales in the form of a smoothed frequency polygon. Note the location of the mean, median, and mode on the *X*-axis.
(b) Is the distribution symmetrical, positively skewed, or negatively skewed? Explain.

Exercises

25. The number of minutes that it takes an auditor to process an invoice is given in the table below:

7.8	8.2	7.6	7.2	6.6	6.6	6.1	5.8	5.9	5.7	6.3	6.8

a. What is the arithmetic mean of processing time?
b. Find the median and the mode of the processing times.
c. Is the data symmetrical, positively skewed, or negatively skewed? Explain.

26. Big Orange Trucking is designing an information system for use in "in-cab" communications. It must summarize data from eight sites throughout a region to describe typical conditions. Compute an appropriate measure of central location for each of the three variables shown in the table below.

City	Wind Direction	Temperature	Pavement
Winnipeg	West	0	Dry
Grand Rapids	Northwest	−2	Wet
Garden Hill	Southwest	2	Wet
Brandon	South	1	Dry
Portage La Prairie	Southwest	2	Dry
Selkirk	South	2	Trace
The Pas	Southwest	3	Wet
Flin Flon	Southwest	3	Trace

The Geometric Mean

The geometric mean is never greater than the arithmetic mean.

The geometric mean is useful in finding the average of percentages, ratios, indexes, or growth rates over time. It has a wide application in business and economics because we are often interested in finding the percentage changes in sales, salaries, or economic figures, such as the Gross Domestic Product, which compound or build on each other. The geometric mean of a set of n positive numbers is defined as the nth root of the product of the n values. The formula for the geometric mean is written:

GEOMETRIC MEAN $$GM = \sqrt[n]{(X_1)(X_2)\cdots(X_n)} \qquad [3\text{–}4]$$

The geometric mean will always be less than or equal to (never more than) the arithmetic mean. Also all the data values must be positive.

As an example of the geometric mean, suppose you receive a 5 percent increase in salary this year and a 15 percent increase next year. The average percent increase is 9.886, not 10.0. Why is this so? We begin by calculating the geometric mean. Recall, for example, that a 5 percent increase in salary is 105 percent or 1.05. We will write it as 1.05.

$$GM = \sqrt{(1.05)(1.15)} = 1.09886$$

This can be verified by assuming that your monthly earning was \$3000 to start and you received two increases of 5 percent and 15 percent.

Raise 1 = \$3000 (.05) = \$150.00
Raise 2 = \$3150 (.15) = 472.50
Total \$622.50

Your total salary increase is \$622.50. This is equivalent to:

\$3000.00 (.09886) = \$296.58
\$3296.58 (.09886) = 325.90
\$622.48 is about \$622.50

The following example shows the geometric mean of several percentages.

example

The return on investment earned by Atkins Construction Company for four successive years was: 30 percent, 20 percent, −40 percent, and 200 percent. What is the geometric mean rate of return on investment?

solution

The number 1.3 represents the 30 percent return on investment, which is the "original" investment of 1.0 plus the "return" of 0.3. The number 0.6 represents the loss of 40 percent, which is the original investment of 1.0 reduced by 40 percent (−0.4). This calculation assumes the total return each period is reinvested or becomes the base for the next period. In other words, the base for the second period is 1.3 and the base for the third period is (1.3)(1.2) and so forth.

Then the geometric mean rate of return is 29.4 percent, found by

$$GM = \sqrt[n]{(X_1)(X_2)\cdots(X_n)} = \sqrt[4]{(1.3)(1.2)(0.6)(3.0)} = 1.294$$

The geometric mean is the fourth root of 2.808. So, the average rate of return (compound annual growth rate) is 29.4 percent.

Notice also that if you compute the arithmetic mean [(30 + 20 − 40 + 200)/4 = 52.5], you would have a much larger number, which would overstate the true rate of return!

A second application of the geometric mean is to find an average percent increase over a period of time. For example, if you earned \$30 000 in 1992 and \$50 000 in 2002, what is your annual rate of increase over the period? The rate of increase is determined from the following formula.

AVERAGE PERCENT INCREASE OVER TIME

$$GM = \sqrt[n]{\frac{\text{Value at end of period}}{\text{Value at beginning of period}}} - 1 \qquad [3\text{–}5]$$

In the above box n is the number of periods. An example will show the details of finding the average annual percent increase.

example

The population of Alberta grew from 2 974 807 in 2001 to 3 290 350 in 2006. What was the average annual rate of percentage increase during the period?

solution

There are 5 years between 2001 and 2006 so $n = 5$. The formula (3–5) for the geometric mean as applied to this type of problem is:

$$GM = \sqrt[n]{\frac{\text{Value at end of period}}{\text{Value at beginning of period}}} - 1$$

$$= \sqrt[5]{\frac{3\,290\,350}{2\,974\,807}} - 1 = 1.0204 - 1 = .0204$$

The final value is 0.0204. So the annual rate of increase is 2.04 percent. This means that the average rate of population growth in the province is 2.04 percent per year from 2001 to 2006.

self-review 3–5

1. The percent increase in sales, for the last four years at Combs Cosmetics are: 4.91, 5.75, 8.12, and 21.60.
   (a) Find the geometric percent increase.
   (b) Find the arithmetic percent increase.
   (c) Is the arithmetic mean equal to or greater than the geometric mean?
2. Production of Cablos trucks increased from 23 000 units in 1988 to 120 520 units in 2008. Find the geometric mean annual percent increase.

Exercises

27. Compute the geometric mean of the following percent increases: 8, 12, 14, 26, and 5.

28. Compute the geometric mean of the following percent increases: 2, 8, 6, 4, 10, 6, 8, and 4.

29. Listed below is the percent increase in sales for the MG Corporation over the last five years. Determine the geometric mean percent increase in sales over the period.

9.4	13.8	11.7	11.9	14.7

30. In 1978, the CPI for Canada was 43.6, but in 1988, the CPI was 84.8. What was the geometric mean annual increase for the period?

31. The population of Canada has increased from 21 961 999 in 1971 to 31 241 030 in 2006. What was the geometric mean annual increase for the period?

32. Gas prices in St. John's, Newfoundland and Labrador have increased from 64.1 cents per litre for regular unleaded in 1990, to 116.0 cents per litre in 2007. What was the geometric mean annual increase for the period?

33. In 1999 there were 42.0 million pager subscribers. By 2004 the number of subscribers increased to 70.0 million. What is the geometric mean annual increase for the period?

34. Tuition fees for dentistry in Canada increased from \$7863 for the 1999–2000 academic year to \$11 733 in the 2003–2004 academic year. What was the geometric mean annual increase for the period?

Why Study Dispersion?

A measure of location, such as the mean or the median, only describes the centre of the data. It is valuable from that standpoint, but it does not tell us anything about the spread of the data. For example, if your nature guide told you that the river ahead averaged 1 m in depth, would you want to wade across on foot without additional information? Probably not. You would want to know something about the variation in the depth. Is the maximum depth of the river 1.25 m and the minimum 0.5 m? If that is the case, you would probably agree to cross. What if you learned the river depth ranged from 0.50 m to 2 m? Your decision would probably be not to cross. Before making a decision about crossing the river, you want information on both the typical depth and the dispersion in the depth of the river.

A small value for a measure of dispersion indicates that the data are clustered closely, say, around the arithmetic mean. The mean is therefore considered representative of the data. Conversely, a large measure of dispersion indicates that the mean is not reliable. Refer to Chart 3–5. The 100 employees of Hammond Iron Works Inc., a steel fabricating company, are organized into a histogram based on the number of years of employment with the company. The mean is 4.9 years, but the spread of the data is from 6 months to 16.8 years. The mean of 4.9 years is not very representative of all the employees.

The average is not representative because of the large spread.

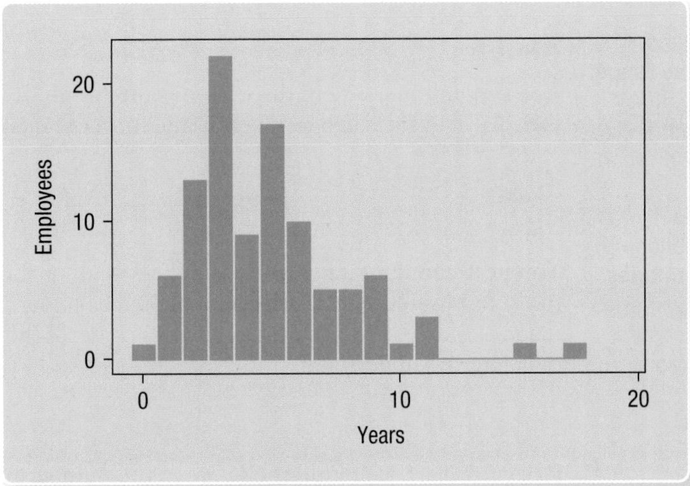

CHART 3–5 Histogram of Years of Employment at Hammond Iron Works Inc.

A second reason for studying the dispersion in a set of data is to compare the spread in two or more distributions. Suppose, for example, that the new Vision Quest LCD computer monitor is assembled in Kanata and also in Waterloo. The arithmetic mean hourly output in both the Kanata plant and the Waterloo plant is 50. Based on the two means, you might conclude that the distributions of the hourly outputs are identical. Production records for nine hours at the two plants, however, reveal that this conclusion is not correct (see Chart 3–6). Kanata production varies from 48 to 52 assemblies per hour. Production at the Waterloo plant is more erratic, ranging from 40 to 60 per hour. Therefore, the hourly output for Kanata is clustered near the mean of 50; the hourly output for Waterloo is more dispersed.

A measure of dispersion can be used to evaluate the reliability of two or more measures of location.

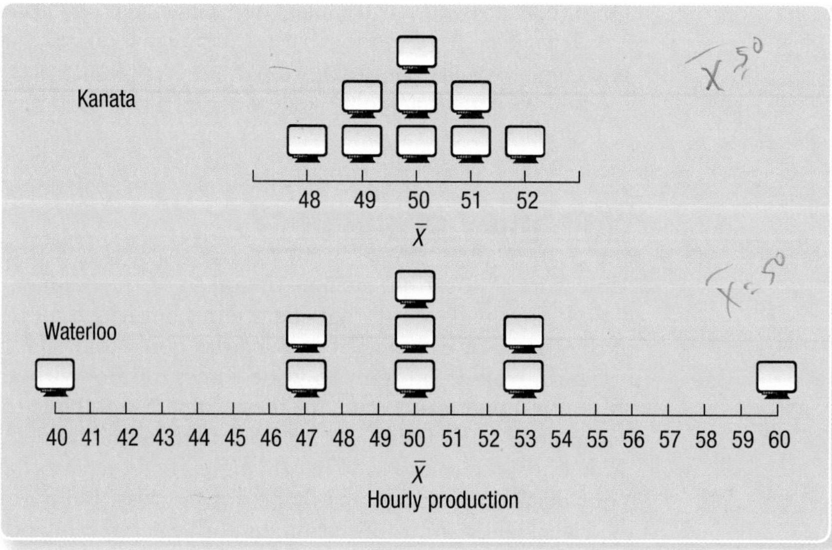

CHART 3–6 Hourly Production of Computers at the Kanata and Waterloo Plants

Measures of Dispersion

We will consider several measures of dispersion. The range is based on the largest and the smallest values in the data set. The mean deviation, the variance, and the standard deviation are all based on deviations from the arithmetic mean.

4 Compute and interpret the *range*, *mean deviation*, *variance*, and *standard deviation*.

5 Explain the characteristics, uses, advantages, and disadvantages of each *measure of dispersion*.

Range

The simplest measure of dispersion is the **range.** It is the difference between the largest and the smallest values in a data set. In the form of an equation:

RANGE	**Range = Largest value − Smallest value**	**[3–6]**

You hear about a range every day. The weather forecast is given in high and low temperatures. In business, stock prices are quoted as highs and lows for the day, week, etc. Also, the range is widely used in statistical process control (SPC) applications because it is very easy to calculate and understand.

example

Refer to Chart 3–6. Find the range in the number of computer monitors produced per hour for the Kanata and the Waterloo plants. Interpret the two ranges.

solution

The range of the hourly production of computer monitors at the Kanata plant is 4, found by the difference between the largest hourly production of 52 and the smallest of 48. The range in the hourly production for the Waterloo plant is 20 computer monitors, found by 60−40. We therefore conclude that (1) there is less dispersion in the hourly production in the Kanata plant than in the Waterloo plant because the range of 4 computer monitors is less than a range of 20 computer monitors, and (2) the production is clustered more closely around the mean of 50 at the Kanata plant than at the Waterloo plant (because a range of 4 is less than a range of 20). Thus, the mean production in the Kanata plant (50 computer monitors) is a more representative measure of location than the mean of 50 computer monitors for the Waterloo plant.

4 Compute and interpret the *range*, *mean deviation*, *variance*, and *standard deviation*.

Mean Deviation

A defect of the range is that it is based on only two values, the highest and the lowest; it does not take into consideration all of the values. The **mean deviation** does. It measures the mean amount by which the values in a population, or sample, vary from their mean.

In terms of a formula, the mean deviation, designated *MD*, is computed for a sample by:

mean deviation The arithmetic mean of the absolute values of the deviations from the arithmetic mean.

MEAN DEVIATION $$MD = \frac{\Sigma|X - \bar{X}|}{n}$$ **[3–7]**

where:

X is the value of each observation.
$\bar{X}$ is the arithmetic mean of the values.
n is the number of observations in the sample.
$||$ indicates the absolute value.

Why do we ignore the signs of the deviations from the mean? If we didn't, the positive and negative deviations from the mean would exactly offset each other, and the mean deviation would always be 0. Such a measure (0) would be a useless statistic.

example

The numbers of cappuccinos sold at the coffee shop in the Kings County Municipal Airport between 4 and 7 p.m. for a sample of 5 days last year were 20, 40, 50, 60, and 80. In the Sydney Airport, the number of cappuccinos sold at the coffee shop between 4 and 7 p.m. for a sample of 5 days last year were 20, 49, 50, 51, and 80. Determine the mean, median, range, and mean deviation for each location. Compare the differences.

solution

For the Kings County Municipal Airport the mean, median and range are:

Mean	(20 + 40 + 50 + 60 + 80)/5 = 50 cappuccinos per day
Median	50 (the middle value when the data is ordered) cappuccinos per day
Range	80 − 20 = 60 cappuccinos per day

The mean deviation is the mean of the differences between individual observations and the arithmetic mean. For the Kings County Municipal Airport, the mean number of cappuccinos sold is 50. Next we find the differences between each observation and the mean. Then we sum these differences while ignoring the signs, and divide the sum by the number of observations. The result is the mean difference between the observations and the mean.

Number of Cappuccinos Sold	$X - \bar{X}$	Absolute Deviation
20	(20 − 50) = −30	30
40	(40 − 50) = −10	10
50	(50 − 50) = 0	0
60	(60 − 50) = 10	10
80	(80 − 50) = 30	30
	Total	80

$$MD = \frac{\Sigma|X - \bar{X}|}{n} = \frac{80}{5} = 16$$

The mean deviation is 16 cappuccinos per day and shows that the number of cappuccinos sold deviates, on average, by 16 from the mean of 50 cappuccinos per day. The summary of the mean, median, range, and mean deviation for the Sydney Airport follows. You should perform the calculations to verify the results.

Mean	50	cappuccinos per day
Median	50	cappuccinos per day
Range	60	cappuccinos per day
Mean Deviation	12.4	cappuccinos per day

Recall in the previous chapter that we described data using graphical methods. In this chapter, we describe data using numerical measures. When we use numerical measures, it is very important to always report measures of location and dispersion.

Let's interpret and compare the results of our measures for the coffee shop locations. The mean and median of the two locations are exactly the same, 50 cappuccinos per day. Therefore, the location of both distributions is the same. The range for both locations is also the same, 60. However, recall that the range provides limited information about the dispersion of the distribution.

Notice that the mean deviations are not the same because they are based on the differences between all observations and the arithmetic mean, which show the relative closeness or clustering of the data relative to the mean or centre of the distribution. Compare the mean deviation for the Kings County Municipal Airport of 16 to the mean deviation of the Sydney Airport of 12.4. Based on the mean deviation, we can say that the dispersion for the sales distribution of the Sydney Airport coffee shop is more concentrated near the mean of 50 than the Kings County Municipal Airport location.

5 **Explain the characteristics, uses, advantages, and disadvantages of each *measure of dispersion.***

Advantages of mean deviation

The mean deviation has two advantages. First, it uses all the values in the computation. Recall that the range uses only the highest and the lowest values. Second, it is easy to understand—it is the average amount by which values deviate from the mean. However, its major drawback is the use of absolute values. Generally, absolute values are difficult to work with, so the mean deviation is not used as frequently as other measures of dispersion, such as the standard deviation.

self-review 3–6

The masses of a group of crates being shipped to Ireland are (in kilograms):

95	103	105	110	104	105	112	90

(a) What is the range of the masses?
(b) Compute the arithmetic mean mass.
(c) Compute the mean deviation of the masses.

Exercises

For Exercises 35–38, calculate the (a) range, (b) arithmetic mean, and (c) mean deviation, and (d) interpret the range and the mean deviation.

35. There were five customer service representatives on duty at the Electronic Super Store during last Friday's sale. The number of HDTVs these representatives sold are: 5, 8, 4, 10, and 3.

36. The Business School at a local college offers eight sections of basic statistics. Following are the number of students enrolled in these sections: 34, 46, 52, 29, 41, 38, 36, and 28.

37. Dave's Automatic Door installs automatic garage door openers. The following list indicates the number of minutes needed to install a sample of 10 doors: 28, 32, 24, 46, 44, 40, 54, 38, 32, and 42.

38. A sample of eight companies in the aerospace industry was surveyed as to their return on investment last year. The results are (in percent): 10.6, 12.6, 14.8, 18.2, 12.0, 14.8, 12.2, and 15.6.

39. Ten randomly selected young adults living in British Columbia rated the taste of a newly developed sushi pizza topped with tuna, rice, and kelp on a scale of 1 to 50 with 1 indicating they did not like the taste and 50 that they did. The ratings were:

34	39	40	46	33	31	34	14	15	45

In a parallel study 10 randomly selected young adults in Manitoba rated the taste of the same pizza. The ratings were:

28	25	35	16	25	29	24	26	17	20

As a market researcher, compare the potential markets for sushi pizza.

40. A sample of the personnel files of eight sales employees at the Clean Carpet Company revealed that during the last six-month period they lost the following number of days due to illness:

2	0	6	3	10	4	1	2

A sample of eight warehouse employees of the same company during the same period revealed that they lost the following number of days due to illness:

2	0	1	0	5	0	1	0

As the director of human resources, compare the two sets of data. Is there a difference in the number of days lost due to illness in the two locations? What would you recommend?

4 Compute and interpret the *range*, *mean deviation*, *variance*, and *standard deviation*.

Variance and Standard Deviation

The **variance** and **standard deviation** are also based on deviations from the mean. However, instead of using the absolute value of the deviations, the variance, and the standard deviation, square the deviations.

Note that the variance is non-negative, and it is 0 only if all observations are the same.

Variance and standard deviation are based on squared deviations from the mean.

variance The arithmetic mean of the squared deviations from the mean.

standard deviation The square root of the variance.

Population Variance The formulas for the population variance and the sample variance are slightly different. The population variance is considered first. (Recall that a population is the totality of all observations being studied.) The **population variance** is found by:

POPULATION VARIANCE

$$\sigma^2 = \frac{\Sigma(X - \mu)^2}{N} \qquad \textbf{[3–8]}$$

where:

σ^2 is the symbol for the population variance (σ is the lowercase Greek letter sigma). It is usually referred to as "sigma squared."
X is the value of an observation in the population.
μ is the arithmetic mean of the population.
N is the number of observations in the population.

Note the steps in computing the population variance:

1. Begin by finding the mean.
2. Next, find the difference between each observation and the mean.
3. Square the difference.
4. Sum all of the squared differences.
5. Divide the sum by the total number of observations.

For populations whose values are near the mean, the variance will be small. For populations whose values are dispersed from the mean, the population variance will be large.

5 Explain the characteristics, uses, advantages, and disadvantages of each *measure of dispersion*.

The variance overcomes the weakness of the range by using all the values in the population, whereas the range uses only the largest and smallest. We overcome the issue of absolute values in the mean deviation by squaring the differences. Squaring the differences between each observation and the mean will always result in non-negative values, and will be 0 only when all values in the data set are the same.

example

The ages of all the patients in the isolation ward of Mountainview Hospital are 38, 26, 13, 41, and 22 years. Determine the population variance.

solution

We will consider the data as population data as we are studying all of the patients in the isolation ward.

Age (X)	$X - \mu$	$(X - \mu)^2$
38	+10	100
26	−2	4
13	−15	225
41	+13	169
22	−6	36
140	0*	534

$$\mu = \frac{\Sigma X}{N} = \frac{140}{5} = 28$$

$$\sigma^2 = \frac{\Sigma(X - \mu)^2}{N} = \frac{534}{5} = 106.8$$

Sum of the deviations from mean must equal 0.

5 Explain the characteristics, uses, advantages, and disadvantages of each *measure of dispersion*.

4 Compute and interpret the *range*, *mean deviation*, *variance*, and *standard deviation*.

Like the range and the mean deviation, the variance can be used to compare the dispersion in two or more sets of observations. For example, the variance for the ages of the patients in isolation was just computed to be 106.8. If the variance in the ages of the cancer patients in the hospital is 342.9, we conclude that (1) there is less dispersion in the distribution of the ages of patients in isolation than in the age distribution of all cancer patients (because 106.8 is less than 342.9); and (2) the ages of the patients in isolation are clustered more closely about the mean of 28 years than the ages of those in the cancer ward. Thus, the mean age for the patients in isolation is a more representative measure of location than the mean for all cancer patients.

Variance is difficult to interpret because the units are squared.

Standard deviation is in the same units as the data.

Population Standard Deviation Both the range and the mean deviation are easy to interpret. The range is the difference between the high and low values of a set of data, and the mean deviation is the mean of the deviations from the mean. However, the variance is difficult to interpret for a single set of observations. The variance of 106.8 for the ages of the patients in isolation is not in terms of years, but rather "years squared."

There is a way out of this difficulty. By taking the square root of the population variance, we can transform it to the same unit of measurement used for the original data. The square root of 106.8 years-squared is 10.3 years. The units are now simply years. The square root of the population variance is called the **population standard deviation**.

POPULATION STANDARD DEVIATION

$$\sigma = \sqrt{\frac{\Sigma(X - \mu)^2}{N}} \qquad [3\text{–}9]$$

self-review 3–7

An office of Price Waterhouse Coopers LLP hired five accounting trainees this year. Their monthly starting salaries were: $3536; $3173; $3448; $3121; and $3622.

(a) Compute the population mean.
(b) Compute the population variance.
(c) Compute the population standard deviation.
(d) Another location hired six trainees. Their mean monthly salary was $3380, and the standard deviation was $250. Compare the two groups.

Exercises

41. Consider these five values a population: 8, 3, 7, 3, and 4.
   a. Determine the mean of the population.
   b. Determine the variance.
42. Consider these six values a population: 13, 3, 8, 10, 8, and 6.
   a. Determine the mean of the population.
   b. Determine the variance.
43. The annual report of Dennis Industries cited these primary earnings per common share for the past five years: \$2.68, \$1.03, \$2.26, \$4.30, and \$3.58. If we assume these are population values, what is:
   a. The arithmetic mean primary earnings per share of common stock?
   b. The variance?
44. Referring to Exercise 43, the annual report of Dennis Industries also gave these returns on stockholder equity for the same five-year period (in percent): 13.2, 5.0, 10.2, 17.5, and 12.9.
   a. What is the arithmetic mean return?
   b. What is the variance?
45. Plywood Inc. reported these returns on stockholder equity for the past five years: 4.3, 4.9, 7.2, 6.7, and 11.6. Consider these as population values.
   a. Compute the range, the arithmetic mean, the variance, and the standard deviation.
   b. Compare the return on stockholder equity for Plywood Inc. with that for Dennis Industries cited in Exercise 44.
46. The annual incomes of the five vice-presidents of TMV Industries are: \$125 000; \$128 000; \$122 000; \$133 000; and \$140 000. Consider this a population.
   a. What is the range?
   b. What is the arithmetic mean income?
   c. What is the population variance? The standard deviation?
   d. The annual incomes of officers of another firm similar to TMV Industries were also studied. The mean was \$129 000 and the standard deviation \$8612. Compare the means and dispersions in the two firms.

Statistics in Action

Chris Osgood of the Detroit Red Wings played 19 games in the 2007–2008 post season of the National Hockey League. He played a total of 1160 minutes and his team was charged with 30 goals against making his 60-minute goals against average (GAA) 1.55. The second ranked goalie was Marc-Andre Fleury of the Pittsburgh Penguins with a GAA of 1.97.

Sample Variance The formula for the population mean is $\mu = \Sigma X/N$. We just changed the symbols for the sample mean, that is $\bar{X} = \Sigma X/n$. Unfortunately, the conversion from the population variance to the sample variance is not as direct. It requires a change in the denominator. Instead of substituting n (number in the sample) for N (number in the population), the denominator is $n - 1$. Thus the formula for the **sample variance** is:

SAMPLE VARIANCE, DEVIATION FORMULA

$$s^2 = \frac{\Sigma(X - \bar{X})^2}{n - 1} \quad [3\text{–}10]$$

where:

s^2 is the sample variance.
X is the value of each observation in the sample.
$\bar{X}$ is the mean of the sample.
n is the number of observations in the sample.

Why is this change made in the denominator? Although the use of n is logical, it tends to underestimate the population variance, σ^2. The use of $(n - 1)$ in the denominator provides the appropriate correction for this tendency. For example, in a sample, if we did not have to estimate the population mean using the sample mean, then we could divide by n. But the first estimate we make is the sample mean, and so, we lose a degree of freedom, and hence use $(n - 1)$.

An easier way to compute the variance follows. This formula is much easier to use, even with a hand calculator, because it avoids all but one subtraction. Hence, we recommend formula (3–11) for calculating a sample variance.

SAMPLE VARIANCE, DIRECT FORMULA

$$s^2 = \frac{\Sigma X^2 - \dfrac{(\Sigma X)^2}{n}}{n - 1} \quad [3\text{–}11]$$

example

The hourly wages for a sample of part-time employees at Fruit Packers Inc. are: \$12, \$20, \$16, \$18, and \$19. What is the sample variance?

solution

The sample variance is computed using two methods. On the left is the deviation method, using formula (3–10). On the right is the direct method, using formula (3–11).

$$\bar{X} = \frac{\Sigma X}{n} = \frac{\$85}{5} = \$17$$

Using squared deviations from the mean:

Hourly Wage (\$) X	\$ $X - \bar{X}$	\$^{2} $(X - \bar{X})^2$
12	−5	25
20	3	9
16	−1	1
18	1	1
19	2	4
85	0	40

$$s^2 = \frac{\Sigma(X - \bar{X})^2}{n - 1} = \frac{\$^2 40}{5 - 1}$$

$$= 10\$^2 \text{ (dollars squared)}$$

Using the direct formula:

Hourly Wage (\$) X	\$^{2} X^2
12	144
20	400
16	256
18	324
19	361
85	1485

$$s^2 = \frac{\Sigma X^2 - \frac{(\Sigma X)^2}{n}}{n - 1}$$

$$= \frac{1485 - \frac{(85)^2}{5}}{5 - 1} = \frac{40}{5 - 1}$$

$$= 10\$^2 \text{ (dollars squared)}$$

5 Explain the characteristics, uses, advantages, and disadvantages of each *measure of dispersion*.

Sample Standard Deviation The sample standard deviation is used as an estimator of the population standard deviation. As noted previously, the population standard deviation is the square root of the population variance. Likewise, the *sample standard deviation is the square root of the sample variance*. The sample standard deviation is most easily determined by:

STANDARD DEVIATION, DIRECT FORMULA

$$s = \sqrt{\frac{\Sigma X^2 - \frac{(\Sigma X)^2}{n}}{n - 1}} \qquad [3\text{–}12]$$

example

The sample variance in the previous example involving hourly wages was computed to be 10\$^{2}. What is the sample standard deviation?

solution

The sample standard deviation is \$3.16, found by $\sqrt{10}$. Note again that the sample variance is in terms of dollars squared, but taking the square root of 10 gives us \$3.16, which is in the same units (dollars) as the original data.

self-review 3–8

The years of service for a sample of seven employees at an insurance claims office are: 4, 2, 5, 4, 5, 2, and 6. What is the sample variance? Compute the sample standard deviation.

Statistics in Action

An average is a value used to represent all the data. However, often an average does not give the full picture of the set of data. Stockbrokers are often faced with this problem when they are considering two investments, where the mean rate of return is the same. They usually calculate the standard deviation of the rates of return to assess the risk associated with the two investments. The investment with the larger standard deviation is considered to have the greater risk. In this context the standard deviation plays a vital part in making critical decisions regarding the composition of an investor's portfolio.

Exercises

For Exercises 47–52, do the following:

a. Compute the variance using the deviation formula.
b. Compute the variance using the direct formula.
c. Determine the sample standard deviation.

47. Consider these values a sample: 7, 2, 6, 2, and 3.

48. The following five values are a sample: 11, 6, 10, 6, and 7.

49. Dave's Automatic Door, referred to in Exercise 37, installs automatic garage door openers. Based on a sample, following are the times, in minutes, required to install 10 doors: 28, 32, 24, 46, 44, 40, 54, 38, 32, and 42.

50. The sample of eight companies in the aerospace industry was surveyed as to their return on investment last year. The results are: 10.6, 12.6, 14.8, 18.2, 12.0, 14.8, 12.2, and 15.6.

51. The provincial Motel Owner Association conducted a survey regarding weekday motel rates in the northern part of the province. Listed below is the room rate for fishermen for a sample of 10 motels.

$101	$97	$103	$110	$78	$87	$101	$80	$106	$88

52. A consumer watchdog organization is concerned about credit card debt. A survey of 10 young adults with credit card debt of more than $2000 showed they paid an average of just over $100 per month against their balances. Listed below are the amounts each young adult paid last month.

$110	$126	$103	$93	$99	$113	$87	$101	$109	$100

6 Understand *Chebyshev's theorem* and the *Empirical Rule* as they relate to a set of observations.

Interpretation and Uses of the Standard Deviation

The standard deviation is commonly used as a measure to compare the spread in two or more sets of observations. For example, the price of two stocks may have about the same mean, but different standard deviations. The stock with the larger standard deviation has more variability in its mean price, and therefore, could be considered more risky.

Chebyshev's Theorem

Chebyshev's theorem For any set of observations (sample or population), the proportion of the values that lie within k standard deviations of the mean is at least $1 - 1/k^2$, where k is any constant greater than 1.

We have stressed that a small standard deviation for a set of values indicates that these values are located close to the mean. Conversely, a large standard deviation reveals that the observations are widely scattered about the mean. The Russian mathematician P. L. Chebyshev (1821–1894) developed a theorem that allows us to determine the minimum proportion of the values that lie within a specified number of standard deviations of the mean. For example, according to **Chebyshev's theorem**, at least three of four values, or 75 percent, must lie between the mean plus two standard deviations and the mean minus two standard deviations. This relationship applies regardless of the shape of the distribution. Further, at least eight of nine values, or 88.9 percent, will lie between plus 3 standard deviations and minus 3 standard deviations of the mean. At least 24 of the 25 values, or 96 percent, will lie between plus and minus five standard deviations of the mean.

example

The average biweekly amount contributed by the Dupree Paint employees to the company's profit-sharing plan is $51.54, and the standard deviation is $7.51. At least what percent of the contributions lie within plus and minus 3.5 standard deviations of the mean?

solution

About 92 percent, found by $1 - 1/k^2 = 1 - 1/(3.5)^2 = 1 - 1/12.25 = 0.92$

6 **Understand *Chebyshev's theorem* and the *Empirical Rule* as they relate to a set of observations.**

The Empirical Rule

Chebyshev's theorem is concerned with any set of values; that is, the distribution of values can have any shape. However, for a symmetrical, bell-shaped distribution such as the one in Chart 3–7, we can be more precise in describing the dispersion about the mean. These relationships involving the standard deviation and the mean are called the **Empirical Rule**, or the **Normal Rule**.

These relationships are portrayed graphically in Chart 3–7 for a bell-shaped distribution with a mean of 100 and a standard deviation of 10.

Empirical Rule applies only to symmetrical, bell-shaped distributions.

It has been noted that if a distribution is symmetrical and bell-shaped, practically all of the observations lie between the mean plus and minus 3 standard deviations. Thus, if $\bar{X} = 100$ and $s = 10$, practically all the observations lie between $100 + 3(10)$ and $100 - 3(10)$, or 70 and 130. The range is therefore 60, found by $130 - 70$.

Conversely, if we know that the range is 60, we can approximate the standard deviation by dividing the range by 6. For this illustration: range $\div 6 = 60 \div 6 = 10$, the standard deviation. We will discuss this topic further in Chapter 6 when we discuss the normal distribution.

It should be noted that the Empirical Rule does not violate Chebyshev's theorem by increasing the percentages.

Empirical Rule For a symmetrical, bell-shaped frequency distribution, approximately 68 percent of the observations will lie within plus and minus 1 standard deviation of the mean; about 95 percent of the observations will lie within plus and minus 2 standard deviations of the mean; and practically all (99.7 percent) will lie within plus and minus 3 standard deviations of the mean.

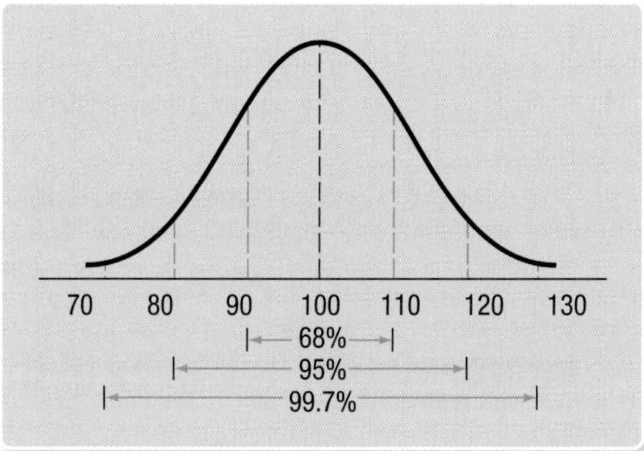

CHART 3–7 A Symmetrical, Bell-Shaped Curve Showing the Relationships between the Standard Deviation and the Observations

example

A sample of the rental rates at the College Park apartments approximates a symmetrical, bell-shaped distribution. The sample mean is \$500; the standard deviation is \$20. Using the Empirical Rule, answer these questions:

1. About 68 percent of the rental rates are between what two amounts?
2. About 95 percent of the rental rates are between what two amounts?
3. Almost all of the rental rates are between what two amounts?

solution

1. About 68 percent are between \$480 (\$500 − \$20) and \$520 (\$500 + \$20).
2. About 95 percent are between \$460 (\$500 − 2(\$20)) and \$540 (\$500 + 2(\$20)).
3. Almost all (99.7 percent) are between \$440 (\$500 − 3(\$20)) and \$560 (\$500 + 3(\$20)).

self-review 3–9

The Superior Metal Company is one of several domestic manufacturers of PVC pipe. The quality control department sampled 600 10 m lengths. At a point 1 m from the end of the pipe they measured the outside diameter. The mean was 1.2 m and the standard deviation 0.1 m.

(a) If the shape of the distribution is not known, at least what percent of the observations will lie between 1.05 m and 1.35 m?

(b) If we assume that the distribution of diameters is symmetrical and bell-shaped, about 68 percent of the observations will be between what two values?

(c) If we assume that the distribution of diameters is symmetrical and bell-shaped, about 95 percent of the observations will be between what two values?

Exercises

53. According to Chebyshev's theorem, at least what percent of any set of observations will be within 1.8 standard deviations of the mean?
54. The mean income of a group of sample observations is \$500; the standard deviation is \$40. According to Chebyshev's theorem at least what percent of the incomes will lie between \$400 and \$600?
55. The distribution of the weights of a sample of 1400 cargo containers is somewhat normally distributed. According to the Empirical Rule, what percent of the weights will lie
    a. Between $\bar{X} - 2s$ and $\bar{X} + 2s$?
    b. Between $\bar{X}$ and $\bar{X} + 2s$? Below $\bar{X} - 2s$?
56. The following figure portrays the appearance of a distribution of efficiency ratings for employees of Nale Nail Works Inc.

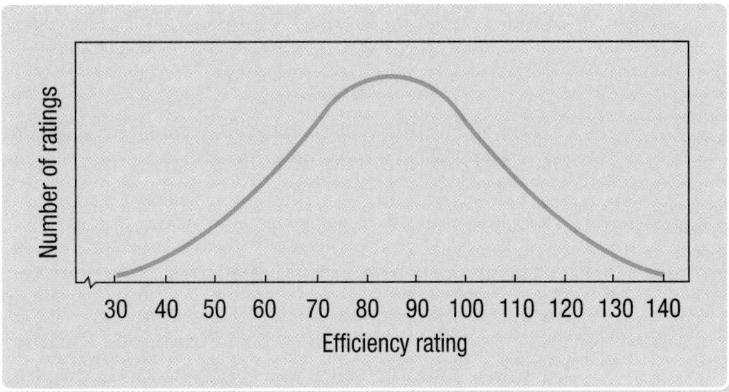

    a. Estimate the mean efficiency rating.
    b. Estimate the standard deviation to the nearest whole number.
    c. About 68 percent of the efficiency ratings are between what two values?
    d. About 95 percent of the efficiency ratings are between what two values?

Statistics in Action

Joe Mauer of the Minnesota Twins had the highest batting average at .347 during the 2006 season. Tony Gwynn hit .394 in the strikeshortened season of 1994, and Ted Williams hit .406 in 1941. No one has hit over .400 since 1941. The mean batting average has remained constant at about .260 for more than 100 years, but the standard deviation declined from .049 to .031. This indicates less dispersion in the batting averages today and helps explain the lack of any .400 hitters in recent times.

Relative Dispersion

7 Compute and interpret the *coefficient of skewness* and the *coefficient of variation*.

A direct comparison of two or more measures of dispersion—say, the standard deviation for a distribution of annual incomes and the standard deviation of a distribution of absenteeism for this same group of employees—is impossible. Can we say that the standard deviation of \$1200 for the income distribution is greater than the standard deviation of 4.5 days for the distribution of absenteeism? Obviously not, because we cannot directly compare dollars and days absent from work. In order to make a meaningful comparison of the dispersion in incomes and absenteeism, we need to convert each of these measures to a *relative value*—that is, a percent. Karl Pearson (1857–1936), who contributed significantly to the science of statistics, developed a relative measure called the **coefficient of variation** (CV). It is a very useful measure when:

coefficient of variation The ratio of the standard deviation to the arithmetic mean, expressed as a percent.

When to use CV

1. The data are in different units (such as dollars and days absent).
2. The data are in the same units, but the means are far apart (such as the incomes of the top executives and the incomes of the unskilled employees).

In terms of a formula for a sample:

COEFFICIENT OF VARIATION $$CV = \frac{s}{\bar{X}}(100) \leftarrow$$ **Multiplying by 100 converts the decimal to a percent** **[3–13]**

example

A study of the amount of bonus paid and the years of service of employees at Sea Pro Marine Inc. resulted in these statistics: The mean bonus paid was \$200; the standard deviation was \$40; the mean number of years of service was 20 years; the standard deviation was 2 years. Compare the relative dispersion in the two distributions using the coefficient of variation.

solution

The distributions are in different units (dollars and years of service). Therefore, they are converted to coefficients of variation.

For the bonus paid:

$$CV = \frac{s}{\overline{X}}(100) = \frac{\$40}{\$200}(100) = 20 \text{ percent}$$

For years of service:

$$CV = \frac{s}{\overline{X}}(100) = \frac{2}{20}(100) = 10 \text{ percent}$$

Interpreting, there is more dispersion relative to the mean in the distribution of bonus paid compared with the distribution of years of service (because 20 percent > 10 percent).

The same procedure is used when the data are in the same units but the means are far apart. (See the following example.)

example

The variation in the annual incomes of executives at Nash-Rambler Products Inc. is to be compared with the variation in incomes of unskilled employees. For a sample of executives, $\overline{X} = \$500\ 000$ and $s = \$50\ 000$. For a sample of unskilled employees, $\overline{X} = \$32\ 000$ and $s = \$3200$. We are tempted to say that there is more dispersion in the annual incomes of the executives because \$50 000 > \$3200. The means are so far apart, however, that we need to convert the statistics to coefficients of variation to make a meaningful comparison of the variations in annual incomes.

solution

For the executives:

$$CV = \frac{s}{\overline{X}}(100) = \frac{\$50\ 000}{\$500\ 000}(100) = 10 \text{ percent}$$

For the unskilled employees:

$$CV = \frac{s}{\overline{X}}(100) = \frac{\$3200}{\$32\ 000}(100) = 10 \text{ percent}$$

There is no difference in the relative dispersion of the two groups.

self-review 3–10

A large group of Air Force inductees was given two experimental tests—a mechanical aptitude test and a finger dexterity test. The arithmetic mean score on the mechanical aptitude test was 200, with a standard deviation of 10. The mean and standard deviation for the finger dexterity test were: $\overline{X} = 30$, $s = 6$. Compare the relative dispersion in the two groups.

Exercises

57. For a sample of students in a college studying Business Administration, the mean grade point average is 3.10 with a standard deviation of 0.25. Compute the coefficient of variation.

58. Skipjack Airlines is studying the mass of luggage for each passenger. For a large group of domestic passengers, the mean is 21 kg with a standard deviation of 5 kg. For a large group of overseas passengers, the mean is 35 kg and the standard deviation is 7 kg. Compute the relative dispersion of each group. Comment on the difference in relative dispersion.

59. The research analyst for the Sidde Financial stock brokerage firm wants to compare the dispersion in the price-earnings ratios for a group of common stocks with the dispersion of their return on investment. For the price-earnings ratios, the mean is 4.9 and the standard deviation 1.8. The mean return on investment is 10 percent and the standard deviation 5.2 percent.
    a. Why should the coefficient of variation be used to compare the dispersion?
    b. Compare the relative dispersion for the price-earnings ratios and return on investment.

60. The spread in the annual prices of stocks selling for under \$10 and the spread in prices of those selling for over \$60 are to be compared. The mean price of the stocks selling for under \$10 is \$5.25 and the standard deviation \$1.52. The mean price of those stocks selling for over \$60 is \$92.50 and the standard deviation \$5.28.
    a. Why should the coefficient of variation be used to compare the dispersion in the prices?
    b. Compute the coefficients of variation. What is your conclusion?

7 Compute and interpret the *coefficient of skewness* and the *coefficient of variation.*

Statistics in Action

The late Stephen Jay Gould (1941–2002) was a professor of zoology and professor of geology at Harvard University. In 1982, he was diagnosed with cancer and had an expected survival time of eight months. However, never to be discouraged, his research showed that the distribution of survival time is dramatically skewed to the right and showed that not only do 50 percent of similar cancer patients survive more than eight months, but that the survival time could be years rather than months! Based on his experience, he wrote a widely published essay titled, "The Median Is Not the Message."

Skewness

In this chapter we have described measures of central location for a set of observations by reporting the mean, median, and mode. We also described measures that show the amount of spread or variation in a set of data, such as the range and the standard deviation.

Another characteristic of a set of data is the shape. There are four shapes commonly observed: symmetric, positively skewed, negatively skewed, and bimodal. In a **symmetric** set of observations the mean and median are equal and the data values are evenly spread around these values. The data values below the mean and median are a mirror image of those above. A set of values is **skewed to the right** or **positively skewed** if there is a single peak and the values extend much further to the right of the peak than to the left of the peak. In this case the mean is larger than the median. In a **negatively skewed** distribution there is a single peak but the observations extend further to the left, in the negative direction, than to the right. In a negatively skewed distribution the mean is smaller than the median. Positively skewed distributions are more common. Salaries often follow this pattern. Think of the salaries of those employed in a small company of about 100 people. The president and a few top executives would have very large salaries relative to the other workers and hence the distribution of salaries would exhibit positive skewness. A **bimodal distribution** will have two or more peaks. This is often the case when the values are from two or more populations. This information is summarized in Chart 3–8.

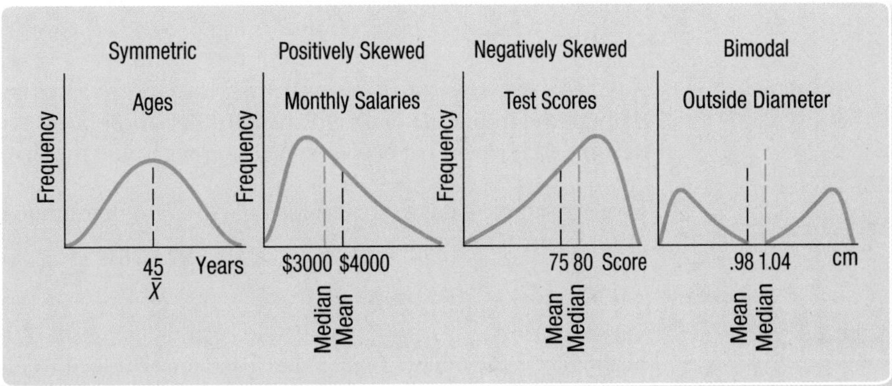

CHART 3–8 Shapes of Frequency Polygons

There are several formulas in the statistical literature used to calculate skewness. The simplest, developed by Professor Karl Pearson, is based on the difference between the mean and the median.

PEARSON'S COEFFICIENT OF SKEWNESS

$$sk = \frac{3(\bar{X} - \text{Median})}{s} \qquad [3\text{–}14]$$

Using this relationship the coefficient of skewness can range from -3 up to 3. A value near -3, such as -2.57, indicates considerable negative skewness. A value such as 1.63 indicates moderate positive skewness. A value of 0, which will occur when the mean and median are equal, indicates the distribution is symmetrical and that there is no skewness present.

In this text we present output from the statistical software packages **Excel**, with the Add-in MegaStat, and MINITAB. Both of these software packages calculate the coefficient of skewness using a formula that is slightly different from formula 3–14, that is based on the cubed deviations from the mean. The formula is:

$$sk = \frac{n}{(n-1)(n-2)}\left[\Sigma\left(\frac{X-\bar{X}}{s}\right)^3\right]$$

This formula offers an insight into skewness. The right-hand side of the formula is the difference between each value and the mean, divided by the standard deviation. That is the portion $(X - \bar{X})/s$ of the formula. This idea is called **standardizing.** We will discuss the idea of standardizing a value in more detail in Chapter 6 when we describe the normal probability distribution. At this point, observe that the result is to report the difference between each value and the mean in units of the standard deviation. If this difference is positive, the particular value is larger than the mean; if the variation is negative, the standardized quantity is smaller than the mean. When we cube these values, we retain the information on the direction of the difference. Recall that in the formula for the standard deviation (see formula 3–11), we squared the difference between each value and the mean, so that the result was all non-negative values.

If the set of data values under consideration is symmetric, when we cube the standardized values and sum over all the values, the result would be near 0. If there are several large values, clearly separate from the others, the sum of the cubed differences would be a large positive value. Several values much smaller will result in a negative cubed sum.

An example will illustrate the idea of skewness.

example

Following are the earnings per share, in dollars, for a sample of 15 software companies for the year 2008. The earnings per share are arranged from smallest to largest.

\$0.09	0.13	0.41	0.51	1.12	1.20	1.49	3.18
3.50	6.36	7.83	8.92	10.13	12.99	16.40	

Compute the mean, median, and standard deviation. Find the coefficient of skewness using Pearson's estimate. What is your conclusion regarding the shape of the distribution?

solution

These are sample data, so we use formula (3–2) to determine the mean

$$\bar{X} = \frac{\Sigma X}{n} = \frac{\$74.26}{15} = \$4.95$$

The median is the middle value in a set of data, arranged from smallest to largest. In this case the middle value is \$3.18, so the median earnings per share is \$3.18.

We use formula (3–12) on page 80 to determine the sample standard deviation.

$$s = \sqrt{\frac{\Sigma X^2 - \frac{(\Sigma X)^2}{n}}{n-1}} = \sqrt{\frac{749.372 - \frac{(74.26)^2}{15}}{15-1}} = \$5.22$$

minitab

Pearson's coefficient of skewness is 1.017, found by

$$sk = \frac{3(\bar{X} - \text{Median})}{s} = \frac{3(\$4.95 - \$3.18)}{\$5.22} = 1.017$$

This indicates there is moderate positive skewness in the earnings per share data.

We obtain a similar, but not exactly the same value when using software. The details are shown below.

X	$\bar{X}$	$(X - \bar{X})$	s	$\left(\frac{X - \bar{X}}{s}\right)^3$
0.09	4.95067	−4.86067	5.22176	−0.80656
0.13	4.95067	−4.82067	5.22176	−0.78681
0.41	4.95067	−4.54067	5.22176	−0.65752
0.51	4.95067	−4.44067	5.22176	−0.61502
1.12	4.95067	−3.83067	5.22176	−0.39479
1.20	4.95067	−3.75067	5.22176	−0.37057
1.49	4.95067	−3.46067	5.22176	−0.29109
3.18	4.95067	−1.77067	5.22176	−0.03899
3.50	4.95067	−1.45067	5.22176	−0.02144
6.36	4.95067	1.40933	5.22176	0.01966
7.83	4.95067	2.87933	5.22176	0.16766
8.92	4.95067	3.96933	5.22176	0.43924
10.13	4.95067	5.17933	5.22176	0.97582
12.99	4.95067	8.03933	5.22176	3.64929
16.40	4.95067	11.44933	5.22176	10.54117
			Total	11.81004

$$sk = \frac{n}{(n-1)(n-2)}\left[\Sigma\left(\frac{X - \bar{X}}{s}\right)^3\right] = \frac{15}{(15-1)(15-2)}(11.81004) = 0.9734$$

The preceding values were produced by an **Excel** spreadsheet and appear rounded in the table. The MegaStat output follows and you can see the value of 0.9734 in the output. We can conclude that the earnings per share values are somewhat positively skewed.

The MegaStat commands and output are shown below.

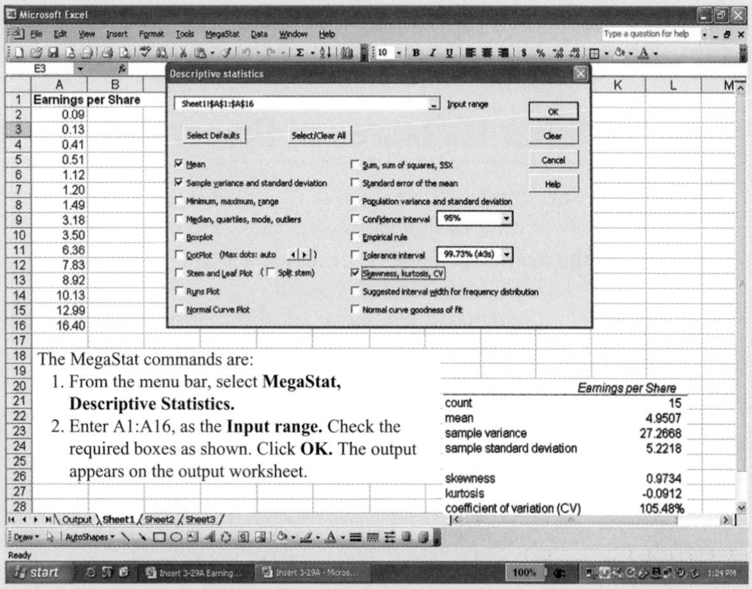

self-review 3–11

A sample of five data entry clerks employed in the customer service department of a large pharmaceutical distribution company revised the following number of records last hour: 73, 98, 60, 92, and 84.

(a) Find the mean, median, and the standard deviation.
(b) Compute the coefficient of skewness using Pearson's method.
(c) What is your conclusion regarding the skewness of the data?

Exercises

For Exercises 61–64, do the following:

a. Determine the mean, median, and the standard deviation.
b. Determine the coefficient of skewness using Pearson's method.

61. The following values are the starting salaries, in thousands of dollars, for a sample of five accounting graduates who accepted positions in public accounting last year.

$36.0	26.0	33.0	28.0	31.0

62. Listed below are the salaries, in thousands of dollars, for a sample of 15 chief financial officers in the electronics industry.

$516.0	548.0	566.0	534.0	586.0	529.0
546.0	523.0	538.0	523.0	551.0	552.0
486.0	558.0	574.0			

63. Listed below are the commissions earned, in thousands of dollars, last year by the sales representatives at the Furniture Patch Inc.

$3.9	5.7	7.3	10.6	13.0	13.6	15.1	15.8	17.1
17.4	17.6	22.3	38.6	43.2	87.7			

64. Listed below are the average commissions of top producing financial advisors in the firm A2Z Securities.

$15 000	13 000	21 600	1250	12 000	382
396	5667	389	382	456	3000
432	23 429	13 000	10 000	385	490
750	382	1500	16 000	10 500	
491	4000	11 070	600	380	

8 Compute and interpret *quartiles*, *interquartile range*, and *percentiles*.

Other Measures of Dispersion

The standard deviation is the most widely used measure of dispersion. However, there are other ways of describing the variation or spread in a set of data. One method is to determine the *location* of values that divide a set of observations into equal parts. These measures include *quartiles*, *deciles*, and *percentiles*.

Quartiles divide a set of observations into four equal parts. To explain further, think of any set of values arranged from smallest to largest. Earlier in this chapter we called the middle value of a set of data arranged from smallest to largest the median. That is, 50 percent of the observations are larger than the median and 50 percent are smaller. The median is a measure of location because it pinpoints the centre of the data. In a similar fashion **quartiles** divide a set of observations into four equal parts. The first quartile, usually labeled Q_1, is the value below which 25 percent of the observations occur, and the third quartile, usually labeled Q_3, is the value below which 75 percent of the observations occur. Logically, Q_2 is the median. The values corresponding to Q_1, Q_2, and Q_3 divide a set of data into four equal parts. Q_1 can be thought of as the "median" of the lower half of the data and Q_3 the "median" of the upper half of the data.

In a similar fashion **deciles** divide a set of observations into 10 equal parts and **percentiles** into 100 equal parts. So if you found that your GPA was in the 8th decile at your school, you could conclude that 80 percent of the students had a GPA lower than yours and 20 percent had a higher GPA. A GPA in the 33rd percentile means that 33 percent of the students have a lower GPA and 67 percent have a higher GPA. Percentile scores are frequently used to report results on such national standardized tests as the SAT, ACT, GMAT (used to judge entry into many Master of Business Administration programs), and LSAT (used to judge entry into law school).

8 Compute and interpret *quartiles*, *interquartile range*, and *percentiles*.

Quartiles, Deciles, and Percentiles

To formalize the computational procedure, let L_p refer to the location of a desired percentile. So if we wanted to find the 33rd percentile we would use L_{33} and if we wanted the median, the 50th percentile, then L_{50}. The number of observations is n, so if we want to locate the middle observation, its position is at $(n + 1)/2$, or we could write this as $(n + 1)(P/100)$, where P is the desired percentile.

LOCATION OF A PERCENTILE

$$L_p = (n+1)\frac{P}{100} \quad [3\text{–}15]$$

An example will help to explain further.

example

Listed below are the commissions earned, in dollars, last month by a sample of 15 brokers at Salomon Smith Barney's office.

\$2038	1758	1721	1637	2097	2047	2205	1787	2287
1940	2311	2054	2406	1471	1460			

Locate the median, the first quartile, and the third quartile for the commissions earned.

solution

The first step is to organize the data from the smallest commission to the largest.

\$1460	1471	1637	1721	1758	1787	1940	2038
2047	2054	2097	2205	2287	2311	2406	

The median value is the observation in the centre. The centre value or L_{50} is located at $(n + 1)(50/100)$, where n is the number of observations. In this case that is position number 8, found by $(15 + 1)(50/100)$. The eighth largest commission is \$2038. So we conclude this is the median and that half the brokers earned commissions more than \$2038 and half earned less than \$2038.

Recall the definition of a quartile. Quartiles divide a set of observations into four equal parts. Hence, 25 percent of the observations will be less than the first quartile. Seventy-five percent of the observations will be less than the third quartile. To locate the first quartile, we use formula (3–15), where $n = 15$ and $P = 25$:

$$L_{25} = (n+1)\frac{P}{100} = (15+1)\frac{25}{100} = 4$$

and to locate the third quartile, $n = 15$ and $P = 75$:

$$L_{75} = (n+1)\frac{P}{100} = (15+1)\frac{75}{100} = 12$$

Therefore, the first and third quartile values are located at positions 4 and 12. The fourth value in the ordered array is \$1721 and the twelfth is \$2205. These are the first and third quartiles, respectively.

In the above example the location formula yielded a whole number result. That is, we wanted to find the first quartile and there were 15 observations, so the location formula indicated we should find the fourth ordered value. What if there were 20 observations in the sample, that is $n = 20$, and we wanted to locate the first quartile? From the location formula (3–15):

$$L_{25} = (n+1)\frac{P}{100} = (20+1)\frac{25}{100} = 5.25$$

We would locate the fifth value in the ordered array and then move .25 of the distance between the fifth and sixth values and report that as the first quartile. Like the median, the quartile does not need to be one of the actual values in the data set.

To explain further, suppose a data set contained the six values: 91, 75, 61, 101, 43, and 104. We want to locate the first quartile. We order the values from smallest to largest: 43, 61, 75, 91, 101, and 104. The first quartile is located at

$$L_{25} = (n+1)\frac{P}{100} = (6+1)\frac{25}{100} = 1.75$$

The position formula tells us that the first quartile is located between the first and the second value and that it is .75 of the distance between the first and the second values. The first value is 43 and the second is 61. So the distance between these two values is 18. To locate the first quartile, we need to move .75 of the distance between the first and second values, so .75(18) = 13.5. To complete the procedure, we add 13.5 to the first value and report that the first quartile is 56.5.

We can extend the idea to include both deciles and percentiles. If we wanted to locate the 23rd percentile in a sample of 80 observations, we would look for the 18.63 position.

$$L_{25} = (n+1)\frac{P}{100} = (80+1)\frac{23}{100} = 18.63$$

minitab

To find the value corresponding to the 23rd percentile, we would locate the 18th value and the 19th value and determine the distance between the two values. Next, we would multiply this difference by 0.63 and add the result to the smaller value. The result would be the 23rd percentile.

excel

With a statistical software package, it is quite easy to sort the data from smallest to largest and to locate percentiles and deciles. Either MINITAB or **Excel** could be used. The **Excel** commands to calculate quartiles and percentiles follow. The method used is not as precise as that described above, but the result is a good approximation. Using the real estate example data (Table 02-1), we will calculate the 1st quartile (25th percentile) and the 56th percentile. Use the Paste Function, Statistical category, Quartile and then Percentile. The result appears in the dialogue boxes, and by clicking OK, the result will appear in the worksheet.

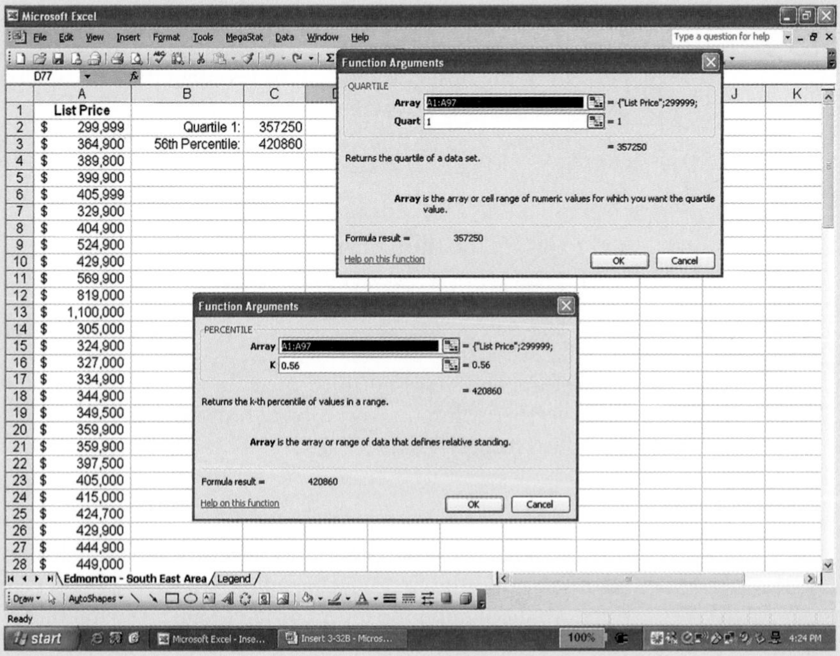

self-review 3–12

The quality control department of the Plainsville Peanut Company is responsible for checking the mass of the 500g jar of peanut butter. The masses of a sample of nine jars produced last hour are:

490	495	496	498	500	500	501	504	505

(a) What is the median mass?
(b) Determine the masses corresponding to the first and third quartiles.

Exercises

65. Determine the median and the values corresponding to the first and third quartiles in the following data.

46	47	49	49	51	53	54	54	55	55	59

66. Determine the median and the values corresponding to the first and third quartiles in the following data.

5.24	6.02	6.67	7.30	7.59	7.99	8.03	8.35	8.81	9.45
9.61	10.37	10.39	11.86	12.22	12.71	13.07	13.59	13.89	15.42

67. The Thomas Supply Company Inc. is a distributor of small electrical motors. As with any business, the length of time customers take to pay their invoices is important. Listed below, arranged from smallest to largest, is the time, in days, for a sample of The Thomas Supply Company Inc. invoices.

13	13	13	20	26	27	31	34	34	34	35	35	36	37	38
41	41	41	45	47	47	47	50	51	53	54	56	62	67	82

a. Determine the first and third quartiles.
b. Determine the second decile and the eighth decile.
c. Determine the 67th percentile.

68. Kevin Horn is the national sales manager for National Textbooks Inc. He has a sales staff of 40 who visit college and university professors. Each Saturday morning he requires his sales staff to send him a report. This report includes, among other things, the number of professors visited during the previous week. Listed below, ordered from smallest to largest, are the number of visits last week.

38	40	41	45	48	48	50	50	51	51	52	52	53	54	55	55	55	56	56	57
59	59	59	62	62	62	63	64	65	66	66	67	67	69	69	71	77	78	79	79

a. Determine the median number of calls.
b. Determine the first and third quartiles.
c. Determine the first decile and the ninth decile.
d. Determine the 33rd percentile.

Box Plots

A **box plot** is a graphical display, based on quartiles, that helps us picture a set of data. To construct a box plot, we need only five statistics: the minimum value, Q_1 (the first quartile), the median, Q_3 (the third quartile), and the maximum value. An example will help to explain.

example

Alexander's Pizza offers free delivery of its pizza within 15 km. Alex, the owner, wants some information on the time it takes for delivery. How long does a typical delivery take? Within what range of times will most deliveries be completed? For a sample of 20 deliveries, he determined the following information:

Minimum value = 13 minutes
Q_1 = 15 minutes
Median = 18 minutes
Q_3 = 22 minutes
Maximum value = 30 minutes

Develop a box plot for the delivery times. What conclusions can you make about the delivery times?

solution

The first step in drawing a box plot is to create an appropriate scale along the horizontal axis. Next, we draw a box that starts at Q_1 (15 minutes) and ends at Q_3 (22 minutes). Inside the box we place a vertical line to represent the median (18 minutes). Finally, we extend horizontal lines from the box out to the minimum value (13 minutes) and the maximum value (30 minutes). These horizontal lines outside of the box are sometimes called "whiskers" because they look a bit like a cat's whiskers.

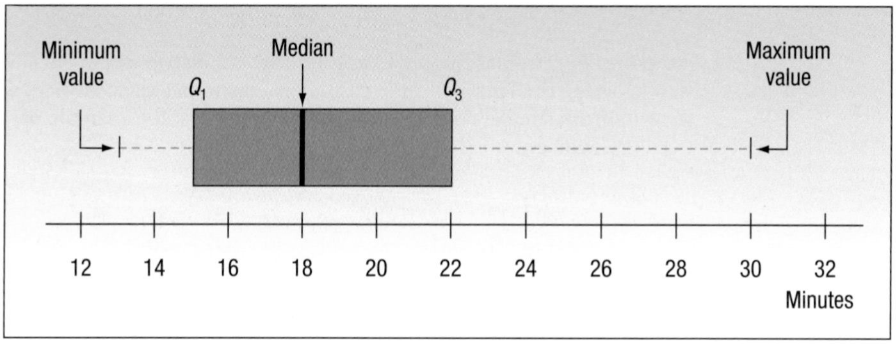

The box plot shows that the middle 50 percent of the deliveries take between 15 minutes and 22 minutes. The distance between the ends of the box, 7 minutes, is the **interquartile range.** The interquartile range is the distance between the first and the third quartile. It shows the spread or dispersion of the majority of deliveries.

The box plot also reveals that the distribution of delivery times is positively skewed. How do we know this? In this case there are actually two pieces of information that suggest that the distribution is positively skewed. First, the dashed line to the right of the box from 22 minutes (Q_3) to the maximum time of 30 minutes is longer than the dashed line from the left of 15 minutes (Q_1) to the minimum value of 13 minutes. To put it another way, the 25 percent of the data larger than the third quartile is more spread out than the 25 percent less than the first quartile. A second indication of positive skewness is that the median is not in the centre of the box. The distance from the first quartile to the median is smaller than the distance from the median to the third quartile. We know that the number of delivery times between 15 minutes and 18 minutes is the same as the number of delivery times between 18 minutes and 22 minutes.

example

Refer to the real estate data in Table 2–1. Develop a box plot of the data. What can we conclude about the distribution of the list prices?

solution

MegaStat was used to develop the following chart. The commands follow.

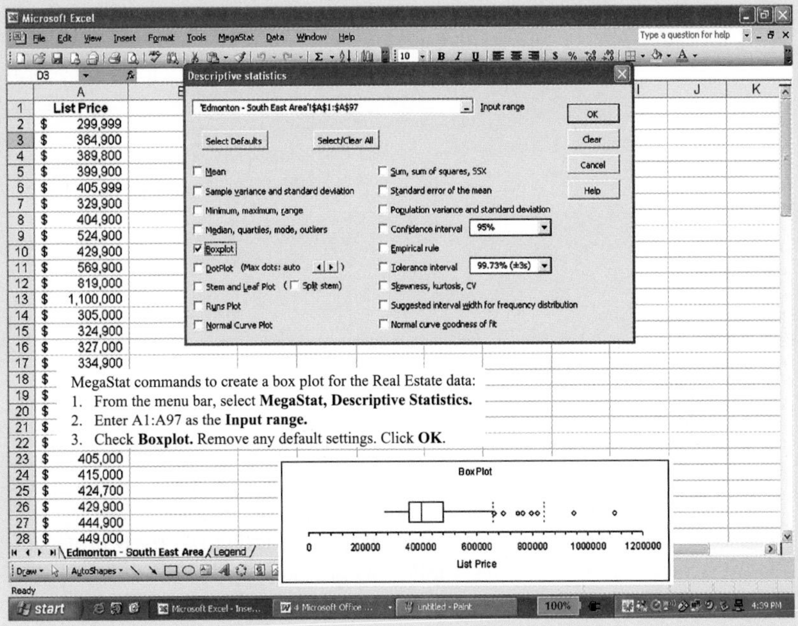

From the box plot we can conclude that the median list price is about \$400 000, that about 25 percent of the list prices are below \$360 000, and that about 25 percent are above \$480 000. The middle 50 percent of the list prices are between \$360 000 and \$480 000. The distribution is positively skewed because the line above \$480 000 is somewhat longer than the line below \$360 000.

There are several small circles above the \$480 000 list price. The circles represent outliers. An **outlier** is a value that is more than 1.5 times the interquartile range larger than Q_3 or smaller than Q_1. We use the **Excel** commands to find Q_1 = \$357 250, Q_3 = \$479 150, and the interquartile range = \$479 150 − \$357 250 = \$121 900. So a high outlier would be a value larger than \$388 675, found by

$$\textbf{Outlier} > Q_3 + 1.5(Q_3 - Q_1) = \$479\,150 + 1.5(\$121\,900) = \$662\,000.$$

A value less than \$174 400 is also an outlier, but would be described as a low outlier. Since there are no list prices less than \$250 000, there are no low outliers for this data.

$$\textbf{Outlier} < Q_1 - 1.5(Q_3 - Q_1) = \$357\,250 - 1.5(\$121\,900) = \$174\,400.$$

self-review 3–13

The following box plot is given.

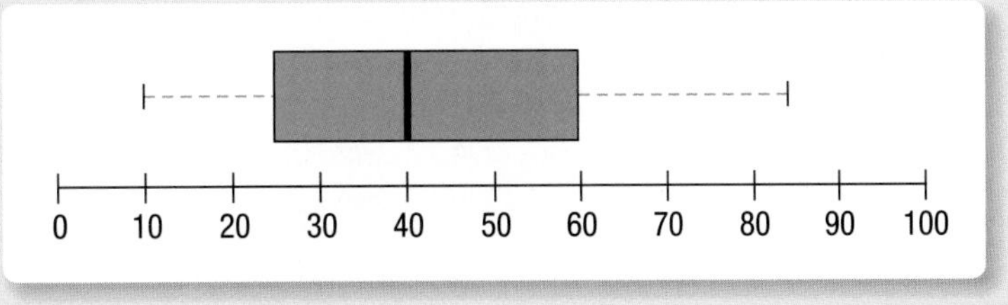

What are the median, the largest and smallest values, and the first and third quartiles? Would you agree that the distribution is symmetrical?

Exercises

69. The box plot below shows the amount spent for books and supplies per year by students at community colleges.

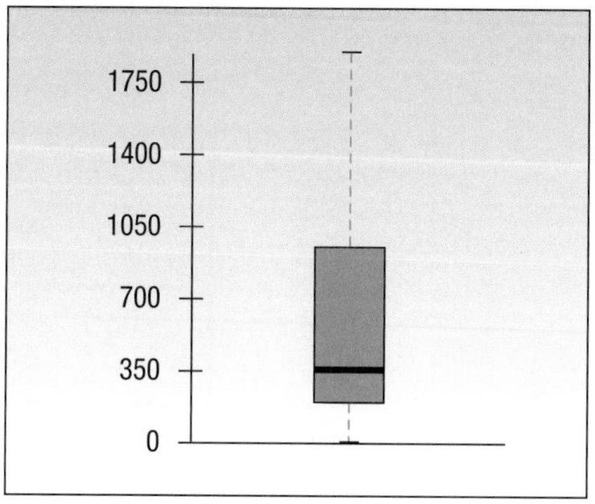

a. Estimate the median.
b. Estimate the first and third quartiles.
c. Determine the interquartile range.
d. Beyond what point is a value considered an outlier?
e. Identify any outliers and estimate their value.
f. Is the distribution symmetrical or positively or negatively skewed?

70. Refer to the following box plot.

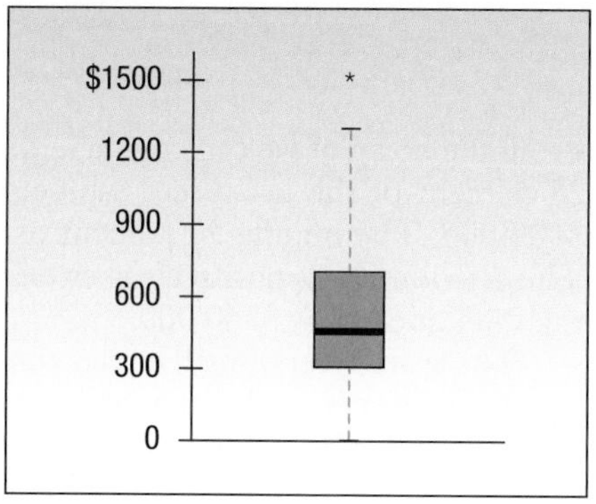

a. Estimate the median.
b. Estimate the first and third quartiles.
c. Determine the interquartile range.
d. Beyond what point is a value considered an outlier?
e. Identify any outliers and estimate their value.
f. Is the distribution symmetrical or positively or negatively skewed?

71. In a study of the fuel efficiency of model year 2008 automobiles, the mean efficiency was 12 km/L and the median was 11.7 km/L. The smallest value in the study was 5.5 km/L, and the largest was 22 km/L. The first and third quartiles were 7.8 km/L and 15.5 km/L, respectively. Develop a box plot and comment on the distribution. Is it a symmetric distribution?

72. A sample of 28 time-shares revealed the following daily charges, in dollars, for a one-bed suite. For convenience the data are ordered from smallest to largest. Construct a box plot to represent the data. Comment on the distribution. Be sure to identify the first and third quartiles and the median.

$116	121	157	192	207	209	209
229	232	236	236	239	243	246
260	264	276	281	283	289	296
307	309	312	317	324	341	353

The Mean, Median, and Standard Deviation of Grouped Data

In most instances measures of location, such as the mean, and measures of variability, such as the standard deviation, are determined by using the individual values. **Excel** makes it easy to calculate these values, even for large data sets. However, sometimes we are only given the frequency distribution and wish to estimate the mean or standard deviation. In the following discussion we show how we can estimate the mean and standard deviation from data organized into a frequency distribution. We should stress that a mean or a standard deviation from grouped data is an *estimate* of the corresponding actual values.

The Arithmetic Mean of Grouped Data

To approximate the arithmetic mean of data organized into a frequency distribution, we begin by assuming the observations in each class are represented by the *midpoint* of the class. The mean of a sample of data organized in a frequency distribution is computed by:

ARITHMETIC MEAN OF GROUPED DATA $$\bar{X} = \frac{\Sigma fX}{n}$$ **[3–16]**

where:

$\bar{X}$ is the designation for the sample mean.
X is the midpoint of each class.
f is the frequency in each class.
fX is the frequency in each class times the midpoint of the class.
ΣfX is the sum of these products.
n is the total number of frequencies.

example

The computations for the arithmetic mean of data grouped into a frequency distribution will be shown based on the real estate data, from the south-east area of Edmonton. Recall in Chapter 2, in Table 2–7 we constructed a frequency distribution for the list prices. The information is repeated below. Determine the arithmetic mean list price.

List Price ($ thousands)	Frequency
$250 to under $375	33
375 to under 500	41
500 to under 625	11
625 to under 750	5
750 to under 875	4
875 to under 1000	1
1000 to under 1125	1
Total	96

solution

The mean list price can be estimated from data grouped into a frequency distribution. To find the estimated mean, assume the midpoint of each class is representative of the data values in that class. Recall that the midpoint of a class is halfway between the upper and the lower class limits. To find the midpoint of a particular class, we add the upper and the lower class limits and divide by two. Hence, the midpoint of the first class is $312.5, (found by $250 + $375)/2. We assume that the value of $312.5 is representative of the 33 values in that class. To put it another way, we assume the sum of the 33 values is $10 312.5, found by 33($312.5). We continue the process of multiplying the class midpoint by the class frequency for each class and then sum these products. The results are summarized in Table 3–1.

TABLE 3–1 List Prices, South-East Area of Edmonton

List Price ($ thousands)	Frequency f	Midpoint ($) X	fX ($)
$250 to under $375	33	$312.5	$10 312.5
375 to under 500	41	437.5	17 937.5
500 to under 625	11	562.5	6187.5
625 to under 750	5	687.5	3437.5
750 to under 875	4	812.5	3250.0
875 to under 1000	1	937.5	937.5
1000 to under 1125	1	1062.5	1062.5
Total	96		$43 125.0

Solving for the arithmetic mean using formula (3–16), we get:

$$\bar{X} = \frac{\Sigma fX}{n} = \frac{\$43125}{96} = \$449.2 \text{ (thousands)}$$

So we conclude that the mean list price is about $449 200

The Median of Grouped Data

Recall that the **median** is defined as the midpoint of the observations after they have been ordered from the lowest to the highest. If the data is grouped some of the raw data values may not be available, and so we cannot necessarily determine the exact value of the median. But we can estimate the median by first finding the position of the median (which class it falls in), and then calculating an estimate of the median within this median class.

MEDIAN, GROUPED DATA

$$Median = L + \frac{\frac{N}{2} - f_c}{f}(i) \qquad [3\text{–}17]$$

where:

L is the lower limit of the median class.
N is the size of the population.
f is the frequency of the median class.
f_c is the cumulative frequencies up to but excluding the median class.
i is the class width of the median class.

In the following example, the raw data is available.

example

Professor Law lists the following quiz marks for his class of 30 students. Determine the median quiz mark.

Quiz Mark	10	9	8	7	6	5	4	3	2	1	0
Number of Students	2	3	5	12	4	2	1	0	1	0	0

solution

1. Arrange the data from the lowest mark (2) to the highest mark (10) as follows.

Quiz Mark	0	1	2	3	4	5	6	7	8	9	10
Number of Students	0	0	1	0	1	2	4	12	5	3	2

2. Find the position of the median mark by using formula (3–15):

$$L_p = (n + 1)\frac{P}{100} = (30 + 1)\frac{50}{100} = 15.5$$

Therefore, the median quiz mark will be the 15.5th observation. Finally, count the number of students until the 15.5th observation is reached. The table below shows the cumulative number of observations until the 15.5th observation.

Quiz Mark	Number of Students	f_c
0	0	0
1	0	0
2	1	1
3	0	1
4	1	2
5	2	4
6	4	8
7	12	20 ←
8	5	25
9	3	28
10	2	30

3. The value of the median falls in the class where the number of students is 12 and the quiz mark is 7. Therefore, the median quiz mark is 7. Since the raw data values are listed, we are able to determine the exact value of the median.

The next example does not have the raw data listed. Instead the data is grouped into a frequency distribution.

example

Refer to the frequency distribution for the real estate data reported in Table 3–1. Compute the median of the list prices.

List Price ($ thousands)	Frequency
$250 to under $375	33
375 to under 500	41
500 to under 625	11
625 to under 750	5
750 to under 875	4
875 to under 1000	1
1000 to under 1125	1
Total	96

solution

1. The data is arranged from lowest to highest in the frequency distribution.
2. Find the position of the median list price by using formula (3–15):

$$L_p = (n + 1)\frac{P}{100} = (96 + 1)\frac{50}{100} = 48.5$$

Therefore, the median list price will be in the class where the 48.5th observation is found. Count the number of list prices until the 48.5th observation is reached. The table below shows the cumulative number of observations until the 48.5th observation.

List Price ($ thousands)	Frequency f	f_c	
\$250 to under \$375	33	33	
375 to under 500	41	74	← median class
500 to under 625	11	85	
625 to under 750	5	90	
750 to under 875	4	94	
875 to under 1000	1	95	
1000 to under 1125	1	96	
Total	96		

3. Find the value of the median by using formula (3–17).

$$Median = L + \frac{\frac{N}{2} - f_c}{f}(i) = 375 + \frac{\frac{96}{2} - 33}{41}(125) = 420.73$$

Therefore, the median list price is \$420 730. Since the original observations are not available, we can only estimate the median.
Note: the median of the raw data from Table 3–1 is \$402 400. The estimate is \$18 330 larger, which is a 4.6 percent difference.

Standard Deviation of Grouped Data

Recall that for *ungrouped* data, one formula for the sample standard deviation is:

$$s = \sqrt{\frac{\Sigma X^2 - \frac{(\Sigma X)^2}{n}}{n-1}} \quad [3\text{–}12]$$

If the data of interest are in *grouped* form (in a frequency distribution), the sample standard deviation can be approximated by substituting ΣfX^2 for ΣX^2 and ΣfX for ΣX. The formula for the *sample standard deviation* then converts to:

STANDARD DEVIATION, GROUPED DATA

$$s = \sqrt{\frac{\Sigma fX^2 - \frac{(\Sigma fX)^2}{n}}{n-1}} \quad [3\text{–}18]$$

where:

s is the symbol for the sample standard deviation.
X is the midpoint of a class.
f is the class frequency.
n is the total number of sample observations.

example

Refer to the frequency distribution for the real estate data reported in Table 3–1. Compute the standard deviation of the list prices.

solution

Following the same practice used earlier for computing the mean of data grouped into a frequency distribution, X represents the midpoint of each class.

TABLE 3–1 List Prices, South-East Area of Edmonton

List Price ($ thousands)	Frequency f	Midpoint ($) X	fX ($)	fX^2
$250 to under $375	33	$312.5	$10 312.5	3 222 656.25
375 to under 500	41	437.5	17 937.5	7 847 656.25
500 to under 625	11	562.5	6187.5	3 480 468.75
625 to under 750	5	687.5	3437.5	2 363 281.25
750 to under 875	4	812.5	3250.0	2 640 625.00
875 to under 1000	1	937.5	937.5	878 906.25
1000 to under 1125	1	1062.5	1062.5	1 128 906.24
Total	96		$43 125.0	21 562 499.99

To find the standard deviation:

Step 1: Each class frequency is multiplied by its class midpoint. That is, multiply f times X. Thus, for the first class, 33($312.5) = $10 312.50. For the second class, fX = 41($437.5) = $17 937.50, and so on.

Step 2: Calculate fX^2. This could be written as $fX \, x \, X$. For the first class it would be (10 312.50)(312.5) = 3 222 656.25, and so on.

Step 3: Sum the fX and fX^2 columns. The totals are $43 125.0 and 21 562 499.99. We have omitted the units involved with the fX^2 column, but it is "dollars squared".

These values are used in the following formula (3–18):

$$s = \sqrt{\frac{\Sigma fX^2 - \frac{(\Sigma fx)^2}{n}}{n-1}} = \sqrt{\frac{21\,562\,499.99 - \frac{(43\,125.0)^2}{96}}{96-1}} = 151.83$$

The mean and standard deviation calculated from grouped data into a frequency distribution are usually close to the values calculated from raw data. The grouping results in some loss of information. For the list prices, the mean price reported in the **Excel** output is $447 403.14 and the standard deviation is $143 390.76. The respective values estimated from data grouped into a frequency distribution are $449 218.75, and $151 828.90. The difference in the means is $1815.61 or 0.4 percent. Based on the percentage difference, the estimated values are very close to the actual values.

self-review 3–14

The net incomes of a sample of large importers of antiques were organized into the following table:

Net Income ($ millions)	Number of Importers
$2 to under $6	1
6 to under 10	4
10 to under 14	10
14 to under 18	3
18 to under 22	2

(a) What is the table called?
(b) Based on the distribution, what is the estimate of the arithmetic mean net income?
(c) Based on the distribution, what is the estimate of the median net income?
(d) Based on the distribution, what is the estimate of the standard deviation?

Exercises

73. When we compute the mean of a frequency distribution, why do we refer to this as an *estimated* mean?

74. Determine the mean, median, and the standard deviation of the following frequency distribution.

Class	Frequency
0 to under 5	2
5 to under 10	7
10 to under 15	12
15 to under 20	6
20 to under 25	3

75. Determine the mean, median, and the standard deviation of the following frequency distribution.

Class	Frequency
20 to under 30	7
30 to under 40	12
40 to under 50	21
50 to under 60	18
60 to under 70	12

76. SCCoast, an Internet provider, developed the following frequency distribution on the age of Internet users. Find the mean, median, and the standard deviation.

Age (years)	Frequency
10 to under 20	3
20 to under 30	7
30 to under 40	18
40 to under 50	20
50 to under 60	12

77. The following frequency distribution reports the amount, in thousands of dollars, owed by a sample of 50 public accounting firms. Find the mean, median, and the standard deviation.

Amount ($ thousands)	Frequency
$20 to under $30	1
30 to under 40	15
40 to under 50	22
50 to under 60	8
60 to under 70	4

78. Advertising expenses are a significant component of the cost of goods sold. Listed below is a frequency distribution showing the advertising expenditures for 60 manufacturing companies. Estimate the mean, median, and the standard deviation of advertising expense.

Advertising Expenditure ($ millions)	Number of Companies
$25 to under $35	5
35 to under 45	10
45 to under 55	21
55 to under 65	16
65 to under 75	8
Total	60

Ethics and Reporting Results

In Chapter 1, we discussed the ethical and unbiased reporting of statistical results. While you are learning about how to organize and interpret data using statistics, it is also important to understand statistics so that you can be an intelligent consumer of information.

In this chapter, we learned how to compute descriptive statistics. Specifically, we showed how to compute and interpret measures of location for a data set: the mean, median, and mode. We also discussed the advantages and disadvantages for each statistic. For example, if a real estate developer tells a client that the average home in a particular subdivision sold for \$350 000, we assume that \$350 000 is a representative selling price for all the homes. But suppose that the client also asks what the median sales price is, and the median is \$200 000. Why was the developer only reporting the mean price? This information is extremely important to a person's decision making when buying a home. Knowing the advantages and disadvantages of the mean, median, and mode is important as we report statistics and we use statistical information to make decisions.

We also learned how to compute measures of dispersion: range, mean deviation, variance, and standard deviation. Each of these statistics also has advantages and disadvantages. Remember that the range provides information about the overall spread of a distribution. However, it does not provide any information about how the data is clustered or concentrated around the centre location of the distribution.

As we learn more about statistics, we need to remember that when we use statistics we must maintain an independent and principled point of view. Any statistical report requires objective and honest communication of the results.

Chapter Summary

I. A measure of location is a value used to describe the centre of a set of data.

A. The arithmetic mean is the most widely reported measure of location.

1. It is calculated by adding the values of the observations and dividing by the total number of observations.

a. The formula for a population mean of ungrouped or raw data is:

$$\mu = \frac{\Sigma X}{N} \qquad [3\text{–}1]$$

b. The formula for the mean of a sample is

$$\bar{X} = \frac{\Sigma X}{n} \qquad [3\text{–}2]$$

c. The formula for the sample mean of data in a frequency distribution is

$$\bar{X} = \frac{\Sigma fX}{n} \qquad [3\text{–}16]$$

2. The major characteristics of the arithmetic mean are:

a. At least the interval scale of measurement is required.
b. All the data values are used in the calculation.
c. A set of data has only one mean. That is, it is unique.
d. The sum of the deviations from the mean equals 0.

B. The weighted mean is found by multiplying each observation by its corresponding weight.

1. The formula for determining the weighted mean is:

$$\bar{X}_w = \frac{w_1X_1 + w_2X_2 + w_3X_3 + \cdots + w_nX_n}{w_1 + w_2 + w_3 + \cdots + w_n} \qquad [3\text{–}3]$$

2. It is a special case of the arithmetic mean.

C. The median is the value in the middle of a set of ordered data.

1. To find the median, sort the observations from smallest to largest and identify the middle value.

2. The major characteristics of the median are:

a. At least the ordinal scale of measurement is required.
b. It is not influenced by extreme values.
c. Fifty percent of the observations are larger than the median.
d. It is unique to a set of data.

3. The formula for the median of grouped data is:

$$Median = L + \frac{\frac{N}{2} - f_c}{f}(i) \qquad [3\text{–}17]$$

D. The mode is the value that occurs most often in a set of data.
1. The mode can be found for nominal-level data.
2. A set of data can have more than one mode.

E. The geometric mean is the nth root of the product of n values.
1. The formula for the geometric mean is:

$$GM = \sqrt[n]{(X_1)(X_2)(X_3)\cdots(X_n)} \qquad [3\text{–}4]$$

2. The geometric mean is also used to find the rate of change from one period to another.

$$GM = \sqrt[n]{\frac{\text{Value at end of period}}{\text{Value at beginning of period}}} - 1 \qquad [3\text{–}5]$$

3. The geometric mean is always equal to or less than the arithmetic mean.

II. The dispersion is the variation or spread in a set of data.

A. The range is the difference between the largest and the smallest value in a set of data.
1. The formula for the range is:

$$\text{Range} = \text{Largest value} - \text{Smallest value} \qquad [3\text{–}6]$$

2. The major characteristics of the range are:
   a. Only two values are used in its calculation.
   b. It is influenced by extreme values.
   c. It is easy to compute and to understand.

B. The mean absolute deviation is the sum of the absolute deviations from the mean divided by the number of observations.
1. The formula for computing the mean absolute deviation is

$$MD = \frac{\Sigma|X - \bar{X}|}{n} \qquad [3\text{–}7]$$

2. The major characteristics of the mean absolute deviation are:
   a. It is not unduly influenced by large or small values.
   b. All observations are used in the calculation.
   c. The absolute values are somewhat difficult to work with.

C. The variance is the mean of the squared deviations from the arithmetic mean.
1. The formula for the population variance is:

$$\sigma^2 = \frac{\Sigma(X - \mu)^2}{N} \qquad [3\text{–}8]$$

2. The formula for the sample variance is:

$$s^2 = \frac{\Sigma(X - \bar{X})^2}{n - 1} \qquad [3\text{–}10]$$

3. The major characteristics of the variance are:
   a. All observations are used in the calculation.
   b. It is not unduly influenced by extreme observations.
   c. The units are somewhat difficult to work with; they are the original units squared.

D. The standard deviation is the square root of the variance.
1. The major characteristics of the standard deviation are:
   a. It is in the same units as the original data.
   b. It is the square root of the average squared deviation from the mean.
   c. It cannot be negative.
   d. It is the most widely reported measure of dispersion.
2. The formula for the sample standard deviation is:

$$s = \sqrt{\frac{\Sigma X^2 - \frac{(\Sigma X)^2}{n}}{n - 1}} \qquad [3\text{–}12]$$

3. The formula for the standard deviation of grouped data is:

$$s = \sqrt{\frac{\Sigma fX^2 - \frac{(\Sigma fX)^2}{n}}{n-1}} \quad \textbf{[3–18]}$$

III. We interpret the standard deviation using two measures.

A. Chebyshev's theorem states that regardless of the shape of the distribution, at least $1 - 1/k^2$ of the observations will be within k standard deviations of the mean, where k is greater than 1.

B. The Empirical Rule states that for a bell-shaped distribution about 68 percent of the values will be within 1 standard deviation of the mean, about 95 percent within 2, and virtually all within 3.

IV. The coefficient of variation is a measure of relative dispersion.

A. The formula for the coefficient of variation is:

$$CV = \frac{s}{\bar{X}}(100) \quad \textbf{[3–13]}$$

B. It reports the variation relative to the mean.

C. It is useful for comparing distributions with different units.

V. The coefficient of skewness measures the symmetry of a distribution.

A. In a positively skewed set of data the long tail is to the right.

B. In a negatively skewed distribution the long tail is to the left.

VI. Measures of location also describe the spread in a set of observations.

A. A quartile divides a set of observations into four equal parts.
1. Twenty-five percent of the observations are less than the first quartile, 50 percent are less than the second quartile (the median), and 75 percent are less than the third quartile.
2. The interquartile range is the difference between the third and the first quartile.

B. Deciles divide a set of observations into 10 equal parts.

C. Percentiles divide a set of observations into 100 equal parts.

D. A box plot is a graphic display of a set of data.
1. It is drawn enclosing the first and third quartiles.
   a. A line through the inside of the box shows the median.
   b. Dotted line segments from the third quartile to the largest value and from the first quartile to the smallest value show the range of the largest 25 percent of the observations and the smallest 25 percent.
2. A box plot is based on five statistics: the largest and smallest observation, the first and third quartiles, and the median.

Pronunciation Key

SYMBOL	MEANING	PRONUNCIATION
μ	Population mean	*mu*
Σ	Operation of adding	*sigma*
ΣX	Adding a group of values	*sigma X*
$\bar{X}$	Sample mean	*X bar*
$\bar{X}_w$	Weighted mean	*X bar sub w*
GM	Geometric mean	*GM*
ΣfX	Adding the product of the frequencies and the class midpoints	*sigma fX*
σ^2	Population variance	*sigma squared*
σ	Population standard deviation	*sigma*
s^2	Sample Variance	s^2
s	Standard Deviation	s
CV	Coefficient of Variation	*CV*
sk	Pearson's Coefficient of Skewness	*sk*
ΣfX^2	Sum of the product of the class midpoints squared and the class frequency	*sigma fX squared*
L_p	Location of percentile	*L sub p*
Q_1	First quartile	*Q sub 1*
Q_3	Third quartile	*Q sub 3*

Chapter Exercises

79. The accounting firm of Crawford and Associates has five senior partners. Yesterday the senior partners saw six, four, three, seven, and five clients, respectively.
  a. Compute the mean number and median number of clients seen by a partner.
  b. Is the mean a sample mean or a population mean?
  c. Verify that $\Sigma(X - \mu) = 0$.

80. Owens Orchards sells apples in a large bag by weight. A sample of seven bags contained the following number of apples: 23, 19, 26, 17, 21, 24, 22.
  a. Compute the mean number and median number of apples in a bag.
  b. Verify that $\Sigma(X - \bar{X}) = 0$.

81. A sample of households that subscribe to a local phone company revealed the following number of calls received last week. Determine the mean and the median number of calls received.

52	43	30	38	30	42	12	46	39	37
34	46	32	18	41	5				

82. The Citizens Banking Company is studying the number of times the ATM, located in a Loblaws Supermarket at the foot of Market Street, is used per day. Following are the number of times the machine was used over each of the last 30 days. Determine the mean number of times the machine was used per day.

83	64	84	76	84	54	75	59	70	61
63	80	84	73	68	52	65	90	52	77
95	36	78	61	59	84	95	47	87	60

83. The Canadian Government wants to know the relative age of its workforce. As the baby boom generation becomes older, the government is concerned about the availability of younger, qualified workers. To become more informed, the government hired ABC Consulting Services to survey many industries regarding employee ages. The mean and median age for two industries, communication and retail trade, are listed in the following table.

	Communication and Other Utilities		Retail Trade and Consumer Services	
	Mean	**Median**	**Mean**	**Median**
Managers	52.6	53	48.6	48
Professionals	50.8	50	50.0	49
Technical/Trades	51.4	52	47.1	47
Marketing/Sales	NA	NA	43.7	41
Clerical/Administrative	50.8	51	48.0	48
Production Workers	47.2	50	42.0	34

Comment on the distribution of age. Which industry appears to have older workers? Younger workers? In each industry, which job types show the greatest difference between mean and median age?

84. Trudy Green works for the True-Green Lawn Company. Her job is to solicit lawn care business via the telephone. Listed below are the number of appointments she made in each of the last 25 hours of calling. What is the arithmetic mean number of appointments she made per hour? What is the median number of appointments per hour? Write a brief report summarizing the findings.

9	5	2	6	5	6	4	4	7	2	3	6	3
4	4	7	8	4	4	5	5	4	8	3	3	

85. The Split-A-Rail Fence Company sells three types of fence to homeowners. Grade A costs \$5.00/m to install, Grade B costs \$6.50/m, and Grade C, the premium quality, costs \$8.00/m. Yesterday, Split-A-Rail installed 270 m of Grade A, 300 m of Grade B, and 100 m of Grade C. What was the mean cost per metre of fence installed?

86. Rolland Poust is a business student. Last semester he took courses in statistics and accounting, three hours each, and earned an A in both. He earned a B in a five-hour history course and a B in a two-hour history of jazz course. In addition, he took a one-hour course dealing with the rules of basketball so he could get his license to officiate high school basketball games. He got an A in this course. What was his GPA for the semester? Assume that he receives 4 points for an A, 3 for a B, and so on. What measure of central tendency did you just calculate?

87. The uncertainty in the stock market led Sam to diversify his investments. However, he still felt that stock options would earn the most, and so he left the bulk of his funds in stock options. The table below lists Sam's earnings from investments last year. What is the average rate of return on his investments?

Investment Type	Performance (%)	Amount Invested ($)
Mutual Funds	4.5%	$15 300
GICs	3.0	10 400
Stock Options	10.2	150 600

88. Listed below are the commuting distances, in kilometres, of students attending college for their first year.

5.2	6.3	7.5	4.3	6.8	4.6	4.6	8.2	7.8	9.4	9.3	7.4	5.3	5.3	5.4

a. What is the arithmetic mean distance travelled?
b. What is the median distance travelled?
c. What is the modal distance travelled?

89. The Carter Construction Company pays its summer students an hourly rate of $13.00 for general labour, $15.50 for landscaping, or $18.00 for road work. Forty students were hired for the summer, 20 for general labour, 12 for landscaping, and 8 for road work. What is the mean hourly rate paid to the 40 summer students? Calculate the variance and standard deviation.

90. A recent article suggested that if you earn $25 000 a year today and the inflation rate continues at 3 percent per year, you'll need to make $33 598 in 10 years to have the same buying power. You would need to make $44 771 if the inflation rate jumped to 6 percent. Confirm that these statements are accurate by finding the geometric mean rate of increase.

91. The ages of a sample of Canadian tourists flying from Toronto to Hong Kong were: 32, 21, 60, 47, 54, 17, 72, 55, 33, and 41.
a. Compute the range.
b. Compute the mean deviation.
c. Compute the standard deviation.
d. Using Chebyshev's Theorem, at least what percent of the observations must be within 2 standard deviations of the mean? Verify.
e. Using the Empirical Rule, about 95 percent of the values would occur between what values? Verify.

92. The masses (in kilograms) of a sample of five boxes being sent by UPS are: 12, 6, 7, 3, and 10.
a. Compute the range.
b. Compute the mean deviation.
c. Compute the standard deviation.
d. Using Chebyshev's Theorem, at least what percent of the observations must be within 2.5 standard deviations of the mean? Verify.
e. Using the Empirical Rule, about 68 percent of the values would occur between what values? Verify.

93. A library has seven branches in its system. The number of volumes (in thousands) held in the branches are 83, 510, 33, 256, 401, 47, and 23.
a. Is this a sample or a population?
b. Compute the standard deviation.
c. Compute the coefficient of variation. Interpret.

94. Health issues are a concern of managers, especially as they evaluate the cost of medical insurance. A recent survey of 150 executives at Elvers Industries, a large insurance and financial firm, reported the number of kilograms by which the executives were overweight. Compute the range and the standard deviation.

Number of Kilograms	Frequency
0 to under 6	14
6 to under 12	42
12 to under 18	58
18 to under 24	28
24 to under 30	8

95. A major airline wanted some information on those enrolled in its "frequent flyer" program. A sample of 48 members resulted in the following distance flown last year, in thousands of kilometres, by each participant. Develop a box plot of the data and comment on the information.

22	29	32	38	39	41	42	43	43	43	44	44
45	45	46	46	46	47	50	51	52	54	54	55
56	57	58	59	60	61	61	63	63	64	64	67
69	70	70	70	71	71	72	73	74	76	78	88

96. The National Muffler Company claims they will change your muffler in less than 30 minutes. An investigative reporter for WTOL Channel 11 monitored 30 consecutive muffler changes at the National outlet on Liberty Street. The number of minutes to perform changes is reported below.

44	12	22	31	26	22	30	26	18	28	12
40	17	13	14	17	25	29	15	30	10	28
16	33	24	20	29	34	23	13			

a. Develop a box plot for the time to change a muffler.
b. Does the distribution show any outliers?
c. Summarize your findings in a brief report.

97. The Walter Gogel Company is an industrial supplier of fasteners, tools, and springs. The amounts of its invoices vary widely, from less than $20.00 to over $400.00. During the month of January it sent out 80 invoices. Here is a box plot of these invoices. Write a brief report summarizing the amounts of its invoices. Be sure to include information on the values of the first and third quartile, the median, and whether there is any skewness. If there are any outliers, approximate the value of these invoices.

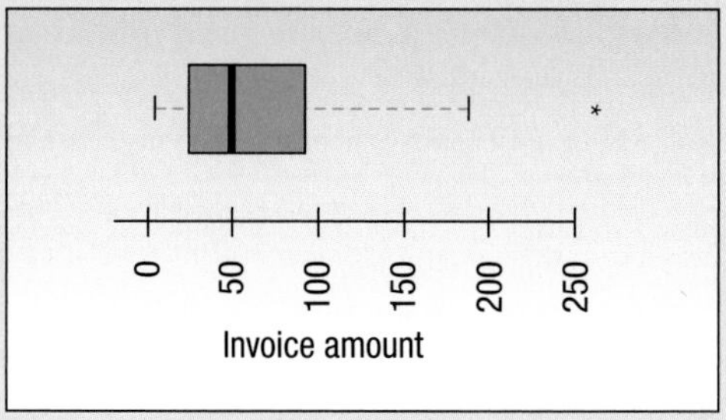

98. The following box plot shows the number of daily newspapers published. Summarize the findings. Be sure to include information on the values of the first and third quartiles, the median, and whether there is any skewness. If there are any outliers, estimate their value.

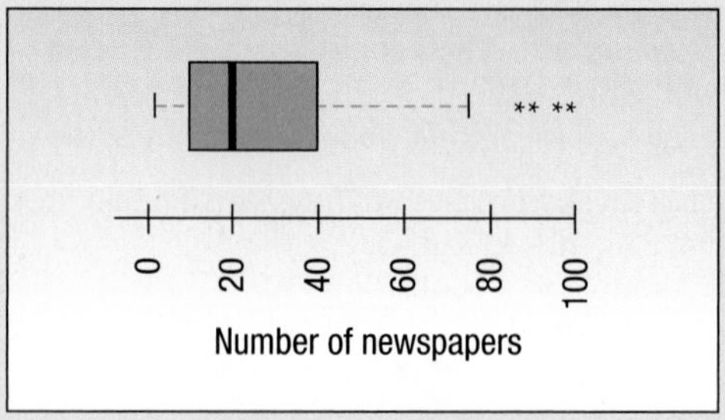

99. The following data are the estimated market values (in millions of dollars) of 50 companies in the auto parts business.

$26.8	8.6	6.5	30.6	15.4	18.0	7.6	21.5	11.0	10.2
28.3	15.5	31.4	23.4	4.3	20.2	33.5	7.9	11.2	1.0
11.7	18.5	6.8	22.3	12.9	29.8	1.3	14.1	29.7	18.7
6.7	31.4	30.4	20.6	5.2	37.8	13.4	18.3	27.1	32.7
6.1	0.9	9.6	35.0	17.1	1.9	1.2	16.6	31.1	16.1

a. Determine the mean and the median of the market values.
b. Determine the standard deviation of the market values.
c. Using the Empirical Rule, about 95 percent of the values would occur between what values?
d. Determine the coefficient of variation.
e. Determine the coefficient of skewness.
f. Estimate the values of Q_1 and Q_3. Draw a box plot.
g. Summarize the results.

100. On the Coast is a very popular restaurant located along the coast of Lake Erie. They serve a variety of steak and seafood dinners. During the summer beach season, they do not take reservations or accept "call ahead" seating. Management of the restaurant is concerned with the time a patron must wait before being seated for dinner. Listed below is the wait time, in minutes, for the 25 tables seated last Saturday night.

28	39	23	67	37	28	56	40	28	50
51	45	44	65	61	27	24	61	34	44
64	25	24	27	29					

a. Explain why the wait times, in minutes, are a sample.
b. Find the mean and median of the wait times.
c. Find the range and the standard deviation of the wait times.

101. The Apollo space program lasted from 1967 until 1972 and included 13 missions. The missions lasted from as little as 7 hours to as long as 301 hours. The duration of each flight is listed below.

9	195	241	301	216	260	7	244	192	147
10	295	142							

a. Find the mean, median, and standard deviation of the duration for the Apollo flights. Treat as sample data.
b. Compute the coefficient of variation and the coefficient of skewness. Comment on your findings.
c. Find the 45th and 82nd percentiles.
d. Draw a box plot and comment on your findings.

102. A recent report in *Woman's World* magazine suggested that the typical family of four with an intermediate budget spends about \$106 per week on food. The following frequency distribution was included in the report. Compute the mean, median, and the standard deviation. How do your results compare with those of the report?

Amount Spent (\$)	Frequency
\$80 to under \$85	6
85 to under 90	12
90 to under 95	23
95 to under 100	35
100 to under 105	24
105 to under 110	10

103. Bidwell Electronics Inc. recently surveyed a sample of employees to determine how far they lived from corporate headquarters. The results are shown below. Compute the mean, median and the standard deviation.

Distance (km)	Frequency
0 to under 5	4
5 to under 10	15
10 to under 15	27
15 to under 20	18
20 to under 25	6

104. A survey showed that in a class of 30 students, nine had purchased their own computer systems. The cost of the computer systems, in dollars, is listed below.

\$2235	2150	1850	1500	2025	5750	2800	2750	3300

a. Calculate the mean and median cost of the computer systems.
b. Draw a box plot and comment on your findings.
c. Would you use the mean or median as a measure of location of your data? Explain.

For the following two questions, find the mean, median, mode, standard deviation, and the interquartile range. Consider this sample data.

105.

Grade on Quiz	3	4	5	7	8	10
Number of Students	4	4	6	20	6	1

106.

Grade on Quiz	50	60	70	80	90	100
Number of Students	2	17	21	40	13	8

Data Set Exercises

107. Refer to the CREA data on the CD-ROM, which reports information on average house prices nationally and in a selection of cities across Canada.
   a. Select the cities only for the variable July 2008.
      1. Find the mean, median, and the standard deviation.
      2. Determine the coefficient of skewness. Is the distribution positively or negatively skewed?
      3. Develop a box plot. Are there any outliers? Estimate the first and third quartiles.
      4. Summarize the results.
   b. Select the cities only for the variable January 2008
      1. Find the mean, median, and the standard deviation.
      2. Determine the coefficient of skewness. Is the distribution positively or negatively skewed?
      3. Develop a box plot. Are there any outliers? Estimate the first and third quartiles.
      4. Summarize the results.

108. Refer to the real estate data from the central area of Edmonton on the CD-ROM, which reports information on listed homes.
   a. Select the variable size (sq. ft.).
      1. Find the mean, median, and the standard deviation.
      2. Determine the coefficient of skewness. Is the distribution positively or negatively skewed?
      3. Develop a box plot. Are there any outliers? Estimate the first and third quartiles.
      4. Summarize the results.
   b. Select the variable no. of bedrooms.
      1. Find the mean, median, and the standard deviation.
      2. Determine the coefficient of skewness. Is the distribution positively or negatively skewed?
      3. Develop a box plot. Are there any outliers? Estimate the first and third quartiles.
      4. Summarize the results.

109. Refer to the International data, which reports demographic and economic information on 46 countries.
   a. Select the variable Life Expectancy.
      1. Find the mean, median, and the standard deviation.
      2. Determine the coefficient of skewness. Is the distribution positively or negatively skewed?
      3. Develop a box plot. Are there any outliers? Estimate the first and third quartiles.
      4. Summarize the results.
   b. Select the variable GDP/cap.
      1. Find the mean, median, and the standard deviation.
      2. Determine the coefficient of skewness. Is the distribution positively or negatively skewed?
      3. Develop a box plot. Are there any outliers? Estimate the first and third quartiles.
      4. Summarize the results.
   c. Select the variable Labour Force.
      1. Find the mean, median, and the standard deviation.
      2. Determine the coefficient of skewness. Is the distribution positively or negatively skewed?
      3. Develop a box plot. Are there any outliers? Estimate the first and third quartiles.
      4. Summarize the results.

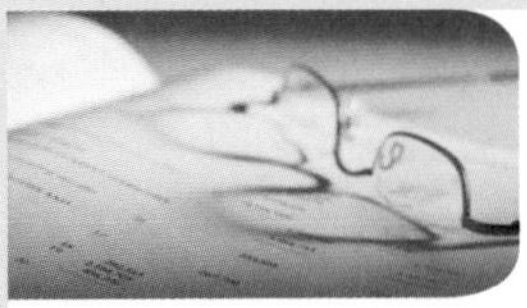

Case

Continue with the Whitner Pontiac data and case from Chapter 2. Rob would like you to further develop tables and charts that he could review monthly and would like you to report where the selling prices tend to cluster, where the variation is in the selling prices, and to note any trends. The data is on the CD-ROM, Data Files, Whitner-2007.

exercises.com

Additional exercises that require you to access information at related Internet sites are available on the CD-ROM included with this text.

Answers to Self-Reviews

3–1 **1. (a)** $\bar{X} = \frac{\$267\,100}{4} = \$66\,775$

(b) Statistic, because it is a sample value.

(c) \$66 775. The sample mean is our best estimate of the population mean.

2. (a) $\mu = \frac{498}{6} = 83$

(b) Parameter, because it was computed using all the population values.

3–2 **(a)** \$237, found by:

$$\frac{(95 \times \$400) + (126 \times \$200) + (79 \times \$100)}{95 + 126 + 79} = \$237.00$$

(b) The profit per suit is \$12, found by \$237 − \$200 cost − \$25 commission. The total profit for the 300 suits is \$3600, found by 300 × \$12.

3–3 **1. (a)** \$323

(b) 3, 3

2. (a) 7, found by (6 + 8)/2 = 7

(b) 3, 3

(c) 0

3–4 **(a)**

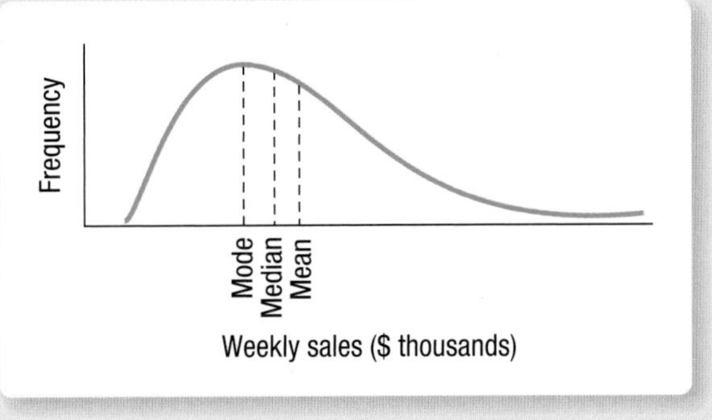

(b) Positively skewed, because the mean is the largest average and the mode is the smallest.

3–5 **1. (a)** About 8.39 percent, found by $\sqrt[4]{4951.75464}$

(b) About 10.095 percent

(c) Greater than, because 10.095 > 8.39

2. 8.63 percent, found by $\sqrt[20]{\frac{120\,520}{23\,000}} - 1 = 1.0863 - 1$

3–6 **(a)** 22, found by 112 − 90

(b) $\bar{X} = \frac{824}{8} = 103$

(c)

X	$\lvert X-\bar{X}\rvert$	Absolute Deviation
95	| −8 |	8
103	| 0 |	0
105	| +2 |	2
110	| +7 |	7
104	| +1 |	1
105	| +2 |	2
112	| +9 |	9
90	| −13 |	13
	Total	42

$$MD = \frac{42}{8} = 5.25\text{ kg}$$

3–7 **(a)** $\mu = \frac{\$16\,900}{5} = \$3380$

(b) $\sigma^2 = \frac{(3536 - 3380)^2 + \cdots + (3622 - 3380)^2}{5}$

$= \frac{197\,454}{5} = 39\,490.8$

(c) $\sigma = \sqrt{39\,490.8} = 198.72$

(d) There is more variation in the second office because the standard deviation is larger.

3–8 2.33, found by:

$$\bar{X} = \frac{\Sigma X}{n} = \frac{28}{7} = 4$$

X	$X-X$	$(X-\bar{X})^2$	X^2
4	0	0	16
2	−2	4	4
5	1	1	25
4	0	0	16
5	1	1	25
2	−2	4	4
6	2	4	36
28	0	14	126

$$s^2 = \frac{\Sigma(X-\bar{X})^2}{n-1} \quad \text{or} \quad s^2 = \frac{\Sigma X^2 - \frac{(\Sigma X)^2}{n}}{n-1}$$

$$= \frac{14}{7-1} \qquad = \frac{126 - \frac{(28)^2}{7}}{7-1}$$

$$= 2.33 \qquad = \frac{126-112}{6}$$

$$= 2.33$$

$$s = \sqrt{2.33} = 1.53$$

3–9 (a) $k = \frac{1.35 - 1.2}{0.1} = 1.5$

$$1 - \frac{1}{(1.5)^2} = 1 - 0.44 = 0.56$$

$$= 56 \text{ percent}$$

(b) 1.1 to 1.3
(c) 1.0 to 1.4

3–10 *CV* for mechanical is 5 percent, found by (10/200) (100). For finger dexterity, *CV* is 20 percent, found by (6/30) (100). Thus, relative dispersion in finger dexterity scores is greater than relative dispersion in mechanical, because 20 percent > 5 percent.

3–11 (a) $\bar{X} = \frac{407}{5} = 81.4$, Median = 84

$$s = \sqrt{\frac{34\,053 - \frac{(407)^2}{5}}{5-1}} = 15.19$$

(b) $sk = \frac{3(81.4 - 84.0)}{15.19} = -0.51$

(c) The distribution is somewhat negatively skewed.

3–12 (a) 500
(b) $Q_1 = 495.5$, $Q_2 = 502.5$

3–13 The smallest value is 10 and the largest 85; the first quartile is 25 and the third is 60. About 50 percent of the values are between 25 and 60. The median value is 40. The distribution is somewhat positively skewed.

3–14 a. Frequency distribution.

b.

f	Midpoint (x)	fX	fX^2
1	4	4	16
4	8	32	256
10	12	120	1440
3	16	48	768
2	20	40	800
20		244	3280

$$\bar{X} = \frac{\Sigma fX}{N} = \frac{\$244}{20} = \$12.20$$

c.

Net Income ($ millions)	f	f_c
$2 to under $6	1	1
6 to under 10	4	5
10 to under 14	10	15
14 to under 18	3	18
18 to under 22	2	20
Total	20	

Position of the median = (20 + 1)/2 = 10.5th observation

$$\text{Value of the median} = 10 + \frac{\frac{20}{2} - 5}{10}(4) = 12$$

d. $s = \sqrt{\frac{3280 - \frac{(244)^2}{20}}{20-1}} = \$3.99$

chapter 4

A Survey of Probability Concepts

LEARNING GOALS

When you have completed this chapter, you will be able to:

1. Define *probability*.
2. Understand the terms *experiment*, *event*, *outcome*, *permutations*, and *combinations*.
3. Describe the *classical*, *empirical*, and *subjective* approaches to probability.
4. Calculate probabilities using the *rules of addition* and *rules of multiplication*.
5. Define the terms *conditional probability* and *joint probability*.
6. Use a tree diagram to organize and compute probabilities.

Introduction

The emphasis in Chapters 2 and 3 is on descriptive statistics. In Chapter 2 we organize the list prices of 96 homes in the south-east area of Edmonton into a frequency distribution. This frequency distribution shows the lowest and the highest list prices and where the largest concentration of data occurs. In Chapter 3 we use measures of location and dispersion to locate a typical list price and to examine the spread in the data. We describe the spread in the list prices with such measures of dispersion as the range and the standard deviation.

Descriptive statistics is concerned with summarizing data collected from past events. For example, we described the list prices of 96 homes in the south-east area of Edmonton. We now turn to the second facet of statistics, namely, *computing the chance that something will occur in the future*. This facet of statistics is called **statistical inference** or **inferential statistics**.

Seldom does a decision maker have complete information from which to make a decision. For example:

- Toys and Things, a toy and puzzle manufacturer, recently developed a new game based on sports trivia. They want to know whether sports buffs will purchase the game. "Slam Dunk" and "Home Run" are two of the names under consideration. One way to minimize the risk of making an incorrect decision is to hire a market research firm to take a sample of, say, 2000 consumers from the population and ask each respondent for a reaction to the new game and its proposed titles. Using the sample results, the company can estimate the proportion of the population that will purchase the game.

- The quality control department of a Hamilton Steel mill must assure management that the 3 mm wire being produced has an acceptable tensile strength. Obviously, not all the wire produced can be tested for tensile strength because testing requires the wire to be stretched until it breaks—thus, destroying it. So a random sample of 10 pieces is selected and tested. Based on the test results, all the wire produced is deemed to be either acceptable or unacceptable.
- Other questions involving uncertainty are: Should the daytime drama *Days of Our Lives* be discontinued immediately? Will a newly developed mint-flavoured cereal be profitable if marketed? How many new television reality shows will be developed for the fall season?

Statistical inference deals with conclusions about a population based on a sample taken from that population. (The populations for the preceding illustrations are: all consumers who like sports trivia games, all the 3 mm steel wire produced, all television viewers who watch daytime drama, all who purchase breakfast cereal, and so on.)

Because there is uncertainty in decision making, it is important that all the known risks involved be scientifically evaluated. Helpful in this evaluation is *probability theory*, which has often been referred to as the science of uncertainty. The use of probability theory allows the decision maker with only limited information to analyze the risks and minimize the gamble inherent, for example, in marketing a new product or accepting an incoming shipment possibly containing defective parts.

Because probability concepts are so important in the field of statistical inference (to be discussed starting with Chapter 7), this chapter introduces the basic language of probability, including such terms as *experiment*, *event*, *subjective probability*, and *addition* and *multiplication rules*.

1 Define *probability*.

What Is a Probability?

probability A value between 0 and 1, inclusive, describing the relative possibility (chance or likelihood) an event will occur.

No doubt you are familiar with terms such as **probability**, *chance*, and *likelihood*. They are often used interchangeably. The weather forecaster announces that there is a 70 percent chance of snow for the Grey Cup game. Based on a survey of consumers who tested a newly developed pickle with a banana taste, the probability is .03 that, if marketed, it will be a financial success. (This means that the chance of the banana-flavoured pickle being accepted by the public is rather remote.) What is a probability? In general, it is a number that describes the chance that something will happen.

A probability is frequently expressed as a decimal, such as .70, .27, or .50. However, it may be given as a fraction such as 7/10, 27/100, or 1/2. It can assume any number from 0 to 1, inclusive. If a company has only five sales regions, and each region's name or number is written on a slip of paper and the slips put in a hat, the probability of selecting one of the five regions is 1. The probability of selecting from the hat a slip of paper that reads "Edmonton Oilers" is 0. Thus, the probability of 1 represents something that is certain to happen, and the probability of 0 represents something that cannot happen.

The closer a probability is to 0, the more improbable it is the event will happen. The closer the probability is to 1, the more sure we are it will happen. The relationship is shown in the following diagram along with a few of our personal beliefs. You might, however, select a different probability for Slo Poke's chances to win the Queen's Plate or for an increase in federal taxes.

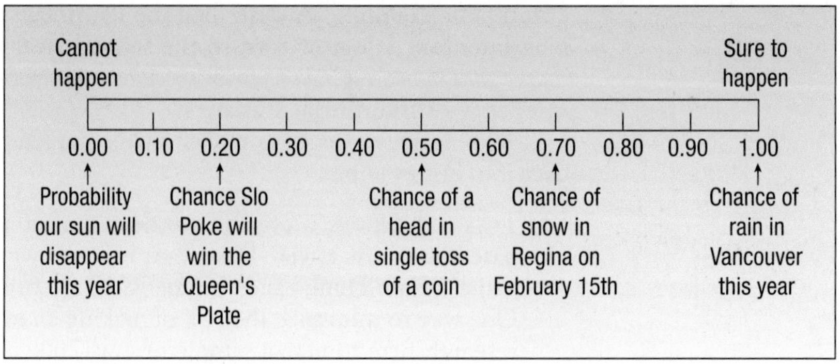

2 **Understand the terms *experiment*, *event*, *outcome*, *permutations*, and *combinations*.**

experiment A process that leads to the occurrence of one and only one of several possible observations.

outcome A particular result of an experiment.

event A collection of one or more outcomes of an experiment.

Three key words are used in the study of probability: **experiment**, **outcome**, and **event**. These terms are used in our everyday language, but in statistics they have specific meanings.

The definition of an experiment is more general than the one used in the physical sciences, where we picture someone manipulating test tubes or microscopes. In reference to probability, an experiment has two or more possible results, and it is uncertain which will occur.

For example, the tossing of a coin is an experiment. You may observe the toss of the coin, but you are unsure whether it will come up "heads" or "tails." Similarly, asking 500 college students whether they would purchase a new Dell computer system at a particular price is an experiment. If the coin is tossed, one particular outcome is a "head." The alternative outcome is a "tail." In the computer purchasing experiment, one possible outcome is that 273 students indicate they would purchase the computer. Another outcome is that 317 students would purchase the computer. Still another outcome is that 423 students indicate that they would purchase it. When one or more of the experiment's outcomes are observed, we call this an event.

Examples to clarify the definitions of the terms *experiment*, *outcome*, and *event* are presented in the following figure.

In the die-rolling experiment there are six possible outcomes, but there are many possible events. When counting the number of members of the board of directors for Fortune 500 companies over 60 years of age, the number of possible outcomes can be anywhere from zero to the total number of members. There are an even larger number of possible events in this experiment.

Experiment	Roll a die	Count the number of members of the board of directors for Fortune 500 companies who are over 60 years of age
All possible outcomes	Observe a 1 Observe a 2 Observe a 3 Observe a 4 Observe a 5 Observe a 6	None are over 60 One is over 60 Two are over 60 ... 29 are over 60 ... ... 48 are over 60
Some possible events	Observe an even number Observe a number greater than 4 Observe a number 3 or less	More than 13 are over 60 Fewer than 20 are over 60

self-review 4–1

Video Games Inc. recently developed a new video game. Its market potential is to be tested by 80 veteran game players.

(a) What is the experiment?
(b) What is one possible outcome?
(c) Suppose 65 players tried the new game and said they liked it. Is 65 a probability?
(d) The probability that the new game will be a success is computed to be −1.0. Comment.
(e) Specify one possible event.

3 Describe the *classical*, *empirical*, and *subjective* approaches to probability.

Approaches to Probability

Two approaches to probability will be discussed, namely, the *objective* and the *subjective* viewpoints. **Objective probability** is subdivided into (1) *classical probability* and (2) *empirical probability*.

Classical Probability

Classical probability is based on the assumption that the outcomes of an experiment are *equally likely*. Using the classical viewpoint, the probability of an event happening is computed by dividing the number of favourable outcomes by the number of possible outcomes:

DEFINITION OF CLASSICAL PROBABILITY

$$\text{Probability of an event} = \frac{\text{Number of favourable outcomes}}{\text{Total number of possible outcomes}} \qquad [4\text{–}1]$$

example

Consider an experiment of rolling a six-sided die. What is the probability of the event "an even number of spots appear face up"?

solution

The possible outcomes are:

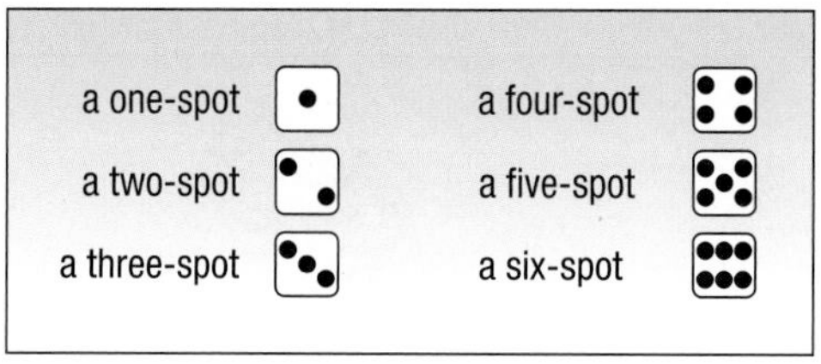

There are three "favourable" outcomes (a two, a four, and a six) in the collection of six equally likely possible outcomes. Therefore:

$$\text{Probability of an even number} = \frac{3}{6} \begin{array}{l} \leftarrow \text{Number of favourable outcomes} \\ \leftarrow \text{Total number of possible outcomes} \end{array}$$

$$= .5$$

mutually exclusive The occurrence of one event means that none of the other events can occur at the same time.

The **mutually exclusive** concept appeared earlier in our study of frequency distributions in Chapter 2. Recall that we create classes so that a particular event is included in only one of the classes and there is no overlap between classes. Thus, only one of several events can occur at a particular time.

The variable "gender" presents two mutually exclusive outcomes, male and female. An employee selected at random is either male or female but cannot be both. A manufactured part is defective or non defective. The part cannot be both defective and non defective at the same time. In a sample of manufactured parts, the event of selecting a non defective part and the event of selecting a defective part are mutually exclusive.

If an experiment has a set of events that includes every possible outcome, such as the events "an even number" and "an odd number" in the die-tossing experiment, then the set of events is **collectively exhaustive**. For the die-tossing experiment, every outcome will be either even or odd. So the set is collectively exhaustive.

collectively exhaustive At least one of the events must occur when an experiment is conducted.

If the set of events is collectively exhaustive and the events are mutually exclusive, the sum of the probabilities equals 1.

Historically, the classical approach to probability was developed and applied in the seventeenth and eighteenth centuries to games of chance, such as cards and dice. It is unnecessary to do an experiment to determine the probability of an event occurring using the classical approach because the total number of outcomes is known before the experiment. The flip of a coin has two possible outcomes; the roll of a die has six possible outcomes. We can logically arrive at the probability of getting a tail on the toss of one coin or three heads on the toss of three coins.

The classical approach to probability can also be applied to lotteries. For example, in a game of "Pick 3," a person buys a lottery ticket and selects three numbers between zero and nine. When the draw is made, three numbers are randomly selected from a machine that tumbles three containers each with balls numbered zero through nine. One way to win is to match the numbers and the order of the numbers. Then, there are 1000 possible outcomes, from 000 to 999. The probability of winning with any three-digit number is 1 in 1000 or 1/1000 = .001.

empirical probability The probability of an event happening is the fraction of the time similar events happened in the past.

Empirical Probability

Empirical or **relative frequency** is the second type of objective probability. It is based on the number of times an event occurs as a proportion of a known number of trials.

In terms of a formula:

$$\textbf{Probability of event happening} = \frac{\textbf{Number of times event occurred in past}}{\textbf{Total number of observations}}$$

The empirical approach to probability is based on what is called the law of large numbers. The key to establishing probabilities empirically is that more observations will provide a more accurate estimate of the probability.

law of large numbers Over a large number of trials, the empirical probability of an event will approach its true probability.

To explain the **law of large numbers**, suppose we toss a fair coin. The result of each toss is either a head or a tail. With just one toss of the coin, the empirical probability for heads is either zero or one. If we toss the coin a great number of times, the probability of the outcome of heads will approach .5. The following table reports the results of an experiment of flipping a fair coin 1, 10, 50, 500, 1000, and 10 000 times, and then computes the relative frequency of heads. Note as we increase the number of trials the empirical probability of a head appearing approaches .5, which is its value based on the classical approach to probability.

Number of Trials	Number of Heads	Relative Frequency of Heads
1	0	.00
10	3	.30
50	26	.52
100	52	.52
500	236	.472
1000	494	.494
10 000	5027	.5027

What have we demonstrated? Based on the classical definition of probability, the likelihood of obtaining a head in a single toss of a fair coin is .5. Based on the empirical or relative frequency approach to probability, the probability of the event happening approaches the same value based on the classical definition of probability.

This reasoning allows us to use the empirical or relative frequency approach to finding a probability. Here are some examples.

- Last semester 40 students registered for Business Statistics 101. Six students earned an A. Based on this information and the empirical rule of probability, we estimate the likelihood a student will earn an A is .15.
- Sidney Crosby of the Pittsburgh Penguins scored 36 goals from 250 shots during the 2006-07 NHL season (www.nhl.com). Based on the empirical rule of probability, the likelihood of Sidney Crosby scoring his next goal is 14.4 percent (36/250 = 0.144). Jordan Staal of the same team scored 29 goals from 131 shots. We estimate that the likelihood of Jordan Staal scoring his next goal is 22.1 percent (29/131 = 0.221).

Life insurance companies rely on past data to determine the acceptability of an applicant as well as the premium to be charged. Mortality tables list the likelihood a person of a particular age will die within the upcoming year. For example, the likelihood a 20-year old female will die within the next year is 0.00105.

The empirical concept is illustrated with the following example.

example

A study of 750 business administration graduates revealed 450 of the 750 were *not* employed in their major area of study in college. For illustration, a person who majored in accounting is now the marketing manager of an e-commerce firm. What is the probability that a particular business graduate will be employed in an area other than his or her college major?

solution

To simplify, letters or numbers may be used. P stands for probability, and in this case $P(A)$ stands for the probability a graduate is not employed in his or her major area of college study.

$$\textbf{Probability of event happening} = \frac{\textbf{Number of times event occurred in past}}{\textbf{Total number of observations}}$$

$$P(A) = \frac{450}{750} = .60$$

We can use this as an estimate of probability. In other words, based on past experience, the probability is .60 that a new business graduate will be employed in a field other than his or her college major.

Subjective Probability

If there is little or no experience or information on which to base a probability, it may be arrived at subjectively. Essentially, this means evaluating the available opinions and other information and then estimating or assigning the probability. This probability is aptly called a **subjective probability**.

subjective probability
The likelihood (probability) of a particular event happening that is assigned by an individual based on whatever information is available.

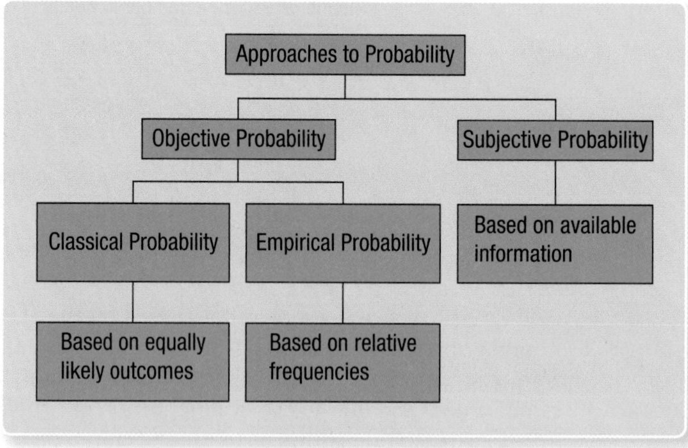

CHART 4–1 Summary of Approaches to Probability

Illustrations of subjective probability are:

1. Estimating when the next provincial election will be.
2. Estimating the likelihood you will be married before the age of 30.
3. Estimating the chance of the Maple Leafs winning the Stanley Cup.

The types of probability are summarized in Chart 4–1. A probability statement always assigns a likelihood to an event that has not yet occurred. There is, of course, a considerable latitude in the degree of uncertainty that surrounds this probability, based primarily on the knowledge possessed by the individual concerning the underlying process. The individual possesses a great deal of knowledge about the toss of a die and can state that the probability that a one-spot will appear face up on the toss of a true die is one-sixth. But we know very little concerning the acceptance in the marketplace of a new and untested product. For example, even though a market research director tests a newly developed product in 40 retail stores and states that there is a 70 percent chance that the product will have sales of more than 1 million units, she still has little knowledge of how consumers will react when it is marketed nationally. In both cases (the case of the person rolling a die and the testing of a new product) the individual is assigning a probability value to an event of interest, and a difference exists only in the predictor's confidence in the precision of the estimate. However, regardless of the viewpoint, the same laws of probability (presented in the following sections) will be applied.

self-review 4–2

1. One card will be randomly selected from a standard 52-card deck. What is the probability the card will be a queen? Which approach to probability did you use to answer this question?
2. The Centre for Child Care reports on the parental status of 539 children. The parents of 333 children are married, 182 divorced, and 24 widowed. What is the probability a particular child chosen at random will have a parent who is divorced? Which approach did you use?
3. What is the probability that the S&P/TSX Composite Index will exceed 15 000 during the next 12 months? Which approach to probability did you use to answer this question?

Exercises

1. Some people are in favour of reducing federal taxes in order to increase consumer spending and others are against it. Two persons are selected and their opinions are recorded. List the possible outcomes.

2. A quality control inspector selects a part to be tested. The part is then declared acceptable, repairable, or scrapped. Then another part is tested. List the possible outcomes of this experiment regarding two parts.

3. A survey of 34 students at a business school showed the following majors:

Accounting	10
Finance	5
E-Commerce	3
Management	6
Marketing	10

Suppose you select a student and observe his or her major.

a. What is the probability he or she is a management major?
b. Which concept of probability did you use to make this estimate?

4. A large company that must hire a new president prepares a final list of five candidates, all of whom are equally qualified. Two of these candidates are members of a minority group. The company decides to select the president by lottery.

a. What is the probability one of the minority candidates is hired?
b. Which concept of probability did you use to make this estimate?

5. In each of the following cases, indicate whether classical, empirical, or subjective probability is used.

a. A basketball player makes 30 out of 50 free throws. The probability is .6 that she makes the next free throw attempted.
b. A seven-member committee of students is formed to study environmental issues. What is the likelihood that any one of the seven is chosen as the spokesperson?
c. You purchase one of five million tickets sold for Lotto Canada. What is the likelihood you win the next jackpot?
d. The probability of an earthquake in northern California in the next 10 years is .80.

6. A firm will promote two employees out of a group of six men and three women.

a. List the outcomes of this experiment if there is particular concern about gender equity.
b. Which concept of probability would you use to estimate these probabilities?

7. A sample of 40 executives in the oil industry were selected to answer a questionnaire. One question about environmental issues required a yes or no answer.
   a. What is the experiment?
   b. List one possible event.
   c. Ten of the 40 executives responded "yes." Based on these sample responses, what is the probability an executive responded "yes"?
   d. What concept of probability does this illustrate?
   e. Are each of the possible outcomes equally likely and mutually exclusive?
8. A sample of 2000 licensed drivers revealed the following number of speeding violations.

Number of Violations	Number of Drivers
0	1910
1	46
2	18
3	12
4	9
5 or more	5
Total	2000

   a. What is the experiment?
   b. List one possible event.
   c. What is the probability that a particular driver had exactly two violations?
   d. What concept of probability does this illustrate?
9. CIBC customers select their own four-digit personal identification number (PIN) for use at ATMs.
   a. Think of this as an experiment and list four possible outcomes.
   b. What is the probability Mr. Jones and Mrs. Smith select the same PIN?
   c. Which concept of probability did you use to answer the question above?
10. An investor buys 100 shares of AT&T stock and records its price change daily.
   a. List several possible events for this experiment.
   b. Estimate the probability for each event you described in a.
   c. Which concept of probability did you use in b.?

Principles of Counting

If the number of possible outcomes in an experiment is small, it is relatively easy to count them. There are six possible outcomes, for example, resulting from the roll of a die, namely:

If, however, there are a large number of possible outcomes, such as the number of heads and tails for an experiment with 10 tosses, it would be tedious to count all the possibilities. They could have all heads, one head and nine tails, two heads and eight tails, and so on. To facilitate counting, three counting formulas will be examined: the **multiplication formula** (not to be confused with the multiplication *rule* described earlier in the chapter), the **permutation formula**, and the **combination formula**.

The Multiplication Formula

multiplication formula
If there are m ways of doing one thing and n ways of doing another thing, there are $m \times n$ ways of doing both.

In terms of a formula:

MULTIPLICATION FORMULA **Total number of arrangements = $(m)(n)$** **[4–2]**

This can be extended to more than two events. For three events m, n, and o:

$$\textbf{Total number of arrangements} = (m)(n)(o)$$

example

An automobile dealer wants to advertise that for \$29 999 you can buy a convertible, a two-door or a four-door model, with your choice of either wire wheel covers or solid wheel covers. How many different arrangements of models and wheel covers can the dealer offer?

solution

Of course the dealer could determine the total number of arrangements by picturing and counting them. There are six.

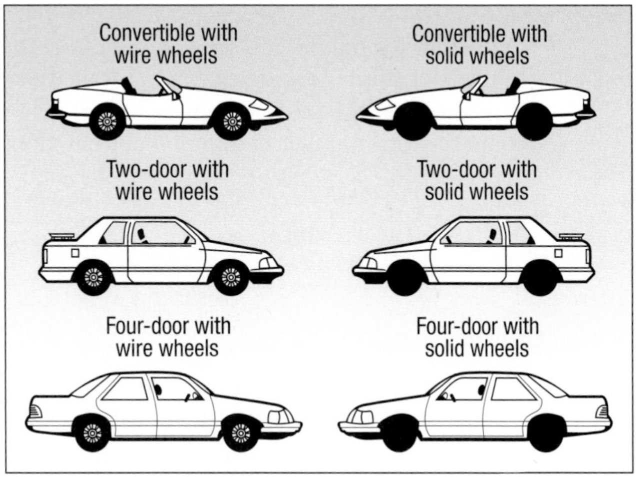

We can employ the multiplication formula as a check (where m is the number of models and n the wheel cover type). Using formula (4–2):

$$\textbf{Total possible arrangements} = (m)(n) = (3)(2) = 6$$

It was not difficult to count all the possible model and wheel cover combinations in this example. Suppose, however, that the dealer decided to offer eight models and six types of wheel covers. It would be tedious to picture and count all the possible alternatives. Instead, the multiplication formula can be used. In this case, there are $(m)(n) = (8)(6) = 48$ possible arrangements.

Note in the preceding applications of the multiplication formula that there were *two or more groupings from which you made selections.* The automobile dealer, for example, offered a choice of models and a choice of wheel covers. If a home builder offered you four different exterior styles of a home to choose from and three interior floor plans, the multiplication formula would be used to find how many different arrangements were possible. There are $(4 \times 3) = 12$ possibilities.

self-review 4–3

1. The Shopping Channel offers sweaters and slacks for women. The sweaters and slacks are offered in coordinating colours. If sweaters are available in five colours and the slacks are available in four colours, how many different outfits can be advertised?
2. Pioneer manufactures three models of stereo receivers, two cassette decks, four speakers, and three CD carousels. When the four types of components are sold together, they form a "system." How many different systems can the electronics firm offer?

The Permutation Formula

As noted, the multiplication formula is applied to find the number of possible arrangements for two or more groups. The **permutation formula** is applied to find the possible number of arrangements when there is only *one* group of objects. Illustrations of this type of problem are:

- Three electronic parts are to be assembled into a plug-in unit for a television set. The parts can be assembled in any order. The question involving counting is: In how many different ways can the three parts be assembled?
- A machine operator must make four safety checks before starting his machine. It does not matter in which order the checks are made. In how many different ways can the operator make the checks?

permutation Any arrangement of r objects selected from a single group of n possible objects.

One order for the first illustration might be: the transistor first, the LEDs second, and the synthesizer third. This arrangement is called a **permutation**.

Note that the arrangements *a b c* and *b a c* are different permutations. The formula to count the total number of different permutations is:

PERMUTATION FORMULA $${}_nP_r = \frac{n!}{(n-r)!} \quad [4\text{–}3]$$

where:

n is the total number of objects.
r is the number of objects selected.

Before we solve the two problems illustrated, note that permutations and combinations (to be discussed shortly) use a notation called *n factorial*. It is written $n!$ and means the product $n(n-1)(n-2)(n-3)\cdots(1)$. For instance, $5! = 5 \cdot 4 \cdot 3 \cdot 2 \cdot 1 = 120$.

Many of your calculators have a button with $x!$ that will perform this calculation for you. It will save you a great deal of time.

The factorial notation can also be cancelled when the same number appears in both the numerator and the denominator, as shown below:

$$\frac{6!3!}{4!} = \frac{6 \cdot 5 \cdot \cancel{4} \cdot \cancel{3} \cdot \cancel{2} \cdot \cancel{1}(3 \cdot 2 \cdot 1)}{\cancel{4} \cdot \cancel{3} \cdot \cancel{2} \cdot \cancel{1}} = 180$$

By definition, zero factorial, written 0!, is 1. That is, 0! = 1.

example

Referring to the group of three electronic parts that are to be assembled in any order, in how many different ways can they be assembled?

solution

There are three electronic parts to be assembled, so $n = 3$. Because all three are to be inserted in the plug-in unit, $r = 3$.

$${}_nP_r = \frac{n!}{(n-r)!} = \frac{3!}{(3-3)!} = \frac{3!}{0!} = \frac{3!}{1} = 6$$

We can check the number of permutations arrived at using the permutation formula. We determine how many "spaces" have to be filled and the possibilities for each "space." In the problem involving three electronic parts, there are three locations in the plug-in unit for the three parts. There are three possibilities for the first place, two for the second (one has been used up), and one for the third, as follows:

$$(3)(2)(1) = 6 \text{ permutations}$$

The six ways in which the three electronic parts, lettered A, B, C, can be arranged are:

ABC	ACB	BAC	BCA	CAB	CBA

In the previous example we selected and arranged all the objects, that is $n = r$. In many cases, only some objects are selected and arranged from the n possible objects. We explain the details of this application in the following example.

example

The Betts Machine Shop Inc. has eight screw machines but only three spaces available in the production area for the machines. In how many different ways can the eight machines be arranged in the three spaces available?

solution

There are eight possibilities for the first available space in the production area, seven for the second space (one has been used up), and six for the third space. Thus:

$$(8)(7)(6) = 336$$

That is, there are a total of 336 different possible arrangements. This could also be found using formula (4–3). If $n = 8$ machines, and $r = 3$ spaces available, the formula leads to

$$_nP_r = \frac{n!}{(n-r)!} = \frac{8!}{(8-3)!} = \frac{8!}{5!} = \frac{(8)(7)(6)5!}{5!} = 336$$

excel

The MegaStat commands to determine the number of permutations using the Betts Machine Shop data follow.

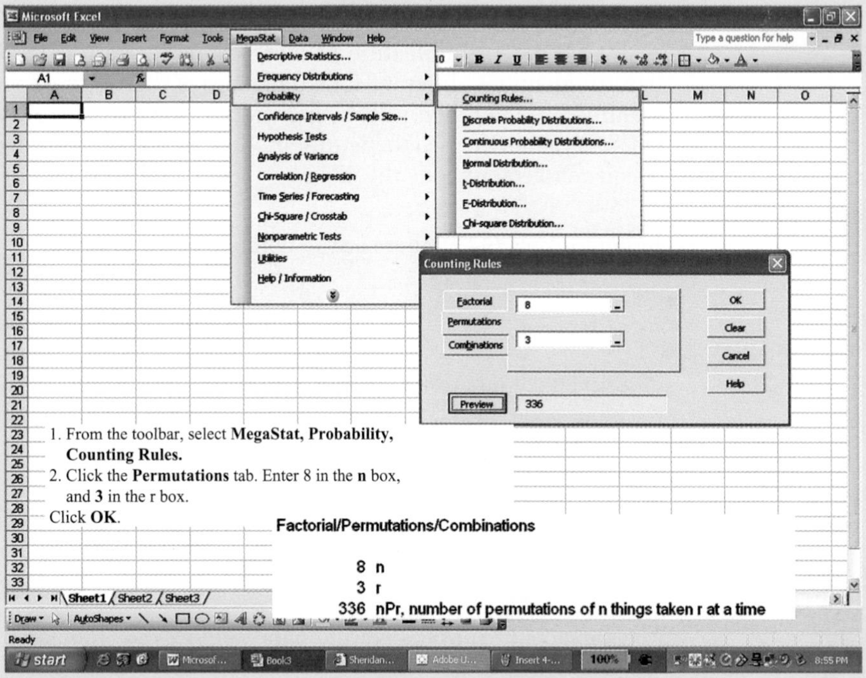

The **Excel** function to determine the number of permutations is PERMUT. The PERMUT function is found in the Statistical category. An example using the Betts Machine Shop data follows.

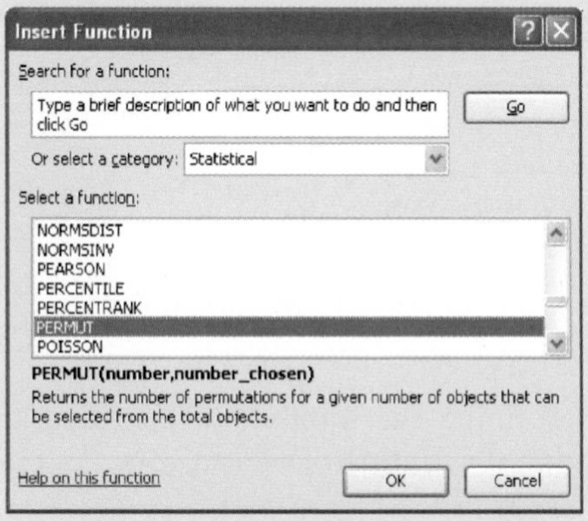

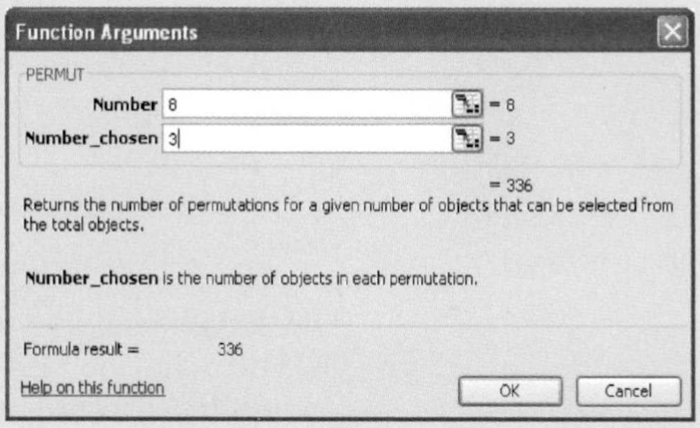

The result of 336 is the same using the formula, calculator, MegaStat, or the **Excel** function.

The Combination Formula

If the order of the selected objects is not important, any selection is called a **combination**. The formula to count the number of r object combinations from a set of n objects is:

COMBINATION FORMULA $${}_nC_r = \frac{n!}{r!(n-r)!} \quad [4\text{–}4]$$

For example, if executives Able, Baker, and Chauncy are to be chosen as a committee to negotiate a merger, there is only one possible combination of these three; the committee of Able, Baker, and Chauncy is the same as the committee of Baker, Chauncy, and Able. Using the combination formula:

$${}_nC_r = \frac{n!}{r!(n-r)!} = \frac{3 \cdot 2 \cdot 1}{3 \cdot 2 \cdot 1(1)} = 1$$

example

The marketing department has been given the assignment of designing colour codes for the 42 different lines of compact disks sold by Goody Records. Three colours are to be used on each CD, but a combination of three colours used for one CD cannot be rearranged and used to identify a different CD. This means that if green, yellow, and violet were used to identify one line, then yellow, green, and violet (or any other combination of these three colours) cannot be used to identify another line. Would seven colours taken three at a time be adequate to colour code the 42 lines?

solution

Using formula (4–4), there are 35 combinations, found by

$${}_7C_3 = \frac{n!}{r!(n-r)!} = \frac{n!}{3!(7-3)!} = \frac{7!}{3!4!} = 35$$

The seven colours taken three at a time (i.e., three colours to a line) would not be adequate to colour code the 42 different lines because they would provide only 35 combinations. Eight colours taken three at a time would give 56 different combinations. This would be more than adequate to colour code the 42 different lines.

excel

MegaStat commands to determine the number of combinations using the Goody Records Inc. data follow.

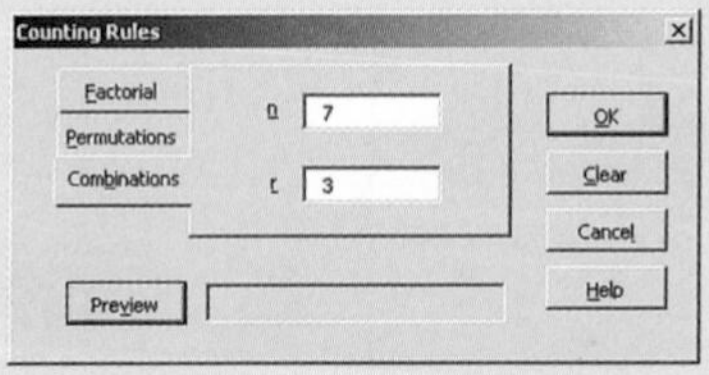

1. From the toolbar, select **MegaStat, Probability, Counting Rules.**
2. Click the **Combinations** tab. Enter 7 in the **n** box, and **3** in the r box.
3. Click **OK**.

Factorial/Permutations/Combinations
7 n
3 r
35 nCr, number of combinations of n things taken r at a time

The **Excel** function to determine the number of combinations is COMBIN. The COMBIN function is found in the Math & Trig category. An example using the Goody Records Inc. data follows.

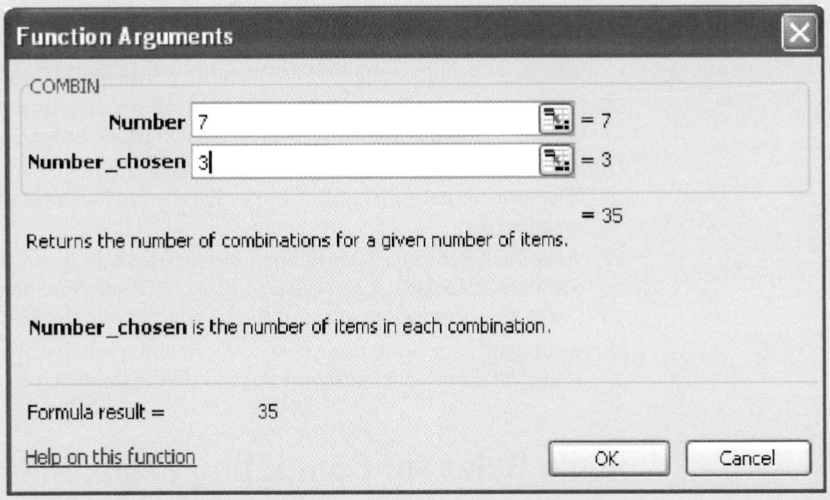

The result of 35 is the same using the formula, calculator, MegaStat, or the **Excel** function.

self-review 4–4

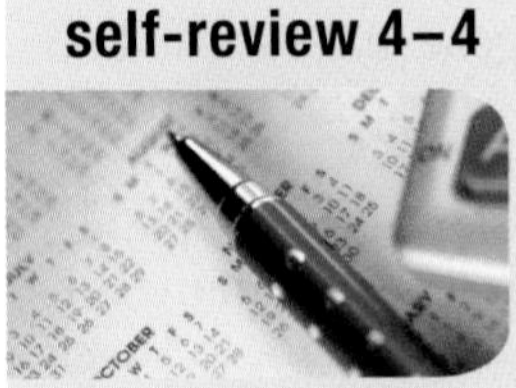

1. A musician wants to write a score based on only five chords: B-flat, C, D, E, and G. However, only three chords out of the five will be used in succession, such as C, B-flat, and E. Repetitions, such as B-flat, B-flat, and E, will not be permitted.
   (a) How many permutations of the five chords, taken three at a time, are possible?
   (b) Using formula (4–3), how many permutations are possible?
2. A machine operator must make four safety checks before starting to machine a part. It does not matter in which order the checks are made. In how many different ways can the operator make the checks?
3. The 10 numbers 0 through 9 are to be used in code groups of four to identify an item of clothing. Code 1083 might identify a blue blouse, size medium; the code group 2031 might identify a pair of pants, size 18; and so on. Repetitions of numbers are not permitted. That is, the same number cannot be used twice (or more) in a total sequence. For example, 2256, 2562, or 5559 would not be permitted. How many different code groups can be designed?
4. In the above example involving Goody Records, we said that eight colours taken three at a time would give 56 different combinations.
   (a) Use formula (4–4) to show this is true.
   (b) As an alternative plan for colour coding the 42 different lines, it has been suggested that only two colours be placed on a disk. Would 10 colours be adequate to colour code the 42 different lines? (Again, a combination of two colours could be used only once–that is, if pink and blue were coded for one line, blue and pink could not be used to identify a different line.)
5. In a lottery game, three numbers are randomly selected from a number of balls, numbered 1 though 50.
   (a) How many permutations are possible?
   (b) How many combinations are possible?

Exercises

11. Solve the following:
  a. 40!/35!
  b. $_7P_4$
  c. $_5C_2$

12. Solve the following:
  a. 20!/17!
  b. $_9P_3$
  c. $_7C_2$

13. A pollster randomly selected 4 of 10 available people. How many different groups of four are possible?
14. A telephone number consists of seven digits, the first three representing the exchange. How many different telephone numbers are possible within the 537 exchange?
15. An overnight express company must include five cities on its route. How many different routes are possible, assuming that it does not matter in which order the cities are included in the routing?
16. A representative of the Ministry of the Environment wants to select samples from 10 landfills. The director has 15 landfills from which she can collect samples. How many different samples are possible?
17. A national pollster has developed 15 questions designed to rate the performance of the Prime Minister of Canada. The pollster will select 10 of these questions. How many different arrangements are there for the order of the 10 selected questions?
18. A company is creating three new divisions and seven managers are eligible to be appointed head of a division. How many different ways could the three new heads be appointed?

Some Rules for Computing Probabilities

Now that we have defined probability and described the different approaches to probability, we turn our attention to combining events by applying rules of addition and multiplication.

4 Calculate probabilities using the *rules of addition* and *rules of multiplication*.

Rules of Addition

There are two rules of addition, the special rule of addition and the general rule of addition. We begin with the special rule of addition.

Mutually exclusive events cannot both happen at the same time.

Special Rule of Addition To apply the **special rule of addition**, the events must be mutually exclusive. Recall that *mutually exclusive* means that when one event occurs, none of the other events can occur at the same time. An illustration of mutually exclusive events in the die-tossing experiment is the events "a number 4 or larger" and "a number 2 or smaller." If the outcome is in the first group (4, 5, and 6), then it cannot also be in the second group (1 and 2). Another example is a part coming off the assembly line. It cannot be both defective and non-defective at the same time.

If two events A and B are mutually exclusive, the special rule of addition states that the probability of occurrence of one event *or* the other equals the sum of their probabilities. This rule is expressed in the following formula:

SPECIAL RULE OF ADDITION $$P(A \text{ or } B) = P(A) + P(B) \quad [4\text{–}5]$$

For three mutually exclusive events designated A, B, and C, the rule is written:

$$P(A \text{ or } B \text{ or } C) = P(A) + P(B) + P(C)$$

An example will help to show the details.

example

An automatic Shaw machine fills plastic bags with a mixture of beans, broccoli, and other vegetables. Most of the bags contain the correct weight, but because of the variation in the size of the beans and other vegetables, a package might be underweight or overweight. A check of 4000 packages filled in the past month revealed:

Weight	Event	Number of Packages	Probability of Occurrence	
Underweight	*A*	100	.025	← $\frac{100}{4000}$
Satisfactory	*B*	3600	.900	
Overweight	*C*	300	.075	
		4000	1.000	

solution

What is the probability that a particular package will be either underweight or overweight? The outcome "underweight" is the event A. The outcome "overweight" is the event C. Applying the special rule of addition:

$$P(A \text{ or } C) = P(A) + P(C) = .025 + .075 = .10$$

Note that the events are mutually exclusive, meaning that a package of mixed vegetables cannot be underweight, satisfactory, and overweight at the same time. They are also collectively exhaustive; that is, a selected package must be either underweight, satisfactory, or overweight.

A Venn diagram is a useful tool to depict addition or multiplication rules.

English logician J. Venn (1834–1923) developed a diagram to portray graphically the outcome of an experiment. The *mutually exclusive* concept and various other rules for combining probabilities can be illustrated using this device. To construct a Venn diagram, a space is first enclosed representing the total of all possible outcomes. This space is usually in the form of a rectangle. An event is then represented by a circular area which is drawn inside the rectangle proportional to the probability of the event. The following Venn diagram represents the *mutually exclusive* concept. There is no overlapping of events, meaning that the events are mutually exclusive.

Statistics in Action

If you wish to get some attention at the next gathering you attend, announce that you believe that at least two people present were born on the same date–that is, the same day of the year but not necessarily the same year. If there are 30 people in the room, the probability of a duplicate is .706. If there are 60 people in the room, the probability is .994 that at least two people share the same birthday. With as few as 23 people the chances are even, that is .50, that at least two people share the same birthday. Hint: To compute this, find the probability everyone was born on a different day and use the complement rule.

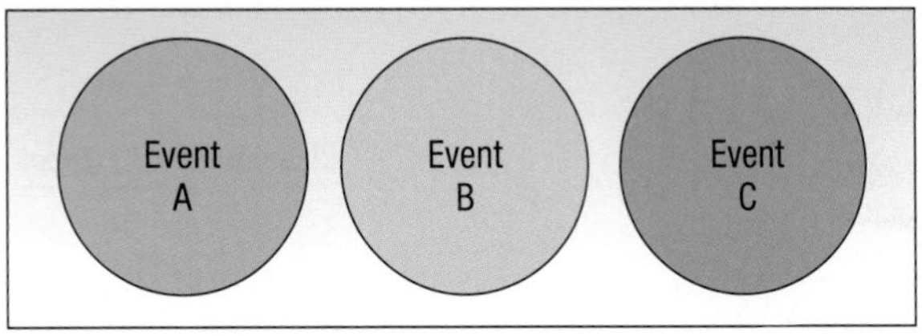

COMPLEMENT RULE: The probability that a bag of mixed vegetables selected is underweight, $P(A)$, plus the probability that it is not an underweight bag, written $P(\sim A)$ and read "not A," must logically equal 1. This is written:

$$P(A) + P(\sim A) = 1$$

This can be revised to read:

COMPLEMENT RULE $$P(A) = 1 - P(\sim A)$$ **[4–6]**

This is the **complement rule**. It is used to determine the probability of an event occurring by subtracting the probability of the event not occurring from 1. This rule is useful because sometimes it is easier to calculate the probability of an event happening by determining the probability of it not happening and subtracting the result from 1. Notice that the events A and $\sim A$ are mutually exclusive and collectively exhaustive. Therefore, the probabilities of A and $\sim A$ sum to 1. A Venn diagram illustrating the complement rule is shown as:

example

Recall the probability a bag of mixed vegetables is underweight is .025 and the probability of an overweight bag is .075. Use the complement rule to show the probability of a satisfactory bag is .900. Show the solution using a Venn diagram.

solution

The probability the bag is unsatisfactory equals the probability the bag is overweight plus the probability it is underweight. That is, $P(A \text{ or } C) = P(A) + P(C) = .025 + .075 = .100$. The bag is satisfactory if it is not underweight or overweight, so $P(B) = 1 - [P(A) + P(C)] = 1 - [.025 + .075] = .900$. The Venn diagram portraying this situation is:

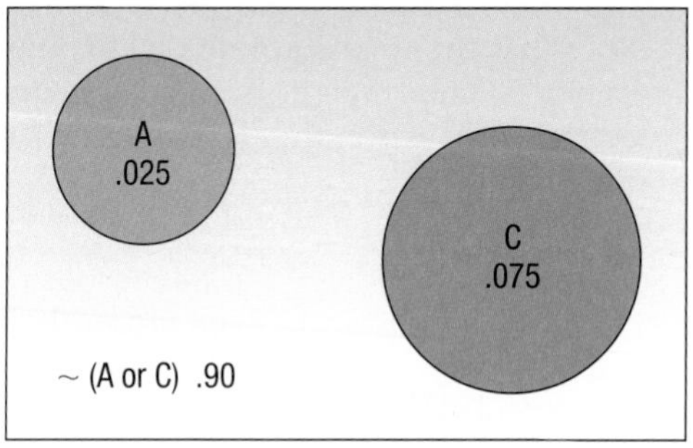

self-review 4–5

A sample of employees of Worldwide Enterprises is to be surveyed about a new pension plan. In-depth interviews are to be conducted with each employee selected in the sample. The employees are classified as follows:

Classification	Event	Number of Employees
Supervisors	*A*	120
Maintenance	*B*	50
Production	*C*	1460
Management	*D*	302
Secretarial	*E*	68

(a) What is the probability that the first person selected is:
 (i) either in maintenance or a secretary?
 (ii) not in management?
(b) Draw a Venn diagram illustrating your answers to part (a).
(c) Are the events in part (a)(i) complementary or mutually exclusive or both?

4 Calculate probabilities using the *rules of addition* and *rules of multiplication*.

The General Rule of Addition The outcomes of an experiment may not be mutually exclusive. Suppose, for example, that the Caribana Festival selected a sample of 200 tourists who visited the Toronto area during the year. The survey revealed that 120 tourists visited the CN Tower, and 100 went to the Toronto Islands. What is the probability that a person selected visited either the CN Tower or the Toronto Islands? If the special rule of addition is used, the probability of selecting a tourist who went to the CN Tower is 0.60, found by 120/200. Similarly, the probability of a tourist going to the Toronto Islands is 0.50. The sum of these probabilities is 1.10. But, we know that this probability cannot be greater than 1. So, the explanation is that some of the tourists visited both attractions and are being counted twice! A check of the survey responses reveals that 60 of the 200 sampled did visit both attractions.

To answer our question, "What is the probability a selected person visited either the CN Tower or the Toronto Islands?", we need to add the probability that a tourist visited the CN Tower and the probability that a tourist visited the Toronto Islands and then subtract the probability of visiting both. Thus:

$$\begin{aligned} \mathbf{P(\text{CN Tower or Toronto Islands})} &= \mathbf{P(\text{CN Tower}) + P(\text{Toronto Islands}) - P(\text{both})} \\ &= \mathbf{.60 + .50 - .30 = .80} \end{aligned}$$

5 **Define the terms *conditional probability* and *joint probability*.**

joint probability A probability that measures the likelihood two or more events will happen concurrently.

When two events both occur, the probability is called a **joint probability**. The probability that a tourist visits both attractions (.30) is an example of a joint probability.

In summary, the general rule of addition refers to events that are not mutually exclusive. This rule for two events designated A and B is written:

GENERAL RULE OF ADDITION $$P(A \text{ or } B) = P(A) + P(B) - P(A \text{ and } B) \quad [4\text{–}7]$$

For the expression $P(A$ or $B)$, the word *or* suggests that A may occur or B may occur. This also includes the possibility that A and B may occur. This use of *or* is sometimes called **inclusive**. You could also write $P(A$ or B or both) to emphasize that the union of the events includes the intersection of A and B.

If we compare the general and special rules of addition, the important difference is determining if the events are mutually exclusive. If the events are mutually exclusive, then the joint probability $P(A$ or $B)$ is 0, and we could use the special rule of addition. Otherwise, we must account for the joint probability and use the general rule of addition.

example

What is the probability that a card chosen at random from a standard deck of cards will be either a king or a heart?

solution

We may be inclined to add the probability of a king and the probability of a heart. But this creates a problem. If we do that, the king of hearts is counted with the kings and also with the hearts. So, if we simply add the probability of a king (there are 4 in a deck of 52 cards) to the probability of a heart (there are 13 in a deck of 52 cards) and report that 17 out of 52 cards meet the requirement, we have counted the king of hearts twice. We need to subtract 1 card from the 17 so the king of hearts is counted only once. Thus, there are 16 cards that are either hearts or kings. So the probability is 16/52 = .3077.

Card	Probability	Explanation
King	$P(A)$ = 4/52	4 kings in a deck of 52 cards
Heart	$P(B)$ = 13/52	13 hearts in a deck of 52 cards
King of hearts	$P(A$ and $B)$ = 1/52	1 king of hearts in a deck of 52 cards

Using formula (4–7):

$$\begin{aligned} P(A \text{ or } B) &= P(A) + P(B) - P(A \text{ and } B) \\ &= 4/52 + 13/52 - 1/52 \\ &= 16/52, \text{ or } .3077 \end{aligned}$$

A Venn diagram portrays these outcomes, which are not mutually exclusive.

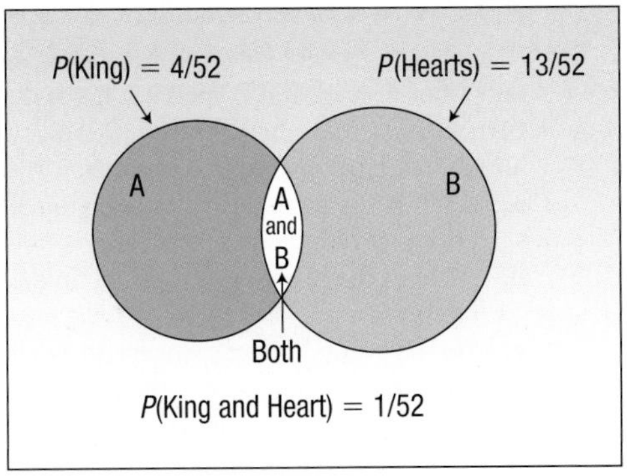

self-review 4–6

Routine physical examinations are conducted annually as part of a health service program for General Concrete Inc. employees. It was discovered that 8 percent of the employees need corrective shoes, 15 percent need major dental work, and 3 percent need both corrective shoes and major dental work.

(a) What is the probability that an employee selected at random will need either corrective shoes or major dental work?

(b) Show this situation in the form of a Venn diagram.

Exercises

19. The events A and B are mutually exclusive. Suppose $P(A) = .30$ and $P(B) = .20$. What is the probability of either A or B occurring? What is the probability that neither A nor B will happen?

20. The events X and Y are mutually exclusive. Suppose $P(X) = .05$ and $P(Y) = .02$. What is the probability of either X or Y occurring? What is the probability that neither X nor Y will happen?

21. A study of 200 advertising firms revealed their incomes after taxes:

Income after Taxes	Number of Firms
Under $1 million	102
$1 million to $20 million	61
$20 million or more	37

a. What is the probability an advertising firm selected at random has under $1 million in income after taxes?

b. What is the probability an advertising firm selected at random has either an income between $1 million and $20 million, or an income of $20 million or more? What rule of probability was applied?

22. The chair of the board of directors says, "There is a 50 percent chance this company will earn a profit, a 30 percent chance it will break even, and a 20 percent chance it will lose money next quarter."

a. Use an addition rule to find the probability the company will not lose money next quarter.

b. Use the complement rule to find the probability the company will not lose money next quarter.

23. Suppose the probability you will get a grade of A in this class is .25 and the probability you will get a B is .50. What is the probability your grade will be above a C?

24. Two coins are tossed. If A is the event "two heads" and B is the event "two tails," are A and B mutually exclusive? Are they complements?

25. The probabilities of the events A and B are .20 and .30, respectively. The probability that both A and B occur is .15. What is the probability of either A or B occurring?

26. Let $P(X) = .55$ and $P(Y) = .35$. Assume the probability that they both occur is .20. What is the probability of either X or Y occurring?

27. Suppose the two events A and B are mutually exclusive. What is the probability of their joint occurrence?

28. A student is taking two courses, history and math. The probability the student will pass the history course is .60, and the probability of passing the math course is .70. The probability of passing both is .50. What is the probability of passing at least one?

29. A survey of grocery stores in Eastern Canada revealed that 40 percent had a pharmacy, 50 percent had a floral shop, and 70 percent had a deli. Suppose 10 percent of the stores have all three departments, 30 percent have both a pharmacy and a deli, 25 percent have both a floral shop and deli, and 20 percent have both a pharmacy and a floral shop.

a. What is the probability of selecting a store at random and finding it has both a pharmacy and a floral shop?

b. What is the probability of selecting a store at random and finding it has both a pharmacy and a deli?

c. Are the events "select a store with a deli," and "select a store with a pharmacy" mutually exclusive?

d. What is the name given to the event of "selecting a store with a pharmacy, a floral shop, and a deli"?

e. What is the probability of selecting a store that does not have all three departments?

30. A study by the National Park Service revealed that 50 percent of vacationers going to the Rocky Mountain region visit Banff National Park, 40 percent visit Yoho National, and 35 percent visit both.

a. What is the probability a vacationer will visit at least one of these parks?

b. What is the probability .35 called?

c. Are the events mutually exclusive? Explain.

4 Calculate probabilities using the *rules of addition* and *rules of multiplication.*

Rules of Multiplication

When we use the rules of addition we find the likelihood of combining two events. Venn diagrams illustrate this as the "union" of two events. In this section we find the likelihood that two events both happen. For example, a marketing firm may want to estimate the likelihood that a person is 21 years old or older *and* buys a Hummer. Venn diagrams illustrate this as the intersection of two events. To find the likelihood of two events happening we use the rules of multiplication. There are two rules of multiplication, the Special Rule and the General Rule.

independent The occurrence of one event has no effect on the probability of the occurrence of another event.

Special Rule of Multiplication The special rule of multiplication requires that two events, A and B, be **independent**. Two events are independent if the occurrence of one does not alter the probability of the occurrence of the other event.

One way to think about independence is to assume that events A and B occur at different times. For example, when event B occurs, does A have any affect on the likelihood that event B occurs? If the answer is no, then A and B are independent events. To illustrate independence, suppose two coins are tossed. The outcome of a coin toss (head or tail) is unaffected by the outcome of any other prior coin toss (head or tail).

For two independent events, A and B, the probability that A and B will both occur is found by multiplying the two probabilities. This is the **special rule of multiplication** and is written symbolically as:

SPECIAL RULE OF MULTIPLICATION $$P(A \text{ and } B) = P(A)P(B) \qquad [4\text{–}8]$$

For the experiment of tossing two coins, the probability of two heads, $P(H \text{ and } H) = (1/2)(1/2) = 1/4$.

For three independent events, A, B, and C, the special rule of multiplication used to determine the probability that all three events will occur is:

$$P(A \text{ and } B \text{ and } C) = P(A)P(B)P(C)$$

For the experiment of tossing three coins, the probability of three heads, $P(H \text{ and } H \text{ and } H) = (1/2)(1/2)(1/2) = 1/8$.

example

A survey of the final grades in an advanced statistics course reveals that 60 percent of the students are successful. Two students are selected at random. What is the probability that both are successful in the advanced statistics course?

solution

The probability that the first student is successful is .60, written as $P(S_1) = .60$, where S_1 refers to the fact that the first student is successful. The probability that the second student is successful is also .60, written as $P(S_2) = .60$. Since students are required to work on their own assignments and tests, S_1 and S_2 are independent. Consequently, using formula (4–8), the probability that they are both successful is .36, found by:

$$P(S_1 \text{ and } S_2) = P(S_1)P(S_2) = (.60)(.60) = .36$$

The possible outcomes can be shown as follows. S means the student is successful, and NS means the student is not successful.

Outcomes		Joint Probability
S	S	(.60)(.60) = .36
S	NS	(.60)(.40) = .24
NS	S	(.40)(.60) = .24
NS	NS	(.40)(.40) = .16
		1.00

self-review 4–7

From experience, Teton Tire knows the probability is .80 that their XB-70 tire will last 100 000 km before it becomes bald or fails. An adjustment is made on any tire that does not last 100 000 km. You purchase four XB-70s. What is the probability all four tires will last at least 100 000 km?

If two events are not independent, they are referred to as **dependent**. To illustrate dependency, suppose there are 10 rolls of film in a box, 7 colour and 3 black and white. A roll of film is selected from the box. The probability of selecting a black and white roll is 3/10, and the probability of selecting a colour roll is 7/10. Then a second roll of film is selected from the box, without returning the first roll of film. (This means that there are nine rolls of film left in the box.) The probability that the second roll is colour depends on whether the first selected was colour or black and white. The probability that the second roll of film selected was colour is:

5 Define the terms *conditional probability* and *joint probability*.

6/9 if the first roll selected is colour. (Only six colour rolls remain in the box.)
7/9 if the first roll selected is black and white. (All seven colour rolls remain in the box.)

conditional probability The probability of a particular event occurring, given that another event has occurred.

The fraction 6/9 (or 7/9) is aptly called a **conditional probability** because its value is conditional on (or dependent on) whether a colour or black and white roll of film was the first selected from the box.

4 Calculate probabilities using the *rules of addition* and *rules of multiplication*.

General Rule of Multiplication We use the **general rule of multiplication** to find the *joint probability* of two events when the events are not independent. For example, when event B occurs after event A occurs, and A has an effect on the likelihood that event B occurs, then A and B are not independent.

The general rule of multiplication states that for two events, A and B, the joint probability that both events will happen is found by multiplying the probability event A will happen by the conditional probability of event B occurring given that A has occurred. In the formula, "given that" is represented by a vertical line, "|". Symbolically, the joint probability, $P(A \text{ and } B)$, is found by:

GENERAL RULE OF MULTIPLICATION $$P(A \text{ and } B) = P(A)P(B \mid A) \qquad [4\text{–}9]$$

example

Example A golfer has 12 golf shirts in his closet. Suppose nine of these shirts are white and the others blue. He gets dressed in the dark, so he just grabs a shirt and puts it on. He plays golf two days in a row and does not do laundry. What is the probability that he has selected white shirts two days in a row?

B	W	W	W	B	W
W	W	B	W	W	W

solution

The event that the first shirt selected is white is W_1. The probability is $P(W_1) = 9/12$ because 9 of the 12 shirts are white. The event that the second shirt selected is also white is identified as W_2. The conditional probability that the second shirt selected is white, given that the first shirt selected is also white, is $P(W_2 \mid W_1) = 8/11$. Why is this so? Because after the first shirt is selected, there only 11 shirts left in the closet and 8 of these are white. To determine the probability of two white shirts being selected we use formula (4–9).

$$P(W_1 \text{ and } W_2) = P(W_1)P(W_2 \mid W_1) = \left(\frac{9}{12}\right)\left(\frac{8}{11}\right) = .55$$

So the likelihood of selecting two shirts and finding them both to be white is .55.

It is assumed that this experiment was conducted *without replacement*. That is, the first shirt was not laundered and put back in the closet before the second shirt was selected. So, the outcome of the second event is conditional or dependent on the outcome of the first event.

We can extend the general rule of multiplication to more than two events. For three events, A, B, and C the formula is:

$$P(A \text{ and } B \text{ and } C) = P(A)P(B \mid A)P(C \mid A \text{ and } B)$$

In the case of the golf shirt example, the probability of selecting three white shirts without replacement is:

$$P(W_1 \text{ and } W_2 \text{ and } W_3) = P(W_1)P(W_2 \mid W_1)\ P(W_3 \mid W_1 \text{ and } W_2) = \left(\frac{9}{12}\right)\left(\frac{8}{11}\right)\left(\frac{7}{10}\right) = .38$$

So the likelihood of selecting three shirts without replacement and all being white is .38.

self-review 4–8

The board of directors of Tarbell Industries consists of eight men and four women. A four-member search committee is to be chosen at random to conduct a nationwide search for a new company president.

(a) What is the probability all four members of the search committee will be women?
(b) What is the probability all four members will be men?
(c) Does the sum of the probabilities for the events described in parts (a) and (b) equal 1? Explain.

contingency table A table used to classify sample observations according to two or more identifiable characteristics.

Statistics in Action

In 2000, George W. Bush won the American Presidency by the slimmest of margins. Many election stories resulted, some involving voting irregularities, others raising interesting election questions. In a local Michigan election, there was a tie between two candidates for an elected position. To break the tie, the candidates drew a slip of paper from a box that contained two slips of paper, one marked "Winner" and the other unmarked. To determine which candidate drew first, election officials flipped a coin. The winner of the coin flip also drew the winning slip of paper. But was the coin flip really necessary? No, because the two events are independent. Winning the coin flip did not alter the probability of either candidate drawing the winning slip of paper.

Contingency Tables

Often we wish to study the relationship between two variables. Then we can tally the results of a sample into a two-way table and use the results of this tally to determine various probabilities. We refer to this two-way table as a **contingency table**.

A contingency table is a cross tabulation that summarizes two variables of interest and their relationship. The level of measurement can be nominal. Some examples follow.

- A survey of 150 adults classified each as to gender and the number of movies attended last month. Each respondent is classified according to two criteria—the number of movies attended and gender.

	Gender		
Movies Attended	**Men**	**Women**	**Total**
0	20	40	60
1	40	30	70
2 or more	10	10	20
Total	70	80	150

- The Coffee Producers Association reports the following information on age and the amount of coffee consumed in a month.

	Coffee Consumption			
Age (Years)	**Low**	**Moderate**	**High**	**Total**
Under 30	36	32	24	92
30 to under 40	18	30	27	75
40 to under 50	10	24	20	54
50 or more	26	24	29	79
Total	90	110	100	300

According to this table each of the 300 respondents is classified according to two criteria: (1) his or her age and (2) the amount of coffee consumed.

The following example shows how the rules of addition and multiplication are used when we employ contingency tables.

example

A sample of executives was surveyed about loyalty to their company. One of the questions was, "If you were given an offer by another company equal to or slightly better than your present position, would you remain with the company or take the other position"? The responses of the 200 executives in the survey were cross-tabulated with their length of service with the company. (See Table 4–1.)

TABLE 4–1 Loyalty of Executives and Length of Service with Company

	Length of Service				
Loyalty	**Less than 1 Year B_1**	**1–5 Years B_2**	**6–10 Years B_3**	**More than 10 Years B_4**	**Total**
Would remain, A_1	10	30	5	75	120
Would not remain, $\sim A_1$	25	15	10	30	80
	35	45	15	105	200

What is the probability of randomly selecting an executive who is loyal to the company (would remain) and who has more than 10 years of service? What is the probability of selecting an executive that would remain *or* has less than one year of service?

solution

Note that two events occur at the same time—the executive would remain with the company, and he or she has more than 10 years of service.

1. Event A_1 happens if a randomly selected executive will remain with the company despite an equal or slightly better offer from another company. To find the probability that event A_1 will happen, refer to Table 4–1. Note there are 120 executives out of the 200 in the survey who would remain with the company, so $P(A_1) = 120/200$, or .60.
2. Event B_4 happens if a randomly selected executive has more than 10 years of service with the company. Thus, $P(B_4 \mid A_1)$ is the conditional probability that an executive with more than 10 years of service would remain with the company despite an equal or slightly better offer from another company. Referring to the contingency table, Table 4–1, 75 of the 120 executives who would remain have more than 10 years of service, so $P(B_4 \mid A_1) = 75/120$, or .625.

Solving for the probability that an executive randomly selected will be one who would remain with the company and who has more than 10 years of service with the company, using the general rule of multiplication in formula (4–9):

$$P(A_1 \text{ and } B_4) = P(A_1)P(B_4 \mid A_1) = \left(\frac{120}{200}\right)\left(\frac{75}{120}\right) = \frac{75}{200} = .375$$

Note that the joint probability of A_1 and B_4 can be found by looking for the point of intersection of A_1 and B_4, which is 75. Divided by the total of 200, we have $75/200 = .375$.

To find the probability of selecting an executive who would remain with the company *or* has less than one year of experience we use the general rule of addition, formula (4–7).

1. Event A_1 refers to executives that would remain with the company. So $P(A_1) = 120/200 = .60$.
2. Event B_1 refers to executives that have been with the company less than one year. The probability of B_1 is $P(B_1) = 35/200 = .175$.
3. The events A_1 and B_1 are not mutually exclusive. That is, an executive can both be willing to remain with the company and have less than one year of experience. We write this probability, which is called the joint probability, as $P(A_1 \text{ and } B_1)$. There are 10 executives who would both stay with the company and have less than 1 year of service, so $P(A_1 \text{ and } B_1) = 10/200 = .05$. These 10 people are in both groups, those who would

remain with the company and those with less than 1 year with the company. They are actually being counted twice, so we need to subtract out this value.

4. We insert these values in formula (4–7) and the result is as follows.

$$P(A_1 \text{ or } B_1) = P(A_1) + P(B_1) - P(A_1 \text{ and } B_1)$$
$$= .60 + .175 - .05 = .725$$

So the likelihood that a selected executive would either remain with the company or has been with the company less than 1 year is .725. The following chart summarizes the results and emphasizes the need to remove the 10 executives who would remain with the company and have less than 1 year of service.

	Length of Service				
Loyalty	Less than 1 Year B_1	1–5 Years B_2	6–10 Years B_3	More than 10 Years B_4	Total
Would remain, A_1	10	30	5	75	120
Would not remain, $\sim A$	25	15	10	30	80
Total	35	45	15	105	200

self-review 4–9

Refer to Table 4–1 to find the following probabilities.

(a) What is the probability of selecting an executive with more than 10 years of service?
(b) What is the probability of selecting an executive who would not remain with the company, given that he or she has more than 10 years of service?
(c) What is the probability of selecting an executive with more than 10 years of service or one who would not remain with the company?

6 Use a tree diagram to organize and compute probabilities.

Tree Diagrams

The **tree diagram** is a graph that is helpful in organizing calculations that involve several stages. Each segment in the tree is one stage of the problem. The branches of a tree diagram are weighted by probabilities. We will use the data in Table 4–1 to show the construction of a tree diagram.

Steps in constructing a tree diagram

1. To construct a tree diagram, we begin by drawing a heavy dot on the left to represent the root of the tree (see Chart 4–2).
2. For this problem, two main branches go out from the root, the upper one representing "would remain" and the lower one "would not remain." Their probabilities are written on the branches, namely, 120/200 and 80/200. These probabilities could also be denoted $P(A_1)$ and $P(\sim A_1)$.
3. Four branches "grow" out of each of the two main branches. These branches represent the length of service—less than 1 year, 1–5 years, 6–10 years, and more than 10 years. The conditional probabilities for the upper branch of the tree, 10/120, 30/120, 5/120, and so on are written on the appropriate branches. These are $P(B_1 | A_1)$, $P(B_2 | A_1)$, $P(B_3 | A_1)$, and $P(B_4 | A_1)$, where B_1 refers to less than 1 year of service, B_2 1 to 5 years, B_3 6 to 10 years, and B_4 more than 10 years. Next, write the conditional probabilities for the lower branch.
4. Finally, joint probabilities, that the events A_1 and B_i, or the events A_2 and B_i will occur together, are shown on the right side. For example, the joint probability of randomly selecting an executive who would remain with the company and who has less than one year of service, using formula (4–9), is:

$$P(A_1 \text{ and } B_1) = P(A_1)P(B_1 \mid A_1) = \left(\frac{120}{200}\right)\left(\frac{10}{120}\right) = .05$$

Statistics in Action

Many provinces, such as British Columbia, Quebec, and Ontario, have lotteries in which a player buys a single ticket, often for only a dollar, and may win a large sum of money. In some cases, the amount of money to be won exceeds $20 million. In order to win, the player must match all six numbers randomly drawn from a pool of 49 numbers. The odds of winning such a lottery are 1 in 13 983 816. The odds of obtaining 23 heads in a row while flipping a coin are 1 in 8 388 608. To put it another way, you have a better chance of flipping a coin 23 times and getting all heads than you do of winning the lottery.

Because the joint probabilities represent all possible selections (would remain, 6–10 years service; would not remain, more than 10 years of service; etc.), they must sum to 1.00 (see Chart 4–2).

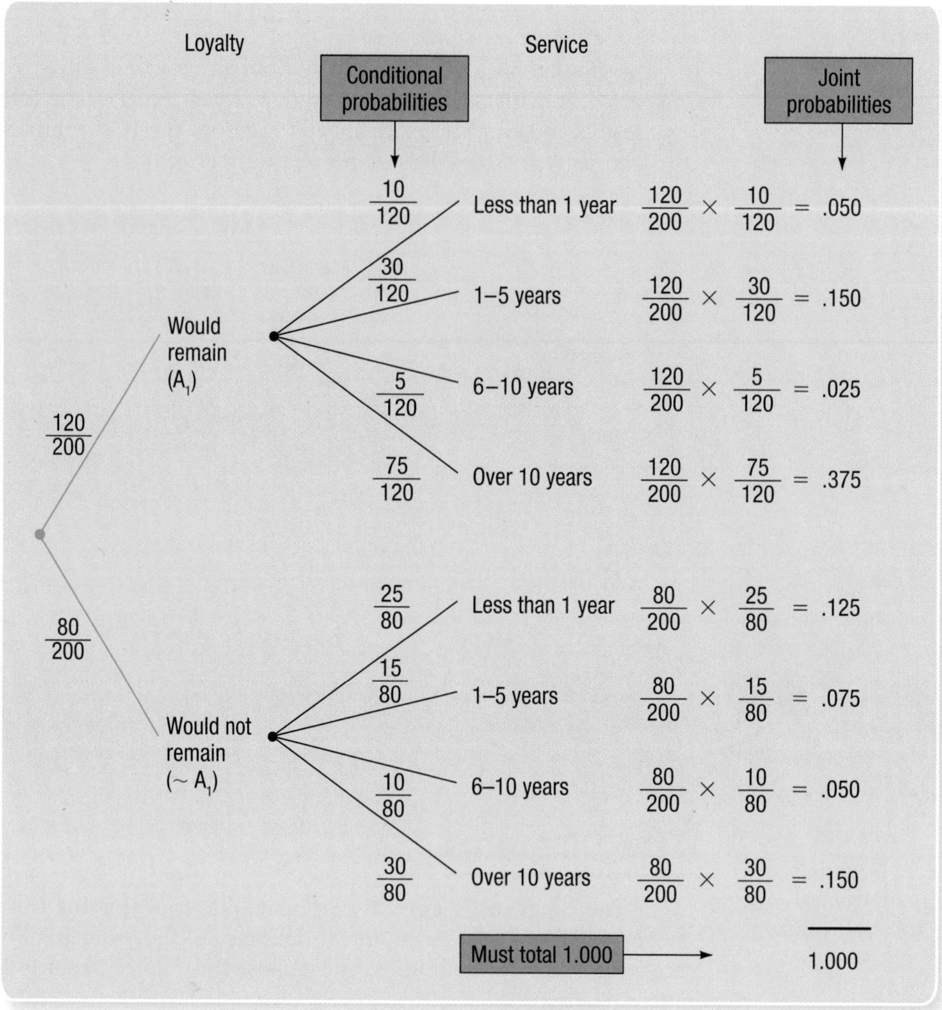

CHART 4–2 Tree Diagram Showing Loyalty and Length of Service

self-review 4–10

A random sample of the employees of the Hardware Manufacturing Company was chosen to determine their retirement plans after age 65. Those selected in the sample were divided into management and production. The results were:

	Plans after Age 65		
Employee	**Retire**	**Not Retire**	**Total**
Management	5	15	20
Production	30	50	80
			100

(a) What is the table called?
(b) Draw a tree diagram, and determine the joint probabilities.
(c) Do the joint probabilities total 1.00? Why?

Exercises

31. Suppose $P(A) = .40$ and $P(B \mid A) = .30$. What is the joint probability of A and B?

32. Suppose $P(X_1) = .75$ and $P(Y_2 \mid X_1) = .40$. What is the joint probability of X_1 and Y_2?

33. A local bank reports that 80 percent of its customers maintain a chequing account, 60 percent have a savings account, and 50 percent have both. If a customer is chosen at random, what is the probability the customer has either a chequing or a savings account? What is the probability the customer does not have either a chequing or a savings account?

34. All Seasons Plumbing has two service trucks which frequently break down. If the probability the first truck is available is .75, the probability the second truck is available is .50, and the probability that both trucks are available is .30, what is the probability neither truck is available?

35. Refer to the following table.

	First Event			
Second Event	A_1	A_2	A_3	**Total**
B_1	2	1	3	6
B_2	1	2	1	4
Total	3	3	4	10

a. Determine $P(A_1)$.
b. Determine $P(B_1 \mid A_2)$.
c. Determine $P(B_2 \text{ and } A_3)$.

36. Three defective electric toothbrushes were accidentally shipped to a drugstore by Cleanbrush Products along with 17 nondefective ones.
a. What is the probability the first two electric toothbrushes sold will be returned to the drugstore because they are defective?
b. What is the probability the first two electric toothbrushes sold will not be defective?

37. Each salesperson at Future Shop is rated either below average, average, or above average with respect to sales ability. Each salesperson is also rated with respect to his or her potential for advancement—either fair, good, or excellent. These traits for the 500 salespeople were cross-classified into the following table.

	Potential for Advancement		
Sales Ability	**Fair**	**Good**	**Excellent**
Below average	16	12	22
Average	45	60	45
Above average	93	72	135

a. What is this table called?
b. What is the probability a salesperson selected at random will have above average sales ability and excellent potential for advancement?
c. Construct a tree diagram showing all the probabilities, conditional probabilities, and joint probabilities.

38. An investor owns three common stocks. Each stock, independently of the other, has equally likely chances of (1) increasing in value, (2) decreasing in value, or (3) remaining the same value. List the possible outcomes of this experiment. Estimate the probability at least two of the stocks increase in value.

39. The board of directors of a small company consists of five people. Three of those are "strong leaders." If they buy an idea, the entire board will agree. The other "weak" members have no influence. Three salespersons are scheduled, one after the other, to make sales presentations to a board member of the salesperson's choice. The salespersons are convincing but do not know who the "strong leaders" are. However, they will know who the previous salespersons spoke to. The first salesperson to find a strong leader will win the account. Do the three salespersons have the same chance of winning the account? If not, find their respective probabilities of winning.

40. If you ask three strangers on campus, what is the probability: (a) All were born on Wednesday? (b) All were born on different days of the week? (c) None were born on Saturday?

41. The manager of a restaurant wishes to study the relationship between the gender of a guest and whether the guest orders dessert. To investigate the relationship the manager collected the following information on 200 recent customers.

	Gender		
Dessert Ordered	Male	Female	Total
Yes	32	15	47
No	68	85	153
	100	100	200

a. What is the level of measurement of the two variables?
b. What is the probability that a man will order dessert?
c. What is the probability that a woman will not order dessert?
d. Does the evidence in the table suggest men are more likely to order dessert than women? Explain.

42. A corporation is evaluating a proposed merger. The board of directors surveyed 50 stockholders concerning their position on the merger. The results are reported below.

	Opinion			
Number of Shares Held	Favour	Opposed	Undecided	Total
Under 200	8	6	2	16
200 to under 1000	6	8	1	15
1000 or more	6	12	1	19
Total	20	26	4	50

a. What is the probability that a stockholder holds 1000 or more shares?
b. What is the probability that a stockholder holds less than 200 shares and is in favour of the merger?
c. What is the probability that a stockholder holds between 200 to under 1000 shares or is opposed to the merger?
d. What is the probability that a stockholder holds under 200 shares given that he/she is opposed to the merger?

43. Wendy's Old Fashioned Hamburgers offers eight different condiments (mustard, ketchup, onion, mayonnaise, pickle, lettuce, tomato, and relish) on hamburgers. A store manager collected the following information on the number of condiments ordered and the age group of the customers.

	Age			
Number of Condiments	Under 18	18 to under 40	40 to under 60	60 +
0	12	18	24	52
1	21	76	50	30
2	39	52	40	12
3 or more	71	87	47	28

a. What is the probability that a customer does not order a condiment?
b. What is the probability that a customer is under 18 years of age?
c. What is the probability that a customer orders 2 condiments and is over 60 years of age?
d. What is the probability that a customer orders 3 or more condiments or is in the 18 to under 40 years age group?
e. What is the probability that a customer orders 2 condiments given that the customer is in the 40 to under 60 years age group?

44. Students were surveyed on the number of visits to a Marc's Milk convenience store (often, occasional, or never) and if the store was conveniently located to their school (yes or no).

	Convenience Store		
Visits	Yes	No	Total
Often	60	20	80
Occasional	25	35	60
Never	5	50	55
Total	90	105	195

a. What is the probability that a student never visited the store?
b. What is the probability that a student visited the store occasionally and found the store conveniently located?
c. What is the probability that a student visited the store often given that the student felt the store was conveniently located?

Chapter Summary

I. A probability is a value between 0 and 1 inclusive that represents the likelihood a particular event will happen.

A. An experiment is the observation of some activity or the act of taking some measurement.

B. An outcome is a particular result of an experiment.

C. An event is the collection of one or more outcomes of an experiment.

II. There are three definitions of probability.

A. The classical definition applies when there are n equally likely outcomes to an experiment.

$$\textbf{Probability of an event} = \frac{\textbf{Number of favourable outcomes}}{\textbf{Total number of possible outcomes}} \qquad [4\text{–}1]$$

B. The empirical definition occurs when the number of times an event happens is divided by the number of observations.

C. A subjective probability is based on whatever information is available.

III. Two events are mutually exclusive if by virtue of one event happening the other cannot happen.

IV. Events are independent if the occurrence of one event does not affect the occurrence of another event.

V. There are three counting rules that are useful in determining the number of outcomes in an experiment.

A. The multiplication rule states that if there are m ways one event can happen and n ways another event can happen, then there are mn ways the two events can happen.

$$\textbf{Number of arrangements} = (m)(n) \qquad [4\text{–}2]$$

B. A permutation is an arrangement in which the order of the objects selected from a specific pool of objects is important.

$$_nP_r = \frac{n!}{(n-r)!} \qquad [4\text{–}3]$$

C. A combination is an arrangement where the order of the objects selected from a specific pool of objects is not important.

$$_nC_r = \frac{n!}{r!(n-r)!} \qquad [4\text{–}4]$$

VI. The rules of addition refer to the union of events.

A. The special rule of addition is used when events are mutually exclusive.

$$P(A \text{ or } B) = P(A) + P(B) \qquad [4\text{–}5]$$

B. The general rule of addition is

$$P(A \text{ or } B) = P(A) + P(B) - P(A \text{ and } B) \qquad [4\text{–}7]$$

C. The complement rule is used to determine the probability of an event happening by subtracting the probability of the event not happening from 1.

$$P(A) = 1 - P(\sim A) \qquad [4\text{–}6]$$

VII. The rules of multiplication refer to the product of events.

A. The special rule of multiplication refers to events that are independent.

$$P(A \text{ and } B) = P(A)P(B) \quad [4\text{–}8]$$

B. The general rule of multiplication refers to events that are not independent.

$$P(A \text{ and } B) = P(A)P(B \mid A) \quad [4\text{–}9]$$

C. A joint probability is the likelihood that two or more events will happen at the same time.

D. A conditional probability is the likelihood that an event will happen, given that another event has already happened.

Pronunciation Key

SYMBOL	MEANING	PRONUNCIATION
$P(A)$	Probability of A	P of A
$P(\sim A)$	Probability of not A	P of not A
$P(A$ and $B)$	Probability of A and B	P of A and B
$P(A$ or $B)$	Probability of A or B	P of A or B
$P(A \mid B)$	Probability of A given B has happened	P of A given B
${}_nP_r$	Permutation of n items selected r at a time	Pnr
${}_nC_r$	Combination of n items selected r at a time	Cnr
$n!$	Product of all positive integers $\leq n$	n factorial
$r!$	Product of all objects selected $\leq r$	r factorial

Chapter Exercises

45. The marketing research department at Vernors plans to survey teenagers about a newly developed soft drink. Each will be asked to compare it with his or her favourite soft drink.
   a. What is the experiment?
   b. What is one possible event?

46. The number of times a particular event occurred in the past is divided by the number of occurrences. What is this approach to probability called?

47. The probability that the cause and the cure for all cancers will be discovered before the year 2010 is .20. What viewpoint of probability does this statement illustrate?

48. Berdine's Chicken Factory has several retail stores. When interviewing applicants for server positions, the owner would like to include information on the amount of tip a server can expect to earn per check (or bill). A study of 500 recent checks indicated the server earned the following tips.

Amount of Tip ($)	Number
$0 to under $5	200
5 to under 10	100
10 to under 20	75
20 to under 50	75
50 or more	50
Total	500

   a. What is the probability of a tip of $50 or more?
   b. Are the categories "$0 to under $5," "$5 to under $10," and so on considered mutually exclusive?
   c. If the probabilities associated with each outcome were totalled, what would that total be?
   d. What is the probability of a tip of up to $10?
   e. What is the probability of a tip of less than $50?

49. Define each of these items:
 a. Conditional probability.
 b. Event.
 c. Joint probability.

50. How many possible outcomes are there when a coin is tossed six times?

51. Canadian postal codes consist of three letters and three digits, which alternate and start with a letter. For example, R2E 0M4 is a postal code from Winnipeg, Manitoba. How many postal codes can be created using this system?

52. A photographer has four pictures to arrange for a gallery showing. In how many ways can the photographer arrange the pictures?

53. How many ways are there of drawing seven cards from a deck of 52 cards? Note—the cards are not replaced.

54. In how many ways can the digits from 0 to 5 be arranged three at a time?

55. Eight-ball pool, one of the most popular pool games, has 15 coloured and striped balls, numbered from 1 to 15, and a white cue ball. In how many ways could six of the numbered balls be arranged?

56. The first card selected from a standard 52-card deck was a king.
 a. If it is returned to the deck, what is the probability that a king will be drawn on the second selection?
 b. If the king is not replaced, what is the probability that a king will be drawn on the second selection?
 c. What is the probability that a king will be selected on the first draw from the deck and another king on the second draw (assuming that the first king was not replaced)?

57. Armco, a manufacturer of traffic light systems, found that under accelerated-life tests, 95 percent of the newly developed systems lasted three years before failing to change signals properly.
 a. If a city purchased four of these systems, what is the probability all four systems would operate properly for at least three years?
 b. Which rule of probability does this illustrate?
 c. Using letters to represent the four systems, write an equation to show how you arrived at the answer to part a.

58. Refer to the following picture.

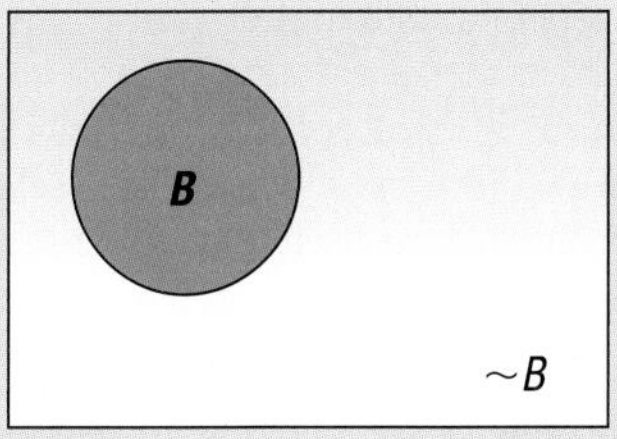

 a. What is the picture called?
 b. What rule of probability is illustrated?
 c. B represents the event of choosing a family that receives welfare payments. What does $P(B) + P(\sim B)$ equal?

59. In a management trainee program at Claremont Enterprises, 80 percent of the trainees are female and 20 percent male. Ninety percent of the females attended college, and 78 percent of the males attended college.
 a. A management trainee is selected at random. What is the probability that the person selected is a female who did not attend college?
 b. Construct a tree diagram showing all the probabilities, conditional probabilities, and joint probabilities.
 c. Do the joint probabilities total 1.00? Why?

60. Assume the likelihood that any flight on Northwest Airlines arrives within 15 minutes of the scheduled time is .90. We select four flights from yesterday for study.
 a. What is the likelihood all four of the selected flights arrived within 15 minutes of the scheduled time?
 b. What is the likelihood that none of the selected flights arrived within 15 minutes of the scheduled time?
 c. What is the likelihood at least one of the selected flights did not arrive within 15 minutes of the scheduled time?

61. There are 100 employees at Kiddie Carts International. Fifty-seven of the employees are production workers, 40 are supervisors, 2 are secretaries, and the remaining employee is the president. Suppose an employee is selected:
 a. What is the probability the selected employee is a production worker?
 b. What is the probability the selected employee is either a production worker or a supervisor?

c. Refer to part b. Are these events mutually exclusive?
d. What is the probability the selected employee is neither a production worker nor a supervisor?

62. In baseball, a batting average is the probability of the number of hits divided by the number of times at bat. A batting average over .300 is very good. This means that a player will get a hit 300 times for every 1000 times at bat. So, assume the probability of getting a hit is .359 for each time a player is at bat. In a particular game assume the batter batted three times.
a. This is an example of what type of probability?
b. What is the probability of getting three hits in a particular game?
c. What is the probability of not getting any hits in a game?
d. What is the probability of getting at least one hit?

63. Assume that when Toronto Raptor forward Chris Bosh takes a free throw there is a probability of .8 that the free throw will be good. In one game, he takes four free throws. Determine each probability.
a. All four free throws are good.
b. None of the four free throws are good.
c. At least one free throw is good.

64. Ninety students will graduate from Lima Shawnee High School this spring. Of the 90 students, 50 are planning to attend college. Two students are to be picked at random to carry flags at the graduation.
a. What is the probability both of the selected students plan to attend college?
b. What is the probability one of the two selected students plans to attend college?

65. Brooks Insurance Inc. wishes to offer life insurance to men aged 60 via the Internet. Mortality tables indicate the likelihood of a 60-year-old man surviving another year is .98. If the policy is offered to five men age 60:
a. What is the probability all five men survive the year?
b. What is the probability at least one does not survive?

66. Forty percent of the homes constructed in the Quail Creek area include a security system. Three homes are selected at random:
a. What is the probability all three of the selected homes have a security system?
b. What is the probability none of the three selected homes have a security system?
c. What is the probability at least one of the selected homes has a security system?
d. Did you assume the events to be dependent or independent?

67. Refer to Exercise 66, but assume there are 10 homes in the Quail Creek area and four of them have a security system. Three homes are selected at random:
a. What is the probability all three of the selected homes have a security system?
b. What is the probability none of the three selected homes have a security system?
c. What is the probability at least one of the selected homes has a security system?
d. Did you assume the events to be dependent or independent?

68. A juggler has a bag containing three green balls, two yellow balls, one red ball, and four blues. The juggler picks a ball at random. Then, without replacing it, he chooses a second ball. What is the probability the juggler first draws a yellow ball followed by a blue ball?

69. The board of directors of Saner Automatic Door Company consists of 12 members, 3 of whom are women. A new policy and procedures manual is to be written for the company. A committee of three is randomly selected from the board to do the writing.
a. What is the probability that all members of the committee are men?
b. What is the probability that at least one member of the committee is a woman?

70. A committee of 5 is selected from a group of 7 faculty and 50 students. In how many different ways can the committee be selected if it must consist of two faculty and three students?

71. A panel discussion of seven employees consists of four women and three men. In how many ways can this group be selected from 15 men and 20 women?

72. If a committee of 6 is being selected from a group of 10 men and 12 women, in how many ways can this committee be arranged if at least 3 must be women?

73. A crew of eight is required for each midnight shift at the airport. There are 50 employees to choose from, and 30 of these are men. In how many ways can the crew be selected if at least half must be men?

74. A survey of undergraduate students in the School of Business at Northern University revealed the following regarding the gender and majors of the students:

	Major			
Gender	**Accounting**	**Marketing**	**Finance**	**Total**
Male	100	150	50	300
Female	100	50	50	200
Total	200	200	100	500

a. What is the probability of selecting a female student?
b. What is the probability of selecting a finance or accounting major?
c. What is the probability of selecting a female or an accounting major? Which rule of addition did you apply?
d. What is the probability of selecting an accounting major, given that the person selected is a male?
e. Suppose two students are selected randomly to attend a lunch with the president of the university. What is the probability that both of those selected are accounting majors?

75. A recent survey reported in *BusinessWeek* concerned the salaries of CEOs at large corporations, and whether company shareholders made or lost money.

	CEO Paid More Than \$1 Million	CEO Paid Less Than \$1 Million	Total
Shareholders made money	2	11	13
Shareholders lost money	4	3	7
Total	6	14	20

If a company is randomly selected from the list of 20 studied, what is the probability:
a. the CEO made more than \$1 million?
b. the CEO made more than \$1 million, or the shareholders lost money?
c. the CEO made more than \$1 million given the shareholders lost money?
d. of selecting two CEOs and finding they both made more than \$1 million?

76. An investor purchased 100 shares of Bank stock and 100 shares of Cooper Electric stock. The probability the Bank stock will appreciate over a year is .70. The probability Cooper Electric stock will increase over the same period is .60.
a. What is the probability both stocks appreciate during the period?
b. What is the probability the Bank stock appreciates and the Cooper Electric stock does not?
c. What is the probability at least one of the stocks appreciate?

77. With each purchase of a large pizza at Tony's Pizza, the customer receives a coupon that can be scratched to see if a prize will be awarded. The odds of winning a free soft drink are 1 in 10, and the odds of winning a free large pizza are 1 in 50. You plan to eat lunch tomorrow at Tony's. What is the probability:
a. That you will win either a large pizza or a soft drink?
b. That you will not win a prize?
c. That you will not win a prize on three consecutive visits to Tony's?
d. That you will win at least one prize on one of your next three visits to Tony's?

78. For a weekly lottery game in Ontario, participants select three numbers between zero and nine. A number cannot be selected more than once, so a winning ticket could be, say, 307. Purchasing one ticket allows you to select one set of numbers. The winning numbers are announced on TV each week.
a. How many different outcomes (three-digit numbers) are possible?
b. If you purchase a ticket for the game tonight, what is the likelihood you will win?
c. Suppose you purchase three tickets for tonight's drawing and select a different number for each ticket. What is the probability that you will not win with any of the tickets?

79. Several years ago Wendy's Old Fashioned Hamburgers advertised that there are 256 different ways to order your hamburger. You may choose to have, or omit, any combination of the following on your hamburger: mustard, ketchup, onion, pickle, tomato, relish, mayonnaise, and lettuce. Is the advertisement correct? Show how you arrive at your answer.

80. It was found that 60 percent of the tourists to China visited the Forbidden City, the Temple of Heaven, the Great Wall, and other historical sites in or near Beijing. Forty percent visited Xi'an with its magnificent terracotta soldiers, horses, and chariots, which lay buried for over 2000 years. Thirty percent of the tourists went to both Beijing and Xi'an. What is the probability that a tourist visited at least one of these places?

81. A new chewing gum has been developed that is helpful to those who want to stop smoking. If 60 percent of those people chewing the gum are successful in stopping smoking, what is the probability that in a group of four smokers using the gum at least one quits smoking?

82. Reynolds Construction Company has agreed not to erect all "look-alike" homes in a new subdivision. Five exterior designs are offered to potential home buyers. The builder has standardized three interior plans that can be incorporated in any of the five exteriors. How many different ways can the exterior and interior plans be offered to potential home buyers?

83. A new sports car model has defective brakes 15 percent of the time and a defective steering mechanism 5 percent of the time. Let's assume (and hope) that these problems occur independently. If one or the other of these problems is present, the car is called a "lemon." If both of these problems are present, the car is a "hazard." Your instructor purchased one of these cars yesterday. What is the probability it is:
a. A lemon?
b. A hazard?

www.mcgrawhill.ca/olc/lind

84. **a.** Some Saskatchewan license plates have three letters and three numbers. How many license plates of this type can there be?
b. Some Ontario license plates have four letters and three numbers. How many license plates of this type can there be?

85. There are four people being considered for the position of chief executive officer of Dalton Enterprises. Three of the applicants are over 60 years of age. Two are female, of which only one is over 60.
a. What is the probability that a candidate is over 60 and female?
b. Given that the candidate is male, what is the probability he is less than 60?
c. Given that the person is over 60, what is the probability the person is female?

86. Tim Bleckie is the owner of Bleckie Investment and Real Estate Company. The company recently purchased four tracts of land in Holly Farms Estates and six tracts in Newburg Woods. The tracts are all equally desirable and sell for about the same amount.
a. What is the probability that the next two tracts sold will be in Newburg Woods?
b. What is the probability that of the next four sold at least one will be in Holly Farms?
c. Are these events independent or dependent?

87. A computer password consists of four characters. The characters can be one of the 26 letters of the alphabet. Each character may be used more than once. How many different passwords are possible?

88. A case of 24 cans contains 1 can that is contaminated. Three cans are to be chosen randomly for testing.
a. How many different combinations of three cans could be selected?
b. What is the probability that the contaminated can is selected for testing?

89. A puzzle in a newspaper presents a matching problem. The names of 10 different Juno award winners are listed in one column, and their 10 winning songs are listed in random order in a second column. The puzzle asks the reader to match each winner with his or her winning song. If you make the matches randomly, how many sets of matches are possible? What is the probability that a randomly selected set of matches has all 10 winners matched correctly?

90. The following diagram represents a system of two components, A and B, which are in series. (Being in series means that for the system to operate, both components A and B must work.) Suppose the system works if *either* A or B works. What is the probability the system works under these conditions? The probability A works is .90 and the probability B functions is also .90.

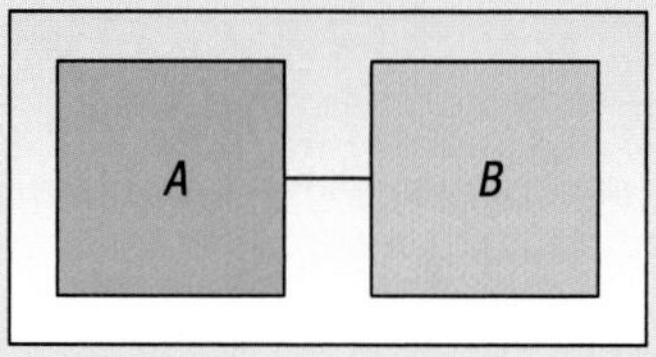

91. A company has a computer system consisting of two components, X and Y, which are in series, meaning that both components X and Y must work in order for the computer system to be operational. The probability of the parts being defective is 1 percent and 2 percent respectively. What is the probability that the computer system is working under these conditions?

Data Set Exercises

92. Refer to the real estate data, from the central area of Edmonton on the CD-ROM, which reports information on list prices, square feet, style, number of bathrooms, and number of bedrooms.
a. Sort the data into a table by style and size (sq. ft. and in class widths of 500) and compute the following probabilities.
1. The house is a two-storey.
2. Given that the house is a bungalow, that it has between 1000 to under 1500 square feet.
3. The house is a two-storey and has between 1000 to under 1500 square feet.

b. Sort the data into a table by list price (class widths of \$100 000) and the number of full baths and compute the following probabilities:
1. The home has four full bathrooms.
2. The home is listed for less than \$400 000.
3. The home is listed for \$200 000 to under \$400 000 and has two full bathrooms.
4. The home has two full bathrooms given that the home is listed for \$200 000 to under \$400 000.

c. Sort the data into a table by list price (class widths of \$100 000) and total square feet and compute the following probabilities:
1. The house size is 1000 square feet or more.
2. Given that the house is listed for less than \$500 000, that is, has 1000 to under 2000 square feet.
3. The house is listed for more than \$400 000.
4. The house size is 1000 square feet or more or is listed for less than \$400 000.

93. Refer to the Baseball 2006 data, which reports information on the 30 Major League Baseball teams for the 2006 season. Set up a variable that divides the teams into two groups, those that had a winning season, and those that did not. That is, create a variable to count the teams that won 81 games or more, and those that won 80 or less. Next, create a new variable for attendance, using three categories: attendance less than 2.0 million, attendance of 2.0 million up to 3.0 million, and attendance of 3.0 million or more.

a. Create a table that shows the number of teams with a winning season versus those with a losing season by the three categories of attendance. If a team is selected at random, compute the following probabilities:
1. Having a winning season.
2. Having a winning season, or attendance of more than 3.0 million.
3. Given attendance of more than 3.0 million, having a winning season.
4. Having a losing season and drawing less than 2.0 million.

b. Create a table that shows the number of teams that play on artificial surfaces and natural surfaces by winning and losing records. If a team is selected at random, compute the following probabilities:
1. Selecting a team with a home field that has a natural surface.
2. Is the likelihood of selecting a team with a winning record larger for teams with natural or artificial surfaces?
3. Having a winning record, or playing on an artificial surface.

exercises.com

Additional exercises that require you to access information at related Internet sites are available on the CD-ROM included with this text.

Answers to Self-Reviews

4–1 **(a)** Testing of the new computer game
(b) Seventy-three players liked the game.
(c) No. Probability cannot be greater than 1. The probability that the game, if put on the market, will be successful is 65/80, or .8125.
(d) Cannot be less than 0. Perhaps a mistake in arithmetic.
(e) More than half of the persons testing the game liked it. (Of course, other answers are possible.)

4–2 **1.** $\frac{\text{4 queens in deck}}{\text{52 cards total}} = \frac{4}{52} = .0769$ Classical.

2. $\frac{182}{539} = .338$ Empirical.

3. The author's view when writing the text of the chance that the index will climb to 12 000 is .25. You may be more optimistic or less optimistic. Subjective.

4–3 **1.** There are 20, found by (5)(4)
2. There are 72, found by (3)(2)(4)(3)

4–4 **1.** **(a)** 60, found by (5)(4)(3).
(b) 60, found by:

$$\frac{5!}{(5-3)!} = \frac{5 \cdot 4 \cdot 3 \cdot \cancel{2 \cdot 1}}{\cancel{2 \cdot 1}}$$

2. 24, found by:

$$\frac{4!}{(4-4)!} = \frac{4!}{0!} = \frac{4!}{1} = \frac{4 \cdot 3 \cdot 2 \cdot 1}{1}$$

3. 5040, found by:

$$\frac{10!}{(10-4)!} = \frac{10 \cdot 9 \cdot 8 \cdot 7 \cdot \cancel{6 \cdot 5 \cdot 4 \cdot 3 \cdot 2 \cdot 1}}{\cancel{6 \cdot 5 \cdot 4 \cdot 3 \cdot 2 \cdot 1}}$$

4. **(a)** 56 is correct, found by:

$${}_8C_3 = \frac{n!}{r!(n-r)!} = \frac{8!}{3!(8-3)!} = 56$$

(b) Yes. There are 45 combinations, found by:

$${}_{10}C_2 = \frac{n!}{r(n-r)!} = \frac{10!}{2!(10-2)!} = 45$$

5. **(a)** ${}_nP_r = \frac{50!}{(50-3)!} = 117\,600$

(b) ${}_nC_r = \frac{50!}{3!(50-3)!} = 19\,600$

4–5 **(a)** **(i)** $\frac{(50+68)}{2000} = .059$

(ii) $1 - \frac{302}{2000} = .849$

(b)

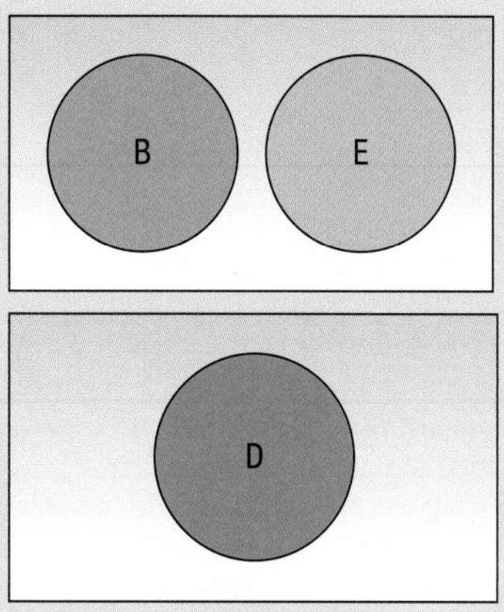

(c) They are not complementary, but are mutually exclusive.

4–6 **(a)** Need for corrective shoes is event A. Need for major dental work is event B.

$$P(A \text{ or } B) = P(A) + P(B) - P(A \text{ and } B)$$
$$= .08 + .15 - .03$$
$$= .20$$

(b) One possibility is:

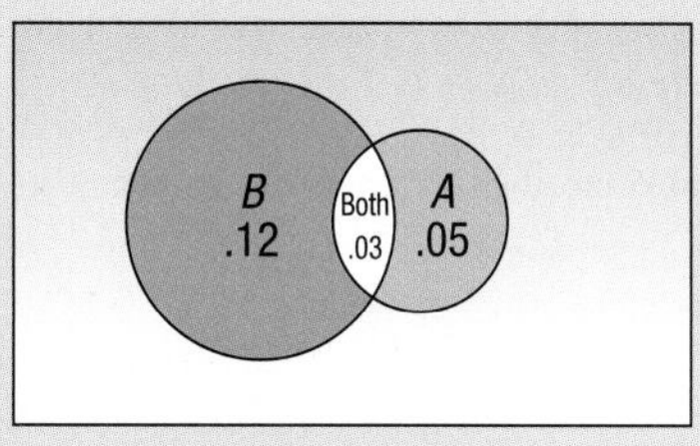

4–7 (.80)(.80)(.80)(.80) = .4096.

4–8 **(a)** .002, found by:

$$\left(\frac{4}{12}\right)\left(\frac{3}{11}\right)\left(\frac{2}{10}\right)\left(\frac{1}{9}\right) = \frac{24}{11\,880} = .002$$

(b) .14, found by:

$$\left(\frac{8}{12}\right)\left(\frac{7}{11}\right)\left(\frac{6}{10}\right)\left(\frac{5}{9}\right) = \frac{1680}{11\,880} = .1414$$

(c) No, because there are other possibilities, such as three women and one man.

4–9 **(a)** $P(B_4) = \frac{105}{200} = .525$

(b) $P(A_2 \mid B_4) = \frac{30}{105} = .286$

(c) $P(A_2 \text{ or } B_4) = \frac{80}{200} + \frac{105}{200} - \frac{30}{200} = \frac{155}{200} = .775$

4–10 **(a)** Contingency table.

(b)

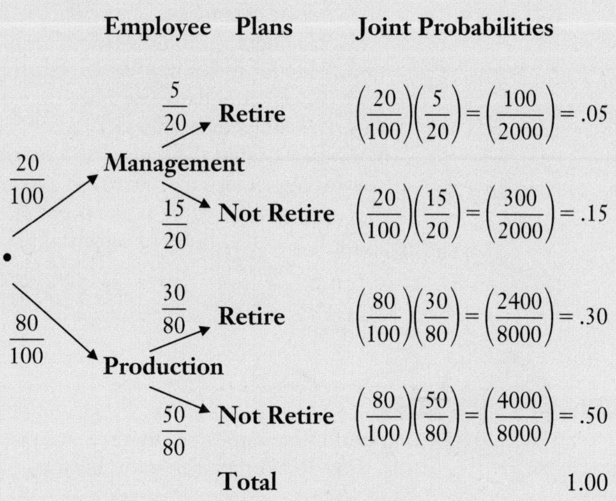

(c) Yes, all possibilities are included.

chapter 5

Discrete Probability Distributions

Croissant Bakery Inc. offers specially decorated cakes for birthdays, weddings, and other occasions. It also has regular cakes available in its display case (see Exercise 47 and Learning Goal 3).

LEARNING GOALS

When you have completed this chapter, you will be able to:

1. Define the terms *probability distribution* and *random variable*.
2. Distinguish between *discrete* and *continuous probability distributions*.
3. Calculate the *mean*, *variance*, and *standard deviation* of a *discrete probability distribution*.
4. Describe the characteristics of and compute probabilities using the *binomial probability distribution*.
5. Describe the characteristics of and compute probabilities using the *hypergeometric probability distribution*.
6. Describe the characteristics of and compute probabilities using the *Poisson probability distribution*.

Introduction

Chapters 2 and 3 are devoted to descriptive statistics. We describe raw data by organizing them into a frequency distribution and portraying the distribution in tables, graphs, and charts. Also, we compute a measure of location—such as the arithmetic mean, median, or mode—to locate a typical value near the centre of the distribution. The range and the standard deviation are used to describe the spread in the data. These chapters focus on describing *something that has already happened*.

Starting with Chapter 4, the emphasis changes—we begin examining *something that would probably happen*. We note that this facet of statistics is called *statistical inference*. The objective is to make inferences (statements) about a population based on a number of observations, called a sample, selected from the population. In Chapter 4, we state that a probability is a value between 0 and 1 inclusive, and we examine how probabilities can be combined using rules of addition and rules of multiplication.

This chapter will begin the study of **probability distributions**. A probability distribution gives the entire range of values that can occur based on an experiment. A probability distribution is similar to a relative frequency distribution. However, instead of describing the past, it describes how likely some future event is. For example, a drug manufacturer may claim a treatment will cause weight loss for 80 percent of the population. A consumer protection agency may test the treatment on a sample of six people. If the manufacturer's claim is true, it is *almost impossible* to have an outcome where no one in the sample loses weight and it is *most likely* that five out of the six do lose weight.

In this chapter we discuss the mean, variance, and standard deviation of a probability distribution. We also discuss three frequently occurring probability distributions: the binomial, the hypergeometric, and the Poisson.

1 Define the terms *probability distribution* and *random variable*.

What is a Probability Distribution?

probability distribution A listing of all the outcomes of an experiment and the probability associated with each outcome.

A **probability distribution** shows the possible outcomes of an experiment and the probability of each of these outcomes.

How can we generate a probability distribution? The following is an example.

example

Suppose we are interested in the number of heads showing face up on three tosses of a coin. This is the experiment. The possible results are: zero heads, one head, two heads, and three heads. What is the probability distribution for the number of heads.

solution

There are eight possible outcomes. A tail might appear face up on the first toss, another tail on the second toss, and another tail on the third toss of the coin. Or we might get a tail, tail, and head. We use the multiplication formula from Chapter 4 (4–2) for counting outcomes. There are (2)(2)(2) = 8 possible outcomes. These results are listed below.

Possible Result	Coin Toss: First	Second	Third	Number of Heads
1	T	T	T	0
2	T	T	H	1
3	T	H	T	1
4	T	H	H	2
5	H	T	T	1
6	H	T	H	2
7	H	H	T	2
8	H	H	H	3

Note that the outcome "zero heads" occurred only once, "one head" occurred three times, "two heads" occurred three times, and the outcome "three heads" occurred only once. That is, "zero heads" happened one out of eight times. Thus, the probability of zero heads is one-eighth, the probability of one head is three-eighths, and so on. The probability distribution is shown in Table 5–1. The total of the probabilities of all possible events is 1. This is always true. The same information is shown in Chart 5–1.

TABLE 5–1 Probability Distribution for the Events of Zero, One, Two, and Three Heads Showing Face Up on Three Tosses of a Coin

Number of Heads, x	Probability of Outcome, $P(x)$
0	$\frac{1}{8} = .125$
1	$\frac{3}{8} = .375$
2	$\frac{3}{8} = .375$
3	$\frac{1}{8} = .125$
Total	$\frac{8}{8} = 1.000$

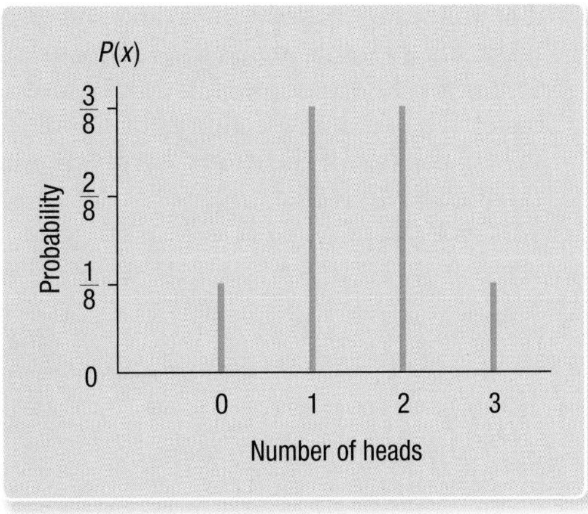

CHART 5–1 Graphical Presentation of the Number of Heads Resulting from Three Tosses of a Coin and the Corresponding Probability

Characteristics of a probability distribution

Before continuing, we should note three important characteristics of a probability distribution.

1. The probability of a particular outcome is between 0 and 1 inclusive.
2. The outcomes are mutually exclusive events.
3. The list is exhaustive. So the sum of the probabilities of the various events is equal to 1.

Refer to the coin-tossing example in Table 5–1. We write the probability of x as $P(x)$. So the probability of zero heads is $P(0 \text{ heads}) = .125$ and the probability of one head is $P(1 \text{ head}) = .375$ and so forth. The sum of these mutually exclusive probabilities is 1; that is, from Table 5–1, $.125 + .375 + .375 + .125 = 1$

self-review 5–1

The possible outcomes of an experiment involving the roll of a six-sided die are: a one-spot, a two-spot, a three-spot, a four-spot, a five-spot, and a six-spot.

(a) Develop a probability distribution for the number of possible spots.
(b) Portray the probability distribution graphically.
(c) What is the sum of the probabilities?

Random Variables

In any experiment of chance, the outcomes occur randomly. So it is often called a *random variable*. For example, rolling a single die is an experiment; any one of six possible outcomes can occur. Some experiments result in outcomes that are quantitative (such as dollars, weight, or number of children), and others result in qualitative outcomes (such as colour or religious preference). Each value of the random variable is associated with a probability to indicate the chance of a particular outcome. A few examples will further illustrate what is meant by a **random variable**.

random variable A variable whose value is determined by the outcome of a random experiment.

- If we count the number of employees absent from the day shift on Monday, the number might be 0, 1, 2, 3, ... The number absent is the random variable.
- If we determine the mass of a steel ingot, it might be 24 928 kg, or 2497 kg, or 2506 kg, and so on. The mass is the random variable.
- Suppose three customers enter a restaurant. The number of these customers who purchase a dessert item after their meal could be zero, one, two, or three. The number purchasing a dessert item is a random variable.
- Other random variables might be: the number of defective light bulbs produced during the week, the heights of the members of the girls' basketball team, and the daily number of drivers charged with driving under the influence of alcohol in British Columbia.

The following diagram illustrates the terms *experiment*, *outcome*, *event*, and *random variable*. First, for the experiment where a coin is tossed three times, there are eight possible outcomes. In this experiment, we are interested in the event that one head occurs in the three tosses. The random variable is the number of heads. In terms of probability, we want to know the probability of the event that the random variable equals 1. The result is P(one head in three tosses) = .375.

Possible *outcomes* for three coin tosses

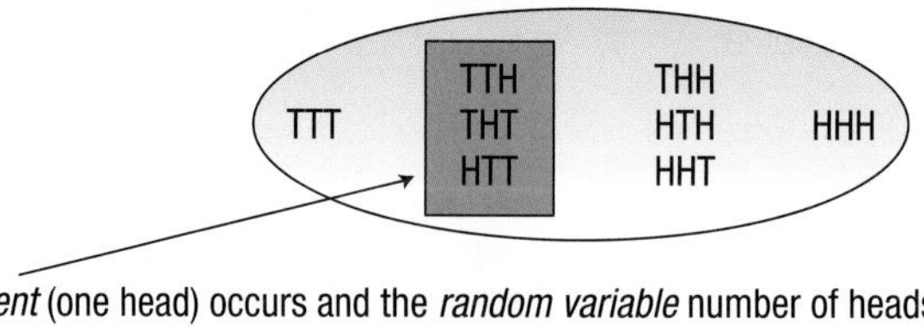

The *event* (one head) occurs and the *random variable* number of heads has the value $x = 1$.

A random variable may be either *discrete* or *continuous*.

2 Distinguish between *discrete* and *continuous* *probability distributions*.

discrete random variable A variable that can assume only certain, clearly separated values.

Discrete Random Variable

A discrete random variable can assume only a certain number of separated values. If there are 100 employees, then the count of the number of workers absent on Monday can only be 0, 1, 2, 3, . . . , 100. A **discrete random variable** is usually the result of counting something.

A discrete variable can, in some cases, assume fractional or decimal values. These values must be separated, that is, have distance between them. As an example, the scores awarded by judges for technical competence and artistic form in a figure skating competition may be decimal values, such as 177.2, 188.9, 169.7 and 183.4. Such values are discrete because there is distance between scores of, say, 183.4 and 183.5. Score cannot be 183.46875 or 184.52738, for example.

Continuous Random Variable

On the other hand, if the random variable is continuous, then the distribution is a continuous probability distribution. If we measure something such as the width of a room, the height of a person, or the pressure in an automobile tire, the variable is a *continuous random variable*. It can assume one of an infinitely large number of values, within certain limitations. As examples:

- The times of commercial flights between Toronto and Ottawa are 1 hour, 1.1 hours, and so on. The random variable is the number of hours.
- Tire pressures, measured in pounds per square inch (psi), for a new Chevy TrailBlazer may be 32 psi, 31 psi, 33 psi, and so on. In other words, any values between 28 and 35 could reasonably occur. The random variable is the tire pressure.

Logically, if we organize a set of possible values from a random variable, the result is a **probability distribution**. So what is the difference between a probability distribution and a random variable? A random variable reports the particular outcome of an experiment. A probability distribution reports all the possible outcomes as well as the corresponding probability.

The tools used, as well as the probability interpretations, are different for discrete and continuous probability distributions. This chapter is limited to the discussion and interpretation of discrete distributions. In the next chapter we discuss continuous distributions. How do you tell the difference between the two types of distributions? Usually a discrete distribution is the result of counting something such as:

- The number of heads appearing when a coin is tossed three times.
- The number of students earning an A in this class.
- The number of production employees absent from the second shift today.
- The number of 30-second commercials during the Super Bowl on Sunday.

Continuous distributions are usually the result of some type of measurement such as:

- The length of each song on the *Best of the Beatles* album.
- The height of each student in the class.
- The temperature outside as you are reading this book.

3 Calculate the *mean*, *variance*, and *standard deviation* of a *discrete probability distribution.*

The Mean, Variance, and Standard Deviation of a Probability Distribution

In Chapter 3 we discussed measures of location and variation for a frequency distribution. The mean reports the central location of the data, and the variance and standard deviation describe the spread in the data. In a similar fashion, a probability distribution is summarized by its mean and standard deviation. Since a probability distribution by definition is a population, we identify the mean of a probability distribution by the Greek letter mu (μ) and the standard deviation by the Greek letter sigma (σ).

Mean

The mean is a typical value used to represent the central location within a probability distribution. It also is the long-run average value of the random variable. The mean of a probability distribution is also referred to as its **expected value**. It is a weighted average where the possible values are weighted by their corresponding probabilities of occurrence.

The mean of a discrete probability distribution is computed by the formula:

MEAN OF A DISCRETE PROBABILITY DISTRIBUTION $\mu = \Sigma[xP(x)]$ **[5–1]**

where $P(x)$ is the probability of a particular value x. In other words, to find the mean, multiply each x value by its probability of occurrence, and then add these products.

Variance and Standard Deviation

As noted, the mean is a typical value used to summarize a discrete probability distribution. However, it does not describe the amount of spread (variation) in a distribution. The variance does this. The formula for the variance of a probability distribution is:

VARIANCE OF A DISCRETE PROBABILITY DISTRIBUTION $\sigma^2 = \Sigma[(x - \mu)^2 P(x)]$ **[5–2]**

The computational steps are:

1. Subtract the mean from each value, and square this difference.
2. Multiply each squared difference by its probability.
3. Sum the resulting products to arrive at the variance.

The standard deviation, σ, is found by taking the square root of σ^2; that is, $\sigma = \sqrt{\sigma^2}$.

An example will help explain the details of the calculation and interpretation of the mean and standard deviation of a probability distribution.

example

John Ragsdale sells developed new cars for Pelican Ford. John usually sells the largest number of cars on Saturday. He has the following probability distribution for the number of cars he expects to sell on a particular Saturday.

Number of Cars Sold, x	Probability, $P(x)$
0	.1
1	.2
2	.3
3	.3
4	.1
Total	1.0

1. What type of distribution is this?
2. On a typical Saturday, how many cars does John expect to sell?
3. What is the variance of the distribution?

solution

1. This is a discrete probability distribution for the random variable "number of cars sold." Note that John expects to sell only within a certain range of cars; he does not expect to sell 5 cars or 50 cars. Further, he cannot sell half a car. He can sell only zero, one, two, three, or four cars. Also, the outcomes are mutually exclusive—he cannot sell a total of both three and four cars on the same Saturday.
2. The mean number of cars sold is computed by weighting the number of cars sold by the probability of selling that number and totalling the products using formula (5–1):

$$\mu = \Sigma[xP(x)]$$
$$= 0(.1) + 1(.2) + 2(.3) + 3(.3) + 4(.1)$$
$$= 2.1$$

These calculations are summarized in the following table.

Number of Cars Sold, x	Probability, $P(x)$	$x \cdot P(x)$
0	.1	.0
1	.2	.2
2	.3	.6
3	.3	.9
4	.1	.4
Total	1.0	$\mu = 2.1$

How do we interpret a mean of 2.1? This value indicates that, over a large number of Saturdays, John Ragsdale expects to sell a mean of 2.1 cars a day. (Of course, it is not possible for him to sell *exactly* 2.1 cars on any particular Saturday.) However, the expected value can be used to predict the arithmetic mean number of cars sold on Saturdays in the long run. For example, if John works 50 Saturdays during a year, he can expect to sell (50)(2.1) = 105 cars on Saturdays during the 50 weeks. Thus, the mean is sometimes called the expected value.

3. Again, a table is useful for organizing the calculations for the variance, which is 1.290.

Number of Cars Sold, x	Probability, $P(x)$	$(x - \mu)$	$(x - \mu)^2$	$(x - \mu)^2P(x)$
0	.1	0 − 2.1	4.41	0.441
1	.2	1 − 2.1	1.21	0.242
2	.3	2 − 2.1	0.01	0.003
3	.3	3 − 2.1	0.81	0.243
4	.1	4 − 2.1	3.61	0.361
				$\sigma^2 = 1.29$

Recall that the standard deviation is the positive square root of the variance. In this example, $\sqrt{\sigma^2} = \sqrt{1.29} = 1.136$ cars. How do we interpret a standard deviation of 1.136 cars? If salesperson Rita Kirsch also sold a mean of 2.1 cars on Saturdays, and the standard deviation in her sales was 1.91 cars, we would conclude that there is more variability in the Saturday sales of Ms. Kirsch than in those of Mr. Ragsdale (because $1.91 > 1.136$).

self-review 5–2

The Pizza Palace offers three sizes of cola—small, medium, and large—to go with its pizza. The colas are sold for \$0.80, \$0.90, and \$1.20, respectively. Thirty percent of the orders are for small, 50 percent are for medium, and 20 percent are for the large sizes. Organize the size of the colas and the probability of a sale into a probability distribution.

(a) Is this a discrete probability distribution? Indicate why or why not.
(b) Compute the mean amount charged for a cola.
(c) What is the variance in the amount charged for a cola? The standard deviation?

Exercises

1. Compute the mean and variance of the following discrete probability distribution.

x	$P(x)$
0	.2
1	.4
2	.3
3	.1

2. Compute the mean and variance of the following discrete probability distribution.

x	$P(x)$
2	.5
8	.3
10	.2

3. Three tables listed below show random variables and their probabilities. However, only one of these is actually a probability distribution.

x	$P(x)$
5	.3
10	.3
15	.2
20	.4

x	$P(x)$
5	.1
10	.2
15	.3
20	.4

x	$P(x)$
5	.5
10	.3
15	−.2
20	.4

a. Which of the above tables is a probability distribution?
b. Using the correct probability distribution, find the probability that x is:
(1) Exactly 15.
(2) No more than 10.
(3) More than 5.
c. Compute the mean, variance, and standard deviation of this distribution.

4. Which of these variables are discrete and which are continuous random variables?
a. The number of new accounts established by a salesperson in a year.
b. The time between customer arrivals to a bank ATM.
c. The number of customers in Big Nick's barber shop.
d. The amount of fuel in your car's gas tank last week.
e. The outside temperature today.

5. The information below is the number of daily emergency assists made to skiers by the volunteer ski team at Alpine Ski Lodge for the last 50 days. To explain, there were 22 days on which there were 2 emergency assists, and 9 days on which there were 3 emergency assists.

Number of Calls	Frequency
0	8
1	10
2	22
3	9
4	1
Total	50

a. Convert this information on the number of calls to a probability distribution.
b. Is this an example of a discrete or continuous probability distribution?
c. What is the mean number of emergency assists per day?
d. What is the standard deviation of the number of assists made daily?

6. The director of admissions at Kinzua University in Nova Scotia estimated the distribution of student admissions for the fall semester based on past experience. What is the expected number of admissions for the fall semester? Compute the variance and the standard deviation.

Admissions	Probability
1000	.60
1200	.30
1500	.10

7. The following table lists the probability distribution for cash prizes in a lottery conducted at Lawson's Department Store.

Prize ($)	Probability
$0	.45
10	.30
100	.20
500	.05

If you buy a single ticket, what is the probability that you win:
a. Exactly $100?
b. At least $10?
c. No more than $100?
d. Compute the mean, variance, and standard deviation of this distribution.

8. You are asked to match three songs with the performers who made those songs famous. If you guess, the probability distribution for the number of correct matches is:

Probability	.333	.500	0	.167
Number correct	0	1	2	3

What is the probability you get:
a. Exactly one correct?
b. At least one correct?
c. Exactly two correct?
d. Compute the mean, variance, and standard deviation of this distribution.

9. Belk Department Store is having a special sale this weekend. Customers charging purchases of more than $50 to their Belk credit card will be given a special Belk Lottery card. The customer will scratch off the card, which will indicate the amount to be taken off the total amount of the purchase. Listed below is the amount of the prize and the percent of the time that amount will be deducted from the total amount of the purchase.

Prize Amount	Probability
$10	.50
25	.40
50	.08
100	.02

a. What is the mean amount deducted from the total purchase amount?
b. What is the standard deviation of the amount deducted from the total purchase?

10. The parking authority in downtown Halifax reported the following information for a sample of 250 customers on the number of hours cars are parked and the amount they are charged.

Number of Hours	Frequency	Amount Charged
1	20	$3
2	38	6
3	53	9
4	45	12
5	40	14
6	13	16
7	5	18
8	36	20

a. Convert the information on the number of hours parked to a probability distribution. Is this a discrete or continuous probability distribution?
b. Find the mean and the standard deviation of the number of hours parked. How would you answer the question, how long is a typical customer parked?
c. Find the mean and the standard deviation of the amount charged.

4 Describe the characteristics of and compute probabilities using the *binomial probability distribution.*

Binomial Probability Distribution

The **binomial probability distribution** is a widely occurring discrete probability distribution. One characteristic of a binomial distribution is that there are only two possible outcomes on a particular trial of an experiment. For example, the statement in a true/false question is either true or false. The outcomes are *mutually exclusive*, meaning that the answer to a true/false question cannot be both true and false at the same time. As other examples, a product is classified as either acceptable or not acceptable by the quality control department, a worker is classified as employed or unemployed, and a sales call results in the customer either purchasing the product or not purchasing the product. Frequently, we classify the two possible outcomes as "success" and "failure." However, this classification does *not* imply that one outcome is good and the other is bad.

Another characteristic of the binomial distribution is that the random variable is the result of counts. That is, we count the number of successes in the total number of trials. We flip a fair coin five times and count the number of times a head appears; we select 10 workers and count the number who are over 50 years of age; or we select 20 boxes of Kellogg's Raisin Bran and count the number that weigh more than the amount indicated on the package.

A third characteristic of a binomial distribution is that the probability of a success remains the same from one trial to another. Two examples are:

- The probability you will guess the first question of a true/false test correctly (a success) is one-half. This is the first "trial." The probability that you will guess correctly on the second question (the second trial) is also one-half, the probability of success on the third trial is one-half, and so on.
- If past experience revealed the swing bridge near Little Current, Ontario was raised 1 out of every 20 times you approach it, then the probability is one-twentieth that it will be raised (a "success") the next time you approach it, one-twentieth the following time, and so on.

The final characteristic of a binomial probability distribution is that each trial is *independent* of any other trial. This means that the outcome of a particular trial does not affect the outcome of any other trial.

In summary, a binomial distribution has these characteristics:

Characteristics of a binomial distribution

BINOMIAL PROBABILITY EXPERIMENT

1. An outcome on each trial of an experiment is classified into one of two mutually exclusive categories—a success or a failure.
2. The random variable counts the number of successes in a fixed number of trials.
3. The probability of success and failure stays the same for each trial.
4. The trials are independent, meaning that the outcome of one trial does not affect the outcome of any other trial.

How is a Binomial Probability Distribution Computed?

To construct a particular binomial probability distribution, we use (1) the number of trials and (2) the probability of success on each trial. For example, if an examination consists of 20 multiple-choice questions, the number of trials is 20. If each question has five choices and only one choice is correct, the probability of success for a person with no knowledge of the subject on each trial is 1/5 = .20. Thus, the probability is .20 that a person with no knowledge of the subject matter will guess the answer to a question correctly. So the conditions of the binomial distribution are met.

The binomial probability distribution is computed by the formula:

BINOMIAL PROBABILITY DISTRIBUTION $$P(x) = {}_nC_x p^x (1-p)^{n-x} \quad [5\text{–}3]$$

where:

C denotes a combination.
n is the number of trials.
x is the number of successes.
p is the probability of a success on each trial.

example

Toss a coin three times. What is the probability of getting exactly two heads?

solution

We can use the probability rules from Chapter 4 to solve the above problem. We will start with tossing the coin three times.

Outcomes	$P(x)$
HHH	1/8
HHT	1/8
HTH	1/8
HTT	1/8
THH	1/8
THT	1/8
TTH	1/8
TTT	1/8
	1.0

We can count the occurrences of two heads as: HHT, HTH, and THH. The probability of two heads is then 3/8 = .375. Or, we could use formula (5–3) to solve the problem, where $X = 2$, $n = 3$, $p = .5$, and $(1-p) = .5$. (Note: $p = .5$ is the probability of a head on a single toss of the coin.)

$$P(2) = {}_nC_x(p)^x(1-p)^{(n-x)}$$
$$P(2) = {}_3C_2(.5)^2(1-.5)^{(3-2)}$$
$$P(2) = (3)(.25)(.5) = .375$$

example

There are five daily morning flights from Edmonton to Calgary. Suppose the probability that any flight arrives late is .20, found by 1/5. What is the probability that none of the flights are late today? What is the probability that exactly one of the flights is late today?

solution

We can use formula (5–3). The probability that a particular flight is late is .20, so let $p = .20$. There are five flights, so $n = 5$, and x refers to the number of successes. In this case a "success" is a plane that arrives late. Because there are no late arrivals $x = 0$.

$$P(0) = {}_nC_x(p)^x(1-p)^{n-x}$$
$$= {}_5C_0(.20)^0(1-.20)^{5-0} = (1)(1)(.3277) = .3277$$

The probability that exactly one of the five flights will arrive late today is .4096 found by

$$P(1) = {}_nC_x(p)^x(1-p)^{n-x}$$
$$= {}_5C_1(.20)^1(1-.20)^{5-1} = (5)(.20)(.4096) = .4096$$

The entire probability distribution is shown in Table 5–2.

TABLE 5–2 Binomial Probability Distribution for $n = 5$, $p = .20$

Number of Late Flights	Probability
0	.3277
1	.4096
2	.2048
3	.0512
4	.0064
5	.0003
Total	1.0000

The random variable in Table 5–2 is plotted in Chart 5–2. Note that the distribution of late arriving flights is positively skewed.

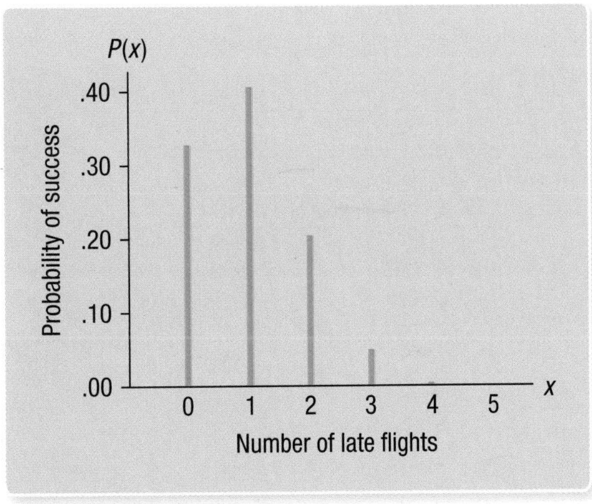

CHART 5–2 Binomial Probability Distribution for $n = 5$, $p = .20$

The mean (μ) and the variance (σ^2) of a binomial distribution can be computed in a "shortcut" fashion by:

MEAN OF A BINOMIAL DISTRIBUTION $$\mu = np$$ **[5–4]**

VARIANCE OF A BINOMIAL DISTRIBUTION $$\sigma^2 = np(1 - p)$$ **[5–5]**

For the example regarding the number of late flights, $p = .20$ and $n = 5$. Hence:

$$\mu = np = (5)(.20) = 1.0$$
$$\sigma^2 = np(1 - p) = 5(.20)(1 - .20) = .80$$

The mean of 1.0 and the variance of .80 can be verified from formulas (5–1) and (5–2). The probability distribution from Table 5–2 and detailed calculations are shown below.

Number of Late Flights x	$P(x)$	$xP(x)$	$x - \mu$	$(x - \mu)^2$	$(x - \mu)^2P(x)$
0	.3277	.0000	−1	1	0.3277
1	.4096	.4096	0	0	0
2	.2048	.4096	1	1	0.2048
3	.0512	.1536	2	4	0.2048
4	.0064	.0256	3	9	0.0576
5	.0003	.0015	4	16	0.0048
		μ = 1.0000			σ^2 = 0.7997

Binomial table: Quick way of determining a probability

Binomial Probability Tables

Formula (5–3) can be used to build a binomial probability distribution for any value of n and p. However, for larger n, the calculations take more time. For convenience, the tables in Appendix A show the result of using the formula for various values of n and p. Table 5–3 shows part of Appendix A for $n = 6$ and various values of probability. We can use the results in this table for the following example.

TABLE 5–3 Binomial Probabilities for $n = 6$ and Selected Values of p

	$n = 6$ Probability										
x	.05	.1	.2	.3	.4	.5	.6	.7	.8	.9	.95
0	.735	.531	.262	.118	.047	.016	.004	.001	.000	.000	.000
1	.232	.354	.393	.303	.187	.094	.037	.010	.002	.000	.000
2	.031	.098	.246	.324	.311	.234	.138	.060	.015	.001	.000
3	.002	.015	.082	.185	.276	.313	.276	.185	.082	.015	.002
4	.000	.001	.015	.060	.138	.234	.311	.324	.246	.098	.031
5	.000	.000	.002	.010	.037	.094	.187	.303	.393	.354	.232
6	.000	.000	.000	.001	.004	.016	.047	.118	.262	.531	.735

example

Five percent of the worm gears produced by an automatic, high-speed milling machine are defective. What is the probability that out of six gears selected at random none will be defective? Exactly one? Exactly two? Exactly three? Exactly four? Exactly five? Exactly six out of six?

solution

The following binomial conditions are met: (a) there are only two possible outcomes (defective or nondefective), (b) there is a fixed number of trials (finite), (c) the probability of success is constant from trial to trial (.05), and (d) the trials are independent.

Refer to Table 5–3 for the probability of exactly zero defective gears. Go down the left margin to an x of 0. Now move horizontally to the column headed by a p of .05 to find the probability. It is .735.

The probability of exactly one defective worm gear in a sample of six is .232. The complete binomial probability distribution for $n = 6$ and $p = .05$ is:

Number of Defective Gears, x	Probability of Occurrence, $P(x)$	Number of Defective Gears, x	Probability of Occurrence, $P(x)$
0	.735	4	.000
1	.232	5	.000
2	.031	6	.000
3	.002		

Of course, there is a slight chance of getting exactly five defective gears out of six random selections. It is .00000178, found by inserting the appropriate values in formula (5–3) for the binomial probability distribution.

$$P(5) = {}_6C_5(.05)^5(.95)^1 = (6)(.05)^5(.95) = .00000178$$

For six out of the six, the exact probability is .000000016. Thus, the probability is very small that five or six defective gears will be selected in a sample of six.

We can compute the mean or expected value of the distribution of the number of defective gears.

$$\mu = np = (6)(.05) = 0.30$$

$$\sigma^2 = np(1 - p) = 6(.05)(.95) = 0.285$$

Statistics in Action

According to the Annals of Internal Medicine, a blood test on a normal person has a 5 percent chance of being read as abnormal by a laboratory computer. If this is true, and your physician submits a profile of 12 independent tests on you, the chance that your tests all appear normal to the computer is only 54 percent.

excel

MegaStat will also compute probabilities for the binomial distribution. The commands and output from the previous example follow.

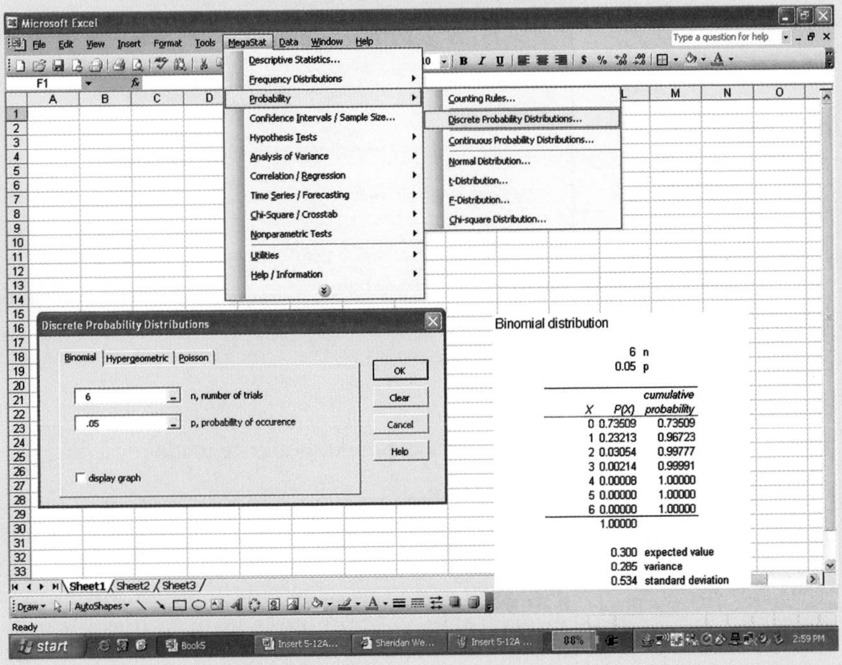

self-review 5–3

Eighty percent of pensioners have their monthly cheques sent directly to their bank by electronic funds transfer. This is also called direct deposit. Suppose we select a random sample of seven recipients.

(a) Does this situation fit the assumptions of the binomial distribution?
(b) What is the probability that all seven recipients use direct deposit?
(c) Use formula (5–3) to determine the exact probability that four of the seven sampled recipients use direct deposit.
(d) Use Appendix A to verify your answers to parts (b) and (c).

Appendix A is limited. It gives probabilities for n values from 1 to 15 and p values of .05, .10, . . . , .90, and .95. A software program can generate the probabilities for any specified number of successes, given n and p. The **Excel** output below shows the probability when $n = 40$ and $p = .09$. Note that the number of successes stops at 12 because the probability for each value between 13 and 40 is very close to 0.

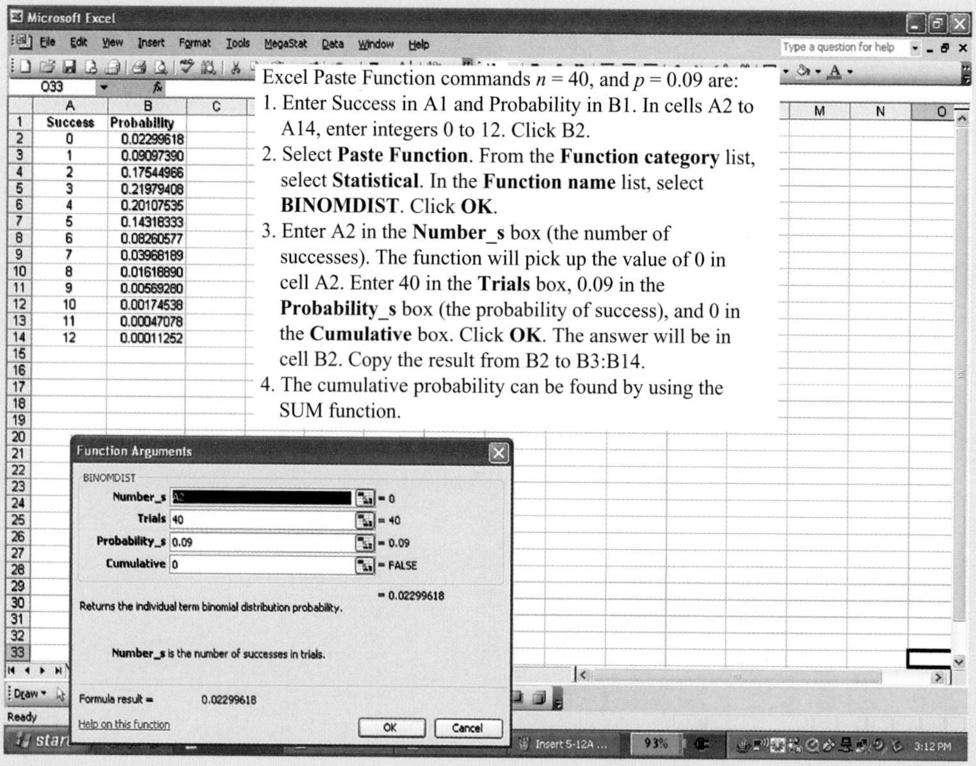

Several additional points should be made regarding the binomial probability distribution.

1. If n remains the same but p increases from .05 to .95, the shape of the distribution changes. Look at Table 5–4 and Chart 5–3. The probabilities for a p of .05 are positively skewed. As p approaches .50, the distribution becomes symmetrical. As p goes beyond .50 and moves toward .95, the probability distribution becomes negatively skewed. Table 5–4 highlights probabilities for $n = 10$ and p values of .05, .10, .20, .50, and .70. The graphs of these probability distributions are shown in Chart 5–3.

TABLE 5–4 Probability of 0, 1, 2, . . . Successes for a *p* of .05, .10, .20, .50, and .70 and an *n* of 10

x	.05	.1	.2	.3	.4	.5	.6	.7	.8	.9	.95
0	.599	.349	.107	.028	.006	.001	.000	.000	.000	.000	.000
1	.315	.387	.268	.121	.040	.010	.002	.000	.000	.000	.000
2	.075	.194	.302	.233	.121	.044	.011	.001	.000	.000	.000
3	.010	.057	.201	.267	.215	.117	.042	.009	.001	.000	.000
4	.001	.011	.088	.200	.251	.205	.111	.037	.006	.000	.000
5	.000	.001	.026	.103	.201	.246	.201	.103	.026	.001	.000
6	.000	.000	.006	.037	.111	.205	.251	.200	.088	.011	.001
7	.000	.000	.001	.009	.042	.117	.215	.267	.201	.057	.010
8	.000	.000	.000	.001	.011	.044	.121	.233	.302	.194	.075
9	.000	.000	.000	.000	.002	.010	.040	.121	.268	.387	.315
10	.000	.000	.000	.000	.000	.001	.006	.028	.107	.349	.599

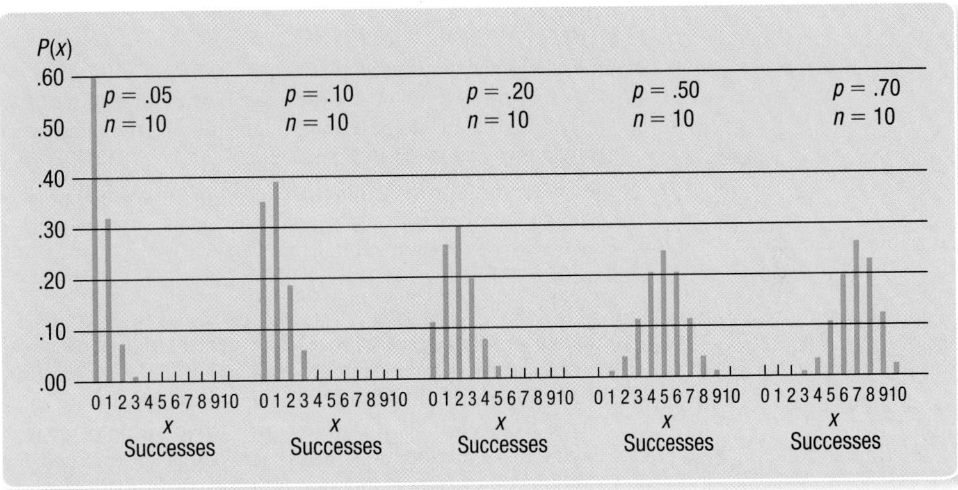

CHART 5–3 Graphing the Binomial Probability Distribution for a *p* of .05, .10, .20, .50, and .70 and an *n* of 10

2. If p, the probability of success, remains the same but n becomes larger, the shape of the binomial distribution becomes more symmetrical. Chart 5–4 shows a situation where p remains constant at .10 but n increases from 7 to 40.

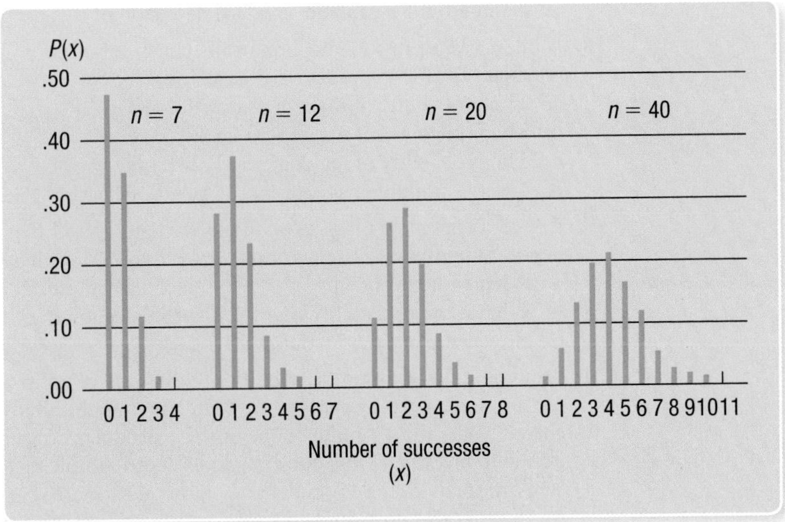

CHART 5–4 Chart Representing the Binomial Probability Distribution for a *p* of .10 and an *n* of 7, 12, 20, and 40

Exercises

11. In a binomial situation $n = 4$ and $p = .25$. Determine the probabilities of the following events using the binomial formula.
 a. $x = 2$
 b. $x = 3$
 c. $x \geq 2$
 d. $x < 3$

12. In a binomial situation $n = 5$ and $p = .40$. Determine the probabilities of the following events using the binomial formula.
 a. $x = 1$
 b. $x = 2$
 c. $x > 2$
 d. $x \leq 4$

13. Assume a binomial distribution where $n = 3$ and $p = .60$.
 a. Refer to Appendix A, and list the probabilities for values of x from 0 to 3.
 b. Determine the mean and standard deviation of the distribution from the general definitions given in formulas (5–1) and (5–2).

14. Assume a binomial distribution where $n = 5$ and $p = .30$.
 a. Refer to Appendix A, and list the probabilities for values of x from 0 to 5.
 b. Determine the mean and standard deviation of the distribution from the general definitions given in formulas (5–1) and (5–2).

15. An investment firm's survey found 30 percent of individual investors have used a discount broker. In a random sample of nine individuals, what is the probability:
 a. Exactly two of the sampled individuals have used a discount broker?
 b. Exactly four of them have used a discount broker?
 c. None of them have used a discount broker?

16. A local courier service reports that 95 percent of bulk parcels within the same city are delivered within two days. Six parcels are randomly sent to different locations.
 a. What is the probability that all six arrive within two days?
 b. What is the probability that exactly five arrive within two days?
 c. Find the mean number of parcels that will arrive within two days.
 d. Compute the variance and standard deviation of the number that will arrive within two days.

17. The industry standards suggest that 10 percent of new vehicles require warranty service within the first year. Jones Nissan, sold 12 Nissans yesterday.
 a. What is the probability that none of these vehicles requires warranty service?
 b. What is the probability exactly one of these vehicles requires warranty service?
 c. Determine the probability that exactly two of these vehicles require warranty service.
 d. What is the probability that less than three of these vehicles require warranty service?
 e. Compute the mean and standard deviation of this probability distribution.

18. A telemarketer makes six phone calls per hour and is able to make a sale on 30 percent of these contacts. During the next two hours, find:
 a. The probability of making exactly four sales.
 b. The probability of making no sales.
 c. The probability of making exactly two sales.
 d. The mean number of sales in the two-hour period.

19. A recent survey of first-year college students found that 23 percent choose accounting as their major. Suppose we select a sample of 15 first-year students.
 a. What is the probability that two selected accounting?
 b. What is the probability that five selected accounting?
 c. How many of the 15 would you expect to select accounting?

20. Can you tell the difference between Coke and Pepsi in a blind taste test? Most people say they can and have a preference for one brand or the other. However, research suggests that people can correctly identify a sample of one of these products only about 60 percent of the time. Suppose we decide to investigate this question and select a sample of 15 college students.
 a. How many of the 15 students would you expect to correctly identify Coke or Pepsi?
 b. What is the probability exactly 10 of the students surveyed will correctly identify Coke or Pepsi?
 c. What is the probability exactly 15 of the students surveyed will correctly identify Coke or Pepsi?

Cumulative Binomial Probability Distributions

We may wish to know the probability of correctly guessing the answers to 6 *or more* true/false questions out of 10. Or we may be interested in the probability of *selecting less than two* defectives at random from production during the previous hour. In these cases we need cumulative frequency distributions similar to the ones developed in Chapter 2. The following example will illustrate.

example

A recent study revealed that 60 percent of student drivers use their seat belts. A sample of 10 student drivers is selected.

1. What is the probability that exactly seven are wearing seat belts?
2. What is the probability that seven or fewer of the drivers are wearing seat belts?

solution

This situation meets the binomial requirements, namely:

- A particular driver either is wearing a seat belt or is not. There are only two possible outcomes.
- There is a fixed number of trials—10 in this case, because 10 drivers are checked.
- The probability of "success" (wearing a seat belt) is the same from driver to driver: 60 percent.
- The trials are independent. If the fourth driver selected in the sample is wearing a seat belt, for example, it has no effect on whether the fifth driver selected is wearing a seat belt.

1. To find the likelihood of *exactly* seven drivers, we use Appendix A. Locate the page for $n = 10$. Next find the column for $p = .60$ and the row for $x = 7$. The value is .215. Thus, the probability of finding 7 out of 10 drivers in the sample wearing their seat belts is .215. This is often written as follows:

$$P(x = 7 \mid n = 10 \text{ and } p = .60) = .215$$

where x refers to the number of successes, n the number of trials, and p the probability of a success. The bar "|" means "given that."

We could also use formula (5–3) to find the likelihood of exactly seven drivers. Again, $x = 7$, $n = 10$, and p = .60.

$$\begin{aligned} P(x) = {}_nC_x p^x(1-p)^{n-x} &= {}_{10}C_7(.60)^7(1-.60)^{10-7} \\ &= 120(.0279936)(.064) \\ &= .214990848 \\ &= .215 \end{aligned}$$

2. To find the probability that seven or fewer of the drivers will be wearing seat belts, we apply the special rule of addition, formula (4–5), from Chapter 4. Because the events are mutually exclusive, we determine the probability that of the 10 drivers stopped, none was wearing a seat belt, 1 was wearing a seat belt, 2 were wearing a seat belt, and so on up to 7 drivers. The probabilities of the eight possible outcomes are then totalled. From Appendix A, $n = 10$, and $p = .60$.

$$\begin{aligned} P(x \le 7 \mid n = 10 \text{ and } p = .60) &= P(x=0) + P(x=1) + P(x=2) + P(x=3) \\ &\quad + P(x=4) + P(x=5) + P(x=6) + P(x=7) \\ &= .000 + .002 + .011 + .042 + .111 + .201 \\ &\quad + .251 + .215 \\ &= .833 \end{aligned}$$

So the probability of stopping 10 cars at random and finding 7 or fewer of the drivers wearing their seat belts is .833.

This value may also be determined, with less computation, using the complement rule. First, find $P(x > 7)$ given that $n = 10$ and $p = .60$. This probability is .167, found by $P(x = 8) + P(x = 9) + P(x = 10) = .121 + .040 + .006$. The probability that $x \le 7$ is equal to $1 - P(x > 7)$, so $P(x \le 7) = 1 - .167 = .833$, the same as computed above.

excel

MegaStat produces cumulative probabilities automatically as shown in the following output.

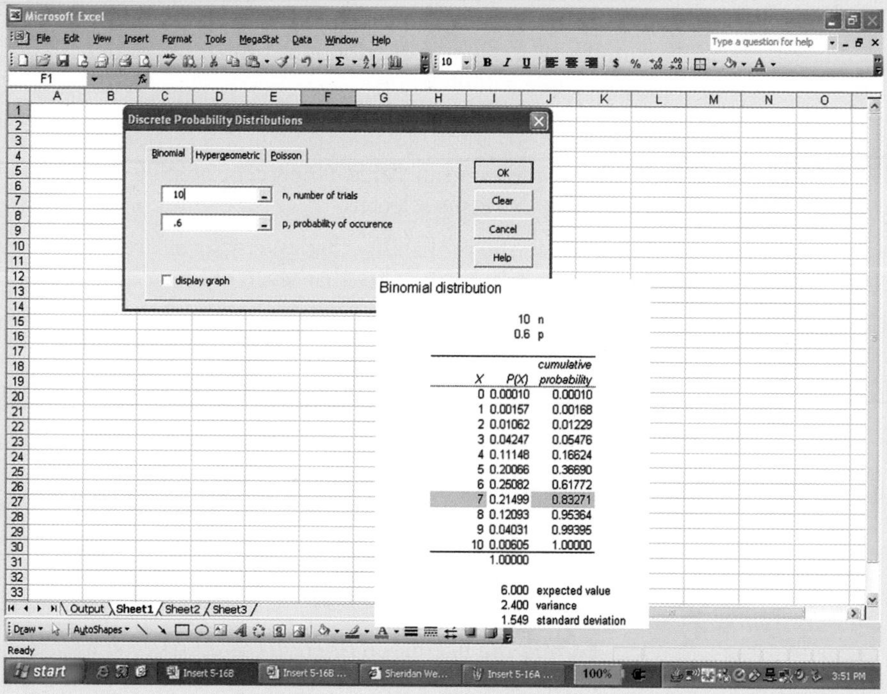

self-review 5–4

For a case where $n = 4$ and $p = .60$, determine the probability that:

(a) $x = 2$.
(b) $x \leq 2$.
(c) $x > 2$.

Exercises

21. In a binomial distribution $n = 8$ and $p = .30$. Find the probabilities of the following events.
  a. $x = 2$.
  b. $x \leq 2$ (the probability that x is equal to or less than 2).
  c. $x \geq 3$ (the probability that x is equal to or greater than 3).

22. In a binomial distribution $n = 12$ and $p = .60$. Find the following probabilities.
  a. $x = 5$.
  b. $x \leq 5$.
  c. $x \geq 6$.

23. In a recent study 90 percent of homes in Canada were found to have large-screen TVs. In a sample of nine homes, what is the probability that:
  a. All nine have large-screen TVs?
  b. Less than five have large-screen TVs?
  c. More than five have large-screen TVs?
  d. At least seven homes have large-screen TVs?

24. A manufacturer of window frames knows from long experience that 5 percent of the production will have some type of minor defect that will require an adjustment. What is the probability that in a sample of 20 window frames:
  a. None will need adjustment?
  b. At least one will need adjustment?
  c. More than two will need adjustment?

25. The speed with which utility companies can resolve problems is very important. GTC, the Georgetown Telephone Company, reports it can resolve customer problems the same day they are reported in 70 percent of the cases. Suppose the 15 cases reported today are representative of all complaints.
   a. How many of the problems would you expect to be resolved today? What is the standard deviation?
   b. What is the probability 10 of the problems can be resolved today?
   c. What is the probability 10 or 11 of the problems can be resolved today?
   d. What is the probability more than 10 of the problems can be resolved today?

26. Steele Electronics Inc. sells expensive brands of stereo equipment in several shopping malls. The marketing research department of Steele reports that 30 percent of the customers entering the store that indicate they are browsing will, in the end, make a purchase. Let the last 20 customers who enter the store be a sample.
   a. How many of these customers would you expect to make a purchase?
   b. What is the probability that exactly five of these customers make a purchase?
   c. What is the probability 10 or more make a purchase?
   d. Does it seem likely at least one will make a purchase?

5 Describe the characteristics of and compute probabilities using the *hypergeometric probability distribution*.

Hypergeometric Probability Distribution

For the binomial distribution to be applied, the probability of a success must stay the same for each trial. For example, the probability of guessing the correct answer to a true/false question is .50. This probability remains the same for each question on an examination. Likewise, suppose that 40 percent of the registered voters in a district are Liberals. If 27 registered voters are to be selected at random, the probability of choosing a Liberal on the first selection is .40. The chance of choosing a Liberal on the next selection is also .40, assuming that the sampling is done *with replacement*, meaning that the person selected is put back in the population before the next person is selected.

Most sampling, however, is done *without replacement*. Thus, if the population is small, the probability for each observation will change. For example, if the population consists of 20 items, the probability of selecting a particular item from that population is 1/20. If the sampling is done without replacement, after the first selection there are only 19 items remaining; the probability of selecting a particular item on the second selection is only 1/19. For the third selection, the probability is 1/18, and so on. This assumes that the population is **finite**—that is, the number in the population is known and relatively small in number. Examples of a finite population are: 37 public schools in the Superior School District, 18 Pontiac Sunbirds currently in stock at North Pontiac, and 30 stocks comprising the Dow Jones Industrial Average.

Recall that one of the criteria for the binomial distribution is that the probability of success remains the same from trial to trial. Since the probability of success does not remain the same from trial to trial when sampling is from a relatively small population without replacement, the binomial distribution should not be used. Instead, the **hypergeometric distribution** should be applied. Therefore, (1) if a sample is selected from a finite population without replacement and (2) if the size of the sample n is more than 5 percent of the population N, then the hypergeometric distribution is used to determine the probability of a specified number of successes or failures. It is especially appropriate when the size of the population is small.

The formula for the hypergeometric distribution is:

HYPERGEOMETRIC DISTRIBUTION

$$P(x) = \frac{({}_{S}C_{x})({}_{N-S}C_{n-x})}{{}_{N}C_{n}} \qquad \textbf{[5–6]}$$

where:

N is the size of the population.
S is the number of successes in the population.
x is the number of successes in the sample. It may be 0, 1, 2, 3, ...
n is the size of the sample or the number of trials.
C is the symbol for a combination.

The following example illustrates the details of determining a probability using the hypergeometric distribution.

example

PlayTime Toys Inc. employs 50 people in the Assembly Department. Forty of the employees belong to a union and 10 do not. Five employees are selected at random to form a committee to meet with management regarding shift starting times. What is the probability that four of the five selected for the committee belong to a union?

The population in this case is the 50 Assembly Department employees. An employee can be selected for the committee only once. Hence, the sampling is without replacement. Thus, the probability of selecting a union employee, for example, changes from one trial to the next. The hypergeometric distribution is appropriate for determining the probability. In this problem,

N is 50, the number of employees.
S is 40, the number of union employees.
x is 4, the number of union employees selected.
n is 5, the number of employees selected.

solution

We wish to find the probability four of the five committee members belong to a union. Inserting these values into formula (5–6):

$$P(4) = \frac{({}_{40}C_4)({}_{50-40}C_{5-4})}{{}_{50}C_5} = \frac{\left(\frac{40!}{4!36!}\right)\left(\frac{10!}{1!9!}\right)}{\frac{50!}{5!45!}} = \frac{(91\ 390)(10)}{2\ 118\ 760} = .431$$

Thus, the probability of selecting 5 assembly workers at random from the 50 workers and finding 4 of the 5 are union members is .431.

Table 5–5 shows the hypergeometric probabilities of finding zero, one, two, three, four, and five union members on the committee.

In order for you to compare the two probability distributions, Table 5–6 shows the hypergeometric and binomial probabilities for the PlayTime Toys Inc. example. Because 40 of the 50 Assembly Department employees belong to the union, we let $p = .80$ for the binomial distribution. The binomial probabilities for Table 5–6 come from the binomial table in Appendix A, with $n = 5$ and $p = .80$.

When the binomial requirement of a constant probability of success cannot be met, the hypergeometric distribution should be used. However, as Table 5–6 shows, under many

TABLE 5–5 Hypergeometric Probabilities ($n = 5$, $N = 50$, and $S = 40$) for the Number of Union Members on the Committee

Union Members	Probability
0	.000
1	.004
2	.044
3	.210
4	.431
5	.311
	1.000

TABLE 5–6 Hypergeometric and Binomial Probabilities for PlayTime Toys Inc. Assembly Department

Number of Union Members on Committee	Hypergeometric Probability, $P(x)$	Binomial Probability ($n = 5$ and $p = 0.80$)
0	.000	.000
1	.004	.006
2	.044	.051
3	.210	.205
4	.431	.410
5	.311	.328
	1.000	1.000

conditions the results of the binomial distribution approximate those of the hypergeometric. This leads to a rule of thumb: if the selected items are not returned to the population and the sample size is less than 5 percent of the population, the binomial distribution can be used to approximate the hypergeometric distribution. That is, when $n < .05N$, the binomial should suffice.

A hypergeometric distribution can be created using **Excel**. See the following output.

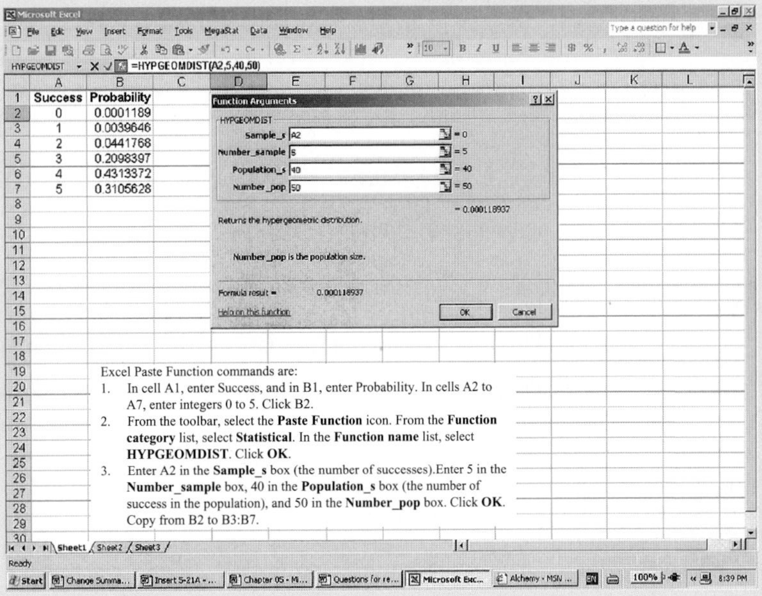

self-review 5–5

Horwege Discount Brokers plans to hire five new financial analysts this year. There is a pool of 12 approved applicants, and George Horwege, the owner, decides to randomly select those who will be hired. There are eight men and four women among the approved applicants. What is the probability that three of the five hired are men?

Exercises

27. A population consists of 10 items, 6 of which are defective. In a sample of three items, what is the probability that exactly two are defective?

28. A population consists of 15 items, 10 of which are acceptable. In a sample of four items, what is the probability that exactly three are acceptable?

29. Kolzak Appliance Outlet just received a shipment of 10 TV sets. Shortly after they were received, the manufacturer called to report that he had inadvertently shipped three defective sets. Ms. Kolzak, the owner of the outlet, decided to test 2 of the 10 sets she received. What is the probability that neither of the two sets tested is defective?

30. The computer systems department has eight faculty, six of whom are tenured. Dr. Vonder, the chairman, wants to establish a committee of three department faculty members to review the curriculum. If she selects the committee at random:

a. What is the probability all members of the committee are tenured?

b. What is the probability that at least one member is not tenured? (Hint: For this question, use the complement rule.)

31. Keith's Florists has 15 delivery trucks used mainly to deliver flowers and flower arrangements. Of these 15 trucks, 6 have brake problems. A sample of five trucks is randomly selected. What is the probability that two of those tested have defective brakes?

32. Professor Jon Hammer has a pool of 15 multiple-choice questions regarding probability distributions. Four of these questions involve the hypergeometric distribution. What is the probability at least one of these hypergeometric questions will appear on the five-question quiz on Monday?

6 Describe the characteristics of and compute probabilities using the *Poisson probability distribution*.

Statistics in Action

Near the end of World War II, the Germans developed rocket bombs, which were fired at the city of London. The Allied military command did not know whether these bombs were fired at random or whether they had some type of aiming device.
To investigate, the city of London was divided into 576 square regions. The distribution of the number of hits in each square was:

Hits	Regions
0	229
1	211
2	93
3	35
4	7
5	1

To interpret, the above chart indicates that 229 regions were not hit with one of the bombs. Seven regions were hit four times. Using the Poisson distribution, with a mean of 0.93 hits per region, the expected number of hits is as follows:

Hits	Regions
0	227.3
1	211.3
2	98.3
3	30.5
4	7.1
5 or more	1.6

Because the actual number of hits was close to the expected number of hits, the military command concluded that the bombs were falling at random. The Germans had not developed a bomb with an aiming device.

Poisson Probability Distribution

The **Poisson probability distribution** describes the number of times some event occurs during a specified interval. The interval may be time, distance, area, or volume.

The distribution is based on two assumptions. The first assumption is that the probability is proportional to the length of the interval. The second assumption is that the intervals are independent. To put it another way, the longer the interval the larger the probability, and the number of occurrences in one interval does not affect the other intervals. This distribution is also a limiting form of the binomial distribution when the probability of a success is very small and n is large. It is often referred to as the "law of improbable events," meaning that the probability, p, of a particular event's happening is quite small. The Poisson distribution is a discrete probability distribution because it is formed by counting.

In summary, a Poisson probability distribution has these characteristics:

POISSON PROBABILITY DISTRIBUTION

1. The random variable is the number of times some event occurs during a defined period.
2. The probability of the event is proportional to the size of the interval.
3. The intervals do not overlap and are independent.

This distribution has many applications. It is used as a model to describe the distribution of errors in data entry, the number of scratches and other imperfections in newly painted car panels, the number of defective parts in outgoing shipments, the number of customers waiting to be served at a restaurant or waiting to get into an attraction at the CNE, and the number of accidents on the Trans-Canada Highway during a three-month period.

The Poisson distribution can be described mathematically using the formula:

POISSON DISTRIBUTION $$P(x) = \frac{\mu^x e^{-\mu}}{x!} \quad [5\text{–}7]$$

where:

μ (mu) is the mean number of occurrences (successes) in a particular interval.
e is the constant 2.71828 (base of the Napierian logarithmic system).
x is the number of occurrences (successes).
$P(x)$ is the probability for a specified value of x.

The mean number of successes, μ, can be determined by np, where n is the total number of trials and p the probability of success.

MEAN OF A POISSON DISTRIBUTION $$\mu = np \quad [5\text{–}8]$$

The variance of the Poisson distribution is equal to its mean. If, for example, the probability that a cheque cashed by a bank will bounce is .0003, and 10 000 cheques are cashed, the mean and the variance for the number of bad cheques is 3.0, found by the formula $\mu = np = 10\,000(.0003) = 3.0$.

Recall that for a binomial distribution there is a fixed number of trials. For example, for a four-question, multiple-choice test there can only be zero, one, two, three, or four successes (correct answers). The random variable, x, for a Poisson distribution, however, can assume an *infinite number of values*—that is, 0, 1, 2, 3, 4, 5, ... However, *the probabilities become very small after the first few occurrences* (successes).

To illustrate the Poisson probability computation, assume baggage is rarely lost by Northwest Airlines. Most flights do not experience any mishandled bags; some have one bag lost; a few have two bags lost; rarely a flight will have three bags lost; and so on. Suppose a random sample of 1000 flights shows a total of 300 bags were lost. Thus, the arithmetic mean number of lost bags per flight is 0.3, found by 300/1000. If the number of lost bags per flight follows a Poisson distribution with $\mu = 0.3$, we can compute the various probabilities by the formula (5–7):

$$P(x) = \frac{\mu^x e^{-\mu}}{x!}$$

For example, the probability of not losing any bags is:

$$P(0) = \frac{(0.3)^0(e^{-0.3})}{0!} = .7408$$

In other words, 74 percent of the flights will have no lost baggage. The probability of exactly one lost bag is:

$$P(1) = \frac{(0.3)^1(e^{-0.3})}{1!} = .2222$$

Thus, we would expect to find exactly one lost bag on 22 percent of the flights.

Poisson probabilities can also be found in the table in Appendix C.

example

Recall from the previous illustration that the number of lost bags follows a Poisson distribution with a mean of 0.3. Use Appendix C to find the probability that no bags will be lost on a particular flight. What is the probability exactly one bag will be lost on a particular flight? When should the supervisor become suspicious that a flight is having too many lost bags?

solution

Part of Appendix C is repeated as Table 5–7. To find the probability of no lost bags, locate the column headed "0.3" and read down that column to the row labeled "0." The probability is .7408. That is the probability of no lost bags. The probability of one lost bag is .2222, which is in the next row of the table, in the same column. The probability of two lost bags is .0333, in the row below; for three lost bags it is .0033; and for four lost bags it is .0003. Thus, a supervisor should not be surprised to find one lost bag but should expect to see more than one lost bag infrequently.

TABLE 5–7 Poisson Table for Various Values of μ (from Appendix C)

	μ								
x	0.1	0.2	0.3	0.4	0.5	0.6	0.7	0.8	0.9
0	0.9048	0.8187	0.7408	0.6703	0.6065	0.5488	0.4966	0.4493	0.4066
1	0.0905	0.1637	0.2222	0.2681	0.3033	0.3293	0.3476	0.3595	0.3659
2	0.0045	0.0164	0.0333	0.0536	0.0758	0.0988	0.1217	0.1438	0.1647
3	0.0002	0.0011	0.0033	0.0072	0.0126	0.0198	0.0284	0.0383	0.0494
4	0.0000	0.0001	0.0003	0.0007	0.0016	0.0030	0.0050	0.0077	0.0111
5	0.0000	0.0000	0.0000	0.0001	0.0002	0.0004	0.0007	0.0012	0.0020
6	0.0000	0.0000	0.0000	0.0000	0.0000	0.0000	0.0001	0.0002	0.0003
7	0.0000	0.0000	0.0000	0.0000	0.0000	0.0000	0.0000	0.0000	0.0000

excel

Use the **Excel** Paste Function commands to determine the Poisson distribution as follows.

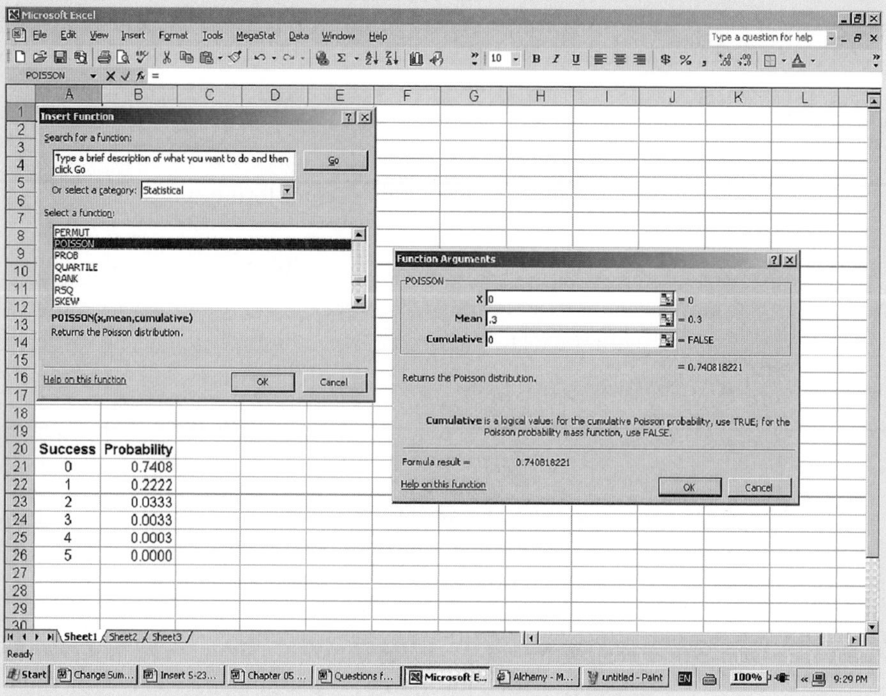

minitab

The Poisson probability distribution is always positively skewed and has no specific upper limit. The Poisson distribution for the lost bags illustration, where $\mu = 0.3$ is highly skewed. As μ becomes larger, the Poisson distribution becomes more symmetrical. For example, Chart 5–5 shows the distributions of the number of transmission services, muffler replacements, and oil changes per day at Avellino's Auto Shop. They follow Poisson distributions with means of 0.7, 2.0, and 6.0, respectively. Observe that the distributions are more symmetrical as μ increases.

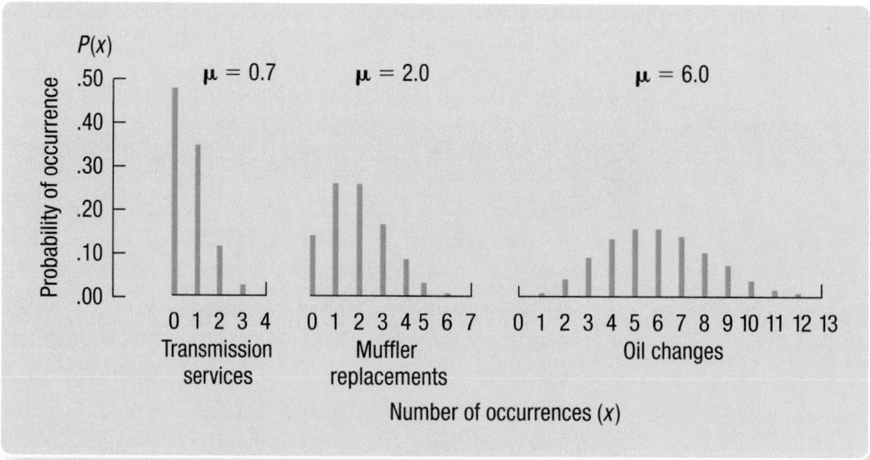

CHART 5–5 Poisson Probability Distributions for Means of 0.7, 2.0, and 6.0

Only μ needed to construct Poisson

In summary, the Poisson distribution is actually a family of discrete distributions. All that is needed to construct a Poisson probability distribution is the mean number of defects, errors, and so on—designated as μ.

self-review 5–6

From actuary tables an insurance company determined the likelihood that a man aged 25 will die within the next year is .0002. If the company sells 4000 policies to 25-year-old men this year, what is the probability it will pay on exactly one policy?

Exercises

33. In a Poisson distribution $\mu = 0.4$.
a. What is the probability that $x = 0$?
b. What is the probability that $x > 0$?

34. In a Poisson distribution $\mu = 4$.
a. What is the probability that $x = 2$?
b. What is the probability that $x \leq 2$?
c. What is the probability that $x > 2$?

35. Ms. Bergen is a loan officer at a trust company. Based on her years of experience, she estimates that the probability is .025 that an applicant will not be able to repay his or her instalment loan. Last month she made 40 loans.
a. What is the probability that three loans will be defaulted?
b. What is the probability that at least three loans will be defaulted?

36. Automobiles frequently arrive at the Bronte exit of the QEW at the rate of two per minute. The distribution of arrivals approximates a Poisson distribution.
a. What is the probability that no automobiles arrive in a particular minute?
b. What is the probability that at least one automobile arrives during a particular minute?

37. It is estimated that 0.5 percent of the callers to the billing department of a local telephone company will receive a busy signal. What is the probability that of today's 1200 callers at least 5 received a busy signal?

38. Textbook authors and publishers work very hard to minimize the number of errors in a text. However, some errors are unavoidable. Ms. Kimberley Redhead, statistics editor, reports that the mean number of errors per chapter is 0.8. What is the probability that there are less than two errors in a particular chapter?

Chapter Summary

I. A random variable is a variable whose value is determined by the outcome of a random experiment.

II. A probability distribution is a listing of all possible outcomes of an experiment and the probability associated with each outcome.

A. A discrete probability distribution can assume only certain values. The main features are:
1. The sum of the probabilities is 1.00.
2. The probability of a particular outcome is between 0.00 and 1.00.
3. The outcomes are mutually exclusive.

B. A continuous distribution can assume an infinite number of values within a specific range.

III. The mean and variance of a discrete probability distribution are computed as follows.

A. The mean is equal to:

$$\mu = \Sigma[xP(x)] \qquad [5\text{–}1]$$

B. The variance is equal to:

$$\sigma^2 = \Sigma[(x - \mu)^2 P(x)] \qquad [5\text{–}2]$$

IV. The binomial distribution has the following characteristics.

A. Each outcome is classified into one of two mutually exclusive categories.

B. The probability of a success remains the same from trial to trial.

C. Each trial is independent.

D. The distribution results from a count of the number of successes in a fixed number of trials.

E. A binomial probability is determined as follows:

$$P(x) = {}_nC_x p^x (1-p)^{n-x} \qquad [5\text{–}3]$$

F. The mean is computed as:

$$\mu = np \qquad [5\text{–}4]$$

G. The variance is

$$\sigma^2 = np(1-p) \qquad [5\text{–}5]$$

V. The hypergeometric distribution has the following characteristics.

A. There are only two possible outcomes.

B. The probability of a success is not the same on each trial.

C. The distribution results from a count of the number of successes in a fixed number of trials.

D. A hypergeometric probability is computed from the following equation.

$$P(x) = \frac{({}_SC_x)({}_{N-S}C_{n-x})}{({}_NC_n)} \qquad [5\text{–}6]$$

VI. The Poisson distribution has the following characteristics.

A. It describes the number of times some event occurs during a specified interval.

B. The probability of a "success" is proportional to the length of the interval.

C. Nonoverlapping intervals are independent.

D. It is a limiting form of the binomial distribution when n is large and p is small.

E. A Poisson probability is determined from the following equation:

$$P(x) = \frac{\mu^x e^{-\mu}}{x!} \qquad [5\text{–}7]$$

F. The mean and the variance of a Poisson distribution are the same and are equal to np.

Chapter Exercises

39. What is the difference between a random variable and a probability distribution?

40. Indicate whether the random variable is discrete or continuous.
- **a.** The length of time to get a haircut.
- **b.** The number of cars a jogger passes each morning while running.
- **c.** The number of hits for a team in a high school girls' softball game.
- **d.** The number of patients treated at the South Strand Medical Center between 6 p.m. and 10 p.m. each night.
- **e.** The number of kilometres your car travelled on the last fill up.
- **f.** The number of customers at the Oak Street Wendy's who used the drive-through facility.
- **g.** The distance between Toronto, Ontario, and all Ontario cities of at least 50 000 people.

41. What are the requirements for the binomial distribution?

42. Under what conditions will the binomial and the Poisson distributions give roughly the same results?

43. Samson Apartments has a large number of units available to rent each month. A concern of management is the number of vacant apartments each month. A recent study revealed the percent of the time that a given number of apartments are vacant. Compute the mean and standard deviation of the number of vacant apartments.

Number of Vacant Units	Probability
0	.10
1	.20
2	.30
3	.40

44. An investment will be worth $1000, $2000, or $5000 at the end of the year. The probabilities of these values are .25, .60, and .15, respectively. Determine the mean and variance of the worth of the investment.

45. The vice president of human resources at Lowes Inc. is studying the number of on-the-job accidents over a period of one month. He developed the following probability distribution. Compute the mean, variance, and standard deviation of the number of accidents in a month.

Number of Accidents	Probability
0	.40
1	.20
2	.20
3	.10
4	.10

46. In a game of heads or tails you win $0.75 if you throw two heads, win $0.50 if you throw a head and a tail, and lose $1.00 if you throw two tails. What are the expected winnings of this game?

47. Croissant Bakery Inc. offers specially decorated cakes for birthdays, weddings, and other occasions. It also has regular cakes available in its display case. The following table gives the total number of cakes sold per day and the corresponding probability. Compute the mean, variance, and standard deviation of the number of cakes sold per day.

Number of Cakes Sold in a Day	Probability
12	.25
13	.40
14	.25
15	.10

48. A recent survey reported that the average adult eats ice cream 28 times per year. The same survey indicated that 33 percent of the respondents said vanilla was their favourite flavour and 19 percent said chocolate was their favourite. There are 10 customers in line waiting for ice cream at the Ben and Jerry's at the Blue Mountain resort.

a. How many would you expect to purchase vanilla ice cream?
b. What is the probability exactly three will purchase vanilla ice cream?
c. What is the probability that exactly three will purchase chocolate ice cream?
d. What is the probability at least one will purchase chocolate ice cream?

49. Which of these variables are discrete and which are continuous random variables?

a. The number of new sales associates hired for the Christmas season.
b. The time between buses from the airport to downtown.
c. The number of students registered in second year accounting.
d. The number of cups of coffee consumed by the average student in a year.
e. The median age of college-age students.

50. Three tables listed below show random variables and their probabilities. However, only one of these is actually a probability distribution.

x	$P(x)$
25	.1
50	.7
75	.2
100	.4

x	$P(x)$
25	−.6
50	.2
75	.1
100	.1

x	$P(x)$
25	.5
50	.3
75	.1
100	.1

a. Which of the above tables is a probability distribution?
b. Using the correct probability distribution, find the probability that x is:
1. Exactly 75.
2. No more than 50.
3. More than 25.
c. Compute the mean, variance, and standard deviation of this distribution.

51. An auditor for an insurance company in Alberta reports 40 percent of the policyholders 55 years or older submit a claim during the year. Fifteen policyholders are randomly selected for company records.
a. How many of the policyholders would you expect to have filed a claim within the last year?
b. What is the probability that 10 of the selected policyholders submitted a claim last year?
c. What is the probability that 10 or more of the selected policyholders submitted a claim last year?
d. What is the probability that less than six of the selected policyholders submitted a claim last year?

52. Tire and Auto Supply is considering a 2-for-1 stock split. Before the transaction is finalized, at least two-thirds of the 1200 company stockholders must approve the proposal. To evaluate the likelihood the proposal will be approved, the director of finance randomly selected a sample of 18 stockholders. He contacted each and found 14 approved of the proposed split. What is the likelihood of this event, assuming two-thirds of the stockholders approve?

53. A study reported that 7.5 percent of the workforce has a drug problem. A drug enforcement official wished to investigate this statement. In his sample of 20 employed workers:
a. How many would you expect to have a drug problem? What is the standard deviation?
b. What is the likelihood that *none* of the workers sampled has a drug problem?
c. What is the likelihood *at least one* has a drug problem?

54. The Bank of Hudson Bay reports that 7 percent of its credit card holders will default at some time in their life. The Moose Factory branch just mailed out 12 new cards today.
a. How many of these new cardholders would you expect to default? What is the standard deviation?
b. What is the likelihood that *none* of the cardholders will default?
c. What is the likelihood *at least one* will default?

55. Recent statistics suggest that 15 percent of those who visit a retail site on the World Wide Web make a purchase. A retailer wished to verify this claim. To do so, she selected a sample of 16 "hits" to her site and found that 4 had actually made a purchase.
a. What is the likelihood of exactly four purchases?
b. How many purchases should she expect?
c. What is the likelihood that four or more "hits" result in a purchase?

56. Dr. Richmond, a psychologist, is studying the daytime television viewing habits of college students. She believes 45 percent of college students watch soap operas during the afternoon. To further investigate, she randomly selects a sample of 10.
a. Develop a probability distribution for the number of students in the sample who watch soap operas.
b. Find the mean and the standard deviation of this distribution.
c. What is the probability of finding exactly four who watch soap operas?
d. What is the probability less than half of the students selected watch soap operas?

57. A recent study conducted by Penn, Shone, and Borland, on behalf of LastMinute.com, revealed that 52 percent of business travellers plan their trips less than 2 weeks before departure. The study is to be replicated in the London area with a sample of 12 frequent business travellers.
a. Develop a probability distribution for the number of travellers who plan their trips within 2 weeks of departure.
b. Find the mean and the standard deviation of this distribution.
c. What is the probability exactly 5 of the 12 selected business travellers plan their trips within 2 weeks of departure?
d. What is the probability 5 or fewer of the 12 selected business travellers plan their trips within 2 weeks of departure?

58. A manufacturer of computer chips claims that the probability of a defective chip is .002. The manufacturer sells chips in batches of 1000 to major computer companies.
a. How many defective chips would you expect in a batch?
b. What is the probability that none of the chips are defective in a batch?
c. What is the probability at least one chip is defective in a batch?

59. The sales of Lexus automobiles in the Calgary area follow a Poisson distribution with a mean of 3 per day.
a. What is the probability that no Lexus is sold on a particular day?
b. What is the probability that for five consecutive days at least one Lexus is sold?

60. Suppose 1.5 percent of the antennas on new Nokia cell phones are defective. For a random sample of 200 antennas, find the probability that:
a. None of the antennas is defective.
b. Three or more of the antennas are defective.

61. A study of the checkout lines at the Safeway Supermarket revealed that between 4 p.m. and 7 p.m. on weekdays there is an average of four customers waiting in line. What is the probability that you visit Safeway today during this period and find:
a. No customers are waiting?
b. Four customers are waiting?
c. Four or fewer are waiting?
d. Four or more are waiting?

62. An internal study at Lahey Electronics, a large software development company, revealed the mean time for an internal email message to arrive at its destination was two seconds. Further, the distribution of the arrival times followed a Poisson distribution.
a. What is the probability a message takes exactly one second to arrive at its destination?
b. What is the probability it takes more than four seconds to arrive at its destination?
c. What is the probability it takes virtually no time, i.e., "zero" seconds?

63. Recent crime reports indicate that 18.4 motor vehicle thefts occur every hour in Canada. Assume that the distribution of thefts per hour can be approximated by a Poisson probability distribution.
a. Calculate the probability exactly *four* thefts occur in an hour.
b. What is the probability there are *no* thefts in an hour?
c. What is the probability there are *at least* 20 thefts in an hour?

64. New Process Inc., a large mail-order supplier of women's fashions, advertises same-day service on every order. Recently the movement of orders has not gone as planned, and there were a large number of complaints. Bud Owens, director of customer service, has completely redone the method of order handling. The goal is to have fewer than five unfilled orders on hand at the end of 95 percent of the working days. Frequent checks of the unfilled orders at the end of the day revealed that the distribution of the unfilled orders follows a Poisson distribution with a mean of two orders.
a. Has New Process Inc. lived up to its internal goal? Cite evidence.
b. Draw a histogram representing the Poisson probability distribution of unfilled orders.

65. NASA (National Aeronautics and Space Administration) has experienced two disasters. *Challenger* exploded over the Atlantic Ocean in 1986 and *Columbia* exploded over east Texas in 2003. There have been a total of 151 space missions. Assume failures continue to occur at the same rate and consider the next 23 missions. What is the probability of exactly two failures? What is the probability of no failures?

66. According to the "January theory," if the stock market is up for the month of January, it will be up for the year. If it is down in January, it will be down for the year. According to an article in *The Wall Street Journal*, this theory held for 29 out of the last 34 years. Suppose there is no truth to this theory. What is the probability this could occur by chance? (You will probably need a software package such as **Excel** or MINITAB.)

67. During the second round of the 1989 U.S. Open golf tournament, four golfers scored a hole-in-one on the sixth hole. The odds of a professional golfer making a hole-in-one are estimated to be 3708 to 1, so the probability is 1/3709. There were 155 golfers participating in the second round that day. Estimate the probability that four golfers would score a hole-in-one on the sixth hole.

68.

Number of big screen TVs sold X	Number of days
0	4
1	15
2	5
3	3
4	2
5	1
Total	30

a. Construct a probability distribution for X = number of big screen TVs sold.
b. What is the expected number of big screen TVs sold per month? Interpret this value.
c. The price of a big screen TV is on average $3575 per TV. If the salesperson's commission on a big screen TV is 15 percent of sales, what is his/her expected monthly commission on the big screen TVs?

Data Set Exercises

69. Refer to the real estate data from the south-east area of Edmonton on the CD-ROM, which reports information on listed homes, March 2008. Create a probability distribution for the number of bedrooms. Compute the mean and the standard deviation of this distribution.

exercises.com

Additional exercises that require you to access information at related Internet sites are available on the CD-ROM included with this text.

Answers to Self-Reviews

5–1 (a)

Number of Spots	Probability
1	$\frac{1}{6}$
2	$\frac{1}{6}$
3	$\frac{1}{6}$
4	$\frac{1}{6}$
5	$\frac{1}{6}$
6	$\frac{1}{6}$
Total	$\frac{6}{6} = 1.00$

(b)

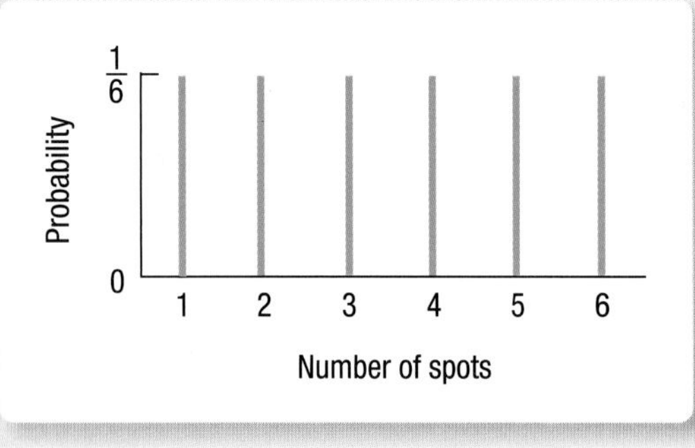

(c) $\frac{6}{6}$, or 1.

5–2 (a) It is discrete, because the values .80, .90, and 1.20 are clearly separated from each other, the sum of the probabilities is 1.00, and the outcomes are mutually exclusive.

(b)

x	$P(x)$	$xP(x)$
\$0.80	.30	0.24
0.90	.50	0.45
1.20	.20	0.24
		0.93

The mean is \$0.93.

(c)

x	$P(x)$	$(x-\mu)$	$(x-\mu)^2 P(x)$
\$0.80	.30	−0.13	.00507
0.90	.50	−0.03	.00045
1.20	.20	0.27	.01458
			.02010

The variance is 0.02010, and the standard deviation is \$0.14.

5–3 (a) It is reasonable because: each retiree either uses direct deposit or does not, the retirees are independent, the probability of using direct deposit is 80 percent for all, and we count the number using the service out of 7.

(b) $P(7) = (.80)^7 = .2097$

(c) $P(4) = {}_7C_4(.80)^4(.20)^3 = (35)(.4096)(.008) = .1147$

(d) Answers are in agreement.

5–4 $n = 4, p = .60$

(a) $P(x = 2) = .3456$

(b) $P(x \leq 2) = .5248$

(c) $P(x > 2) = 1 - .526 = .4752$

5–5
$$P(3) = \frac{{}_8C_3\,{}_4C_2}{{}_{12}C_5} = \frac{\left(\frac{8!}{3!5!}\right)\left(\frac{4!}{2!2!}\right)}{\frac{12!}{5!7!}}$$
$$= \frac{(56)(6)}{792} = .424$$

5–6 $\mu = 4000(.0002) = 0.8$
$$P(1) = \frac{0.8^1 e^{-0.8}}{1!} = .3595$$

chapter 6

The Normal Probability Distribution

LEARNING GOALS

When you have completed this chapter, you will be able to:

1. List the characteristics of the *normal probability distribution*.
2. Define and calculate *z*-values.
3. Determine the probability that an observation is between two points on a *normal probability distribution*.
4. Determine the probability an observation is above or below a point on a *normal probability distribution*.
5. Use the *normal probability distribution* to approximate the binomial probability distribution.

Introduction

Chapter 5 began our study of probability distributions. We considered three discrete probability distributions: the binomial, hypergeometric, and the Poisson. These distributions are based on discrete random variables, which can assume only clearly separated values. For example, the number of correct answers on a 10-question examination can only be 0, 1, 2, 3, . . . , 10. There cannot be a negative number of correct answers, such as −7, nor can there be 7¼ or 15 correct answers.

In this example, only certain outcomes are possible and these outcomes are represented by clearly separated values. In addition, the result is usually found by counting the number of successes or the number of questions answered correctly.

In this chapter, we continue our study of probability distributions by examining a very important *continuous* probability distribution, the **normal probability distribution**.

A continuous probability distribution usually results from measuring something, such as the distance from the residence to the classroom, the weight of an individual, or the amount of bonuses earned by CFOs. Suppose we select five students and find the distance, in kilometres, that they travel to attend class as 12.2, 8.9, 6.7, 3.6, and 14.6. When examining a continuous distribution we are usually interested in information such as the percent of students who travel less than 10 km or the percent of students who travel more than 8 km, or perhaps the percent of observations that occur within a certain range. Then, the number of kilometres travelled could have an infinite number of values within a particular range. So you think of the probability a variable will have a value within a specified range rather than the probability for a specific value.

The normal probability distribution describes the likelihood that a continuous random variable with an infinite number of possible values lies within a specified range. For example, assume the life of an Energizer C size battery follows a normal distribution with a mean of 45 hours and a standard deviation of 10 hours when used in a particular toy. We can determine the likelihood the battery will last more than 50 hours, between 35 and 62 hours, or less than 39 hours. The life of the battery is measured on a continuous scale.

1 List the characteristics of the *normal probability distribution*.

The Family of Normal Probability Distributions

The normal probability distribution and its accompanying normal curve have the following major characteristics:

1. It is **bell-shaped** and has a single peak in the centre of the distribution. The arithmetic mean, median, and mode are equal and located in the centre of the distribution. The total area under the curve is 1. Thus, half the area under the curve is to the right of this centre point, and the other half is to the left of it.
2. It is **symmetrical** about the mean. If we cut the normal curve vertically at this central value, the two halves will be mirror images.
3. It falls off smoothly in either direction from the central value. It is **asymptotic**, meaning that the curve gets closer and closer to the *X*-axis but never actually touches it. That is, the "tails" of the curve extend indefinitely in both directions.
4. The location of a normal distribution is determined by the mean, μ. The dispersion or spread of the distribution is determined by the standard deviation, σ.

These characteristics are shown graphically in Chart 6–1.

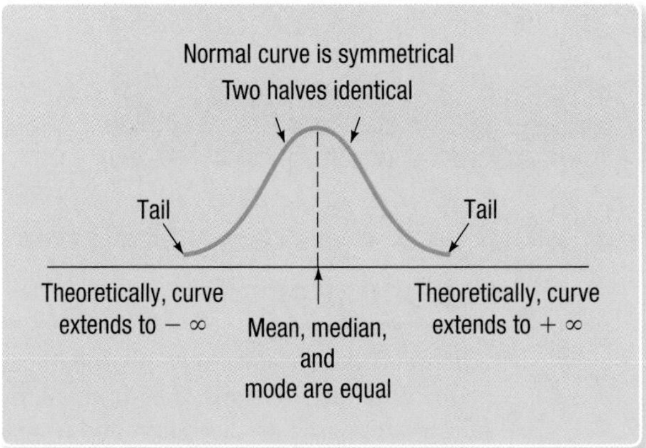

CHART 6–1 Characteristics of a Normal Distribution

There is not just one normal probability distribution, but rather a "family" of them. For example, in Chart 6–2 the probability distributions of length of employee service in three different plants can be compared. In the Camden plant, the mean is 20 years and the standard deviation is 3.1 years. There is another normal probability distribution for the length of service in the Dunkirk plant, where $\mu = 20$ years and $\sigma = 3.9$ years. In the Elmira plant, $\mu = 20$ years and $\sigma = 5.0$. Note that the means are the same but the standard deviations are different.

Equal means, unequal standard deviations

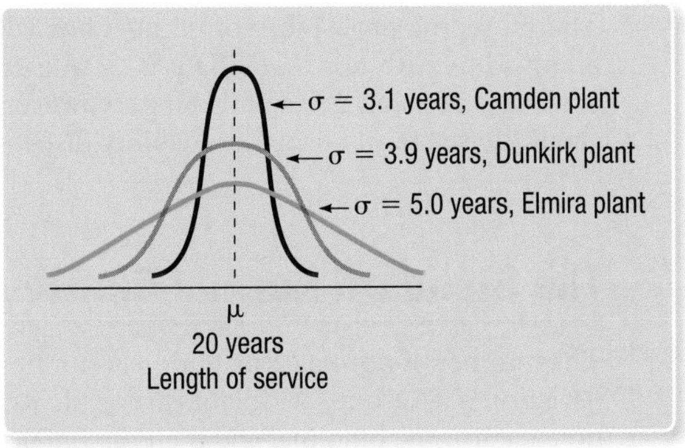

CHART 6–2 Normal Probability Distributions with Equal Means but Different Standard Deviations

Chart 6–3 shows the distribution of box masses of three different cereals. The masses are normally distributed with different means but identical standard deviations.

Unequal means, equal standard deviations

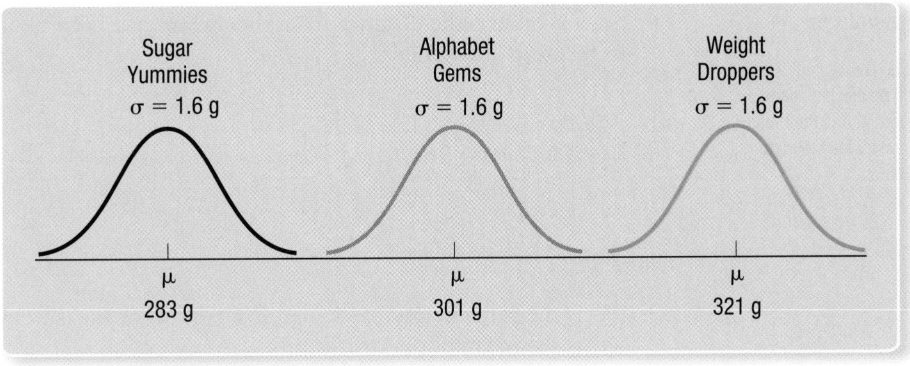

CHART 6–3 Normal Probability Distributions Having Different Means but Equal Standard Deviations

Finally, Chart 6–4 shows three normal distributions having different means and standard deviations. They show the distribution of tensile strengths, measured in kg/m^2, for three types of cables.

Unequal means, unequal standard deviations

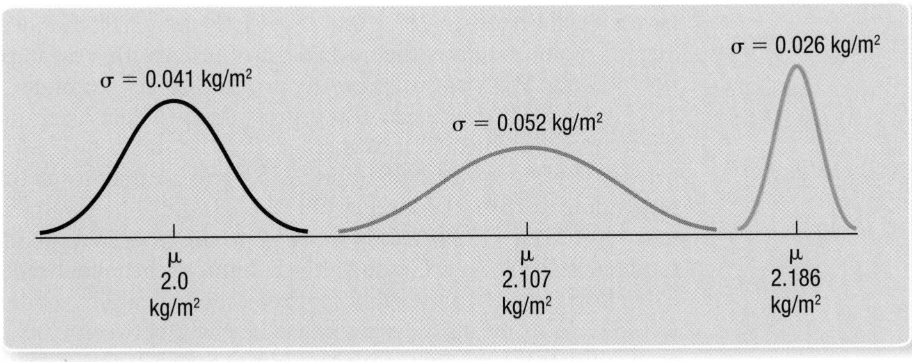

CHART 6–4 Normal Probability Distributions with Different Means and Standard Deviations

In Chapter 5, recall that discrete probability distributions show the specific likelihood a discrete value will occur. For example, the binomial distribution is used to calculate the probability that none of five flights arriving at the Calgary Airport would be late.

With a continuous probability distribution, areas below the curve define probabilities. The total area under the normal curve is 1.0. This accounts for all possible outcomes. Since a normal probability distribution is symmetric, the area under the curve to the left of the mean is 0.5, and the area under the curve to the right of the mean is 0.5. Apply this to the distribution of Sugar Yummies in Chart 6–3. It is normally distributed with a mean of 283 g.

Therefore, the probability of filling a box with more than 283 g is .5 and the probability of filling a box with less than 283 g is .5. We can also determine the probability that the mass of a box is between 280 g and 286 g. However, to determine this probability we need to know about the standard normal probability distribution.

The Standard Normal Distribution

The number of normal distributions is unlimited, each having a different mean (μ), standard deviation (σ), or both. While it is possible to provide probability tables for discrete distributions such as the binomial and the Poisson, providing tables for the infinite number of normal distributions is impossible. Fortunately, one member of the family can be used to determine the probabilities for all normal distributions. It is called the **standard normal distribution**, and it is unique because it has a mean of 0 and a standard deviation of 1.

2 **Define and calculate *z*-values.**

Any normal distribution can be converted into a *standard normal distribution* by subtracting the mean from each observation and dividing this difference by the standard deviation. The results are called **z-values** or **z scores**.

z-value The signed distance between a selected value, designated X, and the mean, μ, divided by the standard deviation, σ.

So, a z-value is the distance from the mean, measured in units of the standard deviation. In terms of a formula:

STANDARD NORMAL VALUE

$$z = \frac{X - \mu}{\sigma} \quad \textbf{[6–1]}$$

where:

X is the value of any particular observation or measurement.
μ is the mean of the distribution.
σ is the standard deviation of the distribution.

As noted in the above definition, a z-value expresses the distance or difference between a particular value of X and the arithmetic mean in units of the standard deviation. Once the normally distributed observations are standardized, the z-values are normally distributed with a mean of 0 and a standard deviation of 1. The table in Appendix D (also on the inside back cover) lists the probabilities for the standard normal probability distribution.

To explain, suppose we wish to compute the probability that boxes of Sugar Yummies have a weight between 283 g and 285.4 g. From Chart 6–3, we know that the box weight of Sugar Yummies follows the normal distribution with a mean of 283 g and a standard deviation of 1.6 g. We want to know the probability or area under the curve between the mean, 283 g, and 285.4 g. We can also express this problem using probability notation, similar to the style used in the previous chapter: $P(283 < \text{mass} < 285.4)$. To find the probability, it is necessary to convert both 283 g and 285.4 g to z-values using formula (6–1). The z-value corresponding to 283 is 0, found by $(283 - 283)/1.6$. The z-value corresponding to 285.4 is 1.50 found by $(285.4 - 283)/1.6$. Next we go to the table in Appendix D. A portion of the table is repeated as Table 6–1. Go down the column of the table headed by the letter z to 1.5. Then move horizontally to the right and read the probability under the column headed 0.00. It is 0.4332. This means the area under the curve between 0.00 and 1.50 is 0.4332. This is the probability that a randomly selected box of Sugar Yummies will have a weight between 283 g and 285.4 g.

3 **Determine the probability that an observation is between two points on a *normal probability distribution*.**

We can summarize this information as follows.

$$\begin{aligned} P(283 < \text{weight} < 285.4) &= P\left(\frac{283 - 283}{1.6} < z < \frac{285.4 - 283}{1.6}\right) \\ &= P(0 < z < 1.50) \\ &= 0.4332 \end{aligned}$$

TABLE 6–1 Areas under the Normal Curve

z	.00	.01	.02	.03	.04	.05	. . .
1.3	0.4032	0.4049	0.4066	0.4082	0.4099	0.4115	
1.4	0.4192	0.4207	0.4222	0.4236	0.4251	0.4265	
1.5	0.4332	0.4345	0.4357	0.4370	0.4382	0.4394	
1.6	0.4452	0.4463	0.4474	0.4484	0.4495	0.4505	
1.7	0.4554	0.4564	0.4573	0.4582	0.4591	0.4599	
1.8	0.4641	0.4649	0.4656	0.4664	0.4671	0.4678	
1.9	0.4713	0.4719	0.4726	0.4732	0.4738	0.4744	
⋮							

The following graph illustrates this information. Notice we show both grams and z-values on the horizontal scale. The values of 285.4 g and a z score of 1.50 are the same distance from $\mu = 283$ and $z = 0$, respectively.

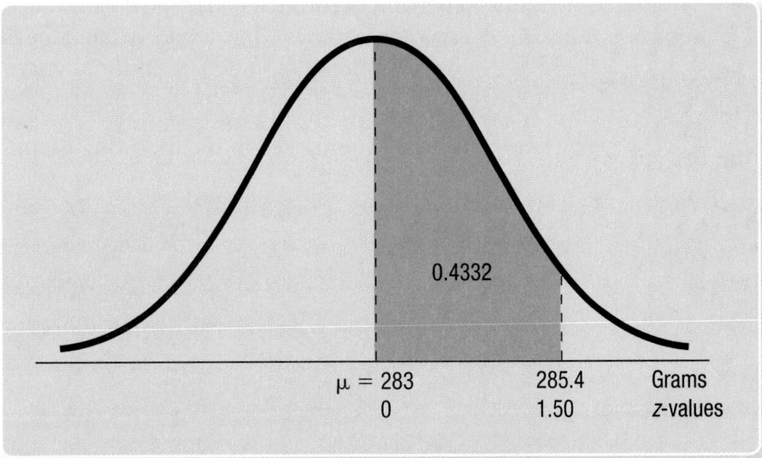

2 **Define and calculate z-values.**

Now we will compute the z-value given the population mean, μ, the population standard deviation, σ, and a selected X.

example

The weekly incomes of shift supervisors in the glass industry are normally distributed with a mean of \$1000 and a standard deviation of \$100. What is the z-value for the income X of a supervisor who earns \$1100 per week? For a supervisor who earns \$900 per week?

solution

Using formula (6–1), the z-values for the two X values (\$1100 and \$900) are:

For $X = \$1100$:

$$z = \frac{X - \mu}{\sigma} = \frac{\$1100 - \$1000}{\$100} = 1.00$$

For $X = \$900$:

$$z = \frac{X - \mu}{\sigma} = \frac{\$900 - \$1000}{\$100} = -1.00$$

The z of 1.00 indicates that a weekly income of \$1100 is 1 standard deviation above the mean, and a z of -1.00 shows that a \$900 income is 1 standard deviation below the mean. Note that both incomes (\$1100 and \$900) are the same distance (\$100) from the mean.

self-review 6–1

Using the information in the preceding example (μ = \$1000, σ = \$100), convert:

(a) The weekly income of \$1225 to a z-value.
(b) The weekly income of \$775 to a z-value.

Statistics in Action

An individual's skills depend on a combination of many hereditary and environmental factors, each having about the same amount of weight or influence on the skills. Thus, much like a binomial distribution with a large number of trials, many skills and attributes follow the normal distribution. For example, scores on the Scholastic Aptitude Test (SAT) are normally distributed with a mean of 1000 and a standard deviation of 140.

The Empirical Rule

Before examining further applications of the standard normal probability distribution, we will consider three areas under the normal curve that will be used extensively in the following chapters. These facts were called the Empirical Rule in Chapter 3.

1. About 68 percent of the area under the normal curve is within one standard deviation of the mean. This can be written as $\mu \pm 1\sigma$. The actual percentage is 68.26 percent.
2. About 95 percent of the area under the normal curve is within two standard deviations of the mean, written $\mu \pm 2\sigma$. The actual percentage is 95.44 percent.
3. Practically all of the area under the normal curve is within three standard deviations of the mean, written $\mu \pm 3\sigma$. The percentage is 99.7 percent.

This information is summarized in the following graph.

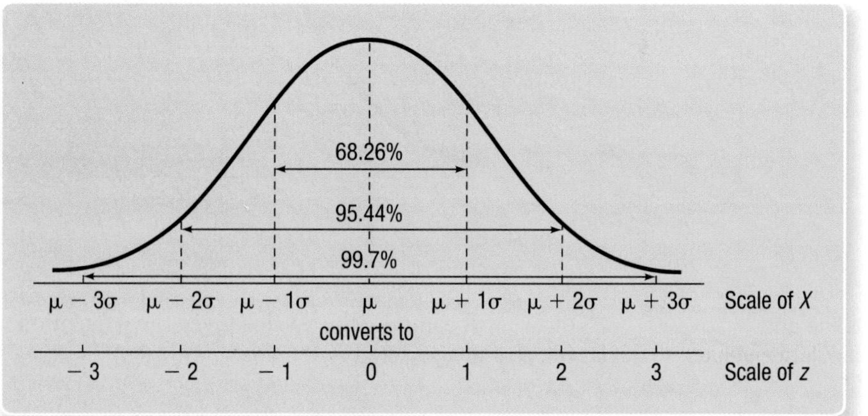

Transforming measurements to z-values changes the scale. The conversions are also shown in the graph. For example, $\mu + 1\sigma$ is converted to a z-value of +1.00. Likewise, $\mu - 2\sigma$ is transformed to a z-value of −2.00. Note that the centre of the z distribution is zero, indicating no deviation from the mean, μ.

example

As part of its quality control program, the Autolite Battery Company conducts tests on battery life. For a particular D cell alkaline battery, the mean life is 19 hours. The useful life of the battery follows a normal distribution with a standard deviation of 1.2 hours. Answer the following questions.

1. $\mu \pm 1\sigma$ of the batteries failed between what two values?
2. $\mu \pm 2\sigma$ of the batteries failed between what two values?
3. $\mu \pm 3\sigma$ of the batteries failed between what two values?

solution

We can use the results of the Empirical Rule to answer these questions.

1. $\mu \pm 1\sigma$ of the batteries will fail between 17.8 and 20.2 hours, found by $19.0 \pm 1(1.2)$ hours.
2. $\mu \pm 2\sigma$ of the batteries will fail between 16.6 and 21.4 hours, found by $19.0 \pm 2(1.2)$ hours.
3. $\mu \pm 3\sigma$ failed between 15.4 and 22.6 hours, found by $19.0 \pm 3(1.2)$ hours.

This information is summarized on the following chart.

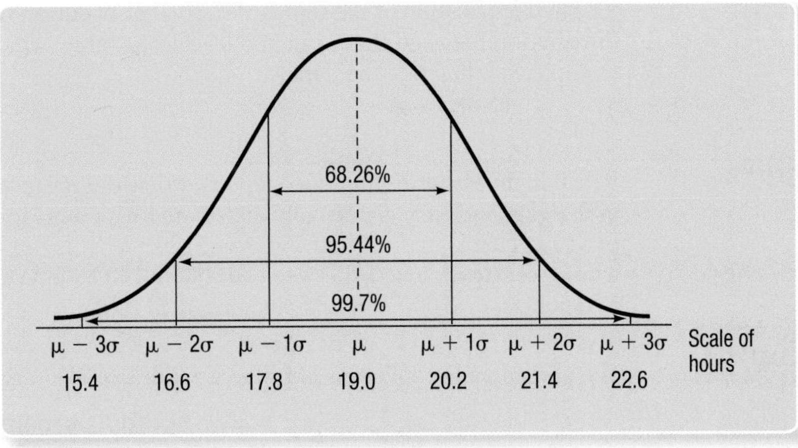

self-review 6–2

The distribution of the annual incomes of a group of middle-management employees at Compton Plastics approximates a normal distribution with a mean of $47 200 and a standard deviation of $800.

(a) $\mu \pm 1\sigma$ of the incomes lie between what two amounts?
(b) $\mu \pm 2\sigma$ of the incomes lie between what two amounts?
(c) $\mu \pm 3\sigma$ of the incomes lie between what two amounts?
(d) What are the median and the modal incomes?
(e) Is the distribution of incomes symmetrical?

Exercises

1. The mean of a normal probability distribution is 500; the standard deviation is 10.
a. $\mu \pm 1\sigma$ of the observations lie between what two values?
b. $\mu \pm 2\sigma$ of the observations lie between what two values?
c. $\mu \pm 3\sigma$ of the observations lie between what two values?

2. The mean of a normal probability distribution is 60; the standard deviation is 5.
a. What percent of the observations lie between 55 and 65?
b. What percent of the observations lie between 50 and 70?
c. What percent of the observations lie between 45 and 75?

3. The mean of a normal probability distribution is 100; the standard deviation is 15.
a. What percent of the observations lie between 85 and 115?
b. What percent of the observations lie between 70 and 130?
c. What percent of the observations lie between 55 and 145?

4. The mean of a normal probability distribution is 350; the standard deviation is 75.
a. $\mu \pm 1\sigma$ of the observations lie between what two values?
b. $\mu \pm 2\sigma$ of the observations lie between what two values?
c. $\mu \pm 3\sigma$ of the observations lie between what two values?

5. The Kamp family has twins, Rob and Rachel. Both Rob and Rachel graduated from college two years ago, and each is now earning $50 000 per year. Rachel works in the retail industry, where the mean salary for executives with less than five years' experience is $35 000 with a standard deviation of $8000. Rob is an engineer. The mean salary for engineers with less than five years' experience is $60 000 with a standard deviation of $5000. Compute the z-values for both Rob and Rachel and comment on your findings.

6. A recent article in the Collingwood *Sun Times* reported that the mean labour cost to repair a heat pump is $90 with a standard deviation of $22. Dawson's Heating Repairs and Services completed repairs on two heat pumps this morning. The labour cost for the first was $75 and it was $100 for the second. Compute z-values for each and comment on your findings.

Finding Areas under the Normal Curve

The first application of the standard normal distribution involves finding the area in a normal distribution between the mean and a selected value, which we identify as X. The following example will illustrate the details.

example

Recall in an earlier example we reported that the mean weekly income of a shift supervisor in the glass industry is normally distributed with a mean of \$1000 and a standard deviation of \$100. That is, $\mu = \$1000$ and $\sigma = \$100$. What is the likelihood of selecting a supervisor whose weekly income is between \$1000 and \$1100? We write this question in probability notation as: $P(\$1000 < \text{weekly income} < \$1100)$.

solution

We have already converted \$1100 to a z-value of 1.00 using formula (6–1). To repeat:

$$z = \frac{X - \mu}{\sigma} = \frac{\$1100 - \$1000}{\$100} = 1.00$$

3 Determine the probability that an observation is between two points on a *normal probability distribution.*

The probability associated with a z of 1.00 is available in Appendix D. A portion of Appendix D follows. To locate the probability, go down the left column to 1.0, and then move horizontally to the column headed 0.00. The value is 0.3413.

z	0.00	0.01	0.02
⋮	⋮	⋮	⋮
0.7	0.2580	0.2611	0.2642
0.8	0.2881	0.2910	0.2939
0.9	0.3159	0.3186	0.3212
1.0	0.3413	0.3438	0.3461
1.1	0.3643	0.3665	0.3686
⋮	⋮	⋮	⋮

Statistics in Action

Many processes, such as filling soft drink bottles and canning fruit, are normally distributed. Manufacturers must guard against both over- and underfilling. If they put too much in the can or bottle, they are giving away their product. If they put too little in, the customer may feel cheated and the government may question the label description. "Control Charts," with limits drawn three standard deviations above and below the mean, are routinely used to monitor this type of production process.

The area under the normal curve between \$1000 and \$1100 is .3413. We estimate that 34.13 percent of the shift supervisors in the glass industry earn between \$1000 and \$1100 weekly, or the likelihood of selecting a supervisor and finding his or her income is between \$1000 and \$1100 is .3413.

This information is summarized in the following chart.

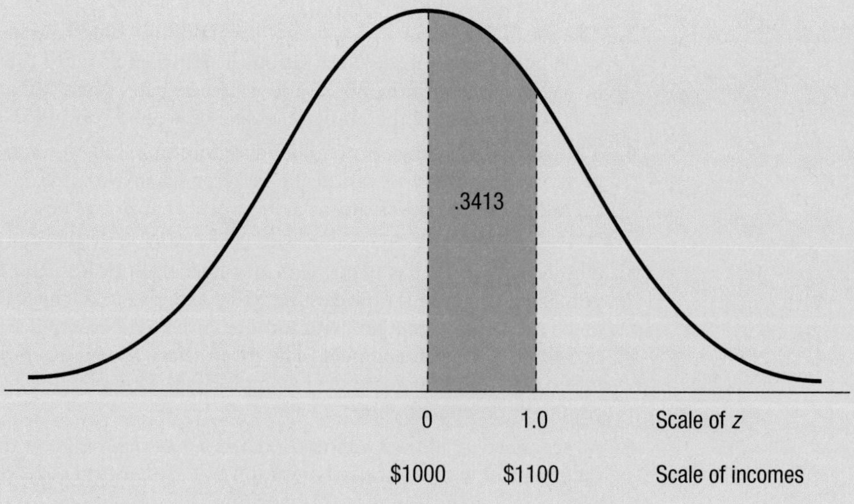

4 Determine the probability an observation is above or below a point on a *normal probability distribution*.

In the example just completed, we are interested in the probability between the mean and a given value. Let's change the question. Instead of wanting to know the probability of selecting a supervisor at random who earned between \$1000 and \$1100, suppose we wanted the probability of selecting a supervisor who earned less than \$1100. In probability notation we write this statement as P(weekly income < \$1100). The method of solution is the same. We find the probability of selecting a supervisor who earns between \$1000, the mean, and \$1100. This probability is .3413. Next, recall that half the area, or probability, is above the mean and half is below. So, the probability of selecting a supervisor earning less than \$1000 is 0.5000. Finally, we add the two probabilities, so .3413 + .5000 = .8413. So, 84.13 percent of the supervisors in the glass industry earn less than \$1100 per month. See the following diagram.

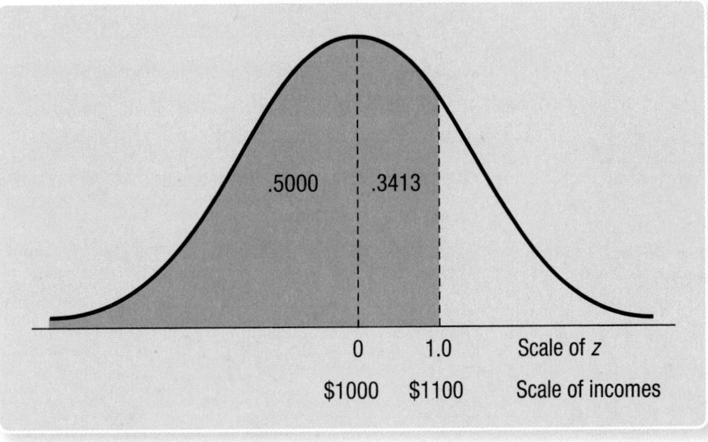

excel

The **Excel** and MegaStat commands to find the output for the weekly incomes of shift supervisors follows. **Excel** and MegaStat calculate the area to the left (lower) and to the right (upper) of the point \$1100.

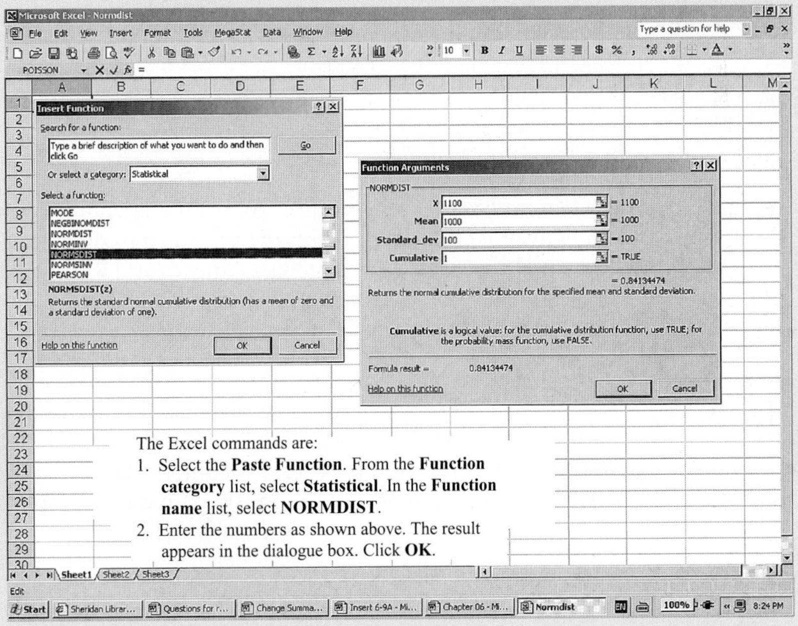

The answer to the above problem using **Excel** is the area in the lower tail, .8413. Since NORMDIST is a cumulative function, it measures the total area to the left of \$1100. However, if you want to find the area under the normal curve between \$1000 (the mean) and \$1100, we subtract the area to the left of the mean (.5). This gives us .8413 − .5 = .3413.

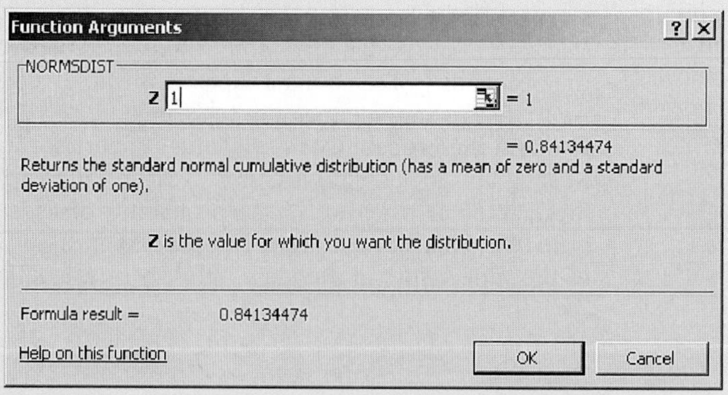

If the z-value is known, then the **Excel** function NORMSDIST can be used. The function gives the same result as noted in the dialogue box above.

The MegaStat commands follow.

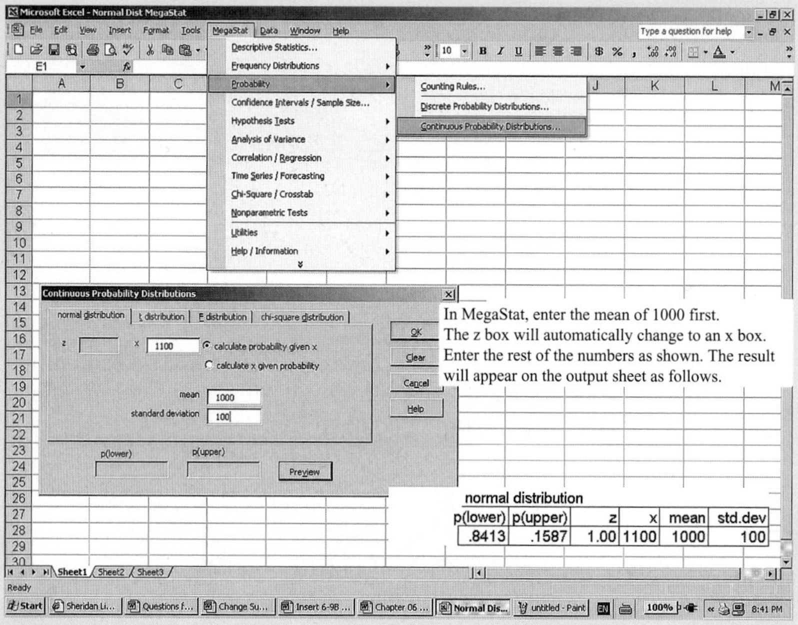

As with **Excel**, MegaStat will return the area in the lower tail as .8413. Since this is a cumulative function, it measures the total area to the left of \$1100. To find the area under the normal curve between \$1000 (the mean) and \$1100, we subtract the area to the left of the mean (.5). This gives us .8413 − .5 = .3413.

example

Refer to the information regarding the weekly income of shift supervisors in the glass industry. The distribution of weekly incomes follows the normal distribution, with a mean of \$1000 and a standard deviation of \$100. What is the probability of selecting a shift supervisor in the glass industry whose income is:

1. Between \$790 and \$1000?
2. Less than \$790?

solution

We begin by finding the z value corresponding to a weekly income of \$790. From formula (6–1):

$$z = \frac{X - \mu}{\sigma} = \frac{\$790 - \$1000}{\$100} = -2.10$$

See Appendix D. Move down the left margin to the row 2.1 and across that row to the column headed 0.00. The value is 0.4821. So the area under the standard normal curve corresponding to a z-value of 2.10 is 0.4821. However, because the normal distribution is symmetric, the area between 0 and a negative z is the same as that between 0 and z. The likelihood of finding a supervisor earning between \$790 and \$1000 is 0.4821. In probability notation we write $P(\$790 < \text{weekly income} < \$1000) = 0.4821$.

z	0.00	0.01	0.02
⋮	⋮	⋮	⋮
2.0	0.4772	0.4778	0.4783
2.1	0.4821	0.4826	0.4830
2.2	0.4861	0.4864	0.4868
2.3	0.4893	0.4896	0.4898
⋮	⋮	⋮	⋮

The mean divides the normal curve into two identical halves. The area under the half to the left of the mean is .5000, and the area to the right is also .5000. Because the area under the curve between \$790 and \$1000 is .4821, the area below \$790 is .0179, found by .5000 − .4821. In probability notation we write $P(\text{weekly income} < \$790) = .0179$.

This means that 48.21 percent of the supervisors have weekly incomes between \$790 and \$1000. Further, we can anticipate that 1.79 percent earn less than \$790 per week. This information is summarized in the following diagram.

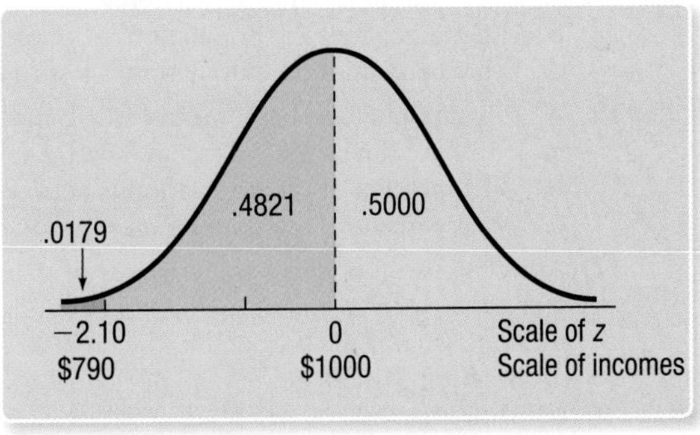

Excel and MegaStat are cumulative functions, and will split the area under the normal curve into two areas at the point in question. So, to find the required probability it may be necessary to add or subtract areas. The MegaStat commands for the above example follow.

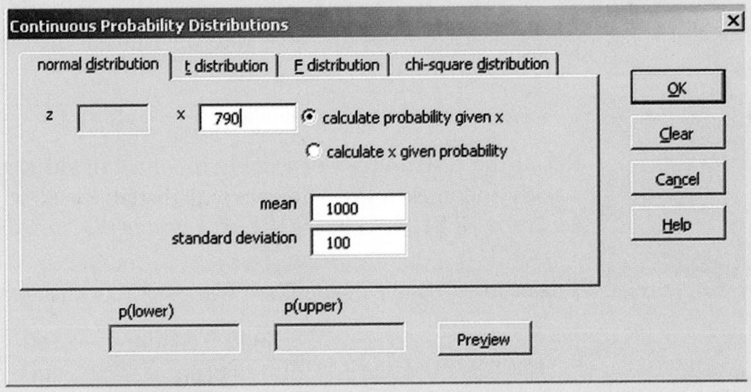

normal distribution

p(lower)	p(upper)	z	X	mean	std. dev.
.0179	.9821	−2.10	790	1000	100

MegaStat returns .9821 in the upper tail. This is the area under the curve from \$790 to the right. To find the area between \$790 and \$1000, we must subtract the area from \$1000 to the right, which is .5. So, the result is .9821 − .5 = .4821.

self-review 6–3

The employees of Cartwright Manufacturing are awarded efficiency ratings. The distribution of the ratings follows a normal distribution. The mean is 400, the standard deviation 50.

(a) What is the area under the normal curve between 400 and 482? Write this area in probability notation.
(b) What is the area under the normal curve for ratings greater than 482? Write this area in probability notation.
(c) Show the details of this problem in a chart.

Exercises

7. Given the following z-values, find the areas under the normal curve to the left and right of the z-value.
- **a.** $z = 1.0$
- **b.** $z = -1.25$
- **c.** $z = 2.83$
- **d.** $z = -2.35$

8. Given the following pairs of z-values, find the area under the normal curve between each pair of z-values.
- **a.** $z = 1.0$ and $z = -1.0$
- **b.** $z = -1.25$ and $z = -2.0$
- **c.** $z = 2.83$ and $z = 1.75$
- **d.** $z = -2.35$ and $z = 1.5$

9. A normal population has a mean of 20.0 and a standard deviation of 4.0.
- **a.** Compute the z-value associated with 25.0.
- **b.** What percent of the population is between 20.0 and 25.0?
- **c.** What percent of the population is less than 18.0?

10. A normal population has a mean of 12.2 and a standard deviation of 2.5.
- **a.** Compute the z-value associated with 14.3.
- **b.** What percent of the population is between 12.2 and 14.3?
- **c.** What percent of the population is less than 10.0?

11. A recent study of the hourly wages of maintenance crews for major airlines showed that the mean hourly salary was \$16.50, with a standard deviation of \$3.50. If we select a crew member at random, what is the probability the crew member earns:
- **a.** Between \$16.50 and \$20.00 per hour?
- **b.** More than \$20.00 per hour?
- **c.** Less than \$15.00 per hour?

12. The mean of a normal distribution is 400 kg. The standard deviation is 10 kg.
- **a.** What is the area between 415 kg and the mean of 400 kg?
- **b.** What is the area between the mean and 395 kg?
- **c.** What is the probability of selecting a value at random and discovering that it has a value of less than 395 kg?

Another application of the normal distribution involves combining two areas, or probabilities. One of the areas is to the right of the mean and the other to the left.

example

Recall the distribution of weekly incomes of shift supervisors in the glass industry. The weekly incomes follow the normal distribution, with a mean of \$1000 and a standard deviation of \$100. What is the area under this normal curve between \$840 and \$1200?

solution

The problem can be divided into two parts. For the area between \$840 and the mean of \$1000:

$$z = \frac{\$840 - \$1000}{\$100} = \frac{-\$160}{\$100} = -1.60$$

For the area between the mean of \$1000 and \$1200:

$$z = \frac{\$1200 - \$1000}{\$100} = \frac{\$200}{\$100} = 2.00$$

The area under the curve for a z of -1.60 is .4452 (from Appendix D). The area under the curve for a z of 2.00 is .4772. Adding the two areas: .4452 + .4772 = .9224. Thus, the probability of selecting an income between \$840 and \$1200 is .9224. In probability notation we write

$P(\$840 < \text{weekly income} < \$1200) = .4452 + .4772 = .9224$. To summarize, 92.24 percent of the supervisors have weekly incomes between \$840 and \$1200. This is shown in a diagram:

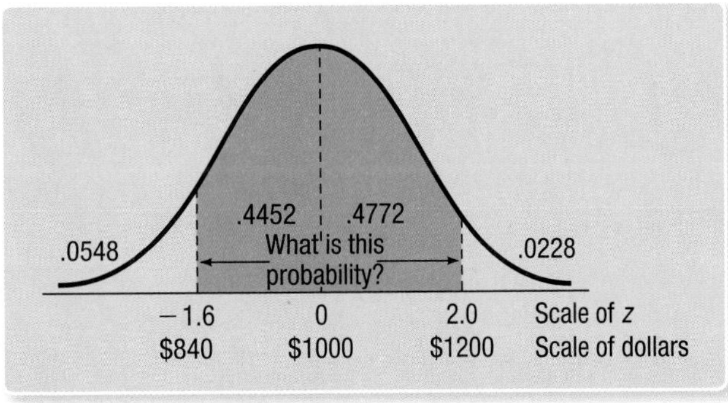

The output from MegaStat for the values of \$840 and \$1200 follow. Note that the area in the two tails of the above example are calculated as $.5 - .4452 = .0548$ in the lower tail and $.5 - .4772 = .0228$ in the upper tail.

normal distribution

p(lower)	p(upper)	z	X	mean	std. dev.
.0548	.9452	−1.60	840	1000	100

normal distribution

p(lower)	p(upper)	z	X	mean	std. dev.
.9772	.0228	2.00	1200	1000	100

The output from MegaStat for the value of \$840 is .0548 in the lower tail and .9452 in the upper tail. The output for the value of \$1200 is .9772 in the lower tail and .0228 in the upper tail. To obtain the required result, take the total area and subtract the areas that you do not need. (This is using the complement rule). The required result is computed as $1 - .0548 - .0228 = .9224$.

Another application of the normal distribution involves determining the area between values on the *same* side of the mean.

example

Returning to the weekly income distribution of shift supervisors in the glass industry ($\mu = \$1000$, $\sigma = \$100$), what is the area under the normal curve between \$1150 and \$1250?

solution

The situation is again separated into two parts, and formula (6–1) is used. First, we find the z-value associated with a weekly salary of \$1250:

$$z = \frac{\$1250 - \$1000}{\$100} = 2.50$$

Next we find the z-value for a weekly salary of \$1150:

$$z = \frac{\$1150 - \$1000}{\$100} = 1.50$$

From Appendix D the area associated with a z-value of 2.50 is 0.4938. So the probability of a weekly salary between \$1000 and \$1250 is 0.4938. Similarly, the area associated with a z-value of 1.50 is 0.4332, so the probability of a weekly salary between \$1000 and \$1150 is 0.4332. The probability of a weekly salary between \$1150 and \$1250 is found by subtracting the area associated with a z-value of 1.50 (0.4332) from that associated with a z of 2.50 (0.4938). Thus, the probability of a weekly salary between \$1150 and \$1250 is 0.0606. In probability notation we write $P(\$1150 \leq \text{weekly income} \leq \$1250) = 0.4938 - 0.4332 = 0.0606$. This information is summarized in the following diagram.

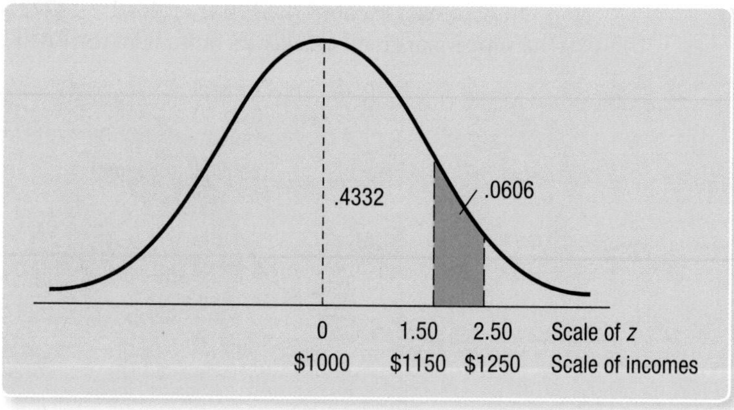

excel

This example is similar to the previous example using MegaStat. The output from MegaStat for the value of $1150 is .9332 (.5 + .4332) in the lower tail and .0668 in the upper tail. The output for the value of $1250 is .9938 in the lower tail and .0062 in the upper tail. Again we will use the complement rule and subtract the areas that we do not need. The required result is 1 − .9332 − .0062 = .0606.

normal distribution

p(lower)	*p*(upper)	*z*	*X*	mean	std. dev.
.9332	.0668	1.50	1150	1000	100

normal distribution

p(lower)	*p*(upper)	*z*	*X*	mean	std. dev.
.9938	.0062	2.50	1250	1000	100

In brief, there are four situations for finding the area under the standard normal distribution.

1. To find the area between 0 and z (or $-z$), look up the probability directly in the table.
2. To find the area beyond z or ($-z$), locate the probability of z in the table and subtract that probability from 0.5000.
3. To find the area between two points on different sides of the mean, determine the z-values and add the corresponding probabilities.
4. To find the area between two points on the same side of the mean, determine the z-values and subtract the smaller probability from the larger.

example

The average list price of 90 homes in Regina is $320 000 with a standard deviation of $99 500. What is the probability that:

1. a house is listed for more than $500 000?
2. a house is listed between $270 995 and $442 500?
3. a house is listed between $186 000 and $242 250?

solution

1. We begin by finding the z-value corresponding to a list price of $350 000. From formula (6–1):

$$z = \frac{X - \mu}{\sigma} = \frac{500\,000 - 320\,000}{99\,500} = 1.81$$

See Appendix D. Move down the left margin to the row 1.8 and across that row to the column headed 0.01. The value is 0.4649. However, the required area is to the right of

\$500 000, so we subtract 0.4649 from 0.5. Then 0.5 − 0.4649 = 0.0351. The probability that a house is listed for more than \$500 000 is 3.51 percent.

2. We will require two z-values corresponding to list prices of \$270 995 and \$442 500. Note that the values are on different sides of the mean. From formula (6–1):

$$z = \frac{X - \mu}{\sigma} = \frac{270\,995 - 320\,000}{99\,500} = -0.49 \quad \text{and} \quad z = \frac{X - \mu}{\sigma} = \frac{442\,500 - 320\,000}{99\,500} = 1.23$$

See Appendix D. Move down the left margin to the row 0.4 and across that row to the column headed 0.09. The value is 0.1879. Then, move down the left margin to the row 1.2 and across that row to the column headed 0.03. The value is 0.3907. But, the required area is between \$270 995 and \$442 500, so we must add the two areas: 0.1879 + 0.3907 = 0.5786. The probability that a house is listed for between \$270 995 and \$442 500 is 57.86 percent.

3. Again, we will require two z-values corresponding to list prices of \$186 000 and \$242 250. Note that the values are on the same side of the mean. From formula (6–1):

$$z = \frac{X - \mu}{\sigma} = \frac{186\,000 - 320\,000}{99\,500} = -1.35 \quad \text{and} \quad z = \frac{X - \mu}{\sigma} = \frac{242\,250 - 320\,000}{99\,500} = -0.78$$

See Appendix D. Move down the left margin to the row 1.3 and across that row to the column headed 0.05. The value is 0.4115. Then, move down the left margin to the row 0.7 and across that row to the column headed 0.08. The value is 0.2823. But, the required area is between \$186 000 and \$242 250, so we must subtract the two areas: 0.4115 − 0.2823 = 0.1292. The probability that a house is listed for between \$186 000 and \$242 250 is 12.92 percent.

MegaStat produces the following output.

1.

p(lower)	*p*(upper)	*z*	*X*	mean	std. dev.
.9649	.0351	1.81	500 000	320 000	99 500

The required area is p(upper) = 3.51 percent.

2.

p(lower)	*p*(upper)	*z*	*X*	mean	std. dev.
.3112	.6888	−0.49	270 995	320 000	99 500

p(lower)	*p*(upper)	*z*	*X*	mean	std. dev.
.8909	.1091	1.23	442 500	320 000	99 500

The p(lower) of .3112 is the area under the normal curve up to \$270 995. We do not need this area. The p(lower) of .8909 is the area under the normal curve up to \$442 500. So, we subtract the area we do not need, .8909 − .3112 = .5797 (57.97 percent). The probability is slightly different than that calculated using tables due to rounding.

3.

p(lower)	*p*(upper)	*z*	*X*	mean	std. dev.
.0890	.9110	−1.35	186 000	320 000	99 500

p(lower)	*p*(upper)	*z*	*X*	mean	std. dev.
.2173	.7827	−0.78	242 250	320 000	99 500

This is calculated in the same manner as #2. The p(lower) of .0890 is the area under the normal curve up to \$186 000. We do not need this area. The p(lower) of .2173 is the area under the normal curve up to \$242 250. So, we subtract the area we do not need, .2173 − .0890 = .1283 (12.83 percent). The probability is slightly different than that calculated using tables due to rounding.

Note: further examples and instructions on using **Excel** and MegaStat are in the appendix section on the CDROM.

self-review 6–4

Refer to the previous example, where the distribution of weekly incomes follows the normal distribution with a mean of \$1000 and the standard deviation is \$100.

(a) What percent of the shift supervisors earn a weekly income between \$750 and \$1225? Draw a normal curve and shade the desired area on your diagram.
(b) What percent of the shift supervisors earn a weekly income between \$1100 and \$1225? Draw a normal curve and shade the desired area on your diagram.

Exercises

13. A normal distribution has a mean of 50 and a standard deviation of 4.
  a. Compute the probability of a value between 44.0 and 55.0.
  b. Compute the probability of a value greater than 55.0.
  c. Compute the probability of a value between 52.0 and 55.0.

14. A normal population has a mean of 80.0 and a standard deviation of 14.0.
  a. Compute the probability of a value between 75.0 and 90.0.
  b. Compute the probability of a value 75.0 or less.
  c. Compute the probability of a value between 55.0 and 70.0.

15. A cola-dispensing machine is set to dispense on average 225 ml of cola per cup. The standard deviation is 10 ml. The distribution amounts dispensed follows a normal distribution.
  a. What is the probability that the machine will dispense between 235 ml and 250 ml of cola?
  b. What is the probability that the machine will dispense 250 ml of cola or more?
  c. What is the probability that the machine will dispense between 205 ml and 250 ml of cola?

16. The amounts of money requested on home loan applications at Down River Federal Savings follow the normal distribution, with a mean of \$70 000 and a standard deviation of \$20 000. A loan application is received this morning. What is the probability:
  a. The amount requested is \$80 000 or more?
  b. The amount requested is between \$65 000 and \$80 000?
  c. The amount requested is \$65 000 or more?

17. WNAE, an all-news AM station, finds that the distribution of the lengths of time listeners are tuned to the station follows the normal distribution. The mean of the distribution is 15.0 minutes and the standard deviation is 3.5 minutes. What is the probability that a particular listener will tune in:
  a. More than 20 minutes?
  b. For 20 minutes or less?
  c. Between 10 and 12 minutes?

18. The mean starting salary for college graduates in the spring of 2009 was \$33 176. Assume that the distribution of starting salaries follows the normal distribution with a standard deviation of \$3500. What percent of the graduates have starting salaries:
  a. Between \$30 000 and \$38 000?
  b. More than \$42 000?
  c. Between \$38 000 and \$42 000?

Previous examples require finding the percent of the observations located between two observations or the percent of the observations above, or below, a particular observation X. A further application of the normal distribution involves finding the value of the observation X when the percent above or below the observation is given.

example

The Layton Tire and Rubber Company wishes to set a minimum distance guarantee on its new MX100 tire. Tests reveal the mean number of kilometres is 109 000 with a standard deviation of 3300 km and that the distribution of kilometres follows the normal distribution. Layton wants to set the minimum guaranteed number of kilometres so that no more than 4 percent of the tires will have to be replaced. What minimum guaranteed kilometres should Layton announce?

solution

The details of this case are shown in the following diagram, where X represents the minimum guaranteed number of kilometres.

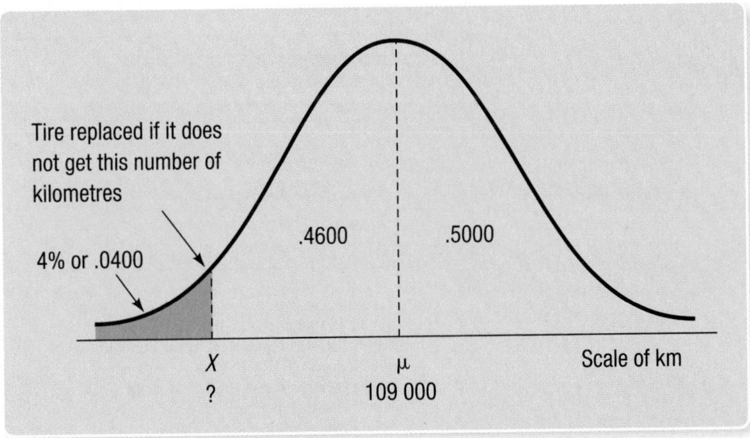

Inserting these values in formula (6–1) for z:

$$z = \frac{X - \mu}{\sigma} = \frac{X - 109\,000}{3300}$$

Notice that there are two unknowns, z and X. To find X, we first find z, and then solve for X. Notice the area under the normal curve to the left of μ is .5000. The area between μ and X is .4600, found by .5000 − .0400. Now refer to Appendix D. Search the body of the table for the area closest to 0.4600. The closest area is 0.4599. Move to the margins from this value and read the z-value of 1.75. Because the value is to the left of the mean, it is actually −1.75. These steps are illustrated in Table 6–2.

TABLE 6–2 Selected Areas under the Normal Curve

z	0.03	0.04	0.05	0.06
⋮				
1.5	0.4370	0.4382	0.4394	0.4406
1.6	0.4484	0.4495	0.4505	0.4515
1.7	0.4582	0.4591	0.4599	0.4608
1.8	0.4664	0.4671	0.4678	0.4686

Knowing that the distance between μ and X is -1.75σ or $z = -1.75$, we can now solve for X (the minimum guaranteed kilometres):

$$z = \frac{X - 109\,000}{3300}$$

$$-1.75 = \frac{X - 109\,000}{3300}$$

$$-1.75(3300) = X - 109\,000$$

$$X = 109\,000 - 1.75(3300) = 103\,225$$

So, Layton can advertise that it will replace for free any tire that wears out before it reaches 103 225 km, and the company will know that only 4 percent of the tires will be replaced under this plan.

Excel and MegaStat will also find the number of kilometres. **Excel** commands follow.

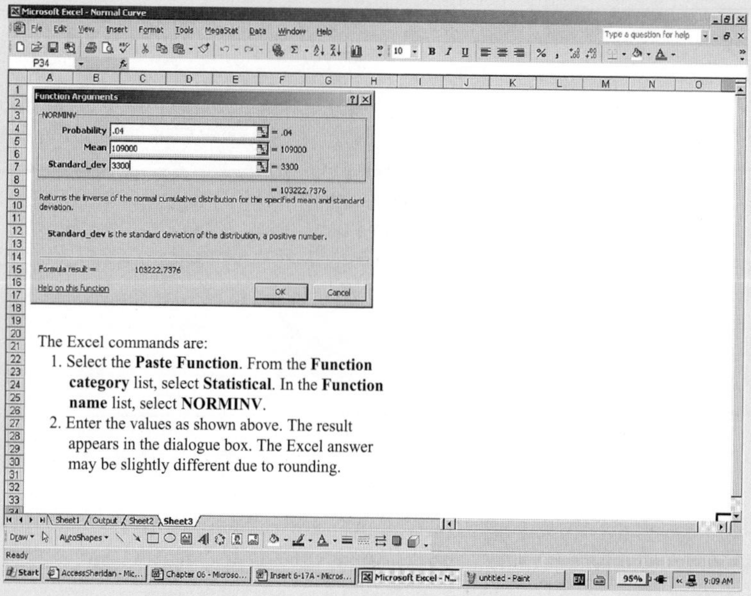

MegaStat commands follow.

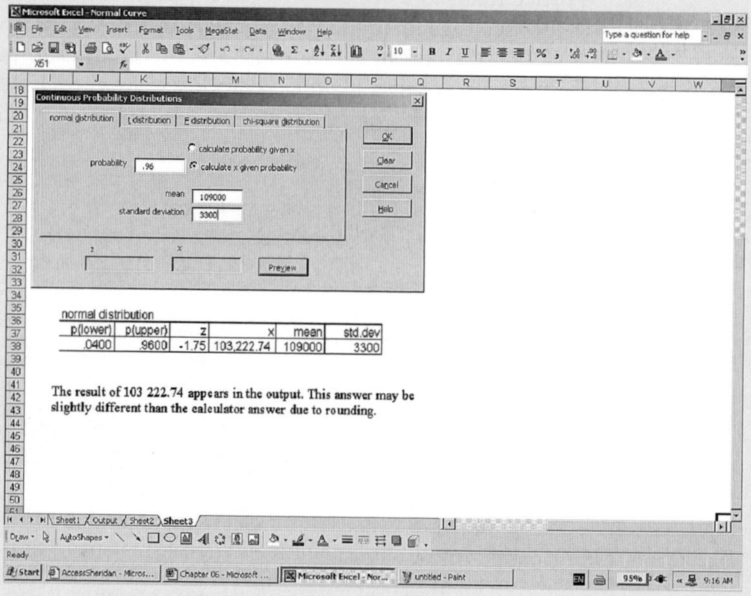

self-review 6–5

An analysis of the final test scores for Introduction to Business reveals the scores follow the normal distribution. The mean of the distribution is 75 and the standard deviation is 8. The professor wants to award an A to students whose scores are in the highest 10 percent. What is the dividing point for those students who earn an A and those earning a B?

Exercises

19. A normal distribution has a mean of 50 and a standard deviation of 4. Determine the value below which 95 percent of the observations will occur.

20. A normal distribution has a mean of 80 and a standard deviation of 14. Determine the value above which 80 percent of the values will occur.

21. The amounts dispensed by a cola machine follow the normal distribution with a mean of 200 ml and a standard deviation of 0.3 ml per cup. How much cola is dispensed in the largest 1 percent of the cups?

22. Refer to Exercise 16, where the amount requested for home loans followed the normal distribution with a mean of \$70 000 and a standard deviation of \$20 000.
   a. What is the minimum amount requested on the largest 3 percent of loans?
   b. What is the maximum amount requested on the smallest 10 percent of loans?

23. Assume that the mean hourly cost to operate a commercial airplane follows the normal distribution with a mean \$2100 per hour and a standard deviation of \$250. What is the maximum operating cost for the lowest 3 percent of the airplanes?

24. The monthly sales of mufflers follow the normal distribution with a mean of 1200 and a standard deviation of 225. The manufacturer would like to establish inventory levels such that there is only a 5 percent chance of running out of stock. Where should the manufacturer set the inventory levels?

5 Use the *normal probability distribution* to approximate the binomial probability distribution.

The Normal Approximation to the Binomial

Chapter 5 describes the binomial probability distribution, which is a discrete distribution. The table of binomial probabilities in Appendix A goes successively from an n of 1 to an n of 20, and then to $n = 25$. If a problem involved taking a sample of 60, generating a binomial distribution for that large a number would be very time consuming. A more efficient approach is to apply the *normal approximation to the binomial.*

Using the normal distribution (a continuous distribution) as a substitute for a binomial distribution (a discrete distribution) for large values of n seems reasonable because, as n increases, a binomial distribution gets closer and closer to a normal distribution. Chart 6–5 depicts the change in the shape of a binomial distribution with $p = .50$ from an n of 1, to an n of 3, to an n of 20. Notice how the case where $n = 20$ approximates the shape of the normal distribution. That is, compare the case where $n = 20$ to the normal curve in Chart 6–1 on page 176.

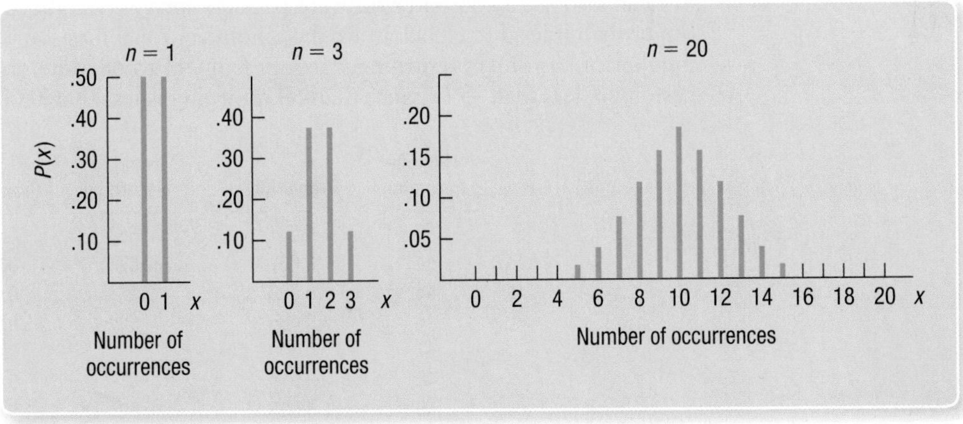

CHART 6–5 Binomial Distributions for an n of 1, 3, and 20, where $p = .50$

When to use the normal approximation

When can we use the normal approximation to the binomial? The normal probability distribution is a good approximation to the binomial probability distribution when np and $n(1 - p)$ are both at least 5. However, before we apply the normal approximation, we must make sure that our distribution of interest is in fact a binomial distribution. Recall from Chapter 5 that four criteria must be met:

1. There are only two mutually exclusive outcomes to an experiment: a "success" and a "failure."
2. The distribution results from counting the number of successes in a fixed number of trials.
3. Each trial is independent.
4. The probability, p, remains the same from trial to trial.

Continuity Correction Factor

To show the application of the normal approximation to the binomial and the need for a correction factor, suppose the management of the Santoni Pizza Restaurant found that 70 percent of its new customers return for another meal. For a week in which 80 new (first-time) customers dined at Santoni's, what is the probability that 60 or more will return for another meal?

Notice the binomial conditions are met: (1) There are only two possible outcomes—a customer either returns for another meal or does not return. (2) We can count the number of successes, meaning, for example, that 57 of the 80 customers return. (3) The trials are independent, meaning that if the 34th person returns for a second meal, that does not affect whether the 58th person returns. (4) The probability of a customer returning remains at .70 for all 80 customers.

Therefore, we could use the binomial formula (5–3) described on page 154.

$$P(x) = {}_nC_x\,(p)^x\,(1 - p)^{n-x}$$

To find the probability 60 or more customers return for another pizza, we need to first find the probability exactly 60 customers return. That is:

$$P(x = 60) = {}_{80}C_{60}\,(.70)^{60}\,(1 - .70)^{20} = .063$$

Next we find the probability that exactly 61 customers return. It is:

$$P(x = 61) = {}_{80}C_{61}\,(.70)^{61}\,(1 - .70)^{19} = .048$$

We continue this process until we have the probability all 80 customers return. Finally, we add the probabilities from 60 to 80. Solving the above problem in this manner is tedious. We can also use a computer software package such as MINITAB or **Excel** to find the various probabilities. Listed below are the binomial probabilities for $n = 80$, $p = 0.70$, and x, the number of customers returning, ranging from 43 to 68. The probability of any number of customers less than 43 or more than 68 returning is less than 0.001.

Number Returning	Probability	Number Returning	Probability
43	0.001	56	0.097
44	0.002	57	0.095
45	0.003	58	0.088
46	0.006	59	0.077
47	0.009	60	0.063
48	0.015	61	0.048
49	0.023	62	0.034
50	0.033	63	0.023
51	0.045	64	0.014
52	0.059	65	0.008
53	0.072	66	0.004
54	0.084	67	0.002
55	0.093	68	0.001

We can find the probability of 60 or more returning by summing $0.063 + 0.048 + \cdots + 0.001$, which is 0.197. However, a look at the plot below shows the similarity of this distribution to a normal distribution. All we need do is "smooth out" the discrete probabilities into a continuous distribution. Furthermore, working with a normal distribution will involve far fewer calculations than working with the binomial.

The trick is to let the discrete probability for 56 customers be represented by an area under the continuous curve between 55.5 and 56.5. Then let the probability for 57 customers be represented by an area between 56.5 and 57.5 and so on. This is just the opposite of rounding off the numbers to a whole number.

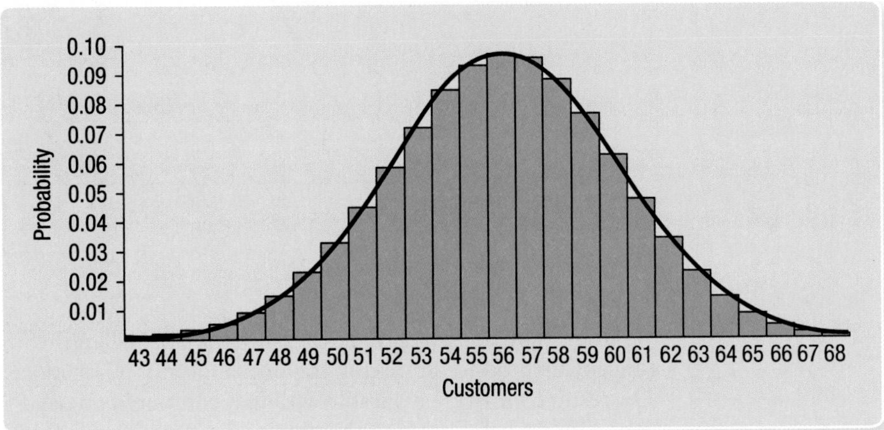

continuity correction factor The value .5 subtracted or added, depending on the question, to a selected value when a discrete probability distribution is approximated by a continuous probability distribution.

Because we use the normal distribution to determine the binomial probability of 60 or more successes, we must subtract, in this case, .5 from 60. The value .5 is called the **continuity correction factor**. This small adjustment must be made because a continuous distribution (the normal distribution) is being used to approximate a discrete distribution (the binomial distribution). Subtracting, 60 − .5 = 59.5.

Statistics in Action

The heights of adults approximate a normal distribution, but those individuals who are very tall can cause design problems. For example, Shaquille O'Neal, a professional basketball player with the Los Angeles Lakers, is 216 cm tall. The height of the standard doorway is 203 cm, so Shaquille and many other NBA players duck to get into most rooms.

As another example, the driver's seat in most vehicles is set to comfortably fit a person who is at least 159 cm tall. The distribution of heights of adult women is approximately a normal distribution with a mean of 161.5 cm and a standard deviation of 6.3 cm. Thus about 35 percent of adult women will not fit comfortably in the driver's seat.

How to Apply the Correction Factor

Only four cases may arise. These cases are:

1. For the probability that *at least* X occur, use the area *above* $(X - .5)$.
2. For the probability that *more than* X occur, use the area *above* $(X + .5)$.
3. For the probability that X *or fewer* occur, use the area *below* $(X + .5)$.
4. For the probability that *fewer than* X occur, use the area *below* $(X - .5)$.

A helpful hint is that the shaded area should always contain the x value.

To use the normal distribution to approximate the probability that 60 or more first-time Santoni customers out of 80 will return, follow the procedure shown below.

Step 1. Find the z corresponding to an X of 59.5 using formula (6–1), and formulas (5–4) and (5–5) for the mean and the variance of a binomial distribution:

$$\mu = np = 80(.70) = 56$$

$$\sigma^2 = np(1 - p) = 80(.70)(1 - .70) = 16.8$$

$$\sigma = \sqrt{16.8} = 4.10$$

$$z = \frac{X - \mu}{\sigma} = \frac{59.5 - 56}{4.10} = 0.85$$

Step 2. Determine the area under the normal curve between a μ of 56 and an X of 59.5. From step 1, we know that the z-value corresponding to 59.5 is 0.85. So we go to Appendix D and read down the left margin to 0.8, and then we go horizontally to the area under the column headed by 0.05. That area is 0.3023.

Step 3. Calculate the area beyond 59.5 by subtracting 0.3023 from 0.5000, that is 0.5000 − 0.3023 = 0.1977. Thus, 0.1977 is the probability that 60 or more first-time Santoni customers out of 80 will return for another meal. In probability notation $P(\text{customers} > 59.5) = 0.5000 - 0.3023 = 0.1977$. The details of this problem are shown graphically:

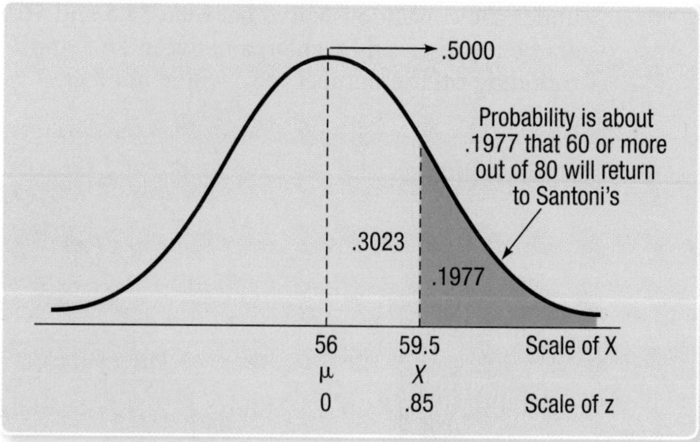

No doubt you will agree that using the normal approximation to the binomial is a more efficient method of estimating the probability of 60 or more first-time customers returning. The result compares favourably with that computed on page 194, using the binomial distribution. The probability using the binomial distribution is 0.197, whereas the probability using the normal approximation is 0.1977.

self-review 6–6

A study by Great Southern Home Insurance revealed that none of the stolen goods were recovered by homeowners in 80 percent of reported thefts.

(a) During a period in which 200 thefts occurred, what is the probability that no stolen goods were recovered in 170 or more of the robberies?
(b) During a period in which 200 thefts occurred, what is the probability that no stolen goods were recovered in 150 or more robberies?

Exercises

25. Assume a binomial probability distribution with $n = 50$ and $p = .25$. Compute the following:
   a. The mean and standard deviation of the random variable.
   b. The probability that X is 15 or more.
   c. The probability that X is 10 or less.

26. Assume a binomial probability distribution with $n = 40$ and $p = .55$. Compute the following:
   a. The mean and standard deviation of the random variable.
   b. The probability that X is 25 or greater.
   c. The probability that X is 15 or less.
   d. The probability that X is between 15 and 25 inclusive.

27. Dottie's Tax Service specializes in tax returns for professional clients, such as physicians, dentists, accountants, and lawyers. A recent audit of the returns she prepared indicated that an error was made on 5 percent of the returns she prepared last year. Assuming this rate continues into this year and she prepares 60 returns, what is the probability that she makes errors on:
   a. More than six returns?
   b. At least six returns?
   c. Exactly six returns?

28. Shorty's Muffler advertises it can install a new muffler in 30 minutes or less. However, the work standards department at corporate headquarters recently conducted a study and found that 20 percent of the mufflers were not installed in 30 minutes or less. The Maumee branch installed 50 mufflers last month. If the corporate report is correct:
   a. How many of the installations at the Maumee branch would you expect to take more than 30 minutes?
   b. What is the likelihood that fewer than eight installations took more than 30 minutes?
   c. What is the likelihood that eight or fewer installations took more than 30 minutes?
   d. What is the likelihood that exactly 8 of the 50 installations took more than 30 minutes?

29. A study conducted by the nationally known Taurus Health Club revealed that 30 percent of its new members are significantly overweight. A membership drive in a metropolitan area resulted in 500 new members.

a. It has been suggested that the normal approximation to the binomial be used to determine the probability that 175 or more of the new members are significantly overweight. Does this problem qualify as a binomial problem? Explain.

b. What is the probability that 175 or more of the new members are significantly overweight?

c. What is the probability that 140 or more new members are significantly overweight?

30. Research on new juvenile delinquents put on probation revealed that 38 percent of them committed another crime.

a. What is the probability that of the last 100 new juvenile delinquents put on probation, 30 or more will commit another crime?

b. What is the probability that 40 or fewer of the delinquents will commit another crime?

c. What is the probability that from 30 to 40 of the delinquents will commit another crime?

Chapter Summary

I. The normal distribution is a continuous probability distribution with the following characteristics.

A. It is bell-shaped and the mean, median, and mode are equal.

B. It is symmetrical.

C. It is asymptotic, meaning the curve approaches but never touches the *X*-axis.

D. It is completely described by the mean and standard deviation.

E. There is a family of normal distributions. Each time the mean or standard deviation changes, a new distribution is created.

F. The area under a normal curve expresses the probability of an outcome.

II. The standard normal distribution is a particular normal distribution.

A. It has a mean of 0 and a standard deviation of 1.

B. Any normal distribution can be converted to the standard normal distribution by the following formula.

$$z = \frac{X - \mu}{\sigma} \quad [6\text{–}1]$$

C. By standardizing a normal distribution, we can report the distance from the mean in units of the standard deviation.

III. The normal distribution can approximate a binomial distribution under certain conditions.

A. np and $n(1 - p)$ must both be at least 5.

1. n is the number of observations.

2. p is the probability of a success.

B. The four conditions for a binomial distribution are:

1. There are only two possible outcomes.

2. p remains the same from trial to trial.

3. The trials are independent.

4. The distribution results from a count of the number of successes in a fixed number of trials.

C. The mean and variance of a binomial distribution are computed as follows:

$$\mu = np$$

$$\sigma^2 = np(1 - p)$$

D. The continuity correction factor of .5 is used to extend the continuous value of *X* one-half unit in either direction. This correction compensates for estimating a discrete distribution by a continuous distribution.

Chapter Exercises

31. Given the following *z*-values, find the areas under the normal curve to the left and right of the *z*-value.

a. $z = 1.56$

b. $z = 1.83$

c. $z = -0.78$

d. $z = -2.45$

www.mcgrawhill.ca/olc/lind

32. Given the following pairs of z-values, find the area under the normal curve between each pair of z-values.
   a. $z = -1.5$ and $z = 1.75$
   b. $z = 1.23$ and $z = 2.71$
   c. $z = -2.58$ and $z = -1.05$
   d. $z = -2.45$ and $z = -0.79$

33. A normal population has a mean of 50 and a standard deviation of 7.
   a. Compute the z-value associated with 45.
   b. What percent of the population is between 45 and 63?
   c. What percent of the population is less than 55?
   d. What percent of the population is more than 40?
   e. What percent of the population is less than 40 or more than 55?
   f. Below what value do 80 percent of the observations lie?

34. The average salary of merchandisers is \$45 000 per year with a standard deviation of \$6000.
   a. What is the probability that a merchandiser earns more than \$55 000 per year?
   b. What is the probability that a merchandiser earns less than \$32 000 per year?
   c. What is the probability that a merchandiser earns between \$40 000 and \$50 000 per year?
   d. What is the probability that a merchandiser will earn between \$36 000 and \$54 000 per year?
   e. What is the average salary below which 20 percent of the merchandisers earn?
   f. What is the average salary above which the top 10 percent of the merchandisers earn?

35. The net sales and the number of employees for aluminum fabricators with similar characteristics are organized into frequency distributions. Both are normally distributed. For the net sales, the mean is \$180 million and the standard deviation is \$25 million. For the number of employees, the mean is 1500 and the standard deviation is 120. Clarion Fabricators had sales of \$170 million and 1850 employees.
   a. Convert Clarion's sales and number of employees to z-values.
   b. Locate the two z-values.
   c. Compare Clarion's sales and number of employees with those of the other fabricators.

36. The accounting department at Weston Materials Inc., a national manufacturer of unattached garages, reports that it takes two construction workers a mean of 32 hours and a standard deviation of 2 hours to erect the Red Barn model. Assume the assembly times follow the normal distribution.
   a. Determine the z-values for 29 and 34 hours. What percent of the garages take between 32 hours and 34 hours to erect?
   b. What percent of the garages take between 29 hours and 34 hours to erect?
   c. What percent of the garages take 28.7 hours or less to erect?
   d. Of the garages, 5 percent take how many hours or more to erect?

37. A recent report indicated a typical family of four spends \$490 per month on food. Assume the distribution of food expenditures for a family of four follows the normal distribution, with a mean of \$490 and a standard deviation of \$90.
   a. What percent of the families spend more than \$30 but less than \$490 per month on food?
   b. What percent of the families spend less than \$430 per month on food?
   c. What percent spend between \$430 and \$600 per month on food?
   d. What percent spend between \$500 and \$600 per month on food?

38. A study of long distance phone calls made from the corporate offices of the Pepsi Bottling Group Inc. showed the calls follow the normal distribution. The mean length of time per call was 4.2 minutes and the standard deviation was 0.60 minutes.
   a. What is the probability the calls lasted between 4.2 and 5 minutes?
   b. What is the probability the calls lasted more than 5 minutes?
   c. What is the probability the calls lasted between 5 and 6 minutes?
   d. What is the probability the calls lasted between 4 and 6 minutes?
   e. As part of her report to the president, the director of communications would like to report the minimum length of the longest (in duration) 4 percent of the calls. What is this time?

39. Shaver Manufacturing Inc. offers dental insurance to its employees. A recent study by the human resource director shows the annual cost per employee per year followed the normal distribution, with a mean of \$1280 and a standard deviation of \$420 per year.
   a. What is the probability that the employees' dental expenses will be more than \$1500 per year?
   b. What is the probability that the employees' dental expenses will be between \$1500 and \$2000 per year?
   c. Estimate the percent that did not have any dental expense.
   d. What was the minimum cost for the 10 percent of employees that incurred the highest dental expense?

40. The annual commissions earned by sales representatives of Machine Products Inc., a manufacturer of light machinery, follow the normal distribution. The mean yearly amount earned is \$40 000 and the standard deviation is \$5000.
   a. What percent of the sales representatives earn more than \$42 000 per year?
   b. What percent of the sales representatives earn between \$32 000 and \$42 000?

c. What percent of the sales representatives earn between $32 000 and $35 000?
d. The sales manager wants to award the sales representatives who earn the largest commissions a bonus of $1000. He can award a bonus to 20 percent of the representatives. What is the cutoff point between those who earn a bonus and those who do not?

41. The weights of cans of Monarch pears follow the normal distribution with a mean of 1000 g and a standard deviation of 50 g. Calculate the percentage of the cans that have weights:
a. Less than 860 g.
b. Between 1055 g and 1100 g.
c. Between 860 g and 1055 g.

42. The number of passengers on the *Queen Elizabeth II* during one-week cruises in the Caribbean follows the normal distribution. The mean number of passengers per cruise is 1820 and the standard deviation is 120.
a. What percent of the cruises will have between 1820 and 1970 passengers?
b. What percent of the cruises will have 1970 passengers or more?
c. What percent of the cruises will have 1600 or fewer passengers?
d. How many passengers are on the cruises with the fewest 25 percent of passengers?

43. Management at Gordon Electronics is considering adopting a bonus system to increase production. One suggestion is to pay a bonus on the highest 5 percent of production based on past experience. Past records indicate weekly production follows the normal distribution. The mean of this distribution is 4000 units per week and the standard deviation is 60 units per week. If the bonus is paid on the upper 5 percent of production, the bonus will be paid on how many units or more?

44. Fast Service Truck Lines uses the Ford Super 1310 exclusively. Management made a study of the maintenance costs and determined the number of kilometres travelled during the year followed the normal distribution. The mean of the distribution was 96 600 km and the standard deviation 3200 km.
a. What percent of the Ford Super 1310s logged 104 970 km or more?
b. What percent of the trucks logged more than 91 800 but less than 93 800 km?
c. What percent of the Fords travelled 99 800 or less during the year?
d. Is it reasonable to conclude that any of the trucks were driven more than 112 700 km? Explain.

45. Best Electronics offers a "no hassle" returns policy. The number of items returned per day follows the normal distribution. The mean number of customer returns is 10.3 per day and the standard deviation is 2.25 per day.
a. In what percent of the days are there eight or fewer customers returning items?
b. In what percent of the days are between 12 and 14 customers returning items?
c. Is there any chance of a day with no returns?

46. A recent study shows that 20 percent of all employees prefer their vacation time during March break. If a company employs 50 people, what is the probability that:
a. Fewer than five employees want their vacation during March break?
b. More than five employees want their vacation during March break?
c. Exactly five employees want their vacation during March break?
d. More than 5 but fewer than 15 employees want their vacation during March break?

47. According to Statistics Canada, the mean number of hours of TV viewing per week is higher among adult women than men. A recent study showed women spent an average of 25.6 hours per week watching TV and men 20.9 per week. (http://www40.statcan.ca/l01/cst01/arts23.htm, December 22, 2006.) Assume that the distribution of hours watched follows a normal distribution for both groups, and that the standard deviations are 4.5 hours for the women and 5.1 hours for the men.
a. What percent of women watch TV less than 30 hours per week?
b. What percent of men watch TV more than 18 hours per week?
c. What minimum number of hours of TV do the 1 percent of women who watch the most TV per week watch? Find the comparable value for the men.

48. The current model Boeing 737 has a capacity of 189 passengers. The distribution of the number of seats sold follows a normal distribution with a mean of 155 seats and a standard deviation of 15 seats.
a. What is the probability of selling more than 134 seats?
b. What is the probability of selling less than 173 seats?
c. What is the probability of selling between 134 and 173 seats?
d. What percent of the time does an airline sell more seats than there are available?

49. The median age in Canada in 2006 was 39.5 years. (Statistics Canada, 2006 Census data, http://www12.statcan.ca/english/census06/data/highlights/agesex/index.cfm, March 2008.) Assume that the distribution of median ages is normally distributed with a standard deviation of 1.5 years.
a. What is the probability that the median age is more than 37.0 years?
b. What is the probability that the median age is less than 41.5 years?
c. What is the probability that the median age is between 36.0 and 37.0 years?
d. What is the probability that the median age is less than 36.0 or more than 37.0 years?

50. The funds dispensed at the ATM at the Queensway site of the Trillium Hospital follows a normal distribution with a mean of $4200 per day and a standard deviation of $720 per day. The machine is programmed to notify the bank if the amount dispensed is very low, less than $2500, or very high, more than $6000.

a. What percent of the time will the bank be notified because the amount dispensed is very low?
b. What percent of the time will the bank be notified because the amount dispensed is very high?
c. What percent of the time will the bank not be notified regarding the amount of funds dispensed?

51. A recent survey reported that 64 percent of men over the age of 18 consider nutrition a top priority in their lives. Suppose we select a sample of 60 men. What is the likelihood that:

a. 32 or more consider nutrition important?
b. 44 or more consider nutrition important?
c. More than 32 but fewer than 43 consider nutrition important?
d. Exactly 44 consider diet important?

52. It is estimated that 10 percent of those taking the quantitative methods portion of the CPA examination fail that section. Sixty students are taking the exam this Saturday.

a. How many would you expect to fail? What is the standard deviation?
b. What is the probability that exactly two students will fail?
c. What is the probability at least two students will fail?

53. The Woodbridge Traffic Division reported 40 percent of the high-speed chases involving automobiles result in a minor or major accident. During a month in which 50 high-speed chases occur, what is the probability that 25 or more will result in a minor or major accident?

54. Cruise ships of the Royal Viking line report that 80 percent of their rooms are occupied during September. For a cruise ship having 800 rooms, what is the probability that 665 or more are occupied in September?

55. The goal at airports handling international flights is to clear these flights within 45 minutes. Let's interpret this to mean that 95 percent of the flights are cleared in 45 minutes, so 5 percent of the flights take longer to clear. Let's also assume that the distribution is approximately normal.

a. If the standard deviation of the time to clear an international flight is five minutes, what is the mean time to clear a flight?
b. Suppose the standard deviation is 10 minutes, not the 5 minutes suggested in part a. What is the new mean?
c. A customer has 30 minutes from the time her flight landed to catch her limousine. Assuming a standard deviation of 10 minutes, what is the likelihood that she will be cleared in time?

56. The Home Lottery states that you have a 1 in 35 chance of winning a prize. A ticket is good for all draws and there are 25 weekly draws.

a. How many prizes would you expect to win in the 25 draws?
b. Evaluate the normal approximation to estimate the probability of at least 1 win in 25 draws. Is this a good approximation? Tell why or why not.

57. The registrar at Elmwood University studied the grade point averages (GPAs) of students over many years. Assume the GPA distribution follows a normal distribution with a mean of 3.10 and a standard deviation of 0.30.

a. What is the probability that a randomly selected Elmwood student has a GPA between 2.00 and 3.00?
b. What percent of the students are on probation, that is, have a GPA less than 2.00?
c. The student population at EU is 10 000. How many students are on the dean's list, that is, have GPAs of 3.70 or higher?
d. To qualify for a Bell scholarship, a student must be in the top 10 percent. What minimum GPA must a student attain to qualify for a Bell scholarship?

58. Jon Molnar will graduate from Cobden High School this year. He took the American College Test (ACT) for college admission and received a score of 30. The high school principal informed him that only 2 percent of the students taking the exam received a higher score. The mean score for all students taking the exam is 18.3. Jon's friends Karrie and George also took the test but were not given any information by the principal other than their scores. Karrie scored 25 and George 18. Based on this information, what were Karrie's and George's percentile ranks? Assume that the distribution of scores follows the normal distribution.

59. The weights of canned hams processed at the Henline Ham Company follow the normal distribution, with a mean of 3.1 kg and a standard deviation of 0.125 kg. The label weight is given as 3 kg.

a. What proportion of the hams actually weigh less than the amount claimed on the label?
b. The owner, Glen Henline, is considering two proposals to reduce the proportion of hams below label weight. He can increase the mean weight to 3.15 kg and leave the standard deviation the same, or he can leave the mean weight at 3.1 kg and reduce the standard deviation from 0.125 kg to 0.10 kg. Which change would you recommend?

60. The Gravenhurst *Enquirer* reported that the mean number of hours worked per week by those employed full time is 43.9. The article further indicated that about one-third of those employed full time work less than 40 hours per week.
   a. Given this information and assuming that number of hours worked follows the normal distribution, what is the standard deviation of the number of hours worked?
   b. The article also indicated that 20 percent of those working full time work more than 49 hours per week. Determine the standard deviation with this information. Are the two estimates of the standard deviation similar? What would you conclude?

61. Most four-year automobile leases allow up to 100 000 km. If the lessee goes beyond this amount, a penalty of $0.08 per kilometre is added to the lease cost. Suppose the distribution of kilometres driven on four-year leases follows the normal distribution. The mean is 85 000 kilometres and the standard deviation is 8000 kilometres.
   a. What percent of the leases will yield a penalty because of excess distance travelled?
   b. If the automobile company wanted to change the terms of the lease so that 25 percent of the leases went over the limit, where should the new upper limit be set?
   c. One definition of a low-mileage car is one that is 4 years old and has been driven less than 72 000 kilometres. What percent of the cars returned are considered low-mileage?

62. The price of shares of the Continental Bank at the end of trading each day for the last year followed the normal distribution. Assume there were 240 trading days in the year. The mean price was $42.00 per share and the standard deviation was $2.25 per share.
   a. What percent of the days was the price over $45.00? How many days would you estimate?
   b. What percent of the days was the price between $38.00 and $40.00?
   c. What was the minimum price of the stock on the *highest* 15 days of the year?

63. The annual sales of romance novels follows the normal distribution. However, the mean and the standard deviation are unknown. Forty percent of the time sales are more than 470 000, and 10 percent of the time sales are more than 500 000. What are the mean and the standard deviation?

64. In establishing warranties on large screen TVs, the manufacturer wants to set the limits so that few will need repair at manufacturer expense. On the other hand, the warranty period must be long enough to make the purchase attractive to the buyer. For a new large screen TV the mean number of months until repairs are needed is 36.84 with a standard deviation of 3.34 months. Where should the warranty limits be set so that only 10 percent of the large screen TVs need repairs at the manufacturer's expense?

65. DeKorte Tele-Marketing Inc. is considering purchasing a machine that randomly selects and automatically dials telephone numbers. DeKorte Tele-Marketing makes most of its calls during the evening, so calls to business phones are wasted. The manufacturer of the machine claims that its programming reduces the calling to business phones to 15 percent of all calls. To test this claim, the director of purchasing at DeKorte programmed the machine to select a sample of 150 phone numbers. What is the likelihood that more than 30 of the phone numbers selected are that of a business, assuming the manufacturer's claim is correct?

Data Set Exercises

66. Refer to the real estate data, from the south-east area of Edmonton, on the CD-ROM, which reports information on listed homes. The mean list price (in $ thousands) of the homes was computed earlier. Use the normal distribution to estimate the percent of homes listed for more than $475 000. Compare this to the actual results. Does the normal distribution yield a good approximation of the actual results?

67. Refer to the CREA (Canadian Real Estate Association) data on the CD-ROM, which reports information on average house prices nationally and in a selection of cities across Canada. Select the cities only.
   a. Calculate the mean and the standard deviation for July 2008. Use the normal distribution to estimate the number of homes listed for less than $360 000. Compare the estimate to the actual results. Does the normal distribution yield a good approximation of the actual results?
   b. Calculate the mean and the standard deviation for January 2008. Use the normal distribution to estimate the number of homes listed for more than $400 000. Compare the estimate to the actual results. Does the normal distribution yield a good approximation of the actual results?

68. Refer to the International data, which reports demographic and economic information on 46 countries.
   a. The mean of the GDP/capita variable is 16.58 with a standard deviation of 9.27. Use the normal distribution to estimate the percentage of countries with GDP/capita above 24. Compare this estimate with the actual proportion. Does the normal distribution appear accurate in this case? Explain.
   b. The mean of the Exports is 116.3 with a standard deviation of 157.4. Use the normal distribution to estimate the percentage of countries with Exports above 170. Compare this estimate with the actual proportion. Does the normal distribution appear accurate in this case? Explain.

www.mcgrawhill.ca/olc/lind

exercises.com

Additional exercises that require you to access information at related Internet sites are available on the CD-ROM included with this text.

Answers to Self-Reviews

6–1 **(a)** 2.25, found by:

$$z = \frac{\$1225 - \$1000}{\$100} = \frac{\$225}{\$100} = 2.25$$

(b) −2.25, found by:

$$z = \frac{\$775 - \$1000}{\$100} = \frac{-\$225}{\$100} = -2.25$$

6–2 **(a)** \$46 400 and \$48 000, found by \$47 200 ± 1(\$800).
(b) \$45 600 and \$48 800, found by \$47 200 ± 2(\$800).
(c) \$44 800 and \$49 600, found by \$47 200 ± 3(\$800).
(d) \$47 200. Mean, median, and mode are equal for a normal distribution.
(e) Yes, a normal distribution is symmetrical.

6–3 **(a)** Computing z:

$$z = \frac{482 - 400}{50} = 1.64$$

Referring to Appendix D, the area is 0.4495.
$P(400 < \text{rating} < 482) = 0.4495$

(b) 0.0505, found by 0.5000 − 0.4495.
$P(\text{rating} > 482) = 0.5000 - 0.4495 = 0.0505$

(c)

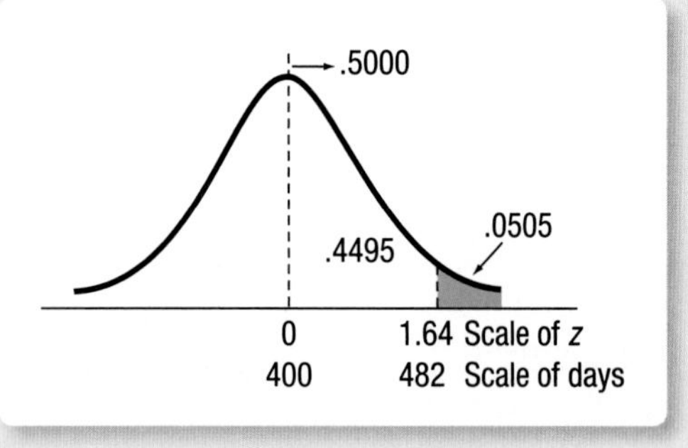

6–4 **(a)** 98.16 percent, found by 0.4938 + 0.4878.

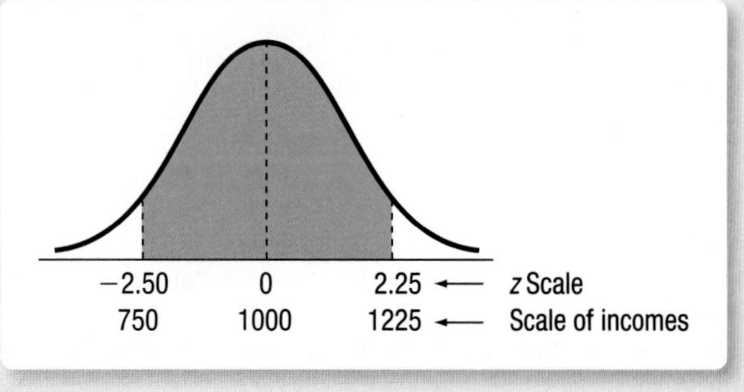

(b) 14.65 percent, found by 0.4878 − 0.3413.

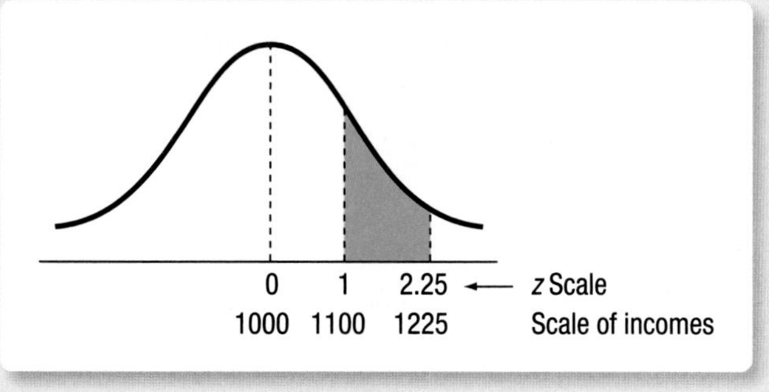

6–5 85.24 (instructor would no doubt make it 85). The closest area to 0.4000 is 0.3997; z is 1.28. Then:

$$1.28 = \frac{X - 75}{8}$$

$$10.24 = X - 75$$

$$X = 85.24$$

6–6 **(a)** 0.0465, found by $\mu = np = 200(.80) = 160$, and $\sigma^2 = np(1-p) = 200(.80)(1 - .80) = 32$. Then,

$$\sigma = \sqrt{32} = 5.66$$

$$z = \frac{169.5 - 160}{5.66} = 1.68$$

Area from Appendix D is 0.4535. Subtracting from 0.5000 gives 0.0465.

(b) 0.9686, found by 0.4686 + 0.5000. First calculate z:

$$z = \frac{149.5 - 160}{5.66} = -1.86$$

Area from Appendix D is 0.4686.

chapter 7

Sampling Methods and the Central Limit Theorem

LEARNING GOALS

When you have completed this chapter, you will be able to:

1. Explain why a sample is often the only feasible way to learn something about a population.
2. Describe methods to select a sample.
3. Define and construct a sampling distribution of the sample mean.
4. Explain the *central limit theorem*.
5. Use the central limit theorem to find probabilities of selecting possible sample means from a specified population.
6. Define and construct a sampling distribution of a proportion.

Introduction

Chapters 1 through 3 emphasize techniques to describe data. To illustrate these techniques, we organize the list prices of 96 homes in the south-east area of Edmonton into a frequency distribution and compute various measures of location and dispersion. Such measures as the mean and the standard deviation describe the typical list price and the spread in the list prices. In these chapters, the emphasis is on describing the condition of the data. That is, we describe something that has already happened.

Chapter 4 starts to lay the foundation for statistical inference with the study of probability. Recall that in statistical inference our goal is to determine something about a *population* based only on the *sample*. The population is the entire group of individuals or objects under consideration, and the sample is a part or subset of that population. Chapter 5 extends the probability concepts by describing three discrete probability distributions: the binomial, the hypergeometric, and the Poisson. Chapter 6 describes the normal probability distribution, a widely applicable continuous probability distribution. Probability distributions encompass all possible outcomes of an experiment and the probability associated with each outcome. We use probability distributions to evaluate something that might occur in the future.

This chapter begins our study of sampling. A sample is a tool to infer something about a population. We begin this chapter by discussing methods of selecting a sample from a population. Next, we construct a distribution of the sample mean to understand how the sample means tend to cluster around the population mean. Finally, we show that for any population, the shape of this sampling distribution tends to follow the normal probability distribution.

1 Explain why a sample is often the only feasible way to learn something about a population.

Sampling Methods

In Chapter 1, we said the purpose of inferential statistics is to find something about a population based on a sample. A sample is a portion or part of the population of interest. In many cases, sampling is more feasible than studying the entire population. In this section, we show major reasons for sampling, and then several methods for selecting a sample.

Reasons to Sample

When studying characteristics of a population, there are many practical reasons why we prefer to select portions or samples of a population to observe and measure. Here are some of the reasons for sampling:

Reasons for sampling

1. **To contact the whole population would often be time consuming.** A candidate for public office may wish to determine her chances for election. A sample poll using the regular staff and field interviews of a professional polling firm would take only one or two days. By using the same staff and interviewers and working seven days a week, it could take years to contact all the voting population! Even if a large staff of interviewers could be assembled, the benefit of contacting all of the voters would probably not be worth the time.
2. **The cost of studying all the items in a population may be prohibitive.** Public opinion polls and consumer testing organizations, such as Gallup Polls, usually contact only a small portion of the population. One consumer panel-type organization charges about $40 000 to mail samples and tabulate responses in order to test a product (such as breakfast cereal, cat food, or perfume). The same product test using all population families would cost a great deal more.
3. **The physical impossibility of checking all items in the population.** Some populations are infinite. It would be impossible to check all the water in Okanagan Lake for bacterial levels, so we select samples at various locations. The populations of fish, birds, snakes, mosquitoes, and the like are large and are constantly moving, being born, and dying. Instead of even attempting to count all the Canada Geese or all the fish in Rainbow Lake, we make estimates using various techniques—such as counting all the ducks on a pond picked at random, making creel checks, or setting nets at predetermined places in the lake.
4. **The destructive nature of some tests.** If the wine tasters in Niagara-on-the-Lake drank all the wine to evaluate the vintage, they would consume the entire crop, and none would be available for sale. In the area of industrial production, steel plates, wires, and similar products must have a certain minimum tensile strength. To ensure that the product meets the minimum standard, samples are selected from the current production. Each piece is stretched until it breaks, and the breaking strength recorded. Obviously, if all the wire or all the plates were tested for tensile strength, none would be available for sale or use. For the same reason, only a sample of photographic film is selected and tested by Kodak to determine the quality of all the film produced, and only a few seeds are tested for germination by Burpee prior to the planting season.
5. **The sample results are adequate.** Even if funds are available, it is doubtful the additional accuracy of a 100 percent sample—that is, studying the entire population—is essential in most problems. For example, the federal government uses a sample of grocery stores scattered throughout Canada to determine the monthly index of food prices. The prices of bread, beans, milk, and other major food items are included in the index. It is unlikely that the inclusion of all grocery stores in Canada would significantly affect the index, since the prices of milk, bread, and other major foods usually do not vary by more than a few cents from one chain store to another.

Statistics in Action

With the significant role played by inferential statistics in all branches of science, the availability of large sources of random numbers has become a necessity. The first book of random numbers, containing 41 600 random digits generated by L. Tippett, was published in 1927. In 1938, R. A. Fisher and F. Yates published 15 000 random digits generated using two decks of cards. In 1955, RAND Corporation published a million random digits, generated by the random frequency pulses of an electronic roulette wheel. By 1970, applications of sampling required billions of random numbers. Methods have since been developed for generating digits, using a computer, that are 'almost' random and hence are called *pseudo-random*. The question of whether a computer program can be used to generate numbers that are truly random remains a debatable issue.

When selecting a sample, researchers or analysts must be very careful that the sample is a fair representation of the population. In other words, the sample must be unbiased. In Chapter 1, an example of abusing statistics was the intentional selection of dentists to report that "two out of three dentists surveyed indicated they would recommend Brand X toothpaste to their patients." Clearly, people can select a sample that supports their own biases. The ethical side of statistics always requires unbiased sampling and objective reporting of results. Next, several sampling methods show how to select a fair and unbiased sample from a population.

2 Describe methods to select a sample.

Simple Random Sampling

simple random sample A sample selected so that each item or person in the population has the same chance of being included.

The most widely used type of sampling is a **simple random sample**.

To illustrate simple random sampling and selection, suppose a population consists of 845 employees of Nitra Industries. A sample of 20 employees is to be selected from that population. One way of ensuring that every employee in the population has the same chance of being chosen is to first write the name of each one on a small slip of paper and deposit all of the slips in a box. After they have been thoroughly mixed, the first selection is made by drawing a slip out of the box without looking at it. This process is repeated until the sample size of 20 is chosen.

A table of random numbers is an efficient way to select members of the sample

A more convenient method of selecting a random sample is to use the identification number of each employee and a **table of random numbers** such as the one in Appendix E. As the name implies, these numbers have been generated by a random process (in this case, by a computer). For each digit of a number, the probability of 0, 1, 2, . . . , 9 is the same. Thus, the probability that employee number 011 will be selected is the same as for employee 722 or employee 382. By using random numbers to select employees, bias is eliminated from the selection process.

A portion of a table of random numbers is shown in the following illustration. All of the digits are random. They are in groups of five for easy reading. To select a sample of employees, you must first choose a starting point in the table. Any starting point will do. Suppose the time is 3:04. You might look at the third column and then move down to the fourth set of numbers. The number is 03759. Since there are only 845 employees, we will use the first three digits of a five-digit random number. Thus, 037 is the number of the first employee to be a member of the sample. Another way of selecting the starting point is to close your eyes and point at a number in the table. To continue selecting employees, you could move in any direction. Suppose you move right. The first three digits of the number to the right of 03759 are 447—the number of the employee selected to be the second member of the sample. The next three-digit number to the right is 961. You skip 961 because there are only 845 employees. You continue to the right and select employee 784, then 189, and so on.

5 0 5 2 5	5 7 4 5 4	2 8 4 5 5	6 8 2 2 6	3 4 6 5 6	3 8 8 8 4	3 9 0 1 8
7 2 5 0 7	5 3 3 8 0	5 3 8 2 7	4 2 4 8 6	5 4 4 6 5	7 1 8 1 9	9 1 1 9 9
3 4 9 8 6	7 4 2 9 7	0 0 1 4 4	3 8 6 7 6	8 9 9 6 7	9 8 8 6 9	3 9 7 4 4
6 8 8 5 1	2 7 3 0 5	0 3 7 5 9	4 4 7 2 3	9 6 1 0 8	7 8 4 8 9	1 8 9 1 0
0 6 7 3 8	6 2 8 7 9	0 3 9 1 0	1 7 3 5 0	4 9 1 6 9	0 3 8 5 0	1 8 9 1 0
1 1 4 4 8	1 0 7 3 4	0 5 8 3 7	2 4 3 9 7	1 0 4 2 0	1 6 7 1 2	9 4 4 9 6
		Starting point	Second employee		Third employee	Fourth employee

Most statistical software packages have a routine that will select a simple random sample.

example

Jane and Joe Miley operate a bed and breakfast called the Foxtrot Inn. There are eight rooms available for rent. Listed below are the dates in June and the number of rooms rented each night. Use **Excel** to select a sample of five of the nights during the month.

June	Rentals	June	Rentals	June	Rentals
1	0	11	3	21	3
2	2	12	4	22	2
3	3	13	4	23	3
4	2	14	4	24	6
5	3	15	7	25	0
6	4	16	0	26	4
7	2	17	5	27	1
8	3	18	3	28	1
9	4	19	6	29	3
10	7	20	2	30	3

solution

Excel will select the random sample and report the results. The information is listed in column C of the following **Excel** spreadsheet. On the first night of the sampled data, four of the eight rooms were rented. On the second night sampled, no rooms were rented, and so on. The **Excel** steps are also shown. **Excel** performs the sampling with replacement, and so, the same day may appear more than once. The results will vary each time the random sample is selected.

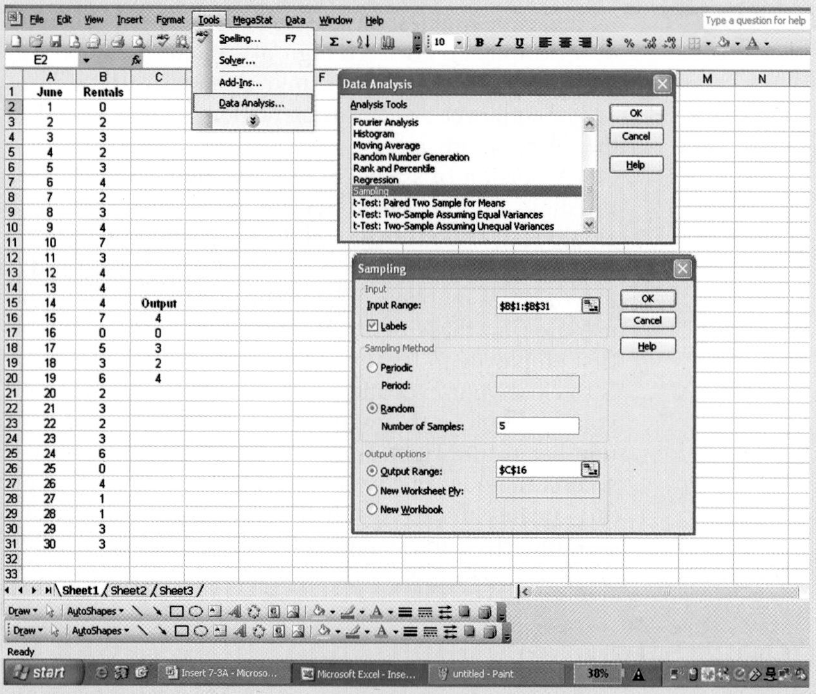

self-review 7–1

The following class roster lists the students enrolling in an introductory course in business statistics. Three students are to be randomly selected and asked various questions regarding course content and method of instruction.

(a) The numbers 00 through 45 are handwritten on slips of paper and placed in a bowl. The three numbers selected are 31, 7, and 25. Which students would be included in the sample?
(b) Now use the table of random digits, Appendix E, to select your own sample.
(c) What would you do if you encountered the number 59 in the table of random digits?

CSPM 264 01 BUSINESS & ECONOMIC STAT

8:00 AM 9:40 AM MW ST 118 LIND D

RANDOM NUMBER	NAME	CLASS RANK	RANDOM NUMBER	NAME	CLASS RANK
00	ANDERSON, RAYMOND	SO	23	MEDLEY, CHERYL ANN	SO
01	ANGER, CHERYL RENEE	SO	24	MITCHELL, GREG R	FR
02	BALL, CLAIRE JEANETTE	FR	25	MOLTER, KRISTI MARIE	SO
03	BERRY, CHRISTOPHER G	FR	26	MULCAHY, STEPHEN ROBERT	SO
04	BOBAK, JAMES PATRICK	SO	27	NICHOLAS, ROBERT CHARLES	JR
05	BRIGHT, M. STARR	JR	28	NICKENS, VIRGINIA	SO
06	CHONTOS, PAUL JOSEPH	SO	29	PENNYWITT, SEAN PATRICK	SO
07	DETLEY, BRIAN HANS	JR	30	POTEAU, KRIS E	JR
08	DUDAS, VIOLA	SO	31	PRICE, MARY LYNETTE	SO
09	DULBS, RICHARD ZALFA	JR	32	RISTAS, JAMES	SR
10	EDINGER, SUSAN KEE	SR	33	SAGER, ANNE MARIE	SO
11	FINK, FRANK JAMES	SR	34	SMILLIE, HEATHER MICHELLE	SO
12	FRANCIS, JAMES P	JR	35	SNYDER, LEISHA KAY	SR
13	GAGHEN, PAMELA LYNN	JR	36	STAHL, MARIA TASHERY	SO
14	GOULD, ROBYN KAY	SO	37	ST. JOHN, AMY J	SO
15	GROSENBACHER, SCOTT ALAN	SO	38	STURDEVANT, RICHARD K	SO
16	HEETFIELD, DIANE MARIE	SO	39	SWETYE, LYNN MICHELE	SO
17	KABAT, JAMES DAVID	JR	40	WALASINSKI, MICHAEL	SO
18	KEMP, LISA ADRIANE	FR	41	WALKER, DIANE ELAINE	SO
19	KILLION, MICHELLE A	SO	42	WARNOCK, JENNIFER MARY	SO
20	KOPERSKI, MARY ELLEN	SO	43	WILLIAMS, WENDY A	SO
21	KOPP, BRIDGETTE ANN	SO	44	YAP, HOCK BAN	SO
22	LEHMANN, KRISTINA MARIE	JR	45	YODER, ARLAN JAY	JR

systematic random sample A random starting point is selected, and then every *k*th member of the population is selected.

Systematic Random Sampling

The simple random sampling procedure may be awkward in some research situations. For example, suppose the sales division of Computer Printers Unlimited needs to quickly estimate the mean dollar revenue per sale during the past month. It finds that 2000 sales invoices were recorded and stored in file drawers, and decides to select 100 invoices to estimate the mean dollar revenue. Simple random sampling requires the numbering of each invoice before using the random number table to select the 100 invoices. The numbering process would be a very time consuming task. Instead, **systematic random sampling** can be used.

First, k is calculated as the population size divided by the sample size. For Computer Printers Unlimited, we would select every 20th (2000/100) invoice from the file drawers; in so doing the numbering process is avoided. If k is not a whole number, then round down.

Random sampling is used in the selection of the first invoice. For example, a number from a random number table between 1 and k, or 20, would be selected. Say, the random number were 18. Then, starting with the 18th invoice, every 20th invoice (18, 38, 58, etc.) would be selected as the sample.

Before using systematic random sampling, we should carefully observe the physical order of the population. When the physical order is related to the population characteristic, then systematic random sampling should not be used. For example, if the invoices in the example were filed in order of increasing sales, systematic random sampling would not guarantee a random sample. Other sampling methods should be used.

Statistics in Action

Is discrimination taking a bite out of your paycheck? Before you answer, consider a recent article in *Personnel Journal*. These findings indicate that attractive men and women earn about 5 percent more than average lookers, who in turn earn about 5 percent more than their plain counterparts. This is true for both men and women. It is also true for a wide range of occupations, from construction workers to auto repair to telemarketing, occupations for which it would seem that looks would not matter.

stratified random sample A population is divided into subgroups, called strata, and a sample is randomly selected from each stratum.

Stratified Random Sampling

When a population can be clearly divided into groups based on some characteristic, then **stratified random sampling** can be used to guarantee that each group is represented in the sample. The groups are also called **strata**. For example, college students can be grouped as full time or part time, male or female, or traditional or nontraditional. Once the strata are defined, we can apply simple random sampling within each group or strata to collect the sample.

For instance, we might study the advertising expenditures for the 200 largest companies in Canada. Suppose the objective of the study is to determine whether firms with high returns on equity (a measure of profitability) spent more of each sales dollar on advertising than firms with a low return or deficit. To make sure that the sample is a fair representation of the 200 companies, the companies are grouped on percent return on equity. Table 7–1 shows the strata and the relative frequencies. If simple random sampling is used, observe that firms in the 3rd and 4th strata have a high chance of selection (probability of 0.87), but firms in the other strata have a low chance of selection (probability of 0.13). We might not select any firms in stratum 1 or 5 *simply by chance*. However, stratified random sampling will guarantee that at least one firm in each of stratum 1 and 5 is represented in the sample. Let's say that 50 firms are selected for intensive study. Then one (0.02 × 50) firm from stratum 1 would be randomly selected, five (0.10 × 50) firms from stratum 2 would be randomly selected, and so on. In this case, the number of firms sampled from each stratum is proportional to the stratum's relative frequency in the population. Stratified sampling has the advantage, in some cases, of more accurately reflecting the characteristics of the population than does simple random or systematic random sampling.

TABLE 7–1 Number Selected for a Proportional Stratified Random Sample

Stratum	Profitability (return on equity)	Number of Firms	Relative Frequency	Number Sampled
1	30 percent and over	4	0.02	1*
2	20 up to 30 percent	20	0.10	5*
3	10 up to 20 percent	108	0.54	27
4	0 up to 10 percent	66	0.33	16
5	Deficit	2	0.01	1
Total		200	1.00	50

*0.02 of 50 = 1, 0.10 of 50 = 5, etc.

Cluster Sampling

cluster sampling
A population is divided into clusters using naturally occurring geographic or other boundaries. Then, clusters are randomly selected and a sample is collected by randomly selecting from each cluster.

Another common type of sampling is **cluster sampling**. It is often employed to reduce the cost of sampling a population scattered over a large geographic area.

Suppose you want to determine the views of residents in a province about provincial and federal environmental protection policies. Selecting a random sample of residents in the province and personally contacting each one would be time consuming and very expensive. Instead, you could employ cluster sampling by subdividing the province into small units—either counties or regions. These are often called *primary units*.

Suppose you divided the province into 12 primary units, then selected at random 4 regions—2, 7, 4, and 12—and concentrated your efforts in these primary units. You could take a random sample of the residents in each of these regions and interview them. (Note that this is a combination of cluster sampling and simple random sampling.)

Many other sampling methods

The discussion of sampling methods in the preceding sections did not include all the sampling methods available to a researcher. Should you become involved in a major research project in marketing, finance, accounting, or other areas, you would need to consult books devoted solely to sample theory and sample design.

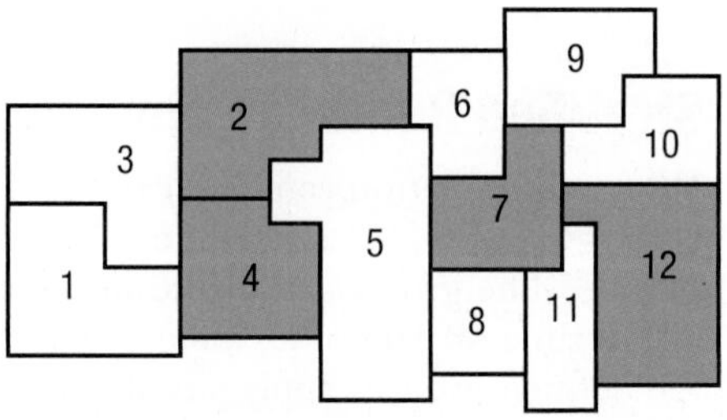

self-review 7–2

Refer to self-review 7–1 and the class roster. Suppose a systematic random sample will select every ninth student enrolled in the class. Initially, the fourth student on the list was selected at random. That student is numbered 03. Remembering that the random numbers start with 00, which students will be chosen to be members of the sample?

Exercises

1. The following is a list of Marco's Pizza stores in Lucas County. Also noted is whether the store is corporate-owned (C) or manager-owned (M). A sample of four locations is to be selected and inspected for customer convenience, safety, cleanliness, and other features.

ID No.	Address	Type	ID No.	Address	Type
00	2607 Starr Av	C	12	2040 Ottawa River Rd	C
01	309 W Alexis Rd	C	13	2116 N Reynolds Rd	C
02	2652 W Central Av	C	14	3678 Rugby Dr	C
03	630 Dixie Hwy	M	15	1419 South Av	C
04	3510 Dorr St	C	16	1234 W Sylvania Av	C
05	5055 Glendale Av	C	17	4624 Woodville Rd	M
06	3382 Lagrange St	M	18	5155 S Main	M
07	2525 W Laskey Rd	C	19	106 E Airport Hwy	C
08	303 Louisiana Av	C	20	6725 W Central	M
09	149 Main St	C	21	4252 Monroe	C
10	835 S McCord Rd	M	22	2036 Woodville Rd	C
11	3501 Monroe St	M	23	1316 Michigan Av	M

a. The random numbers selected are 08, 18, 11, 54, 02, 41, and 54. Which stores are selected?
b. Use the table of random numbers to select your own sample of locations.
c. A sample is to consist of every seventh location. The number 03 is the starting point. Which locations will be included in the sample?
d. Suppose a sample is to consist of three locations, of which two are corporate-owned and one is manager-owned. Select a sample accordingly.

Classify the situations in questions 2 to 4 as stratified random sampling, systematic random sampling, or cluster sampling.

A college decided to survey its students to see how they felt about using a computer in all classes, and how much extra tuition they would be willing to pay for the service.

2. The college made a list of all of the classes registered in the semester and then randomly selected 25 classes. All students in the selected 25 classes were surveyed.
3. The college determined that of its 10 000 students, 500 surveys would be sufficient to achieve satisfactory results. The students attending in that semester were sorted according to their student number, and every 20th student on the list was selected for the survey.
4. The college decided to survey the students according to their programs of study. A random sample was selected from each program.

Sampling "Error"

The previous section discussed sampling methods that can be used to select a sample that is a fair or unbiased representation of the population. In each method, it is important to note that the selection of every possible sample of a specified size from a population has a known chance or probability. This is another way to describe an unbiased sampling method.

Samples are used to estimate population characteristics. For example, the mean of a sample is used to estimate the population mean. However, since the sample is a part or portion

sampling error The difference between a sample statistic and its corresponding population parameter.

of the population, it is unlikely that the sample mean would be *exactly equal* to the population mean. Similarly, it is unlikely that the sample standard deviation would be *exactly equal* to the population standard deviation. We can therefore expect a difference between a *sample statistic* and its corresponding *population parameter*. This difference is called **sampling error**.

example

Refer to the previous example of Jane and Joe Miley who operate a bed and breakfast called the Foxtrot Inn. The population is the number of rooms rented each of the 30 days in June. Find the mean of the population. Use **Excel** or other means to select three random samples of five days. Calculate the mean of each sample and compare it to the population mean. What is the sampling error in each case?

solution

During the month of June there were 94 rentals. So the mean number of units rented per night is 3.13. The population mean, $\mu = 3.13$.

We take three random samples of five nights rented. The first random sample of five nights resulted in the following number of rooms rented: 4, 7, 4, 3, and 1. The mean of this sample is 3.8 rooms, which we call $\bar{x}_1$. The bar over the x reminds us that it is a sample mean and the subscript 1 indicates that it is the mean of the first sample. The mean is calculated by:

$$\bar{x}_1 = \frac{\Sigma x}{n} = \frac{4+7+4+3+1}{5} = \frac{19}{5} = 3.8$$

The sampling error for the first sample is the difference between the population mean (3.13) and the first sample mean (3.8). So, the sampling error is $(3.8 - 3.13) = 0.67$. The second random sample of five nights resulted in the following number of rooms rented: 3, 3, 2, 3, and 6. The mean of this sample is 3.4 rooms, which we call $\bar{x}_2$. The subscript 2 indicates that it is the mean of the second sample. The mean is calculated by:

$$\bar{x}_2 = \frac{\Sigma x}{n} = \frac{3+3+2+3+6}{5} = \frac{17}{5} = 3.4$$

The sampling error is $(3.4 - 3.13) = 0.27$.

In the third sample, the sampling error was found to be -1.33.

Each of these differences, 0.67, 0.27, and -1.33, is the sampling error made in estimating the population mean. Sometimes these errors are positive values, indicating that the sample mean is greater than the population mean, and so, the population mean is overestimated. Other times, the errors are negative values, meaning that they are less than the population mean and therefore, underestimating the population mean.

In this case where we have a population of size 30 (30 nights in June), and a sample size of 5, there is a large number of possible samples, 142 506, to be exact! To find this value, use the combination formula (4–4) from Chapter 4, with $n = 30$, and $r = 5$. Each of the 142 506 different samples has the same chance of being selected. Each sample may have a different sample mean and therefore, a different sampling error. The value of the sampling error depends on the random sample chosen, and so, the sampling errors are also random and occur by chance. If one were to determine the sum of these sampling errors over a large number of samples, the result would be very close to zero. If all possible samples were chosen and the sampling errors determined, their sum would be exactly zero.

Now that we have discovered the possibility of a sampling error when sample results are used to estimate a population parameter, how can we make an accurate prediction about the possible success of a newly developed toothpaste or other product, based only on sample results? How can the quality control department in a mass-production firm release a

3 Define and construct a sampling distribution of the sample mean.

shipment of microchips based only on a sample of 10 chips? How can polling organizations make an accurate prediction about a federal or provincial election based on a sample of 2000 registered voters out of a voting population of millions? To answer these questions, we first develop a *sampling distribution of the sample mean.*

Sample means vary from sample to sample.

sampling distribution of the sample mean
A probability distribution of all possible sample means of a given sample size.

Sampling Distribution of the Sample Mean

The sample means in the previous example varied from one sample to the next. The mean of the first sample of 5 days was 3.8 rooms, and the second sample was 3.4 rooms. The population mean was 3.13 rooms. If we organize the means of all possible samples of five days into a probability distribution, the result is called the **sampling distribution of the sample mean**.

The following example illustrates the construction of a sampling distribution of the sample mean.

example

Tartus Industries has seven production employees (considered the population). The hourly earnings of each employee are given in Table 7–2.

TABLE 7–2 Hourly Earnings of the Production Employees of Tartus Industries

Employee	Hourly Earnings ($)
Joe	$9
Sam	9
Sue	10
Bob	10
Jan	9
Art	10
Ted	11

1. What is the population mean?
2. What is the sampling distribution of the sample mean for samples of size 2?
3. What is the mean of the sampling distribution?
4. What observations can be made about the population and the sampling distribution?

solution

1. The population mean is $9.71, found by:

$$\mu = \frac{\$9 + \$9 + \$10 + \$10 + \$9 + \$10 + \$11}{7} = \$9.71$$

2. To arrive at the sampling distribution of the sample mean, all possible samples of 2 were selected without replacement from the population, and their means were computed. There are 21 possible samples, found by using formula (4–4).

$$_{N}C_{n} = \frac{N!}{n!(N-n)!} = \frac{7!}{2!(7-2)!} = 21$$

where $N = 7$ is the number of items in the population and $n = 2$ is the number of items in the sample.

The 21 distinct sample means from all possible samples of 2 that can be drawn from the population are shown in Table 7–3. This probability distribution is the sampling distribution of the sample mean and is summarized in Table 7–4.

TABLE 7–3 Sample Means for All Possible Samples of 2 Employees

Sample	Employees	Hourly Earnings ($)	Sum ($)	Mean ($)	Sample	Employees	Hourly Earnings ($)	Sum ($)	Mean ($)
1	Joe, Sam	$9, $9	$18	$9.00	12	Sue, Bob	$10, $10	$20	$10.00
2	Joe, Sue	9, 10	19	9.50	13	Sue, Jan	10, 9	19	9.50
3	Joe, Bob	9, 10	19	9.50	14	Sue, Art	10, 10	20	10.00
4	Joe, Jan	9, 9	18	9.00	15	Sue, Ted	10, 11	21	10.50
5	Joe, Art	9, 10	19	9.50	16	Bob, Jan	10, 9	19	9.50
6	Joe, Ted	9, 11	20	10.00	17	Bob, Art	10, 10	20	10.00
7	Sam, Sue	9, 10	19	9.50	18	Bob, Ted	10, 11	21	10.50
8	Sam, Bob	9, 10	19	9.50	19	Jan, Art	9, 10	19	9.50
9	Sam, Jan	9, 9	18	9.00	20	Jan, Ted	9, 11	20	10.00
10	Sam, Art	9, 10	19	9.50	21	Art, Ted	10, 11	21	10.50
11	Sam, Ted	9, 11	20	10.00					

TABLE 7–4 Sampling Distribution of the Sample Mean for $n = 2$

Sample Mean ($)	Number of Means	Probability
$9.00	3	.1429
9.50	9	.4285
10.00	6	.2857
10.50	3	.1429
	21	1.0000

Population mean is equal to the mean of the sample means

3. The mean of the sampling distribution of the sample mean is obtained by summing the various sample means and dividing the sum by the number of samples. The mean of all the sample means is usually written $\mu_{\bar{X}}$. The μ reminds us that it is a population value because we have considered all possible samples. The subscript $\bar{X}$ indicates that it is the sampling distribution of the sample mean.

$$\mu_{\bar{X}} = \frac{\textbf{Sum of all sample means}}{\textbf{Total number of samples}} = \frac{\$9.00 + \$9.50 + \cdots + \$10.50}{21}$$

$$= \frac{\$204}{21} = \$9.71$$

4. Refer to Chart 7–1, which shows both the population distribution and the distribution of the sample mean. These observations can be made:
   a. The mean of the distribution of the sample mean ($9.71) is equal to the mean of the population: $\mu = \mu_{\bar{X}}$.
   b. The spread in the distribution of the sample mean is less than the spread in the population values. The sample mean ranges from $9.00 to $10.50, but the population values vary from $9.00 up to $11.00. In fact, the standard deviation of the distribution of the sample mean is equal to the population standard deviation divided by the square root of the sample size. So, the formula for the standard deviation of the distribution of the sample mean is $\sigma/\sqrt{n}$. Notice, as we increase the size of the sample, $\sigma/\sqrt{n}$ becomes smaller so the spread of the distribution of the sample mean becomes narrower.
   c. The shape of the sampling distribution of the sample mean and the shape of the frequency distribution of the population values are different. The distribution of the sample mean tends to be more bell-shaped and to approximate the normal probability distribution.

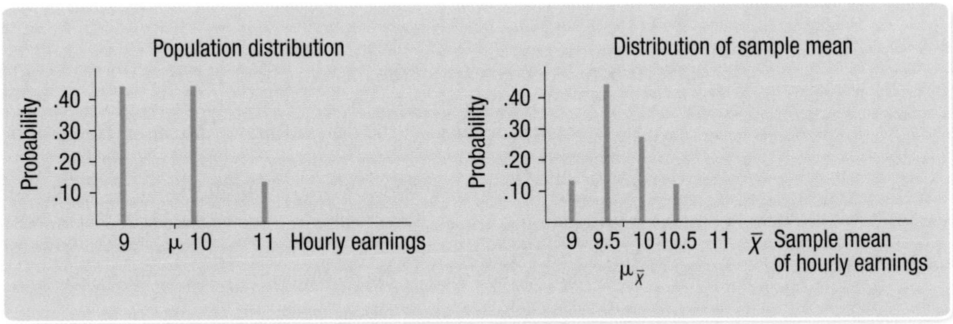

CHART 7–1 Distributions of Population Values and Sample Means

In summary, we took all possible random samples from a population and for each sample calculated a sample statistic (the mean amount earned). This example illustrates important relationships between the population distribution and the sampling distribution of the sample mean:

1. $\mu_{\bar{X}} = \mu$ (the mean of the sample means is exactly equal to the population mean).
2. $\sigma^2_{\bar{X}} = \sigma^2/n$ and $\sigma_{\bar{X}} = \sigma/\sqrt{n}$.
3. The sampling distribution of the sample means tends to become bell-shaped and to approximate the normal probability distribution. This approximation improves with larger samples.

Given a bell-shaped or normal probability distribution, we will be able to apply concepts from Chapter 6 to determine the probability of selecting a sample with a specified sample mean. In the next section, we will show the importance of sample size as it relates to the sampling distribution of sample means.

self-review 7–3

The lengths of service of all the executives employed by Standard Chemicals are:

Name	Years
Mr. Snow	20
Ms. Tolson	22
Mr. Kraft	26
Ms. Irwin	24
Mr. Jones	28

(a) Using the combination formula, how many samples of size 2 are possible?
(b) List all possible samples of two executives from the population and compute their means.
(c) Organize the means into a sampling distribution.
(d) Compare the population mean and the mean of the sample means.
(e) Compare the dispersion in the population with that in the distribution of the sample mean.
(f) A chart portraying the population values follows. Is the distribution of population values normally distributed (bell-shaped)?

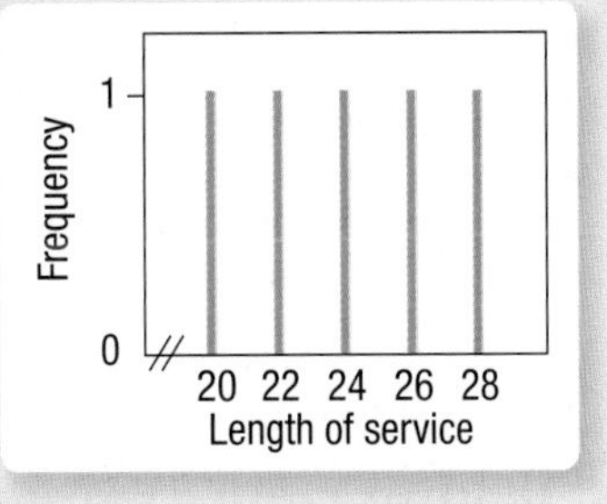

(g) Is the distribution of the sample mean computed in part (c) starting to show some tendency toward being bell-shaped?

Exercises

5. A population consists of the following four values: 12, 12, 14, and 16.
   a. List all samples of size 2, and compute the mean of each sample.
   b. Compute the mean of the distribution of the sample mean and the population mean. Compare the two values.
   c. Compare the dispersion in the population with that of the sample mean.

6. A population consists of the following five values: 2, 2, 4, 4, and 8.
   a. List all samples of size 2, and compute the mean of each sample.
   b. Compute the mean of the distribution of the sample mean and the population mean. Compare the two values.
   c. Compare the dispersion in the population with that of the sample means.

7. A population consists of the following five values: 12, 12, 14, 15, and 20.
   a. List all samples of size 3, and compute the mean of each sample.
   b. Compute the mean of the distribution of the sample mean and the population mean. Compare the two values.
   c. Compare the dispersion in the population with that of the sample means.

8. A population consists of the following five values: 0, 0, 1, 3, 6.
   a. List all samples of size 3, and compute the mean of each sample.
   b. Compute the mean of the distribution of the sample mean and the population mean. Compare the two values.
   c. Compare the dispersion in the population with that of the sample means.

9. In the law firm Tybo and Associates, there are six partners. Listed below is the number of cases each associate actually tried in court last month.

Associate	Number of Cases
Ruud	3
Austin	6
Sass	3
Palmer	3
Wilhelms	0
Schueller	1

   a. How many different samples of size 3 are possible?
   b. List all possible samples of size 3, and compute the mean number of cases in each sample.
   c. Compare the mean of the distribution of the sample mean to the population mean.
   d. On a chart similar to Chart 7–1, compare the dispersion in the population with that of the sample means.

10. There are five sales representatives at Mid-Motors Ford. The five representatives and the number of cars they sold last week are:

Sales Representative	Cars Sold
Peter Hankish	8
Connie Stallter	6
Ron Eaton	4
Ted Barnes	10
Peggy Harmon	6

   a. How many different samples of size 2 are possible?
   b. List all possible samples of size 2, and compute the mean of each sample.
   c. Compare the mean of the sampling distribution of the sample mean with that of the population.
   d. On a chart similar to Chart 7–1, compare the dispersion in the sample mean with that of the population.

4 Explain the *central limit theorem.*

central limit theorem If all samples of a particular size are selected from any population, the sampling distribution of the sample mean is approximately a normal distribution. This approximation improves with larger samples.

The Central Limit Theorem

In this section, we examine the **central limit theorem**. Its application to the sampling distribution of the sample mean, introduced in the previous section, allows us to use the normal probability distribution to create confidence intervals for the population mean (described in Chapter 8) and perform tests of hypothesis (described in Chapter 9). The central limit theorem states that, for large random samples, the shape of the sampling distribution of the sample mean is close to a normal probability distribution. The approximation is more accurate for large samples than for small samples. This is one of the most useful conclusions in statistics. We can reason about the distribution of the sample mean with absolutely no information about the shape of the population distribution from which the sample is taken. In other words, the central limit theorem is true for all distributions.

If the population follows a normal probability distribution, then for any sample size the sampling distribution of the sample mean will also be normal. If the population distribution is symmetrical (but not normal), you will see the normal shape of the distribution of the sample mean emerge with samples as small as 10. On the other hand, if you start with a distribution that is skewed or has thick tails, it may require samples of 30 or more to observe the normality feature. This concept is summarized in Chart 7–2 for various population shapes. Observe the convergence to a normal distribution regardless of the shape of the population distribution. Most statisticians consider a sample of 30 or more to be large enough for the central limit theorem to be employed.

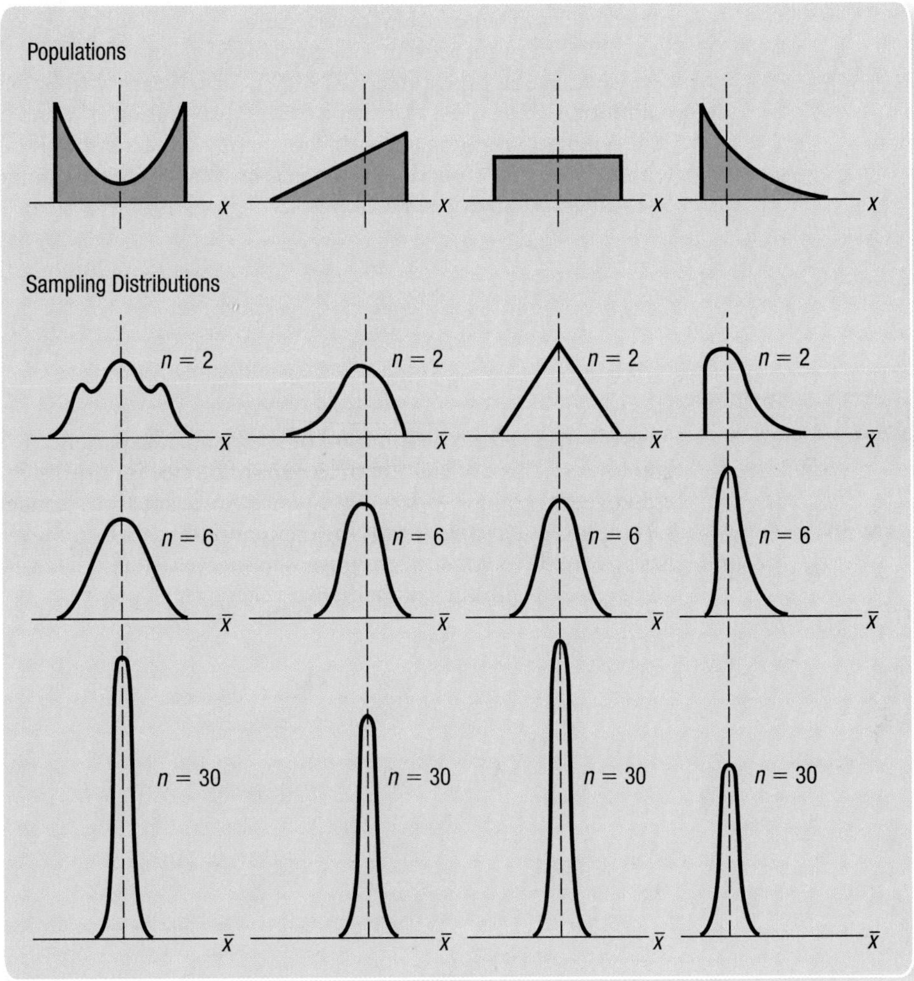

CHART 7–2 Results of the Central Limit Theorem for Several Populations

The idea that the distribution of the sample means from a population that is not normal will converge to normality is also illustrated in Charts 7–3, 7–4, and 7–5. We will discuss this example in more detail shortly, but Chart 7–3 is a graph of a discrete probability distribution that is positively skewed. There are many possible samples of 5 that might be selected from this population. Suppose we randomly select 25 samples of 5 each and compute the mean of each sample. These results are shown in Chart 7–4. Notice that the shape of the distribution of the sample mean has changed from the original population even though we selected only 25 of the many possible samples. To put it another way, we selected 25 random samples of 5 each from a population that is positively skewed and found the distribution of the sample mean has changed from the shape of the population. As we take larger samples, that is, $n = 20$ instead of $n = 5$, we will find the distribution of the sample mean will approach the normal distribution. Chart 7–5 shows the results of 25 random samples of 20 observations each from the same population. Observe the clear trend toward a normal probability distribution. This is the point of the central limit theorem. The following example will underscore this condition.

example

Ed Spence began his sprocket business 20 years ago. The business has grown over the years and now employs 40 people. Spence Sprockets Inc. faces some major decisions regarding health care for these employees. Before making a final decision on what health care plan to purchase, Ed decides to form a committee of five representative employees. The committee will be asked to study the health care issue carefully and make a recommendation as to what plan best fits the employees' needs. Ed feels the views of newer employees toward health care may differ from those of more experienced employees. If Ed randomly selects this committee, what can he expect in terms of the mean years with Spence Sprockets for those on the committee? How does the shape of the distribution of years of experience of all employees (the population) compare with the shape of the sampling distribution of the mean? The lengths of service (rounded to the nearest year) of the 40 employees currently on the Spence Sprockets Inc. payroll are as follows.

11	4	18	2	1	2	0	2	2	4
3	4	1	2	2	3	3	19	8	3
7	1	0	2	7	0	4	5	1	14
16	8	9	1	1	2	5	10	2	3

solution

Chart 7–3 shows the distribution of the years of experience for the population of 40 current employees. This distribution of lengths of service is positively skewed because there are a few employees who have worked at Spence Sprockets for a longer period of time. Specifically, six employees have been with the company 10 years or more. However, because the business has grown, the number of employees has increased in the last few years. Of the 40 employees, 18 have been with the company two years or less.

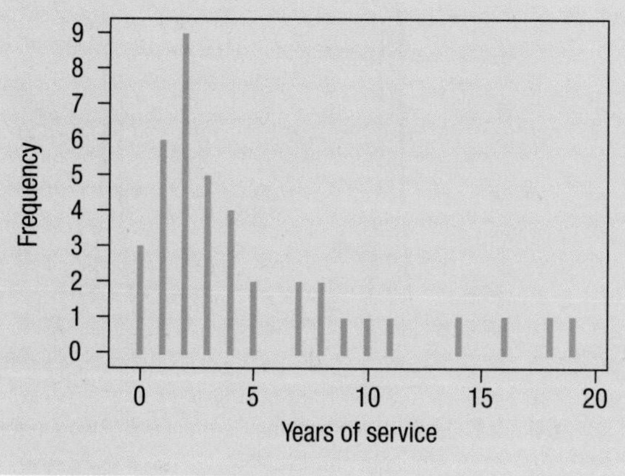

CHART 7–3 Length of Service for Spence Sprockets Inc. Employees

Let's consider the first of Ed Spence's problems. He would like to form a committee of five employees to look into the health care question and suggest what type of health care coverage would be most appropriate for the majority of workers. How should he select the committee? If he selects the committee randomly, what might he expect in terms of mean length of service for those on the committee?

To begin, Ed writes the length of service for each of the 40 employees on pieces of paper and puts them into an old baseball hat. Next, he shuffles the pieces of paper around and randomly selects five slips of paper. The lengths of service for these five employees are 1, 9, 0, 19, and 14 years. Thus, the mean length of service for these five sampled employees is 8.60 years. How does that compare with the population mean? At this point Ed does not know the population mean, but the number of employees in the population is only 40, so he decides to calculate the mean length of service for *all* his employees. It is 4.8 years, found by adding the lengths of service for *all* the employees and dividing the total by 40.

$$\mu = \frac{11 + 4 + 18 + \cdots + 2 + 3}{40} = 4.80$$

The difference between the sample mean ($\bar{X}$) and the population mean (μ) is called **sampling error**. In other words, the difference of 3.80 years between the population mean of 4.80 and the sample mean of 8.60 is the sampling error. It is due to chance. Thus, if Ed selected these five employees to constitute the committee, their mean length of service would be larger than the population mean.

5 Use the central limit theorem to find probabilities of selecting possible sample means from a specified population.

What would happen if Ed put the five pieces of paper back into the baseball hat and selected another sample? Would you expect the mean of this second sample to be exactly the same as the previous one? Suppose he selects another sample of five employees and finds the lengths of service in this sample to be 7, 4, 4, 1, and 3. This sample mean is 3.80 years. The result of selecting 25 samples of five employees each is shown in Table 7–5 and Chart 7–4. There are actually 658 008 possible samples of 5 from the population of 40 employees, found by the combination formula (4–4) for 40 things taken 5 at a time. Notice the difference in the shape of the population and the distribution of these sample means. The population of the lengths of service for employees (Chart 7–3) is positively skewed, but the distribution of these 25 sample means does not reflect the same positive skew. There is also a difference in the range of the sample means versus the range of the population. The population ranged from 0 to 19 years, whereas the sample means range from 1.6 to 8.6 years.

TABLE 7–5 Twenty-five Random Samples of Five Employees

Sample I.D.			Sample Data			Sample Mean
A	1	9	0	19	14	8.6
B	7	4	4	1	3	3.8
C	8	19	8	2	1	7.6
D	4	18	2	0	11	7.0
E	4	2	4	7	18	7.0
F	1	2	0	3	2	1.6
G	2	3	2	0	2	1.8
H	11	2	9	2	4	5.6
I	9	0	4	2	7	4.4
J	1	1	1	11	1	3.0
K	2	0	0	10	2	2.8
L	0	2	3	2	16	4.6
M	2	3	1	1	1	1.6
N	3	7	3	4	3	4.0
0	1	2	3	1	4	2.2
P	19	0	1	3	8	6.2
Q	5	1	7	14	9	7.2
R	5	4	2	3	4	3.6
S	14	5	2	2	5	5.6
T	2	1	1	4	7	3.0
U	3	7	1	2	1	2.8
V	0	1	5	1	2	1.8
W	0	3	19	4	2	5.6
X	4	2	3	4	0	2.6
Y	1	1	2	3	2	1.8

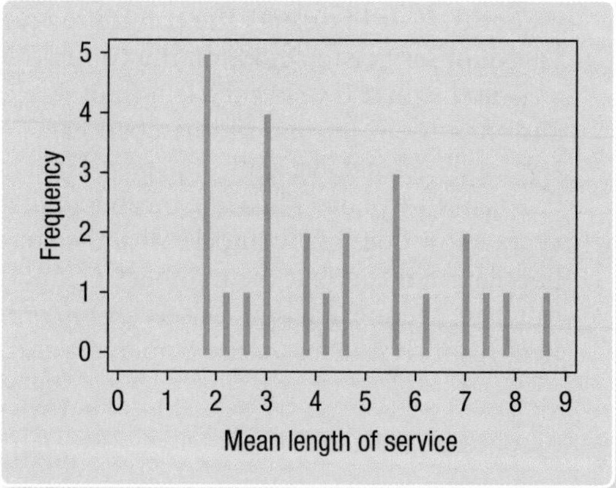

CHART 7–4 Histogram of Mean Lengths of Service for 25 Samples of Five Employees

Table 7–6 reports the result of selecting 25 samples of 20 employees each and computing their sample means. These sample means are shown graphically in Chart 7–5. Compare the shape of this distribution to the population (Chart 7–3) and to the distribution of sample means where the sample is $n = 5$ (Chart 7–4). You should observe two important features:

1. The shape of the distribution of the sample mean is different from that of the population. In Chart 7–3 the distribution of all employees is positively skewed. However, as we select random samples from this population, the shape of the distribution of the sample mean changes. As we increase the size of the sample, the distribution of the sample mean approaches the normal probability distribution. This illustrates the central limit theorem.
2. There is less dispersion in the sampling distribution of sample mean than in the population distribution. In the population the lengths of service ranged from 0 to 19 years. When we selected samples of 5, the sample means ranged from 1.6 to 8.6 years, and when we selected samples of 20, the means ranged from 3.05 to 7.10 years.

TABLE 7–6 Random Samples and Sample Means of 25 Samples of 20 Spence Sprocket Inc. Employees

Sample I.D.	Sample Data (Length of Service)																				Mean
A	3	8	3	0	2	1	2	3	11	5	1	3	4	2	7	1	1	2	4	16	3.95
B	2	3	8	2	1	5	2	0	3	1	0	7	1	4	3	11	4	4	3	1	3.25
C	14	5	0	3	2	14	11	9	2	2	1	2	19	1	0	1	4	2	19	8	5.95
D	9	2	1	1	4	10	0	8	4	3	2	1	0	8	1	14	5	10	1	3	4.35
E	18	1	2	2	4	3	2	8	2	1	0	19	4	19	0	1	4	0	3	14	5.35
F	10	4	4	18	3	3	1	0	0	2	2	4	7	10	2	0	3	4	2	1	4.00
G	5	7	11	8	11	18	1	1	16	2	2	16	2	3	2	16	2	2	2	4	6.55
H	3	0	2	0	5	4	5	3	8	3	2	5	1	1	2	9	8	3	16	5	4.25
I	0	0	18	2	1	7	4	1	3	0	3	2	11	7	2	8	5	1	2	3	4.00
J	2	7	2	4	1	3	3	2	5	10	0	1	1	2	9	3	2	19	3	2	4.05
K	7	4	5	3	3	0	18	2	0	4	2	7	2	7	4	2	10	1	1	2	4.20
L	0	3	10	5	9	2	1	4	1	2	1	8	18	1	4	3	3	2	0	4	4.05
M	4	1	2	1	7	3	9	14	8	19	4	4	1	2	0	3	1	2	1	2	4.40
N	3	16	1	2	4	4	4	2	1	5	2	3	5	3	4	7	16	1	11	1	4.75
O	2	19	2	0	2	2	16	2	3	11	9	2	8	0	8	2	7	3	2	2	5.10
P	2	18	16	5	2	2	19	0	1	2	11	4	2	2	1	4	2	0	4	3	5.00
Q	3	2	3	11	10	1	1	5	19	16	7	10	3	1	1	1	2	2	3	1	5.10
R	2	3	1	2	7	4	3	19	9	2	2	1	1	2	2	2	1	8	0	2	3.65
S	2	14	19	1	19	2	8	4	2	2	14	2	8	16	4	7	2	9	0	7	7.10
T	0	1	3	3	2	2	3	1	1	0	3	2	3	5	2	10	14	4	2	0	3.05
U	1	0	1	2	16	1	1	2	5	1	4	1	2	2	2	2	2	8	9	3	3.25
V	1	9	4	4	2	8	7	1	14	18	1	5	10	11	19	0	3	7	2	11	6.85
W	8	1	9	19	3	19	0	5	2	1	5	3	3	4	1	5	3	1	8	7	5.35
X	4	2	0	3	1	16	1	11	3	3	2	18	2	0	1	5	0	7	2	5	4.30
Y	1	2	1	2	0	2	7	2	4	8	19	2	5	3	3	0	19	2	1	18	5.05

We can also compare the mean of the sample means to the population mean. The mean of the 25 samples reported in Table 7–6 is 4.676 years.

$$\mu_{\bar{X}} = \frac{3.95 + 3.25 + \cdots + 4.30 + 5.05}{25} = 4.676$$

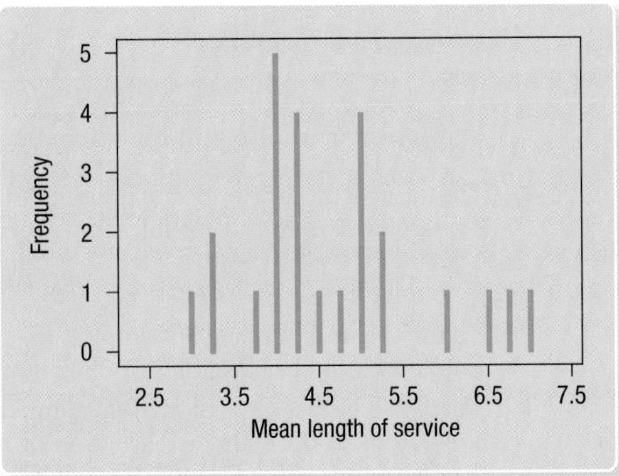

CHART 7–5 Histogram of Mean Lengths of Service for 25 Samples of 20 Employees

We use the symbol $\mu_{\bar{X}}$ to identify the mean of the distribution of the sample mean. The subscript reminds us that the distribution is of the sample mean. It is read "mu sub X bar." We observe that the mean of the sample means, 4.676 years, is very close to the population mean of 4.80.

What should we conclude from this example? The central limit theorem indicates that, regardless of the shape of the population distribution, the sampling distribution of the sample mean will move toward the normal probability distribution. The larger the number of observations in each sample, the stronger the convergence. The Spence Sprockets Inc. example shows how the central limit theorem works. We began with a positively skewed population (Chart 7–3). Next, we selected 25 random samples of 5 observations, computed the mean of each sample, and finally organized these 25 sample means into a graph (Chart 7–4). We observe a change in the shape of the sampling distribution of sample mean from that of the population. The movement is from a positively skewed distribution to a distribution that has the shape of the normal probability distribution.

To further illustrate the effects of the central limit theorem, we increased the number of observations in each sample from 5 to 20. We selected 25 samples of 20 observations each and calculated the mean of each sample. Finally, we organized these sample means into a graph (Chart 7–5). The shape of the histogram in Chart 7–5 is clearly moving toward the normal probability distribution.

If you go back to Chapter 5 where several binomial distributions with a "success" proportion of .10 are shown in Chart 5–4, you can see yet another demonstration of the central limit theorem. Observe as n increases from 7 through 12 and 20 up to 40 that the profile of the probability distributions moves closer and closer to a normal probability distribution. Chart 7–5 also shows the convergence to normality as n increases. This again reinforces the fact that, as more observations are sampled from any population distribution, the shape of the sampling distribution of the sample mean will get closer to a normal distribution.

The central limit theorem itself does not say anything about the dispersion of the sampling distribution of sample mean or about the comparison of the mean of the sampling distribution of sample mean to the mean of the population. However, in our Spence Sprockets example, we did observe that there was less dispersion in the distribution of the sample mean than in the population distribution by noting the difference in the range in the population and the range of the sample means. We observe that the mean of the sample means is close to the mean of the population $\mu_{\bar{x}} = \mu$. It can be demonstrated that the mean of the sampling distribution is the population mean and if the standard deviation in the population is σ, the standard deviation of the sample means is $\sigma/\sqrt{n}$, where n is the number of observations in each sample. We refer to $\sigma/\sqrt{n}$ as the **standard error of the mean**. Its longer name is actually the *standard deviation of the sampling distribution of the sample mean*.

STANDARD ERROR OF THE MEAN

$$\sigma_{\bar{X}} = \frac{\sigma}{\sqrt{n}} \quad [7\text{–}1]$$

In this section we also came to other important conclusions.

1. The mean of the distribution of the sample mean will be *exactly* equal to the population mean if we are able to select all possible samples of a particular size from a given population. That is:

$$\mu = \mu_{\bar{X}}$$

   Even if we do not select all samples, we can expect the mean of the distribution of the sample mean to be close to the population mean.
2. There will be less dispersion in the sampling distribution of the sample mean than in the population. If the standard deviation of the population is σ, the standard deviation of the distribution of the sample mean is $\sigma/\sqrt{n}$. Note that when we increase the size of the sample, the standard error of the mean decreases.

self-review 7–4

Refer to the Spence Sprockets Inc. data. Select 10 random samples of 5 employees each. Use the methods described earlier in the chapter and the Table of Random Numbers (Appendix E) to find the employees to include in the sample. Compute the mean of each sample and plot the sample means on a chart similar to Chart 7–3. What is the mean of the sample means?

Exercises

11. Appendix E is a table of random numbers. Hence, each digit from 0 to 9 has the same likelihood of occurrence.
    a. Draw a graph showing the population distribution. What is the population mean?
    b. Following are the first 10 rows of five digits from Appendix E. Assume that these are 10 random samples of five values each. Determine the mean of each sample and plot the means on a chart similar to Chart 7–3. Compare the mean of the sampling distribution of the sample mean with the population mean.

0	2	7	1	1
9	4	8	7	3
5	4	9	2	1
7	7	6	4	0
6	1	5	4	5
1	7	1	4	7
1	3	7	4	8
8	7	4	5	5
0	8	9	9	9
7	8	8	0	4

12. The Scrapper Elevator Company has 20 sales representatives who sell the company's product throughout the United States and Canada. The number of units sold by each representative is listed below. Assume these sales figures to be the population values.

2	3	2	3	3	4	2	4	3	2	2	7	3	4	5	3	3	3	3	5

a. Draw a graph showing the population distribution.
b. Compute the mean of the population.
c. Select five random samples of 5 each. Compute the mean of each sample. Use the methods described in this chapter and Appendix E to determine the items to be included in the sample.
d. Compare the mean of the sampling distribution of the sample mean to the population mean. Would you expect the two values to be about the same?
e. Draw a histogram of the sample means. Do you notice a difference in the shape of the distribution of sample means compared to the population distribution?

13. Consider all of the coins (pennies, nickels, quarters, etc.) in your pocket or purse as a population. Make a frequency table beginning with the current year and counting backward to record the ages (in years) of the coins. For example, if the current year is 2006, then a coin with 2004 on it is two years old.
a. Draw a histogram or other graph showing the population distribution.
b. Randomly select five coins and record the mean age of the sampled coins. Repeat this sampling process 20 times. Now draw a histogram or other graph showing the distribution of the sample means.
c. Compare the shapes of the two distributions.

14. Consider the digits in the phone numbers on a randomly selected page of your local phone book a population. Make a frequency table of the last four digits of 30 random phone numbers. For example, if a phone number is 555-9704, record 9704.
a. Draw a histogram or other graph of this population distribution.
b. Record the sample mean of the final four digits (9704 has a mean of 5). Draw a histogram or other graph showing the distribution of the sample means.
c. Compare the shapes of the two distributions.

Using the Sampling Distribution of the Sample Mean

The previous discussion is important because most business decisions are made on the basis of sampling results. Here are some examples.

1. Unilever Canada wants to ensure that its laundry detergent actually contains 2.95 L, as indicated on the label. Historical summaries from the filling process indicate the mean amount per container is 2.95 L and the standard deviation is 0.025 L. The quality control technician checked 40 containers in her routine morning sample test, and found the mean amount per container is 2.930 L. Should the technician shut down the filling operation or is the sampling error reasonable?
2. The ACNielsen Company provides information to companies advertising on television. Prior research indicates that adult Americans watch an average of 6.0 hours per day of television. The standard deviation is 1.5 hours. For a sample of 50 adults, would it be likely that we could randomly select a sample and find that they watch an average of 6.5 hours of television per day? Advertisers are especially interested in these viewing habits.
3. The Haughton Elevator Company wishes to develop specifications for the number of people who can ride in a new oversized elevator. Suppose the mean weight for an adult is 73 kg and the standard deviation is 7 kg. However, the distribution of weights does not follow a normal probability distribution. It is positively skewed. What is the likelihood that for a sample of 30 adults their mean weight is 77 kg or more? Safety inspectors and insurance companies would be especially interested in these results.

The sampling distribution will follow a normal distribution under these conditions.

In each of these situations we have a population about which we have some information. We take a sample from that population and wish to conclude whether the sampling error, that is, the difference between the population parameter and the sample statistic, is due to chance.

Using ideas discussed in the previous section, we can compute the probability that a sample mean will fall within a certain range. We know that the sampling distribution of the sample mean will follow a normal probability distribution under two conditions:

1. When the samples are taken from populations known to follow a normal distribution. In this case, the size of the sample is not a factor.
2. When the shape of the population distribution is not known or the shape is known to be non-normal, but our sample contains at least 30 observations.

In this case, the central limit theorem guarantees the sampling distribution of the mean follows a normal distribution.

We can use formula 6–1, from Chapter 6, to convert any normal distribution to the standard normal distribution. We also refer to this as a z-value. Then we can use the standard normal table, Appendix D, to find the probability of selecting an observation that would fall within a specific range. The formula for finding a z-value is:

$$z = \frac{X - \mu}{\sigma}$$

In this formula X is the observed value of the *random variable*, μ is the population mean, and σ the population standard deviation.

However, most business decisions refer to a sample mean—not just one observation. So we are interested in the distribution of $\bar{X}$, the sample mean, instead of X, the value of one observation. That is the first change we make in formula 6–1. The second is that we use the standard error of the mean of n observations instead of the population standard deviation. That is, we use $\sigma/\sqrt{n}$ in the denominator rather than σ. Therefore, to find the likelihood of a sample mean with a specified range, we first use the following formula to find the corresponding z-value. Then we use Appendix D to locate the probability.

FINDING THE z-VALUE OF $\bar{X}$ WHEN THE POPULATION STANDARD DEVIATION IS KNOWN

$$z = \frac{\bar{X} - \mu}{\sigma/\sqrt{n}} \quad \textbf{[7–2]}$$

The following example will show the application.

example

The quality control department for Cola Inc. maintains records regarding the amount of cola in its "Jumbo" bottle. The actual amount of cola in each bottle is critical, but varies a small amount from one bottle to the next. Cola Inc. does not wish to underfill the bottles, because it will have a problem with truth in labelling. On the other hand, it cannot overfill each bottle, because it would be giving cola away, hence reducing its profits. Its records indicate that the amount of cola follows a normal probability distribution. The mean amount per bottle is 1 L and the population standard deviation is 12.8 ml. At 8 a.m. today the quality control technician randomly selected 16 bottles from the filling line. The mean amount of cola contained in the bottles is 1.006 L. Is this an unlikely result? Is it likely the process is putting too much cola in the bottles?

solution

We can use the results of the previous section to find the likelihood that we could select a sample of 16 (n) bottles from a normal population with a mean of 1 L (μ) and a population standard deviation of 12.8 ml (σ) and find the sample mean to be 1.006 L ($\bar{X}$). We use formula 7–2 to find the value of z.

$$z = \frac{\bar{X} - \mu}{\sigma/\sqrt{n}} = \frac{1006 - 1000}{12.8/\sqrt{16}} = 1.875$$

The numerator of this equation, $\bar{X} - \mu = 1006 - 1000 = 6$ ml, is the sampling error. The denominator, $\sigma/\sqrt{n} = 12.8/\sqrt{16} = 3.2$ ml, is the standard error of the sampling distribution of the sample mean. So the z-values express the sampling error in standard units, in other words, the standard error.

Next, we compute the likelihood of a z-value greater than 1.88. In Appendix D locate the probability corresponding to a z-value of 1.88. It is .4699. The likelihood of a z-value greater than 1.88 is .0301, found by $.5 - .4699 = .0301$.

What do we conclude? It is unlikely, about a 3 percent chance, we could select a sample of 16 observations from a normal population with a mean of 1 L and a population standard deviation of 12.8 ml and find the sample mean equal to or greater than 1.006 L. We conclude the process is putting too much cola in the bottles. The quality control technician should see the production supervisor about reducing the amount of cola in each bottle. This information is summarized in Chart 7–6.

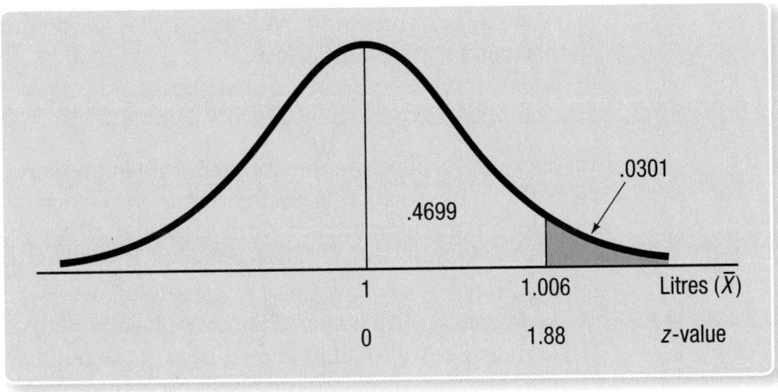

CHART 7–6 Sampling Distribution of the Mean Amount of Cola in a Jumbo Bottle

self-review 7–5

Refer to the Cola Inc. information. Suppose the quality technician selected a sample of 16 Jumbo Cola bottles that averaged 0.996 L. What can you conclude about the filling process?.

Exercises

15. A normal population has a mean of 60 and a standard deviation of 12. You select a random sample of 9. Compute the probability the sample mean is:
- **a.** Greater than 63.
- **b.** Less than 56.
- **c.** Between 56 and 63.

16. A normal population has a mean of 75 and a standard deviation of 5. You select a sample of 40. Compute the probability the sample mean is:
- **a.** Less than 74.
- **b.** Between 74 and 76.
- **c.** Between 76 and 77.
- **d.** Greater than 77.

17. The mean rent for a one-bedroom apartment in Southern Ontario is $1200 per month, with a standard deviation of $250. The distribution of the monthly costs does not follow the normal distribution. In fact, it is positively skewed. What is the probability of selecting a sample of 50 one-bedroom apartments and finding the mean to be at least $950 per month?.

18. According to a study, it takes an average of 330 minutes for taxpayers to prepare, copy, and electronically file an income tax return. The distribution of times follows the normal distribution and the standard deviation is 80 minutes. A random sample of 40 taxpayers is picked.
- **a.** What is the standard error of the mean in this example?
- **b.** What is the likelihood the sample mean is greater than 320 minutes?
- **c.** What is the likelihood the sample mean is between 320 and 350 minutes?
- **d.** What is the likelihood the sample mean is greater than 350 minutes?
- **e.** What assumption or assumptions do you need to make about the shape of the population?

6 Define and construct a sampling distribution of a proportion.

Sampling Distribution of the Proportion

The material presented so far in this chapter uses the ratio scale of measurement. That is, we use such variables as incomes, weights, distances, and ages. We now want to consider situations such as the following:

- A company representative claims that 45 percent of Burger King sales are made at the drive-through window.

- A survey of homes in the Windsor area indicated that 85 percent of the new construction had central air conditioning.
- A recent survey of married men between the ages of 35 and 50 found that 63 percent felt that both partners should earn a living.

These examples illustrate the nominal scale of measurement. When we measure with a nominal scale, an observation is classified into one of two or more mutually exclusive groups. For example, a particular Burger King customer either made a purchase at the drive-through window or did not make a purchase at the drive-through window. There are only two possibilities, and the outcome must be classified into one of the two groups.

proportion The fraction, ratio, or percent indicating the part of the sample or the population having a particular trait of interest.

As an example of a **proportion**, a recent survey indicated that 92 out of 100 people favoured the continued use of daylight savings time in the summer. The sample proportion is 92/100, or .92, or 92 percent. If we let $\bar{p}$ represent the sample proportion, X the number of successes, and n the number of items sampled, we can determine a sample proportion as follows.

SAMPLE PROPORTION $$\bar{p} = \frac{X}{n} \quad [7\text{–}3]$$

The population proportion is identified by p. Therefore, p refers to the percent of successes in the population. Recall from Chapter 5 that p is the proportion of successes in a binomial distribution. Ordinarily we use Greek letters to identify population parameters and Roman letters to identify sample statistics, but in this case we use $\bar{p}$ and p, to avoid confusion with the number $\pi = 3.14159....$

There are many instances when we may be interested only in the proportion of successes in the population such as:

- The proportion of voters who will vote Liberal in the next Federal election
- The percent of customers who preferred the taste of Coke to Pepsi in the recent taste test
- The fraction of students who travel more than 40 km one-way to class each day

In each case, we can take a sample and find the sample proportion, $\bar{p}$, which can be used as an estimate for the population, p. If the sample size is large enough, where np and $n(1 - p)$ are greater than 5, then the distribution of all possible sample proportions will be approximately normally distributed.

sampling distribution of the sampling proportion A probability distribution of all possible sample proportions of a given sample size.

When np and $n(1 - p) > 5$, the **sampling distribution** will be approximately normally distributed with a mean of $\mu_p = p$, and the standard error of the proportion, σ_p.

STANDARD ERROR OF THE PROPORTION $$\sigma_p = \sqrt{\frac{p(1-p)}{n}} \quad [7\text{–}4]$$

and

FINDING THE z-VALUE OF $\bar{p}$ WHEN THE POPULATION PROPORTION IS KNOWN $$z = \frac{\bar{p} - p}{\sqrt{\frac{p(1-p)}{n}}} \quad [7\text{–}5]$$

Using the Sampling Distribution of a Proportion

example

Alpha Corporation receives a shipment of flour every morning from its supplier. The flour is in 40 kg bags and Alpha will reject any shipment that is more than 5 percent underweight. The foreman samples 50 bags with each shipment and if the bags average more than 5 percent underweight, the whole shipment is returned to the supplier. What is the probability that in a sample of 150 bags, the foreman will find that less than 3 percent are underweight?

solution

$$p = .05 \text{ and } n = 150, \text{ so } \sigma_p = \sqrt{\frac{.05(1-.05)}{150}} = .0178$$

$$\text{and } z = \frac{.03 - .05}{.0178} = -1.12$$

We want to know the probability that the foreman will find less than 3 percent underweight, so we are looking for the area to the left of $z = -1.12$. Using the value from Appendix D, we find the probability is .1314 (.5 − .3686).

self-review 7–6

Refer to the Alpha Corporation information. Compute the probability that in a sample of 200, the foreman will find more than 4 percent of the bags underweight.

Exercises

19. Given $p = .45$ and $n = 200$, compute the standard error of the proportion.

20. Given $p = .09$ and $n = 50$, compute the standard error of the proportion.

21. Dawson's Repair Service orders parts from an electronic company who advertises its parts to be no more than 2 percent defective. What is the probability that Bill Dawson finds 3 or more parts out of a sample of 50 to be defective?

22. The college cafeteria finds that 30 percent of students will buy a dessert if it is properly advertised. The cafeteria manager is thinking of hiring an arts student to create a poster of a new apple and ice cream dessert which can be displayed at the front entrance to the cafeteria during the lunch hours. Normally, 650 students use the cafeteria during lunch time. What is the probability that more than 35 percent of the students will buy the apple and ice cream dessert?

23. Ms. Angelina Marie is considering running for mayor of her town for the second time. The first time, she received 75 percent of the popular vote. What is the probability that in a sample of 300 town residents, at least 240 would vote in favour of her for town mayor for the second time?

24. It has been estimated that 25 percent of all university students switch majors within their first two years of starting classes. If a random sample of 500 third-year students is taken at a city university, what is an estimate of the probability that 20 percent or less had switched majors within their first two years?

Chapter Summary

I. There are many reasons for sampling a population.

A. The results of a sample may adequately estimate the value of the population parameter, thus saving time and money.

B. It may be too time consuming to contact all members of the population.

C. It may be impossible to check or locate all the members of the population.

D. The cost of studying all the items in the population may be prohibitive.

E. Often, testing destroys the sampled item and it cannot be returned to the population.

II. In an unbiased sample, all members of the population have a chance of being selected for the sample. There are several probability sampling methods.

A. In a simple random sample, all members of the population have the same chance of being selected for the sample.

B. In a systematic sample, a random starting point is selected, and then every kth item thereafter is selected for the sample.

C. In a stratified sample, the population is divided into several groups, called strata, and then a random sample is selected from each stratum.

D. In cluster sampling, the population is divided into primary units, then samples are drawn from the primary units.

III. The sampling error is the difference between a population parameter and a sample statistic.

IV. The sampling distribution of the sample mean is a probability distribution of all possible sample means of a given size from a population.

A. For a given sample size, the mean of all possible sample means selected from a population is equal to the population mean.

B. There is less variation in the distribution of the sample mean than in the population distribution.

C. The standard error of the mean measures the variation in the sampling distribution of the sample mean. The standard error is found by:

$$\sigma_{\bar{X}} = \frac{\sigma}{\sqrt{n}} \quad \textbf{[7–1]}$$

D. If the population follows a normal distribution, the sampling distribution of the sample mean will also follow a normal distribution for samples of any size.

E. Assume the population standard deviation is known. To determine the probability that a sample mean falls in a particular region, use the following formula.

$$z = \frac{\bar{X} - \mu}{\sigma/\sqrt{n}} \quad \textbf{[7–2]}$$

F. The sampling distribution of the proportion follows a normal distribution if np and $n(1 - p) > 5$.

1. The sample proportion is $\bar{p} = \frac{x}{n}$ **[7–3]**

2. To determine the probability that a sample proportion falls in a particular region, use the following formula:

$$z = \frac{\bar{p} - p}{\sqrt{\frac{p(1-p)}{n}}} \quad \textbf{[7–5]}$$

Pronunciation Key

SYMBOL	MEANING	PRONUNCIATION
$\mu_{\bar{X}}$	Mean of the sampling distribution of the sample mean	*mu sub X bar*
$\sigma_{\bar{X}}$	Population standard error of the sample mean	*sigma sub X bar*
$s_{\bar{X}}$	Estimate of the standard error of the sample mean	*s sub X bar*
$\sigma_{\bar{p}}$	Population standard error of the sample proportion	*sigma sub p bar*

Chapter Exercises

25. The retail stores located in the North Towne Square Mall are:

00	GAP	09	M Studios	18	County Seat
01	Montgomery Ward	10	Bootleggers	19	Kid Mart
02	Deb Shop	11	Formal Man	20	Eddie Bauer
03	Frederick's of Hollywood	12	Leather Ltd.	21	Coach House Gifts
04	Petries	13	B Dalton Bookseller	22	Spence Gifts
05	Easy Dreams	14	Pat's Hallmark	23	CPI Photo Finish
06	Summit Stationers	15	Things Remembered	24	Regis Hairstylists
07	E. B. Brown Opticians	16	Pearle Vision Express		
08	Kay-Bee Toy & Hobby	17	Dollar Tree		

a. If the following random numbers are selected, which retail stores should be contacted for a survey? 11, 65, 86, 62, 06, 10, 12, 77, and 04.

b. Select a random sample of four retail stores. Use Appendix E.
c. A systematic sampling procedure is to be used. The first store is to be contacted and then every third store. Which stores will be contacted?

26. Canada's Wonderland theme park would like to do a survey to find out how often families visit in a season and how long they stay on each visit. How would you suggest taking this sample? What type of sampling have you described?

27. What is sampling error? Could the value of the sampling error be zero? If it were zero, what would this mean?

28. List the reasons for sampling. Give an example of each reason for sampling.

29. The commercial banks in the financial district are to be surveyed. Some of them are very large, with assets of more than $500 million; others are medium-sized, with assets between $100 million and $500 million; and the remaining banks have assets of less than $100 million. Explain how you would select a sample of these banks.

30. Plastic Products is concerned about the inside diameter of the plastic PVC pipe it produces. A machine extrudes the pipe, which is then cut into three-metre lengths. About 720 pipes are produced per machine during a two-hour period. How would you go about taking a sample from the two-hour production period?

31. A study of motel facilities in Rock Hill showed there are 25 facilities. The city's convention and visitors bureau is studying the number of rooms at each facility. The results are as follows:

90	72	75	60	75	72	84	72	88	74	105	115	68	74	80	64	104	82	48	58	60	80	48	58	100

a. Using a table of random numbers (Appendix E), select a random sample of five motels from this population.
b. Obtain a systematic sample by selecting a random starting point among the first five motels and then select every fifth motel.
c. Suppose the last five motels are "cut-rate" motels. Describe how you would select a random sample of three regular motels and two cut-rate motels.

32. As a part of its customer-service program, WestJet randomly selected 10 passengers from today's 9 a.m. Edmonton–Calgary flight. Each sampled passenger is to be interviewed in depth regarding airport facilities, service, food, and so on. To identify the sample, each passenger was given a number as he or she boarded the aircraft. The numbers started with 001 and ended with 250.
a. Select 10 usable numbers at random using Appendix E.
b. The sample of 10 could have been chosen using a systematic sample. Choose the first number using Appendix E, and then list the numbers to be interviewed.
c. Evaluate the two methods by giving the advantages and possible disadvantages.
d. In what other way could a random sample be selected from the 250 passengers?

33. Suppose your statistics instructor gave six examinations during the semester. You received the following grades (percent correct): 79, 64, 84, 82, 92, and 77. Instead of averaging the six scores, the instructor indicated he would randomly select two grades and report that grade to the student records office.
a. How many different samples of two test grades are possible?
b. List all possible samples of size 2 and compute the mean of each.
c. Compute the mean of the sample means and compare it to the population mean.
d. If you were a student, would you like this arrangement? Would the result be different from dropping the lowest score? Explain.

34. At the downtown office of First National Bank there are five tellers. Last week the tellers made the following number of errors each: 2, 3, 5, 3, and 5.
a. How many different samples of two tellers are possible?
b. List all possible samples of size 2 and compute the mean of each.
c. Compute the mean of the sample means and compare it to the population mean.

35. The quality control department employs five technicians during the day shift. Listed below is the number of times each technician instructed the production foreman to shut down the manufacturing process last week.

Technician	Shutdowns
Taylor	4
Hurley	3
Fowler	5
Rousche	3
Telatko	2

a. How many different samples of two technicians are possible from this population?
b. List all possible samples of two observations each and compute the mean of each sample.
c. Compare the mean of the sample means with the population mean.
d. Compare the shape of the population distribution with the shape of the distribution of the sample means.

36. The Appliance Centre has six sales representatives at its store. Listed below is the number of refrigerators sold by each last month.

Sales Representative	Number Sold
Zina Craft	54
Woon Junge	50
Ernie DeBrul	52
Jan Niles	48
Molly Camp	50
Rachel Myak	52

a. How many samples of size 2 are possible?
b. Select all possible samples of two and compute the mean number sold.
c. Organize the sample means into a frequency distribution.
d. What is the mean of the population? What is the mean of the sample means?
e. What is the shape of the population distribution?
f. What is the shape of the distribution of the sample mean?

37. Mattel Corporation produces a remote-controlled car that requires three AA batteries. The mean life of these batteries in this product is 35.0 hours. The distribution of the battery lives closely follows the normal probability distribution with a standard deviation of 5.5 hours. As a part of its testing program, Sony tests samples of 25 batteries.
a. What can you say about the shape of the distribution of sample mean?
b. What is the standard error of the distribution of the sample mean?
c. What fraction of the samples will have a mean useful life of more than 36 hours?
d. What fraction of the sample will have a mean useful life greater than 34.5 hours?
e. What fraction of the sample will have a mean useful life between 34.5 and 36.0 hours?

38. CRA CDs Inc. wants the mean lengths of the "cuts" on a CD to be 135 seconds (2 minutes and 15 seconds). This will allow the disk jockeys to have plenty of time for commercials within each 10-minute segment. Assume the distribution of the length of the cuts follows a normal distribution with a standard deviation of 8 seconds. Suppose we select a sample of 16 cuts from various CDs sold by CRA CDs Inc.
a. What can we say about the shape of the distribution of the sample mean?
b. What is the standard error of the mean?
c. What percent of the sample means will be greater than 140 seconds?
d. What percent of the sample means will be greater than 128 seconds?
e. What percent of the sample means will be greater than 128 but less than 140 seconds?

39. Recent studies indicate that the typical 50-year-old woman spends $350 per year for personal care products with a population standard deviation of $45. The distribution of the amounts spent is positively skewed. We select a random sample of 40 women. The mean amount spent for those sampled is $335. What is the likelihood of finding a sample mean this large or larger from the specified population?

40. The mean amount of life insurance per household is $110 000. This distribution is positively skewed. The standard deviation of the population is $40 000.
a. A random sample of 50 households revealed a mean of $112 000. What is the standard error of the mean?
b. Suppose that you selected 50 samples of households. What is the expected shape of the distribution of the sample mean?
c. What is the likelihood of selecting a sample with a mean of at least $112 000?
d. What is the likelihood of selecting a sample with a mean of more than $100 000?
e. Find the likelihood of selecting a sample with a mean of more than $100 000 but less than $112 000.

41. The mean age at which men in Canada marry for the first time is 30.6 years. The standard deviation of the population distribution is 2.5 years. For a random sample of 60 men, what is the likelihood that the age at which they were married for the first time is less than 31.5 years?

42. A recent study by the Island Resort Taxi Drivers Association showed that the mean fare charged for service from the beach to the airport is $18.00 and the standard deviation is $3.50. We select a sample of 15 fares.
a. What is the likelihood that the sample mean is between $17.00 and $20.00?
b. What must you assume to make the above calculation?

43. The Crossett Trucking Company claims that the mean mass of its delivery trucks when they are fully loaded is 2700 kg and the standard deviation is 68 kg. Assume that the population follows the normal distribution. Forty trucks are randomly selected and their masses measured. Within what limits will 95 percent of the sample means occur?

44. The mean amount purchased by each customer at Churchill's Grocery Store is \$23.50 with a standard deviation of \$5.00. The population is positively skewed. For a sample of 50 customers, answer the following questions.
   a. What is the likelihood the sample mean is at least \$25.00?
   b. What is the likelihood the sample mean is greater than \$22.50 but less than \$25.00?
   c. Within what limits will 90 percent of the sample means occur?

45. The mean SAT score for Division I student-athletes is 947 with a standard deviation of 205. If you select a random sample of 60 of these students, what is the probability the mean is below 900?

46. Suppose we roll a fair die two times.
   a. How many different samples are there?
   b. List each of the possible samples and compute the mean.
   c. On a chart similar to Chart 7–1, compare the distribution of sample means with the distribution of the population.
   d. Compute the mean and the standard deviation of each distribution and compare them.

47. The average grade in a statistics course has been 69 with a standard deviation of 12.5. If a random sample of 50 is selected from this population, what is the probability that the average grade is more than 73?

48. A preliminary survey shows that 35 percent of college students smoke. In a class of 42 students, what is the probability that more than half of the students smoke?

49. A convenience store estimates that 25 percent of its customers come in to buy milk. What is the probability that out of the next 200 customers, 60 or fewer will buy milk?

50. A manufacturing process produces 5 percent defective items. What is the probability that in a sample of 50 items:
   a. 10 percent or more will be defective?
   b. less than 1 percent will be defective?
   c. more than 10 percent or less than 1 percent will be defective?

51. A retailer claims that 90 percent of its customers are pleased or very pleased with the customer service. In a survey of 300 customers taken last week, what is the probability that:
   a. 85 percent or more will be pleased or very pleased with the service?
   b. 92 percent or more will be pleased or very pleased with the service?
   c. between 85 percent and 92 percent will be pleased or very pleased with the service?

Data Set Exercises

52. Refer to the real estate data, from the central area of Edmonton on the CD-ROM, which reports information on listed homes.
   a. Compute the mean and the standard deviation of the distribution of the list prices for the homes. Assume this to be the population. Develop a histogram of the data. Would it seem reasonable from this histogram to conclude that the population of list prices follows a normal distribution?
   b. Select a sample of 35 homes. Compute the mean of the sample. Determine the likelihood of finding a sample mean this large or larger from the population.

53. Refer to the International data, which reports demographic and economic information on 46 countries. Select a random sample of 10 countries. For this sample calculate the mean GDP/capita. Repeat this sampling and calculation process five more times, then find the mean and standard deviation of your six sample means.
   a. How do this mean and standard deviation compare with the mean and standard deviation of the original "population" of 46 countries?
   b. Make a histogram of the six means and discuss whether the distribution is normal.
   c. Suppose the population distribution is normal. For the first sample mean you computed, determine the likelihood of finding a sample mean this large or larger from the population.

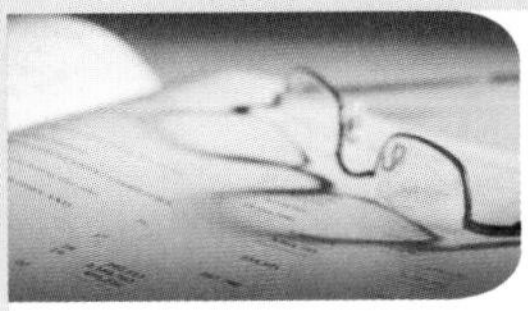

Case

Refer to the Whitner Pontiac data on the CD-ROM (Data Files), which reports information on the selling prices of vehicles sold at Rob Whitner's dealership.

1. Calculate the mean and the standard deviation for the selling prices. Assume this to be the population. Develop a histogram of the data. Would it seem reasonable from this histogram to conclude that the population of selling prices follows a normal distribution?
2. Select a sample of 35 selling prices. Calculate the mean of the sample. Determine the likelihood of finding a sample mean this large or larger from the population.

exercises.com

Additional exercises that require you to access information at related Internet sites are available on the CD-ROM included with this text.

Answers to Self-Reviews

7–1 **(a)** Students selected are Price, Detley, and Molter.
(b) Answers will vary.
(c) Skip it and move to the next random number.

7–2 The students selected are Berry, Francis, Kopp, Poteau, and Swetye.

7–3 **(a)** 10, found by:

$$_5C_2 = \frac{5!}{2!(5-2)!}.$$

(b)

	Service	Sample Mean
Snow, Tolson	20, 22	21
Snow, Kraft	20, 26	23
Snow, Irwin	20, 24	22
Snow, Jones	20, 28	24
Tolson, Kraft	22, 26	24
Tolson, Irwin	22, 24	23
Tolson, Jones	22, 28	25
Kraft, Irwin	26, 24	25
Kraft, Jones	26, 28	27
Irwin, Jones	24, 28	26

(c)

Mean	Number	Probability
21	1	.10
22	1	.10
23	2	.20
24	2	.20
25	2	.20
26	1	.10
27	1	.10
	10	1.00

(d) Identical: population mean, μ, is 24, and mean of sample means $\mu_{\bar{X}}$, is also 24.
(e) Sample means range from 21 to 27. Population values go from 20 to 28.
(f) Non-normal.
(g) Yes.

7–4 The answers will vary. Here is one solution.

	Sample Number										
	1	2	3	4	5	6	7	8	9	10	
	8	2	2	19	3	4	0	4	1	2	
	19	1	14	9	2	5	8	2	14	4	
	8	3	4	2	4	4	1	14	4	1	
	0	3	2	3	1	2	16	1	2	3	
	2	1	7	2	19	18	18	16	3	7	
Total	37	10	29	35	29	33	43	37	24	17	mean
$\bar{X}$	7.4	2	5.8	7.0	5.8	6.6	8.6	7.4	4.8	3.4	= 5.88

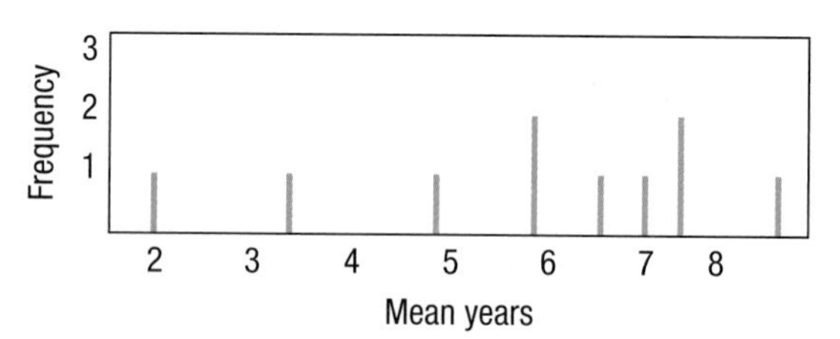

7–5 $z = \dfrac{996 - 1000}{12.8/\sqrt{16}} = -1.25.$

The probability that z is greater than −1.25 is .3944 + .5 = .8944. There is more than an 89 percent chance that the filling operation will produce bottles with at least 0.996 L.

7–6 $p = .05$ and $n = 200$, so $\sigma_P = \sqrt{\dfrac{.05(1-.05)}{200}} = .0154$

and $z = \dfrac{.04 - .05}{.0154} = -0.65.$

The probability is .7422 (.5 + .2422).

chapter 8

Estimation and Confidence Intervals

LEARNING GOALS

When you have completed this chapter, you will be able to:

1. **Define a *point estimate*.**
2. **Define *level of confidence*.**
3. **Construct a confidence interval for the population mean when the population standard deviation is known.**
4. **Define and calculate *t*-values.**
5. **Construct a confidence interval for a population mean when the population standard deviation is unknown.**
6. **Construct a confidence interval for a population proportion.**
7. **Determine the sample size for attribute and variable sampling.**

Introduction

The previous chapter began our discussion of statistical inference. It introduced the reasons and methods of sampling. The possible reasons for sampling are:

- To contact the entire population is too time consuming.
- The cost of studying all the items in the population is often too expensive.
- The sample results are usually adequate.
- Certain tests are destructive.
- Checking all items is physically impossible.

There are several methods of sampling. Simple random sampling is the most widely used method. With this type of sampling, each member of the population has the same chance of being selected to be a part of the sample. Other methods of sampling include systematic sampling, stratified sampling, and cluster sampling.

Chapter 7 assumes information about the population, such as the mean, the standard deviation, or the shape of the population. In most business situations, such information is not available. In fact, the purpose of sampling may be to estimate some of these values. For example, you select a sample from a population and use the mean of the sample to estimate the mean of the population.

1 Define a *point estimate.*

This chapter considers several important aspects of sampling. We begin by studying **point estimates.** A point estimate is a single value (point) derived from a sample and used to estimate a population value. For example, suppose we each select a sample of 50 junior executives and ask the number of hours they worked last week. Compute the mean of this sample of 50 and use the value of the sample mean ($\bar{X}$) as a point estimate of the unknown population mean. However, a point estimate is a single value. A more informative estimate is to present a range of values in which we expect the population parameter to occur. Such a range of values is called a **confidence interval.**

Frequently in business we need to determine the size of a sample. How many voters should a polling organization contact to forecast the election outcome? How many products do we need to examine to ensure our quality level? This chapter also develops a strategy for determining the size of the sample.

Point Estimates and Confidence Intervals for a Mean

We begin the study of point estimates and confidence intervals by studying estimates of the population mean. We will consider two cases, where

- The population standard deviation (σ) is known.
- The population standard deviation is unknown. In this case, we substitute the sample standard deviation (s) for the population standard deviation (σ).

There are important distinctions in the assumptions between these two situations. We consider the case where σ is known first.

Population Standard Deviation (σ) Known

In the previous chapter, the data on the length of service of Spence Sprockets employees is a population because we present the length of service for all 40 employees. In that case we can easily compute the population mean. We have all the data and the population is not too large. In most situations, however, the population is large or it is difficult to identify all members of the population, so we need to rely on sample information. In other words, we do not know the population parameter and we therefore want to estimate the value from a sample statistic. Consider the following business situations.

1. Tourism is a major source of income for many Caribbean countries, such as Barbados. Suppose the Bureau of Tourism for Barbados wants an estimate of the mean amount spent by tourists visiting the country. It would not be feasible to contact each tourist. So 500 tourists are randomly selected as they depart the country and asked in detail about their spending while visiting the island. The mean amount spent by the sample of 500 tourists, is an estimate of the unknown population parameter. That is, we let $\bar{X}$, the sample mean, serve as an estimate of μ, the population mean.
2. Centex Home Builders Inc. builds quality homes. One of the major concerns of new buyers is the date on which the home will be completed. In recent times Centex has been telling customers, "Your home will be completed 45 working days from the date we begin installing drywall." The customer relations department at Centex wishes to compare this pledge with recent experience. A sample of 50 homes completed this year revealed the mean number of working days from the start of drywall to the completion of the home was 46.7 days. Is it reasonable to conclude that the population mean is still 45 days and that the difference between the sample mean (46.7 days) and the proposed population mean is sampling error?
3. Recent medical studies indicate that exercise is an important part of a person's overall health. The director of human resources at OCF, a large glass manufacturer, wants an estimate of the number of hours per week employees spend exercising. A sample of 70 employees reveals the mean number of hours of exercise last week is 3.3. The sample mean of 3.3 hours is an estimate of the unknown population mean, the mean hours of exercise for all employees.

point estimate A single value, computed from sample information, which is used to estimate the population parameter.

A **point estimate** is a single statistic used to estimate a population parameter. Suppose Best Buy Inc. wants to estimate the mean age of buyers of LCD TVs. It selects a random sample of 50 recent purchasers, determines the age of each purchaser, and computes the mean age of the buyers in the sample. The mean of this sample is a point estimate of the mean of the population.

The sample mean, $\bar{X}$, is a point estimate of the population mean, μ; $\bar{p}$, a sample proportion, is a point estimate of p, the population proportion; and s, the sample standard deviation, is a point estimate of σ, the population standard deviation.

2 Define *level of confidence.*

A point estimate, however, tells only part of the story. While we expect the point estimate to be close to the population parameter, we would like to measure how close it really is. A **confidence interval** serves this purpose.

confidence interval A range of values constructed from sample data so that the population parameter is likely to occur within that range at a specified probability. The specified probability is called the *level of confidence.*

For example, we estimate the mean yearly income for construction workers to be \$65 000. The range of this estimate might be from \$61 000 to \$69 000. We can describe how confident we are that the population parameter is in the interval by making a probability statement. We might say, for instance, that we are 90 percent sure that the mean yearly income of construction workers is between \$61 000 and \$69 000.

The information developed about the shape of a sampling distribution of the sample mean, that is, the sampling distribution of $\bar{X}$, allows us to locate an interval that has a specified probability of containing the population mean, μ. For reasonably large samples, the results of the central limit theorem allow us to state the following:

1. Ninety-five percent of the sample means selected from a population will be within 1.96 standard deviations of the population mean, μ.
2. Ninety-nine percent of the sample means will lie within 2.58 standard deviations of the population mean.

The standard deviation discussed here is the standard deviation of the sampling distribution of the sample mean. It is usually called the "standard error." Intervals computed in this fashion are called the **95 percent confidence interval** and the **99 percent confidence interval.** How are the values of 1.96 and 2.58 obtained? The *95 percent* and *99 percent* refer to the percent of the time that similarly constructed intervals would include the parameter being estimated. The *95 percent,* for example, refers to the middle 95 percent of the observations. Therefore, the remaining 5 percent are equally divided between the two tails.

See the following diagram.

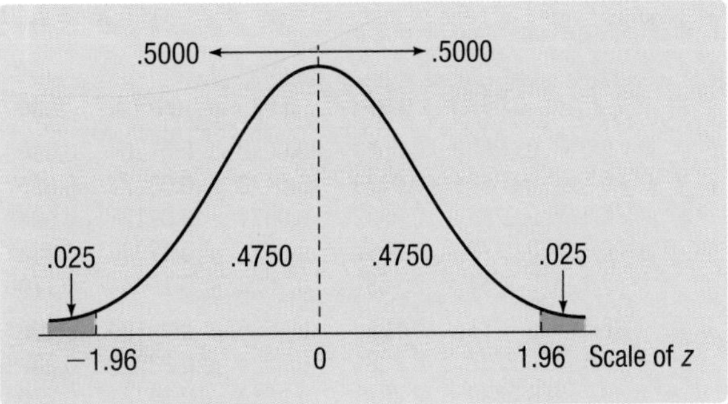

We use Appendix D (a portion of which is shown on the next page) to find the appropriate z-values. Locate .4750 in the body of the table. Read the corresponding row and column values. The value is 1.96. Thus, the probability of finding a z-value between 0 and 1.96 is .4750. Likewise, the probability of being in the interval between −1.96 and 0 is also .4750. When we combine these two, the probability of being in the interval −1.96 to 1.96 is .9500. The z-value for the 80 percent level of confidence is determined in a similar manner. It is 1.28. For a 99 percent level of confidence the z-value is 2.58.

3 Construct a confidence interval for the population mean when the population standard deviation is known.

How do we determine a 95 percent confidence interval for the mean? The width of the interval is determined by the level of confidence and the size of the standard error of the mean. We've described above how to find the z-value for a particular level of confidence. Recall from Chapter 7 that the standard error reports the variation in the distribution of sample means. It is really the standard deviation of the sample means. The formula is repeated below:

$$\sigma_{\bar{X}} = \frac{\sigma}{\sqrt{n}}$$

where:

- $\sigma_{\bar{x}}$ is the symbol for the standard error of the mean. We use a Greek letter because it is a population value, and the subscript $\bar{X}$ reminds us that it refers to a sampling distribution of the sample means.
- σ is the population standard deviation
- n is the number of observations in the sample

The size of the standard error is affected by two values. The first is the standard deviation of the population. The larger the population standard deviation (σ), the larger the standard error ($\sigma/\sqrt{n}$). If the population is homogeneous, resulting in a small population standard deviation, the standard error will also be small. However, the standard error is also affected by the number of observations in the sample. A larger sample will result in a smaller standard error of estimate, indicating that there is less variability in the sample means.

To explain these ideas, consider the following example: Assume your research involves the annual starting salary of business school graduates. You compute the sample mean to be \$39 000 from a sample of 25 graduates. The sample mean of \$39 000 is the point estimate of the population mean. The confidence interval is the point estimate plus or minus the error of estimation. The population standard deviation is known to be \$2000. The standard error is then \$400, found by $\sigma/\sqrt{n} = (2000/\sqrt{25}) = \$400$. The 95 percent confidence interval for the population mean of this particular sample is between \$38 216 and \$39 784, found by \$39 000 ± 1.96(400). Of course, in this case, we observe that the population mean of \$39 000 is in this interval. But that will not always be the case. Theoretically, if we selected 100 samples of 25 graduates from the population, calculated the sample mean, and developed a confidence interval based on each sample mean, we would expect to find the population mean in about 95 of the 100 intervals.

We can summarize the following calculations for a 95 percent confidence interval in the following formula:

$$\bar{X} \pm 1.96\left(\frac{\sigma}{\sqrt{n}}\right)$$

Similarly a 99 percent confidence interval is computed as follows.

$$\bar{X} \pm 2.58\left(\frac{\sigma}{\sqrt{n}}\right)$$

z	0.00	0.01	0.02	0.03	0.04	0.05	0.06	0.07	0.08	0.09
0.0	0.0000	0.0040	0.0080	0.0120	0.0160	0.0199	0.0239	0.0279	0.0319	0.0359
0.1	0.0398	0.0438	0.0478	0.0517	0.0557	0.0596	0.0636	0.0675	0.0714	0.0753
0.2	0.0793	0.0832	0.0871	0.0910	0.0948	0.0987	0.1026	0.1064	0.1103	0.1141
0.3	0.1179	0.1217	0.1255	0.1293	0.1331	0.1368	0.1406	0.1443	0.1480	0.1517
0.4	0.1554	0.1591	0.1628	0.1664	0.1700	0.1736	0.1772	0.1808	0.1844	0.1879
0.5	0.1915	0.1950	0.1985	0.2019	0.2054	0.2088	0.2123	0.2157	0.2190	0.2224
0.6	0.2257	0.2291	0.2324	0.2357	0.2389	0.2422	0.2454	0.2486	0.2517	0.2549
0.7	0.2580	0.2611	0.2642	0.2673	0.2704	0.2734	0.2764	0.2794	0.2823	0.2852
0.8	0.2881	0.2910	0.2939	0.2967	0.2995	0.3023	0.3051	0.3078	0.3106	0.3133
0.9	0.3159	0.3186	0.3212	0.3238	0.3264	0.3289	0.3315	0.3340	0.3365	0.3389
1.0	0.3413	0.3438	0.3461	0.3485	0.3508	0.3531	0.3554	0.3577	0.3599	0.3621
1.1	0.3643	0.3665	0.3686	0.3708	0.3729	0.3749	0.3770	0.3790	0.3810	0.3830
1.2	0.3849	0.3869	0.3888	0.3907	0.3925	0.3944	0.3962	0.3980	0.3997	0.4015
1.3	0.4032	0.4049	0.4066	0.4082	0.4099	0.4115	0.4131	0.4147	0.4162	0.4177
1.4	0.4192	0.4207	0.4222	0.4236	0.4251	0.4265	0.4279	0.4292	0.4306	0.4319
1.5	0.4332	0.4345	0.4357	0.4370	0.4382	0.4394	0.4406	0.4418	0.4429	0.4441
1.6	0.4452	0.4463	0.4474	0.4484	0.4495	0.4505	0.4515	0.4525	0.4535	0.4545
1.7	0.4554	0.4564	0.4573	0.4582	0.4591	0.4599	0.4608	0.4616	0.4625	0.4633
1.8	0.4641	0.4649	0.4656	0.4664	0.4671	0.4678	0.4686	0.4693	0.4699	0.4706
1.9	0.4713	0.4719	0.4726	0.4732	0.4738	0.4744	0.4750	0.4756	0.4761	0.4767
2.0	0.4772	0.4778	0.4783	0.4788	0.4793	0.4798	0.4803	0.4808	0.4812	0.4817
2.1	0.4821	0.4826	0.4830	0.4834	0.4838	0.4842	0.4846	0.4850	0.4854	0.4857
2.2	0.4861	0.4864	0.4868	0.4871	0.4875	0.4878	0.4881	0.4884	0.4887	0.4890
2.3	0.4893	0.4896	0.4898	0.4901	0.4904	0.4906	0.4909	0.4911	0.4913	0.4916
2.4	0.4918	0.4920	0.4922	0.4925	0.4927	0.4929	0.4931	0.4932	0.4934	0.4936

3 Construct a confidence interval for the population mean when the population standard deviation is known.

As we discussed earlier, the values 1.96 and 2.58 are the z-values corresponding to the middle 95 percent and the middle 99 percent of the observations, respectively.

We are not restricted to the 95 and 99 percent levels of confidence. We can select any confidence level between 0 and 100 percent and find the corresponding value for z. In general, a confidence interval for the population mean when the population standard deviation is known is computed by:

CONFIDENCE INTERVAL FOR THE POPULATION MEAN WITH σ KNOWN $$\bar{X} \pm z\frac{\sigma}{\sqrt{n}} \quad \textbf{[8–1]}$$

where z depends on the level of confidence. Thus, for a 92 percent level of confidence, the value of z in formula 8–1 is 1.75. The value of z is from Appendix D. This table is based on half the normal distribution, so .9200/2 = .4600. The closest value in the body of the table is .4599 and the corresponding z value is 1.75.

Frequently, we also use the 90 percent level of confidence. In this case, we want the area between 0 and z to be .4500, found by .9000/2. To find the z-value for this level of confidence, search the body of the table for an area close to .4500. The closest values in the table are .4495 and .4505. Start with .4495. To find the corresponding z-value, in the same row, refer to the left column and read 1.6. Then for the same column, refer to the top margin and find .04. Adding 1.6 and .04, the z-value is 1.64. Move to .4505, and repeat. The z-value is 1.65. Since .4500 is exactly half way between .4495 and .4505, we will use the z-value halfway between 1.64 and 1.65, which is 1.645. Try looking up the following levels of confidence and check your answers with the corresponding z-values given on the right.

Confidence Level	Nearest Probability	z Value
80 percent	.3997	1.28
94 percent	.4699	1.88
96 percent	.4798	2.05

The following example shows the details for calculating a confidence interval and interpreting the result.

example

A marketing company wishes to have information on the mean income of middle managers in the retail industry. A random sample of 256 managers reveals a sample mean of \$45 420. The standard deviation of this population is \$2050. The company would like answers to the following questions:

1. What is the population mean? What is a reasonable value to use as an estimate of the population mean?
2. What is a reasonable range of values for the population mean?
3. What do these results mean?

solution

Generally, distributions of salary and income are positively skewed, because a few individuals earn considerably more than others, thus skewing the distribution in the positive direction. Fortunately, the central limit theorem stipulates that if we select a large sample, the distribution of the sample means will follow a normal distribution. In this instance, a sample of 256 middle managers is large enough that the sampling distribution will follow the normal distribution.

Another issue is that the population standard deviation is not known. Again, it is sound practice to use the sample standard deviation when we have a large sample. Now, to answer the questions posed in the example.

1. **What is the population mean?** In this case, we do not know. We do know the sample mean is \$45 420. Hence, our best estimate of the unknown population value is the corresponding sample statistic. Thus, the sample mean of \$45 420 is a *point estimate* of the unknown population mean.

2. **What is a reasonable range of values for the population mean?** The company decides to use the 95 percent level of confidence. To determine the corresponding confidence interval, we use formula (8–1).

$$\bar{X} \pm z\frac{\sigma}{\sqrt{n}} = \$45\ 420 \pm 1.96\frac{\$2050}{\sqrt{256}} = \$45\ 420 \pm \$251$$

The usual practice is to round these endpoints to \$45 169 and \$45 671. These endpoints are called the *confidence limits*. The degree of confidence or the *level of confidence* is 95 percent and the confidence interval is from \$45 169 to \$45 671. The ± \$251 is often referred to as the *margin of error*.

3. **What do these results mean?** Suppose we select many samples of 256 managers, perhaps several hundred. For each sample, we compute the mean and the standard deviation for the same sample size n and then construct a 95 percent confidence interval, such as we did in the previous section. We could expect about 95 percent of these confidence intervals to contain the *population* mean. About 5 percent of the intervals would not contain the population mean annual income, which is μ. However, a particular confidence interval either contains the population parameter or it does not. The following diagram shows the results of selecting different samples from the population of middle managers in the retail industry, computing the mean of each, and then, using formula (8–1), determining a 95 percent confidence interval for the population mean. Note that not all intervals include the population mean. Both the endpoints of the fifth sample are less than the population mean. We attribute this to sampling error, and it is the risk we assume when we select the level of confidence.

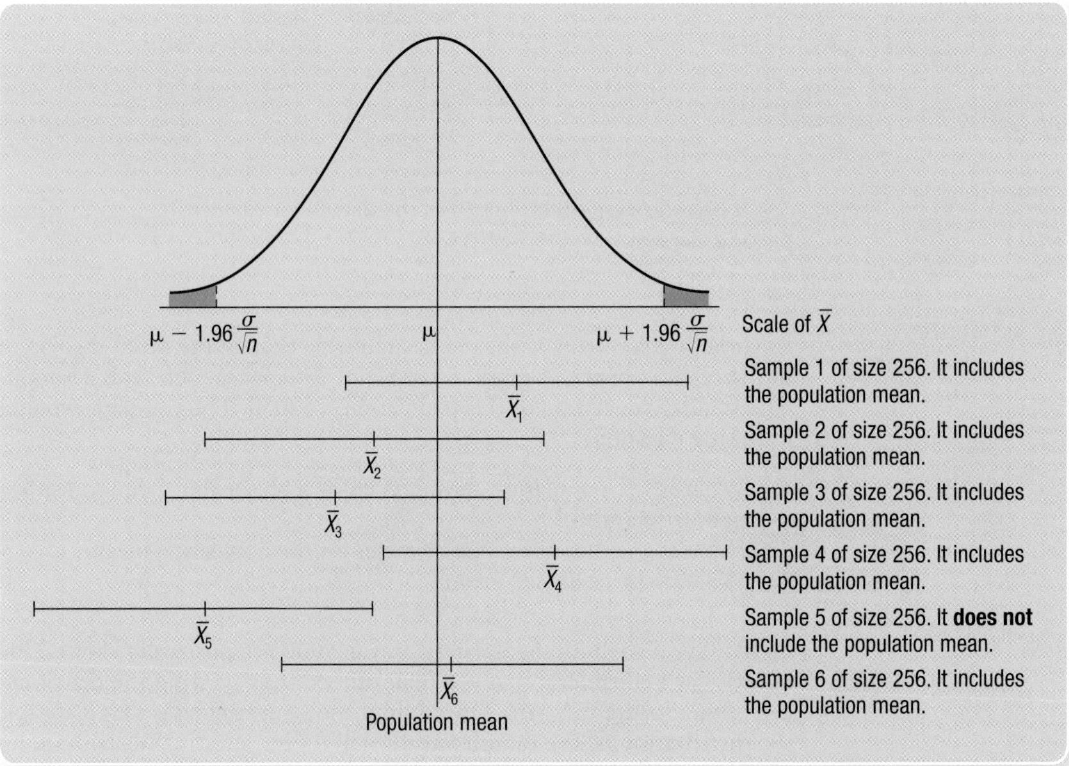

The **Excel** function to find the z-value is NORMSINV. To find the z-value for a 95% confidence level, we would enter '=NORMSINV(97.5%)' into a cell. Remember that the function is cumulative, and so 97.5% includes the 95% confidence level plus the area in the lower tail (5%/2 = 2.5%).

The following MegaStat commands will calculate a confidence interval.

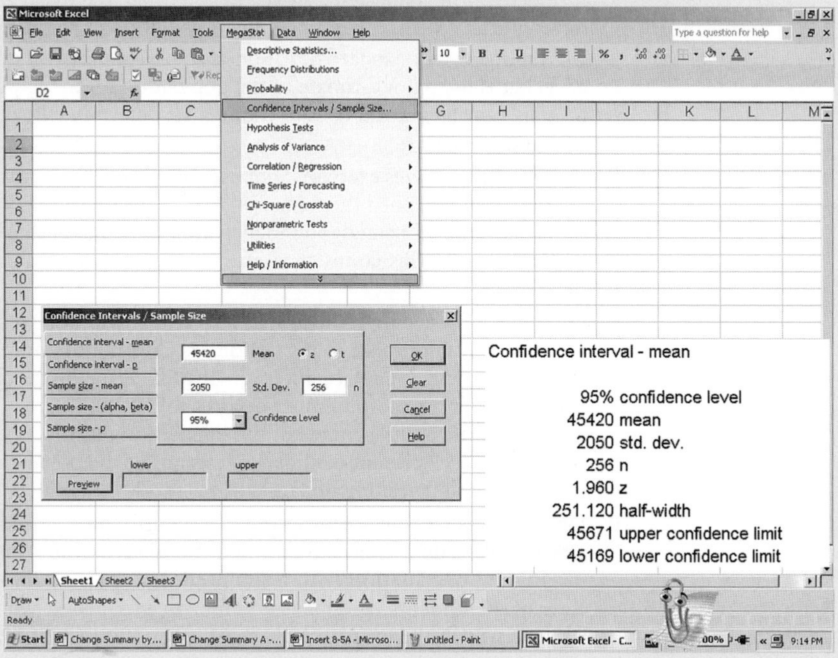

self-review 8–1

The mean daily sales are \$2000 for a sample of 40 days at a fast-food restaurant. The standard deviation of the population is \$300.

(a) What is the estimated mean daily sales of the population? What is this estimate called?
(b) What is the 99 percent confidence interval?
(c) Interpret your findings.

Exercises

1. A sample of 49 observations is taken from a normal population. The sample mean is 55, and the population standard deviation is 10. Determine the 99 percent confidence interval for the population mean.
2. A sample of 81 observations is taken from a normal population with a standard deviation of 5. The sample mean is 40. Determine the 95 percent confidence interval for the population mean.
3. A sample of 10 observations is selected from a normal population for which the population standard deviation is known to be 5. The sample mean is 20.
   a. Determine the standard error of the mean.
   b. Explain why we can use formula (8–1) to determine the 95 percent confidence interval even though the sample size is less than 30.
   c. Determine the 95 percent confidence interval for the population mean.
4. A sample of 40 observations is selected from a normal population where the population standard deviation is 25. The sample mean is 75.
   a. Determine the standard error of the mean.
   b. Determine the 90 percent confidence interval for the population mean.
   c. If you wanted a wider interval, would you increase or decrease the confidence level?
5. A sample of 25 observations is selected from a normal population where the population standard deviation is 4.75. The sample mean is 16.85.
   a. Determine the standard error of the mean.
   b. Determine the 98 percent confidence interval for the population mean.
   c. If you wanted a narrower interval, would you increase or decrease the confidence level?

6. Suppose you want an 85 percent confidence level. What value would you use to multiply the standard error of the mean?
7. A research firm conducted a survey to determine the mean amount steady smokers spend on cigarettes during a week. They found the distribution of amounts spent per week followed the normal distribution with a standard deviation of \$5. A sample of 49 steady smokers revealed that $\bar{X} = \$20$.
   a. What is the point estimate of the population mean? Explain what it indicates.
   b. Using the 95 percent level of confidence, determine the confidence interval for μ. Explain what it indicates.
8. Refer to the previous exercise. Suppose that 64 smokers (instead of 49) were sampled. Assume the sample mean remained the same.
   a. What is the 95 percent confidence interval estimate of μ?
   b. Explain why this confidence interval is narrower than the one determined in the previous exercise.
9. Bob Nale is the owner of Nale's Texaco GasTown. Bob would like to estimate the mean number of litres of gasoline sold to his customers. Assume the number of litres sold follows the normal distribution with a standard deviation of 10 L. From his records, he selects a random sample of 60 sales and finds the mean number of litres sold is 40.
   a. What is the point estimate of the population mean?
   b. Develop a 99 percent confidence interval for the population mean.
   c. Interpret the meaning of part b.
10. Dr. Patton is a Professor of English. Recently she counted the number of misspelled words in a group of student essays. She noted the distribution of misspelled words per essay followed the normal distribution with a standard deviation of 2.44 words per essay. For her Tuesday class of 40 students, the mean number of misspelled words per essay was 6.05. Construct a 95 percent confidence interval for the mean number of misspelled words in the population of student essays.

Population Standard Deviation (σ) Unknown

Statistics in Action

William Gosset was born in England in 1876 and died there in 1937. He worked for many years at Arthur Guinness & Sons Brewery. In fact, in his later years he was in charge of Guinness Brewery in London. Guinness preferred its employees to use pen names when publishing papers, so in 1908, when Gosset wrote "The Probable Error of a Mean," he used the name "Student." In this paper, he first described the properties of the *t* distribution.

In the previous section we assumed the population standard deviation was known. In these cases, there would likely be a history of data. Therefore, it is reasonable to assume the standard deviation of the population is available. However, in most sampling situations the population standard deviation (σ) is not known. Fortunately, we can use the sample standard deviation to estimate the population standard deviation. That is, we use s, the sample standard deviation to estimate σ, the population standard deviation. But in doing so, we can no longer use formula (8–1), and because we do not know σ, we cannot use the z distribution. However, there is a remedy. We use the sample standard deviation and replace the z distribution with the t distribution.

The t distribution is a continuous probability distribution, with many similar characteristics to the z distribution. William Gosset, an English brewmaster, was the first to study the t distribution. He was particularly concerned with the exact behaviour of the distribution of the following statistic:

$$t = \frac{\bar{X} - \mu}{s/\sqrt{n}}$$

when s is an estimate of σ. He was especially worried about the discrepancy between s and σ when s was calculated from a very small sample. The t distribution and the standard normal distribution are shown graphically in Chart 8–1. Note that the t distribution is flatter, more spread out, than the standard normal distribution. This is because the standard deviation of the t distribution is larger than that of the standard normal distribution.

4 **Define and calculate *t*-values.**

The following characteristics of the t distribution are based on the assumption that the population of interest follows the normal distribution.

1. It is, like the z distribution, a continuous distribution.
2. It is, like the z distribution, bell-shaped and symmetrical.
3. There is not one t distribution, but rather a "family" of t distributions. All t distributions have a mean of 0, but their standard deviations differ according to the sample size, n.

There is a t distribution for a sample size of 20, another for a sample size of 22, and so on. The standard deviation for a t distribution with 5 observations is larger than for a t distribution with 20 observations.

4. The t distribution is more spread out and flatter at the centre than is the standard normal distribution (see Chart 8–1). As the sample size increases, however, the t distribution approaches the standard normal distribution, because the errors in using s to estimate σ decrease with larger samples.

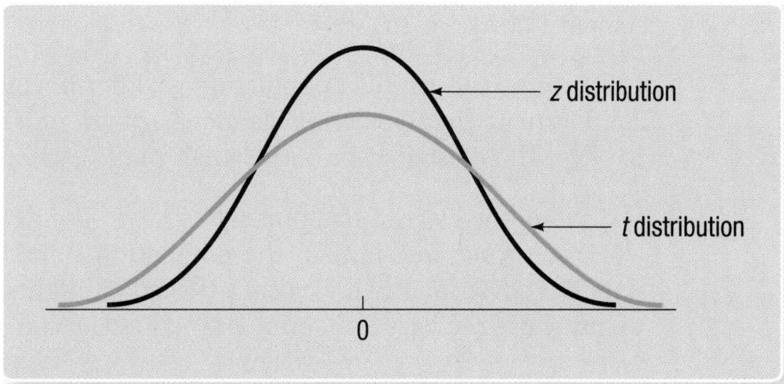

CHART 8–1 The Standard Normal Distribution and Student's *t* Distribution

Because Student's t distribution has a greater spread than the z distribution, the value of t for a given level of confidence is larger in magnitude than the corresponding z-values. Chart 8–2 shows the values of z and of t for a 95 percent level of confidence when the sample size is $n = 5$. How we obtained the actual value of t will be explained shortly. For now, observe that for the same level of confidence the t distribution is more spread out than the standard normal distribution.

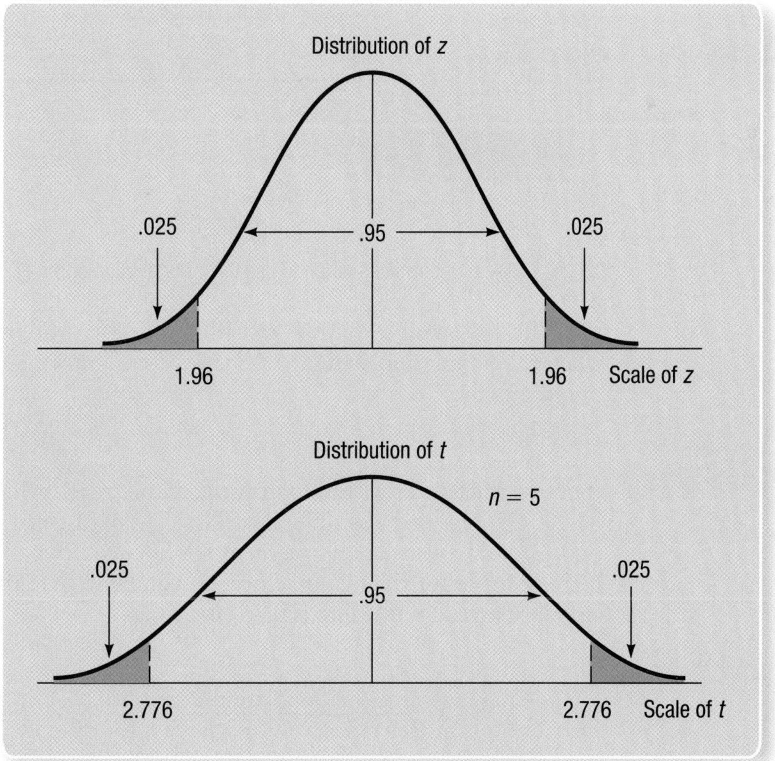

CHART 8–2 Values of *z* and *t* for the 95 Percent Level of Confidence

To develop a confidence interval for the population mean using the *t* distribution, we adjust formula (8–1) as follows.

5 Construct a confidence interval for a population mean when the population standard deviation is unknown.

CONFIDENCE INTERVAL FOR THE POPULATION MEAN, σ UNKNOWN

$$\bar{X} \pm t\frac{s}{\sqrt{n}} \quad \textbf{[8–2]}$$

To develop a confidence interval for the population mean with an unknown population standard deviation (σ) we:

1. Assume the sampled population is either normal or approximately normal.
2. Estimate the population standard deviation (σ) with the sample standard deviation (*s*).
3. Use the *t* distribution rather than the *z* distribution.

We should be clear at this point. We based the decision on whether to use the *t* or the *z* on whether or not we know σ, the population standard deviation. If we know the population standard deviation, then we use *z*. If we do not know the population standard deviation, then we must use *t*. Chart 8–3 summarizes the decision-making process.

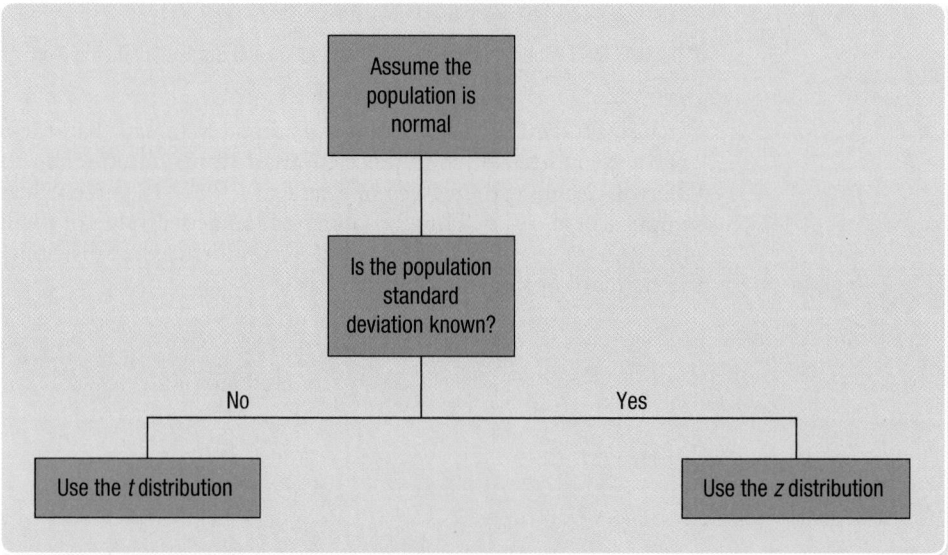

CHART 8–3 Determining When to Use the *z* Distribution or the *t* Distribution

The following example will illustrate a confidence interval for a population mean when the population standard deviation is unknown and how to find the appropriate value of *t* in a table.

example

A tire manufacturer wishes to investigate the tread life of its tires. A sample of 10 tires driven 80 000 km revealed a sample mean of 0.81 cm of tread remaining with a standard deviation of 0.23 cm. Construct a 95 percent confidence interval for the population mean. Would it be reasonable for the manufacturer to conclude that after 80 000 km the population mean amount of tread remaining is 0.76 cm?

solution

To begin, we assume the population distribution of tire wear follows the normal probability distribution. In this case, we don't have a lot of evidence, but the assumption is probably reasonable. We do not know the population standard deviation, but we know the sample standard deviation, which is 0.23 cm. We use formula (8–2):

$$\bar{X} \pm t\frac{s}{\sqrt{n}}$$

From the information given, $\bar{X} = 0.81$, $s = 0.23$, and $n = 10$. To find the value of t we use Appendix F, a portion of which is reproduced as Chart 8–4. The first step for locating t is to move across the row identified for "Confidence Intervals" to the level of confidence requested. In this case we want the 95 percent level of confidence, so we move to the row headed "95%." The column on the left margin is identified as "*df*." This refers to the number of degrees of freedom. The number of degrees of freedom is the number of observations in the sample minus the number of samples, written $n - 1$.[1] In this case it is $10 - 1 = 9$. The value of t is 2.262.

	Confidence Intervals				
	80%	90%	95%	98%	99%
	Level of Significance for One-Tailed Test				
df	0.100	0.050	0.025	0.010	0.005
	Level of Significance for Two-Tailed Test				
	0.20	0.10	0.05	0.02	0.01
1	3.078	6.314	12.706	31.821	63.657
2	1.886	2.920	4.303	6.965	9.925
3	1.638	2.353	3.182	4.541	5.841
4	1.533	2.132	2.776	3.747	4.604
5	1.476	2.015	2.571	3.365	4.032
6	1.440	1.943	2.447	3.143	3.707
7	1.415	1.895	2.365	2.998	3.499
8	1.397	1.860	2.306	2.896	3.355
9	1.383	1.833	2.262	2.821	3.250
10	1.372	1.812	2.228	2.764	3.169

CHART 8–4 A Portion of the *t* Distribution

To determine the confidence interval we substitute the values in formula (8–2).

$$\bar{X} \pm t\frac{s}{\sqrt{n}} = 0.81 \pm 2.262\frac{0.23}{\sqrt{10}} = 0.81 \pm .165$$

The endpoints of the confidence interval are 0.645 and 0.975. How do we interpret this result? It is reasonable to conclude that the population mean is in this interval. The manufacturer can be reasonably sure (95 percent confident) that the mean remaining tread depth is between 0.645 and 0.975 cm. Because the value of 0.76 is in this interval, it is possible that the mean of the population is 0.76.

[1]Why did we decide there were 9 degrees of freedom? When sample statistics are being used, it is necessary to determine the number of values that are *free to vary*. To illustrate: assume that the mean of four numbers is known to be 5. The four numbers are 7, 4, 1, and 8. The deviations of these numbers from the mean must total 0. The deviations of +2, −1, −4, and +3 do total 0. If the deviations of +2, −1, and −4 are known, then the value of +3 is fixed (restricted) in order to satisfy the condition that the sum of the deviations must equal 0. Thus, 1 degree of freedom is lost in a sampling problem involving the standard deviation of the sample because one number (the arithmetic mean) is known. For a 95 percent level of confidence and 9 degrees of freedom, we select the row with 9 degrees of freedom.

The MegaStat commands follow.

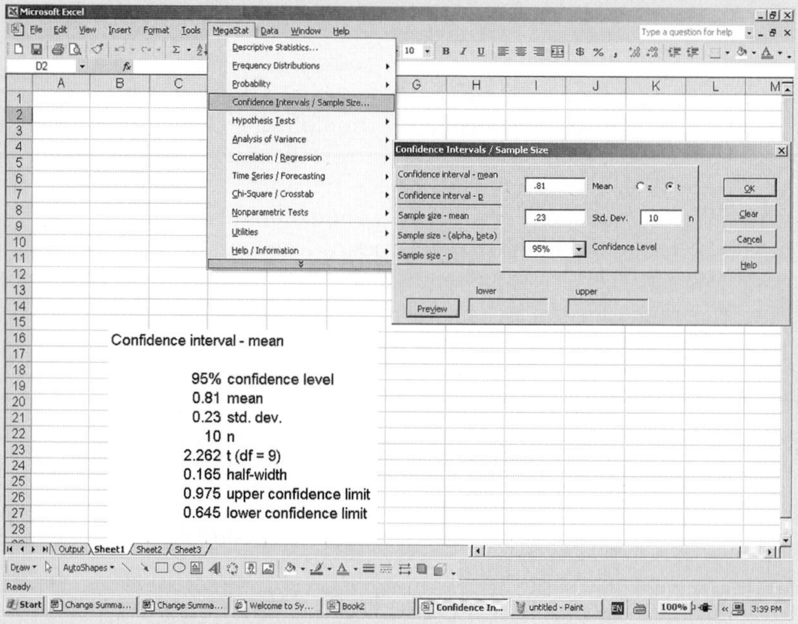

Here is another example to clarify the use of confidence intervals. Suppose an article in your local newspaper reported that the mean time to sell a residential property in the area is 60 days. You select a random sample of 20 homes sold in the last year and find the mean selling time is 65 days. Based on the sample data, you develop a 95 percent confidence interval for the population mean. You find that the endpoints of the confidence interval are 62 days and 68 days. How do you interpret this result? You can be reasonably confident the population mean is within this range. The value proposed for the population mean, that is, 60 days, is not included in the interval. Therefore, it is not likely that the population mean is 60 days. The evidence indicates the statement in the local newspaper may not be correct. To put it another way, it seems unreasonable to obtain the sample you did from a population with a mean selling time of 60 days.

The following example will show additional details for determining and interpreting a confidence interval.

example

The manager of the Inlet Square Mall wants to estimate the mean amount spent per shopping visit by customers. A sample of 20 customers reveals the following amounts spent in dollars.

$48.16	42.22	46.82	51.45	23.78	41.86	54.86
37.92	52.64	48.59	50.82	46.94	61.83	61.69
49.17	61.46	51.35	52.68	58.84	43.88	

What is the best estimate of the population mean? Determine a 95 percent confidence interval. Interpret the result. Would it be reasonable to conclude that the population mean is $50? What about $60?

solution

The mall manager assumes that the population of the amounts spent follows a normal distribution. This is a reasonable assumption in this case. Additionally, the confidence interval technique is quite powerful and tends to commit any errors on the conservative side if the population is not normal.

The population standard deviation is not known and so it is appropriate to use the t distribution and formula (8–2) to find the confidence interval. We use MegaStat to find the mean, standard deviation, and skewness of this sample. The results follow.

excel

minitab

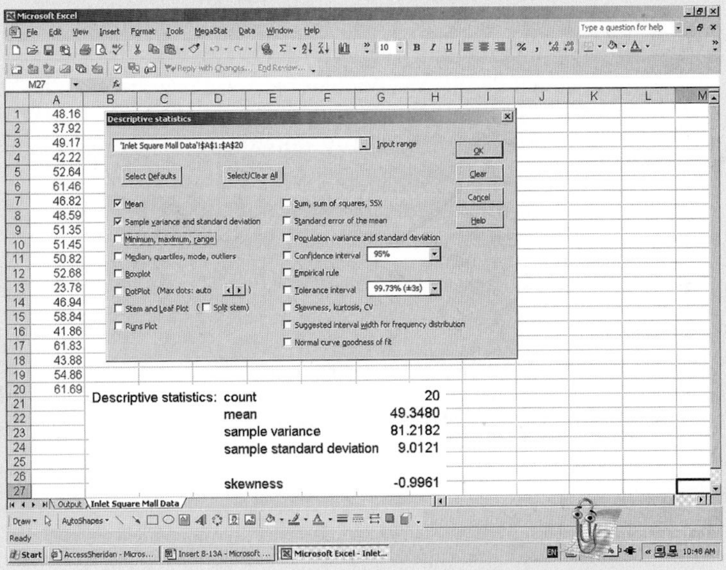

We should not make the normality assumption when the population is severely skewed. However, in this case, the coefficient of skewness is -0.9961, so the normality assumption is reasonable.

The mall manager does not know the population mean. The sample mean is the best estimate of that value. From the above MegaStat output, the mean is \$49.35, which is the best estimate, the *point estimate*, of the unknown population mean.

We use formula (8–2) to find the confidence interval. The value of t is available from Appendix F. There are $n - 1 = 20 - 1 = 19$ degrees of freedom. We move across the row with 19 degrees of freedom to the column for the 95 percent confidence level. The value at this intersection is 2.093. We substitute these values into formula (8–2) to find the confidence interval.

$$\bar{X} \pm t\frac{s}{\sqrt{n}} = \$49.35 \pm 2.093\frac{\$9.01}{\sqrt{20}} = \$49.35 \pm \$4.22$$

The endpoints of the confidence interval are \$45.13 and \$53.57. It is reasonable (with a 95 percent confidence level) to conclude that the population mean is in that interval.

MegaStat steps and output follow.

excel

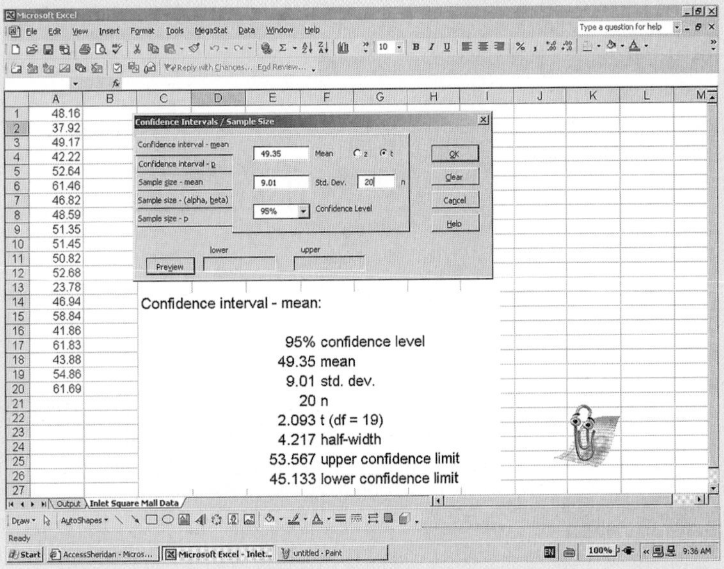

The manager of Inlet Square wondered whether the population mean could have been \$50 or \$60. The value of \$50 is within the confidence interval. It is reasonable that the population mean could be \$50. The value of \$60 is not in the confidence interval. Hence, we conclude that the population mean is unlikely to be \$60.

The **Excel** function to find the *t*-value is TINV. For the Inlet Square example, we would enter '=TINV(5%,19)' into a cell. The 5% is from 100% − 95% = 5%. The number of degrees of freedom is 20 − 1 = 19.

Note: The *t*-table does not show all degrees of freedom. If you want a value that is not shown, then use the smaller value that is shown.

self-review 8–2

Dottie Kleman is the "Cookie Lady." She bakes and sells cookies at 50 different locations. Ms. Kleman is concerned about absenteeism among her workers. The information below reports the number of days absent for a sample of 10 workers during the last two-week pay period.

4	1	2	2	1	2	2	1	0	3

(a) Determine the mean and the standard deviation of the sample.
(b) What is the population mean? What is the best estimate of that value?
(c) Develop a 95 percent confidence interval for the population mean.
(d) Explain why the *t* distribution is used as a part of the confidence interval.
(e) Is it reasonable to conclude that the typical worker does not miss any days during a pay period?

Exercises

11. Use Appendix F, **Excel**, or MegaStat to locate the value of *t* under the following conditions.
  a. The sample size is 12 and the level of confidence is 95 percent.
  b. The sample size is 20 and the level of confidence is 90 percent.
  c. The sample size is 8 and the level of confidence is 99 percent.

12. Use Appendix F, **Excel**, or MegaStat to locate the value of *t* under the following conditions.
  a. The sample size is 15 and the level of confidence is 95 percent.
  b. The sample size is 24 and the level of confidence is 98 percent.
  c. The sample size is 12 and the level of confidence is 90 percent.

13. A sample of 20 observations is selected from a normal population. The sample standard deviation is 26.25, and the sample mean is 75.
  a. Determine the standard error of the mean.
  b. Determine the 90 percent confidence interval for the population mean.
  c. If you wanted a wider interval, would you increase or decrease the confidence level?

14. A sample of 25 observations is selected from a normal population where the sample standard deviation is 4.75. The sample mean is 16.85.
  a. Determine the standard error of the mean.
  b. Determine the 98 percent confidence interval for the population mean.
  c. If you wanted a narrower interval, would you increase or decrease the confidence level?

15. The owner of Britten's Egg Farm wants to estimate the mean number of eggs laid per chicken. A sample of 20 chickens shows they laid an average of 20 eggs per month with a standard deviation of 2 eggs per month.
  a. What is the value of the population mean? What is the best estimate of this value?
  b. Explain why we need to use the *t* distribution. What assumption do you need to make?
  c. For a 95 percent confidence interval, what is the value of *t*?
  d. Develop the 95 percent confidence interval for the population mean.
  e. Would it be reasonable to conclude that the population mean is 21 eggs? What about 25 eggs?

16. The Sugar Producers Association wants to estimate the mean yearly sugar consumption. A sample of 16 people reveals the mean yearly consumption to be 27 kg with a standard deviation of 9 kg. Assume a normal population.
  a. What is the value of the population mean? What is the best estimate of this value?
  b. Explain why we need to use the *t* distribution. What assumption do you need to make?
  c. For a 90 percent confidence interval, what is the value of *t*?
  d. Develop the 90 percent confidence interval for the population mean.
  e. Would it be reasonable to conclude that the population mean is 28 kg?

17. Merrill Lynch Securities and Health Care Retirement Inc. are considering jointly offering child care for their employees. As a part of the feasibility study, they wish to estimate the mean weekly child care cost of their employees. A sample of 10 employees who use child care reveals the following amounts, in dollars, spent last week.

$107	92	97	95	105	101	91	99	95	104

Develop a 90 percent confidence interval for the population mean. Interpret the result.

18. An automobile insurance company wants to estimate the mean time workers who are employed in the downtown area spend getting to work. A sample of 15 workers reveals the following number of minutes travelled.

29	38	38	33	38	21	45	34
40	37	37	42	30	29	35	

Develop a 98 percent confidence interval for the population mean. Interpret the result.

Statistics in Action

Many survey results reported in newspapers, in news magazines, and on TV use confidence intervals. For example, a recent survey of 800 TV viewers found 44 percent watched the evening news on the local CBC affiliate. The article went on to indicate the margin of error was 3.4 percent. The margin of error is actually the amount that is added and subtracted from the point estimate to find the endpoints of a confidence interval. Using formula (8–5) and the 95 percent level of confidence:

$$z\sqrt{\frac{\bar{p}(1-\bar{p})}{n}}$$

$$=1.96\sqrt{\frac{.44(1-.44)}{800}}$$

$$=0.034$$

6 Construct a confidence interval for a population proportion.

A Confidence Interval for a Proportion

Recall from Chapter 7 that a proportion is the fraction, ratio, or percent indicating the part of the sample or the population having a particular trait of interest. We can determine a sample proportion using the following formula:

SAMPLE PROPORTION $$\bar{p}=\frac{X}{n}$$ **[7–3]**

To develop a confidence interval for a proportion, we need to meet the following assumptions.

1. The binomial conditions, discussed in Chapter 5, have been met. Briefly, these conditions are:
   (a) The sample data is the result of counts.
   (b) There are only two possible outcomes. (We usually label one of the outcomes a "success" and the other a "failure.")
   (c) The probability of a success remains the same from one trial to the next.
   (d) The trials are independent. This means the outcome on one trial does not affect the outcome of another.
2. The values np and $n(1-p)$ should both be greater than or equal to 5. This condition allows us to use the normal approximation to the binomial and employ the standard normal distribution, that is, z, as a part of the confidence interval.

Developing a point estimate for a population proportion and a confidence interval for a population proportion is similar to doing so for a mean. To illustrate, a candidate is running for the office of mayor of Calgary. From a random sample of 100 voters in the city, 60 indicate they plan to vote for the candidate in the upcoming election. The sample proportion is .60, but the population proportion is unknown. That is, we do not know what proportion of voters in the *population* will vote for the candidate. The sample value, .60, is the best estimate we have of the unknown population parameter. So we let $\bar{p}$, which is .60, be an estimate of p, which is not known.

To develop a confidence interval for a population proportion, we change formula (8–1) to:

CONFIDENCE INTERVAL FOR A POPULATION PROPORTION $$\bar{p} \pm z\sigma_p \text{ where } \sigma_p=\sqrt{\frac{p(1-p)}{n}}$$ **[8–3]**

The term σ_p is the "standard error" of the proportion. It measures the variability in the sampling distribution of the population proportion. For sample data:

STANDARD ERROR OF THE SAMPLE PROPORTION

$$s_p = \sqrt{\frac{\bar{p}(1-\bar{p})}{n}} \quad [8\text{–}4]$$

We can then construct a confidence interval for a population proportion from the following formula.

CONFIDENCE INTERVAL FOR A SAMPLE PROPORTION

$$\bar{p} \pm z\sqrt{\frac{\bar{p}(1-\bar{p})}{n}} \quad [8\text{–}5]$$

example

The union representing the Bottle Blowers of America (BBA) is considering a proposal to merge with the Teamsters Union. According to BBA union bylaws, at least three-fourths of the union membership must approve any merger. A random sample of 2000 current BBA members reveals 1600 plan to vote for the merger proposal. What is the estimate of the population proportion? Develop a 95 percent confidence interval for the population proportion. Basing your decision on this sample information, can you conclude that the necessary proportion of BBA members favours the merger?

solution

First, calculate the sample proportion from formula (7–3). It is .8, found by

$$\bar{p} = \frac{X}{n} = \frac{1600}{2000} = .8$$

Thus, we estimate that 80 percent of the population favour the merger proposal. We determine the 95 percent confidence interval using formula (8–5). The z-value corresponding to the 95 percent level of confidence is 1.96.

$$\bar{p} \pm z\sqrt{\frac{\bar{p}(1-\bar{p})}{n}} = .8 \pm 1.96\sqrt{\frac{.8(1-.8)}{2000}} = .8 \pm .018$$

The endpoints of the confidence interval are .782 and .818. The lower endpoint is greater than .75. Hence, we conclude that the merger proposal will pass because the interval estimate includes values greater than 75 percent of the union membership.

excel

The MegaStat commands to produce this confidence interval follow.

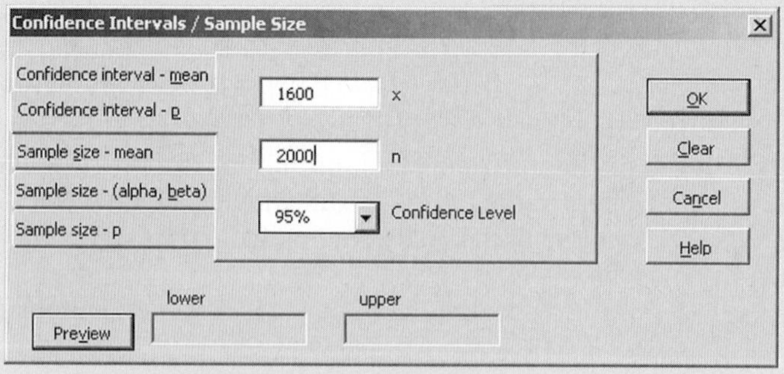

Confidence interval - proportion:

95% confidence level	
0.8 proportion	0.018 half-width
2000 n	0.818 upper confidence limit
1.960 z	0.782 lower confidence limit

The interpretation of a confidence interval can be very useful in decision making and play a very important role on election night. For example, Cliff Obermeyer is running for a federal MP in the riding of Fundy Royal. Suppose 500 voters are contacted upon leaving the polls and 275 indicated they voted for Mr. Obermeyer. We will assume that the 500 voters is a random sample of those voting in the riding. That means that 55 percent of those in the sample voted for Mr. Obermeyer, calculated as follows:

$$\bar{p} = \frac{X}{n} = \frac{275}{500} = .55$$

Now, to be assured of winning the election, he must earn more than 50 percent of the votes in the population of those voting. At this point we know a point estimate, which is .55 of the population of voters that will vote for him, but we do not know the percent in the population that will vote for him. So the question is, could we take a sample of 500 voters from a population where 50 percent or less of the voters support Mr. Obermeyer and find that 55 percent of the sample support him? To put it another way, could the sampling error, which is $\bar{p} - p = (.55 - .50)$ be due to chance, or is the population of voters who support Mr. Obermeyer greater than .50? If we develop a confidence interval for the sample proportion and find that .50 is not in the interval, then we conclude that the proportion of voters supporting Mr. Obermeyer is greater than .50 What does that mean? Well, it means he should be elected! What if .50 is in the interval? Then, we conclude that it is possible that 50 percent or less of the voters support his candidacy and we cannot conclude that he will be elected based on the sample information. In this case, using the 95 percent significance level and formula (8–5):

$$\bar{p} \pm z\sqrt{\frac{\bar{p}(1-\bar{p})}{n}} = .55 \pm 1.96\sqrt{\frac{.55(1-.55)}{500}} = .55 \pm .044$$

So the endpoints of the confidence interval are .55 − .044 = .506 and .55 + .044 = .594. The value of .50 is not in this interval, so we conclude that probably more than 50 percent of the voters support Mr. Obermeyer and that is enough to get him elected. Is this procedure ever used? Yes! It is exactly the procedure used by television networks, news magazines, and polling organizations on election night.

self-review 8–3

A market survey was conducted to estimate the proportion of homemakers who would recognize the brand name of a cleanser based on the shape and the colour of the container. Of the 1400 homemakers sampled, 420 were able to identify the brand by name.

(a) Estimate the value of the population proportion.
(b) Compute the standard error of the proportion.
(c) Develop a 99 percent confidence interval for the population proportion.
(d) Interpret your findings.

Exercises

19. A sample of 200 students indicated that 75 preferred chocolate ice cream to vanilla ice cream.
- **a.** Estimate the value of the population proportion of those who preferred chocolate ice cream.
- **b.** Compute the standard error of the proportion.
- **c.** Determine a 90 percent confidence interval for the population proportion of those who preferred chocolate ice cream.
- **d.** Interpret your findings.

20. Seventy-three percent of the 500 students surveyed voted in favour of the new breakfast menu in the college cafeteria.
- **a.** Estimate the value of the population proportion of those college students who would prefer the new menu.
- **b.** Compute the standard error of the proportion.
- **c.** Determine a 95 percent confidence interval for the population proportion of those college students who would prefer the new menu.
- **d.** Interpret your findings.

21. The owner of the West End Kwick Fill Gas Station wished to determine the proportion of customers who use his pay-at-the-pump feature. This feature allows customers to use a credit

card at the pump and never enter the station. He surveys 100 customers and finds that 80 paid at the pump.
   a. Estimate the value of the population proportion.
   b. Compute the standard error of the proportion.
   c. Develop a 95 percent confidence interval for the population proportion.
   d. Interpret your findings.

22. Ms. Maria Wilson is considering running for mayor of her town. Before completing her nomination papers, she decides to conduct a survey of voters. A sample of 400 voters reveals that 300 would support her in the November election.
   a. Estimate the value of the population proportion.
   b. Compute the standard error of the proportion.
   c. Develop a 99 percent confidence interval for the population proportion.
   d. Interpret your findings.

23. The CTV network is considering replacing one of its prime-time crime investigation shows with a new family-oriented comedy show. Before a final decision is made, network executives commission a sample of 400 viewers. After viewing the comedy, 250 indicated they would watch the new show and suggested it replace the crime investigation show.
   a. Estimate the value of the population proportion.
   b. Compute the standard error of the proportion.
   c. Develop a 99 percent confidence interval for the population proportion.
   d. Interpret your findings.

24. Schadek Silkscreen Printing Inc. purchases plastic cups on which to print logos for sporting events, proms, birthdays, and other special occasions. Zack Schadek, the owner, received a large shipment this morning. To ensure the quality of the shipment, he selected a random sample of 300 cups. He found 15 to be defective.
   a. What is the estimated proportion defective in the population?
   b. Develop a 95 percent confidence interval for the proportion defective.
   c. Zack has an agreement with his supplier that he is to return lots that are 10 percent or more defective. Should he return this lot? Explain your decision.

Finite-Population Correction Factor

The populations we have sampled so far have been very large or infinite. What if the sampled population is not very large? We need to make some adjustments in the way we compute the standard error of the sample means and the standard error of the sample proportions.

A population that has a fixed upper bound is *finite*. For example, there are 21 376 students enrolled at a college, there are 40 employees at Spence Sprockets, DaimlerChrysler assembled 917 Jeep Wranglers at the Alexis Avenue plant yesterday, or there were 65 surgical patients at St. Paul's Memorial Hospital yesterday. A finite population can be rather small; it could be all the students registered for this class. It can also be very large, such as all senior citizens living in Victoria, British Columbia.

For a finite population, where the total number of objects or individuals is N and the number of objects or individuals in the sample is n, we need to adjust the standard errors in the confidence interval formulas. To put it another way, to find the confidence interval for the mean we adjust the standard error of the mean. If we are determining the confidence interval for a proportion, then we need to adjust the standard error of the proportion.

This adjustment is called the **finite-population correction factor**. It is often shortened to *FPC* and is:

$$FPC = \sqrt{\frac{N-n}{N-1}}$$

Why is it necessary to apply a factor, and what is its effect? Logically, if the sample is a substantial percentage of the population, the estimate is more precise. Note the effect of the term $(N - n)/(N - 1)$. Suppose the population is 1000 and the sample is 100. Then this ratio is $(1000 - 100)/(1000 - 1)$, or 900/999. Taking the square root gives the correction factor, .9492. Multiplying this correction factor by the standard error *reduces* the standard error by about 5 percent ($1 - .9492 = .0508$). This reduction in the size of the standard error yields a smaller range of values in estimating the population mean or the population proportion. If the sample is 200, the correction factor is .8949, meaning that the standard error has been reduced by more than 10 percent. Table 8–1 shows the effects of various sample sizes. Note that when the sample is less than about 5 percent of the population, the impact of the correction factor is quite small. The usual rule is if the ratio of n/N is less than .05, the correction factor is ignored.

TABLE 8–1 Finite-Population Correction Factor for Selected Sample Sizes When the Population Is 1000

Sample Size	Fraction of Population	Correction Factor
10	.010	.9955
25	.025	.9879
50	.050	.9752
100	.100	.9492
200	.200	.8949
500	.500	.7075

So, if we wish to develop a confidence interval for the mean or proportion from a finite population, we would adjust the standard error of the mean or proportion as follows:

STANDARD ERROR OF THE SAMPLE MEAN, USING A CORRECTION FACTOR (KNOWN σ)

$$\sigma_{\bar{X}} = \frac{\sigma}{\sqrt{n}}\sqrt{\frac{N-n}{N-1}} \qquad [8\text{–}6]$$

STANDARD ERROR OF THE SAMPLE MEAN, USING A CORRECTION FACTOR (UNKNOWN σ)

$$s_{\bar{X}} = \frac{s}{\sqrt{n}}\frac{\sqrt{N-n}}{\sqrt{N-1}} \qquad [8\text{–}7]$$

STANDARD ERROR OF THE SAMPLE PROPORTION, USING A CORRECTION FACTOR

$$s_p = \sqrt{\frac{\bar{p}(1-\bar{p})}{n}}\sqrt{\frac{N-n}{N-1}} \qquad [8\text{–}8]$$

The following example summarizes the steps to find a confidence interval for the mean.

example

There are 250 families in a small Alberta town. A poll of 40 families reveals the mean annual church contribution is $450 with a standard deviation of $75. Could the population mean be $445 or $425?

1. What is the population mean? What is the best estimate of the population mean?
2. Discuss why the finite-population correction factor should be used.
3. Develop a 90 percent confidence interval for the population mean. What are the endpoints of the confidence interval?
4. Interpret the confidence interval.

solution

1. We do not know the population mean. This is the value we wish to estimate. The best estimate we have of the population mean is the sample mean, which is $450.
2. The sample size is 16 percent of the population size, found by $n/N = 40/250 = .16$. Because the sample size is more than 5 percent of the population size, we should use the *PCF* to adjust the standard error in determining the confidence interval.
3. The formula to find the confidence interval for a population mean follows:

$$\bar{X} \pm t\frac{s}{\sqrt{n}}\left(\sqrt{\frac{N-n}{N-1}}\right)$$

In this case, we know $\bar{X} = 450$, $s = 75$, $N = 450$, and $n = 40$. We do not know the population standard deviation so we use the t distribution. To find the appropriate value of

t we use Appendix F and move across the top row to the column headed 90%. The value is 1.685. We then use these values in the formula.

$$\bar{X} \pm t\frac{s}{\sqrt{n}}\left(\sqrt{\frac{N-n}{N-1}}\right) = \$450 \pm 1.685\frac{75}{\sqrt{40}}\left(\sqrt{\frac{250-40}{250-1}}\right) = \$450 \pm 18.35$$

The endpoints of the confidence interval are \$431.65 and \$468.35.

4. It is likely that the population mean is more than \$431.65 but less than \$468.35. To put it another way, could the population mean be \$445? Yes, but it is not likely that it is \$425. Why is this so? Because the value \$445 is within the confidence interval and \$425 is not within the confidence interval.

self-review 8–4

The same study of church contributions revealed that 15 of the 40 families sampled attend church regularly. Construct the 95 percent confidence interval for the proportion of families attending church regularly. Should the finite-population correction factor be used? Why or why not?

Exercises

25. Thirty-six items are randomly selected from a population of 300 items. The sample mean is 35 and the sample standard deviation 5. Develop a 95 percent confidence interval for the population mean.
26. Forty-nine items are randomly selected from a population of 500 items. The sample mean is 40 and the sample standard deviation 9. Develop a 99 percent confidence interval for the population mean.
27. The attendance at the Foresters Falls baseball game last night was 400. A random sample of 50 of those in attendance revealed that the mean number of soft drinks consumed per person was 1.86 with a standard deviation of 0.50. Develop a 99 percent confidence interval for the mean number of soft drinks consumed per person.
28. Sixty items are randomly selected from a population of 900. The number of defective items is found to be 12. Develop a 95 percent confidence interval for the population proportion of defective items.
29. A shipment of 500 dolls is received by Panda Importers. The quality control manager selects a random sample of 75 to test. Five are found to be defective. Construct a 90 percent confidence interval for the population proportion of defective dolls in the shipment. Would it be reasonable to find 10 defective dolls?
30. There are 300 welders employed at the Weller Shipyards Corporation. A sample of 30 welders revealed that 18 graduated from a registered welding course. Construct the 95 percent confidence interval for the proportion of all welders who graduated from a registered welding course.

7 Determine the sample size for attribute and variable sampling.

Choosing an Appropriate Sample Size

A concern that usually arises when designing a statistical study is "How many items should be in the sample?" If a sample is too large, money is wasted collecting the data. Similarly, if the sample is too small, the resulting conclusions will be uncertain. The necessary sample size depends on three factors:

1. The level of confidence desired.
2. The margin of error the researcher will tolerate.
3. The variability in the population being studied.

The first factor is the *level of confidence*. Those conducting the study select the level of confidence. The 95 percent and the 99 percent levels of confidence are the most common, but any value between 0 and 100 percent is possible. The 95 percent level of confidence corresponds to a z-value of 1.96, and a 99 percent level of confidence corresponds to a z-value of 2.58. The higher the level of confidence selected, the larger the size of the corresponding sample.

The second factor is the *allowable error*. The maximum allowable error, designated as E, is the amount that is added and subtracted to the sample mean (or sample proportion) to determine the endpoints of the confidence interval. It is the amount of error those conducting the study are willing to tolerate. It is also one-half the width of the corresponding confidence interval. A small allowable error will require a large sample. A large allowable error will permit a smaller sample.

The third factor in determining the size of a sample is the *population standard deviation*. If the population is widely dispersed, a large sample is required. On the other hand, if the population is concentrated (homogeneous), the required sample size will be smaller. However, it may be necessary to use an estimate for the population standard deviation. Here are three suggestions for finding that estimate.

1. **Use a comparable study**. Use this approach when there is an estimate of the dispersion available from another study. Suppose we want to estimate the number of hours worked per week by refuse workers. Information from certain provincial or federal agencies who regularly sample the workforce might be useful to provide an estimate of the standard deviation. If a standard deviation observed in a previous study is thought to be reliable, it can be used in the current study to help provide an approximate sample size.
2. **Use a range-based approach**. To use this approach we need to know or have an estimate of the largest and smallest values in the population. Recall from Chapter 3, where we described the Empirical Rule, that virtually all the observations could be expected to be within plus or minus 3 standard deviations of the mean, assuming that the distribution follows the normal distribution. Thus, the distance between the largest and the smallest values is 6 standard deviations, or $6s$. We could estimate the standard deviation as one-sixth of the range. For example, suppose the director of operations at the bank on campus wants an estimate of the number of cheques written per month by college students. She believes that the distribution is approximately normal, the minimum number of cheques written is 2 per month, and the most is 50 per month. The range of the number of cheques written per month is 48, found by $50-2$. The estimate of the standard deviation then would be 8 cheques per month, 48/6.
3. **Conduct a pilot study**. This is the most common method. Suppose we want an estimate of the number of hours per week worked by students enrolled in Seneca College. To test the validity of our questionnaire, we use it on a small sample of students. From this small sample, we compute the standard deviation of the number of hours worked and use this value to determine the appropriate sample size.

We can express the interaction among these three factors and the sample size in the following formula.

$$E = z\frac{\sigma}{\sqrt{n}}$$

Solving this equation for n yields the following result.

SAMPLE SIZE FOR ESTIMATING THE POPULATION MEAN

$$n = \left(\frac{z\sigma}{E}\right)^2 \qquad [8\text{–}9]$$

where:

n is the size of the sample.
z is the standard normal value corresponding to the desired level of confidence.
σ is the population standard deviation.
E is the maximum allowable error.

The result of this calculation is not always a whole number. When the outcome is not a whole number, the usual practice is to round up *any* fractional result. For example, 201.22 would be rounded up to 202.

example

A student in business administration wants to determine the mean amount members of city councils in large cities earn per month as remuneration for being a council member. The error in estimating the mean is to be less than \$100 with a 95 percent level of confidence. The student found a report by the Department of Labour that estimated the standard deviation to be \$1000. What is the required sample size?

solution

The maximum allowable error, E, is \$100. The value of z for a 95 percent level of confidence is 1.96, and the estimate of the standard deviation is \$1000. Substituting these values into formula (8–9), gives the required sample size as:

$$n = \left(\frac{z\sigma}{E}\right)^2 = \left(\frac{(1.96)(\$1000)}{\$100}\right)^2 = 384.16$$

The computed value of 384.16 is rounded up to 385. A sample of 385 is required to meet the specifications. If the student wants to increase the level of confidence, for example to 99 percent, this will require a larger sample. The z-value corresponding to the 99 percent level of confidence is 2.58.

$$n = \left(\frac{z\sigma}{E}\right)^2 = \left(\frac{(2.58)(\$1000)}{\$100}\right)^2 = 665.64$$

We recommend a sample of 666. Observe how much the change in the confidence level changed the size of the sample. An increase from the 95 percent to the 99 percent level of confidence resulted in an increase of 281 observations. This could greatly increase the cost of the study, both in terms of time and money. Hence, the level of confidence should be considered carefully.

The MegaStat commands to find the sample size for the mean follow.

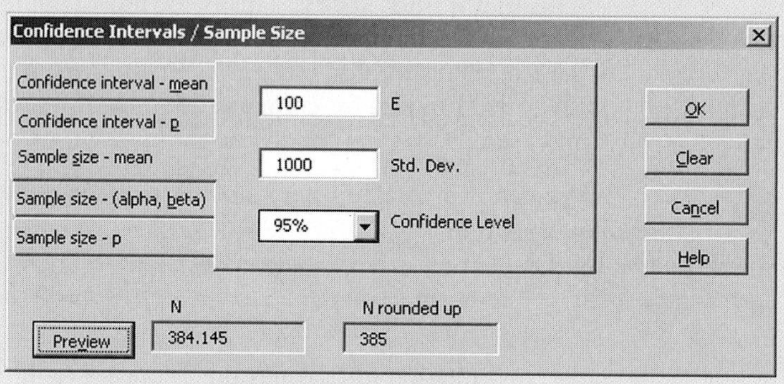

Sample size - mean

100 E, error tolerance	
1000 standard deviation	384.145 sample size
95% confidence level	385 rounded up
1.960 z	

The procedure just described can be adapted to determine the sample size for a proportion. Again, three items need to be specified:

1. The desired level of confidence.
2. The margin of error in the population proportion.
3. An estimate of the population proportion.

The formula to determine the sample size of a proportion is:

SAMPLE SIZE FOR THE POPULATION PROPORTION

$$n = p(1-p)\left(\frac{z}{E}\right)^2 \qquad \textbf{[8–10]}$$

If an estimate of p is available from a pilot study or some other source, it can be used. Otherwise, .50 is used because the term $p(1-p)$ can never be larger than when $p = .50$. For example, if $p = .30$, then $p(1-p) = .3(1-.3) = .21$, but when $p = .50$, $p(1-p) = .5(1-.5) = .25$

example

The study in the previous example also estimates the proportion of cities that have private refuse collectors. The student wants the estimate to be within .10 of the population proportion, the desired level of confidence is 90 percent, and no estimate is available for the population proportion. What is the required sample size?

solution

The estimate of the population proportion is to be within .10, so $E = .10$. The desired level of confidence is .90, which corresponds to a z-value of 1.645. Because no estimate of the population proportion is available, we use .50. The suggested number of observations is

$$n = (.5)(1-.5) = \left(\frac{1.645}{.10}\right)^2 = 67.65$$

The student needs a random sample of 68 cities.

excel

The MegaStat commands to find the sample size follow. The result of 67.639 is slightly different due to rounding.

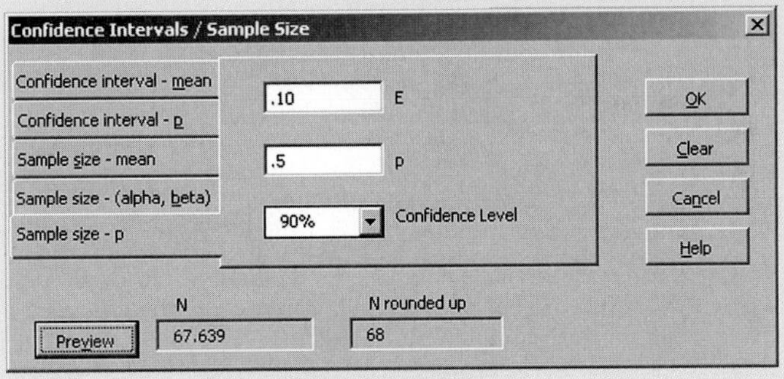

Sample size - proportion

0.1 E, error tolerance
0.5 estimated population proportion
90% confidence level 1.645 z
67.639 sample size 68 rounded up

self-review 8–5

Will you assist the college registrar in determining how many transcripts to study? The registrar wants to estimate the arithmetic mean grade point average (GPA) of all graduating seniors during the past 10 years. GPAs range between 2.0 and 4.0. The mean GPA is to be estimated within plus or minus .05 of the population mean. The standard deviation is estimated to be 0.279. Use the 99 percent level of confidence.

Exercises

31. A population is estimated to have a standard deviation of 10. We want to estimate the population mean within 2, with a 95 percent level of confidence. How large a sample is required?
32. We want to estimate the population mean within 5, with a 99 percent level of confidence. The population standard deviation is estimated to be 15. How large a sample is required?
33. The estimate of the population proportion is to be within plus or minus .05, with a 95 percent level of confidence. The best estimate of the population proportion is .15. How large a sample is required?
34. The estimate of the population proportion is to be within plus or minus .10, with a 99 percent level of confidence. The best estimate of the population proportion is .45. How large a sample is required?
35. A survey is being planned to determine the mean amount of time corporation executives watch television. A pilot survey indicated that the mean time per week is 12 hours, with a standard deviation of 3 hours. It is desired to estimate the mean viewing time within one-quarter hour. The 95 percent level of confidence is to be used. How many executives should be surveyed?
36. A processor of carrots cuts the green top off each carrot, washes the carrots, and inserts six to a package. Twenty packages are inserted in a box for shipment. To test the mass of the boxes, a few were checked. The mean mass was 9.3 kg, the standard deviation 0.23 kg. How many boxes must the processor sample to be 95 percent confident that the sample mean does not differ from the population mean by more than 0.09 kg?
37. Suppose the prime minister wants an estimate of the proportion of the population who support his current policy on health care. The prime minister wants the estimate to be within .04 of the true proportion. Assume a 95 percent level of confidence. The prime minister's political advisors estimated the proportion supporting the current policy to be .60.
    a. How large a sample is required?
    b. How large a sample would be necessary if no estimate were available for the proportion that support current policy?
38. Past surveys reveal that 30 percent of tourists going to Las Vegas to gamble during a weekend spend more than $1000. Management wants to update this percentage.
    a. The new study is to use the 90 percent confidence level. The estimate is to be within 1 percent of the population proportion. What is the necessary sample size?
    b. Management said that the sample size determined above is too large. What can be done to reduce the sample? Based on your suggestion recalculate the sample size.

Chapter Summary

I. A point estimate is a single value (statistic) used to estimate a population value (parameter).

II. A confidence interval is a range of values within which the population parameter is expected to occur.

A. The factors that determine the width of a confidence interval for a mean are:

1. The number of observations in the sample, n.
2. The variability in the population, usually estimated by the sample standard deviation, s.
3. The level of confidence.
    a. To determine the confidence limits when the population standard deviation is known, we use the z distribution. The formula is:

$$\bar{X} \pm z\frac{\sigma}{\sqrt{n}} \qquad [8\text{–}1]$$

    b. To determine the confidence limits when the population standard deviation is unknown, we use the t distribution. The formula is:

$$\bar{X} \pm t\frac{s}{\sqrt{n}} \qquad [8\text{–}2]$$

III. The major characteristics of the t distribution are:

A. It is a continuous distribution.

B. It is mound-shaped and symmetrical.

C. It is flatter, or more spread out, than the standard normal distribution.

D. There is a family of t distributions, depending on the number of degrees of freedom.

IV. A proportion is a ratio, fraction, or percent that indicates the part of the sample or population that has the particular characteristic.

A. A sample proportion is found by X, the number of successes, divided by n, the number of observations.

B. The standard error of the sample proportion reports the variability in the distribution of sample proportions. It is found by

$$s_p = \sqrt{\frac{\bar{p}(1-\bar{p})}{n}} \quad [8\text{–}4]$$

C. We construct a confidence interval for a population proportion from the following formula.

$$\bar{p} \pm z\sqrt{\frac{\bar{p}(1-\bar{p})}{n}} \quad [8\text{–}5]$$

V. For the finite population, the standard error is adjusted by the factor $\sqrt{\frac{N-n}{N-1}}$.

VI. We can determine the sample size for estimating population means and proportions.

A. There are three factors that determine the sample size when we wish to estimate the population mean.

1. The desired level of confidence, which is usually expressed by z.
2. The maximum allowable error, E.
3. The variation in the population, expressed by σ.
4. The formula to determine the sample size for the mean is

$$n = \left(\frac{z\sigma}{E}\right)^2 \quad [8\text{–}9]$$

B. There are three factors that determine the sample size when we wish to estimate a population proportion.

1. The desired level of confidence, which is usually expressed by z.
2. The maximum allowable error, E.
3. An estimate of the population proportion. If no estimate is available, use .50.
4. The formula to determine the sample size for a proportion is

$$n = p(1-p)\left(\frac{z}{E}\right)^2 \quad [8\text{–}10]$$

Pronunciation Key

SYMBOL	MEANING	PRONUNCIATION
$\sigma_{\bar{X}}$	Standard error of the sample means	*sigma sub X bar*
σ_p	Standard error of the population proportion	*sigma sub p*
s_p	Standard error of the sample proportion	*s sub p*
$s_{\bar{x}}$	Sample standard deviation of the sample means	*s sub X bar*

Chapter Exercises

39. A random sample of 85 group leaders, supervisors, and similar personnel at General Motors revealed that, on the average, they spent 6.5 years on the job before being promoted. The standard deviation of the sample was 1.7 years. Construct a 95 percent confidence interval.

40. A meat inspector has been given the assignment of estimating the mean net mass of packages of ground chuck labeled "1.4 kg." Of course, he realizes that the masses cannot be precisely 1.4 kg. A sample of 36 packages reveals the mean mass to be 1.401 kg, with a standard deviation of 0.01 kg.

a. What is the estimated population mean?

b. Determine a 95 percent confidence interval for the population mean.

41. A recent study of 50 self-service gasoline stations in a metropolitan area revealed that the mean price of unleaded gas was \$1.30 per litre. The sample standard deviation was \$0.07 per litre.

a. Determine a 99 percent confidence interval for the population mean price.

b. Would it be reasonable to conclude that the population mean was \$1.40? Why or why not?

42. A recent survey of 50 executives who were laid off from their previous position revealed it took an average of 26 weeks for them to find another position. The standard deviation of the sample was 6.2 weeks. Construct a

www.mcgrawhill.ca/olc/lind

95 percent confidence interval for the population mean. Is it reasonable that the population mean is 28 weeks? Justify your answer.

43. The Badik Construction Company limits its business to constructing decks. The mean time to construct one of its standard decks is 8 hours for a two-person construction crew. The information is based on a sample of 40 decks recently constructed. The standard deviation of the sample was 3 hours.
    a. Determine a 90 percent confidence interval for the population mean.
    b. Would it be reasonable to conclude that the population mean is actually 9 hours? Justify your answer.

44. A restaurant association collected information on the number of meals eaten outside the home per week by young married couples. A survey of 60 couples showed the sample mean number of meals eaten outside the home was 2.76 meals per week, with a population standard deviation of 0.75 meals per week. Construct a 97 percent confidence interval for the population mean.

45. The manager of Apache Burger felt that an average of 70 customers made purchases daily between the hours of 3 p.m. and 5 p.m. A random sample over 50 days showed the sample mean to be 68.6 customers with a standard deviation of 8.2 hours.
    a. Using the sample data, construct a 99 percent confidence interval for the population mean.
    b. Does the 99 percent confidence interval include the value suggested by the manager? Interpret this result.
    c. Suppose you decided to switch from a 99 to a 95 percent confidence interval. Without performing any calculations, will the interval increase, decrease, or stay the same? Which of the values in the formula will change?

46. The employees of Electronics Inc. would like to have a dental plan as part of their benefits package. The question is: How much does a typical employee and his or her family spend per year on dental expenses? A sample of 45 employees reveals the mean amount spent last year was $1820, with a standard deviation of $660.
    a. Construct a 95 percent confidence interval for the population mean.
    b. The information from part (a) was given to the president of Electronics Inc. He indicated he could afford $1700 of dental expenses per employee. Is it possible that the population mean could be $1700? Justify your answer.

47. A student conducted a study and reported that the 95 percent confidence interval for the mean ranged from 46 to 54. He was sure that the mean of the sample was 50, that the standard deviation of the sample was 16, and that the sample was at least 30, but could not remember the exact number. Can you help him out?

48. A recent study by an automobile dealer revealed the mean amount of profit per car sold for a sample of 20 salespeople was $290, with a standard deviation of $125. Develop a 95 percent confidence interval for the population mean.

49. A study of 25 graduates of colleges revealed the mean amount owed by a student was $14 381. The standard deviation of the sample was $1892. Construct a 90 percent confidence interval for the population mean. Is it reasonable to conclude that the mean of the population is actually $15 000? Tell why or why not.

50. An important factor in selling a residential property is the number of people who look through the home. A sample of 15 homes recently sold in the Halifax, Nova Scotia, area revealed the mean number looking through each home was 24 and the standard deviation of the sample was 5 people. Develop a 98 percent confidence interval for the population mean.

51. The Simcoe County Food Emporium claims that "the typical customer spends $60 per visit." A sample of 12 customers revealed the following purchases, in dollars, spent last visit.

$64	66	64	66	59	62	67	61	64	58	54	66

    a. What is the point estimate of the population mean?
    b. Develop a 90 percent confidence interval for the population mean.
    c. Is the restaurant's claim that the "typical customer" spends $60 per visit reasonable? Justify your answer.

52. The manufacturer of a new line of ink jet printers would like to include as part of its advertising the number of pages a user can expect from a print cartridge. A sample of 10 cartridges revealed the following number of pages printed.

2698	2028	2474	2395	2372	2475	1927	3006	2334	2379

    a. What is the point estimate of the population mean?
    b. Develop a 95 percent confidence interval for the population mean.

53. Dr. Susan Benner is an industrial psychologist. She is currently studying stress among executives of Internet companies. She has developed a questionnaire that she believes measures stress. A score above 80 indicates stress at a dangerous level. A random sample of 15 executives revealed the following stress level scores.

94	78	83	90	78	99	97	90	97	90	93	94	100	75	84

a. Find the mean stress level for this sample. What is the point estimate of the population mean?
b. Construct a 95 percent confidence level for the population mean.
c. Is it reasonable to conclude that Internet executives have a mean stress level in the dangerous level, according to Dr. Benner's test?

54. Furniture Land surveyed 600 consumers and found that 414 were enthusiastic about a new home dècor it plans to show in its store in High Point. Construct the 99 percent confidence interval for the population proportion.

55. There are 20 000 eligible voters in York County. A random sample of 500 York County voters revealed 350 plan to vote to re-elect their current member of parliament. Construct a 99 percent confidence interval for the proportion of voters in the county who plan to re-elect the returning member. From this sample information, can you confirm the re-election?

56. In a poll to estimate the prime minister's popularity, each person in a random sample of 1000 voters was asked to agree with one of the following statements:
1. The prime minister is doing a good job.
2. The prime minister is doing a poor job.
3. I have no opinion.

A total of 560 respondents selected the first statement, indicating they thought the prime minister was doing a good job.
a. Construct a 95 percent confidence interval for the proportion of respondents who feel the prime minister is doing a good job.
b. Based on your interval in part (a), is it reasonable to conclude that a majority (more than half) of the population believes the prime minister is doing a good job?

57. Brampton's traffic patrol reports 500 traffic citations were issued last month. A sample of 35 of these citations showed the mean amount of the fine was \$54, with a standard deviation of \$4.50. Construct a 95 percent confidence interval for the mean amount of a citation in Brampton.

58. The bank in Cobden, Ontario has 650 chequing account customers. A recent sample of 50 of these customers showed 26 to have a Visa card with the bank. Construct the 99 percent confidence interval for the proportion of chequing account customers who have a Visa card with the bank.

59. It is claimed that 60 percent of households now subscribe to cable TV. You would like to verify this statement for your class in mass communications. If you want your estimate to be within 5 percentage points, with a 95 percent level of confidence, how large of a sample is required?

60. You need to estimate the mean number of travel days per year for outside salespeople. The mean of a small pilot study was 150 days, with a standard deviation of 14 days. If you must estimate the population mean within 2 days, how many outside salespeople should you sample? Use the 90 percent confidence level.

61. You are to conduct a sample survey to determine the mean family income in a rural area. The question is, how many families should be sampled? In a pilot sample of 10 families, the standard deviation of the sample was \$500. The sponsor of the survey wants you to use the 95 percent confidence level. The estimate is to be within \$100. How many families should be interviewed?

62. You plan to conduct a survey to find what proportion of the workforce has two or more jobs. You decide on the 95 percent confidence level and state that the estimated proportion must be within 2 percent of the population proportion. A pilot survey reveals that 5 of the 50 sampled hold two or more jobs. How many in the workforce should be interviewed to meet your requirements?

63. An employment agency wants to update an estimate of the proportion of accountants who have changed companies within the last three years, to be estimated within 3 percent. A 95 percent level of confidence is to be used. A study conducted several years ago revealed that the percent of accountants changing companies within 3 years was 21.
a. To update this study, the files of how many accountants should be studied?
b. How many accountants should be contacted if no previous estimates of the population proportion are available?

64. The National Bank, like most other large banks, found that using automatic teller machines (ATMs) reduces the cost of routine bank transactions. National installed an ATM in the corporate offices of the Fun Toy Company. The ATM is for the exclusive use of Fun's 605 employees. After several months of operation, a sample of 100 employees revealed the following use of the ATM machine by Fun employees in a month.

Number of Times ATM Used	Frequency
0	25
1	30
2	20
3	10
4	10
5	5

a. What is the estimate of the proportion of employees who do not use the ATM in a month?
b. Develop a 95 percent confidence interval for this estimate. Can National be sure that at least 40 percent of the employees of Fun Toy Company will use the ATM?
c. How many transactions does the average Fun employee make per month?
d. Develop a 95 percent confidence interval for the mean number of transactions per month.
e. Is it possible that the population mean is 0? Explain.

65. In a recent poll of 1000 adults nationwide, 613 said they believe other forms of life exist elsewhere in the universe. Construct the 99 percent confidence interval for the population proportion of those believing life exists elsewhere in the universe. Does your result imply that a majority of Canadians believe life exists outside of Earth?

66. As part of an annual review of its accounts, a discount brokerage selects a random sample of 36 customers. Their accounts are reviewed for total account valuation, which showed a mean of $32 000, with a sample standard deviation of $8200. What is a 90 percent confidence interval for the mean account valuation of the population of customers?

67. A sample of 352 subscribers to *Wired* magazine shows the mean time spent using the Internet is 13.4 hours per week, with a sample standard deviation of 6.8 hours. Find the 95 percent confidence interval for the mean time *Wired* subscribers spend on the Internet.

68. The Manitoba Tourism Board plans to sample information centre visitors entering the province to learn the fraction of visitors who plan to camp in the province. Current estimates are that 35 percent of visitors are campers. How large a sample would you take to estimate at a 95 percent confidence level the population proportion with an allowable error of 2 percent?

Data Set Exercises

69. Refer to the real estate data, from the south-east area of Edmonton, which reports information on listed homes.
a. Develop a 95 percent confidence interval for the mean list price of the homes.
b. Develop a 95 percent confidence interval for the mean number of square feet per home.
c. Develop a 95 percent confidence interval for the proportion of homes that have four or more bedrooms.

70. Refer to the CREA (Canadian Real Estate Association) data on the CD-ROM, which reports information on average house prices nationally and in a selection of cities across Canada. Note: Select the cities only.
a. Develop a 95 percent confidence interval for the mean list price for January 2008.
b. Is it possible that the population mean is $350 000? Explain.

71. Refer to the CREA (Canadian Real Estate Association) data on the CD-ROM, which reports information on average house prices nationally and in a selection of cities across Canada. Note: Select the cities only.
a. Develop a 95 percent confidence interval for the mean list price for January 2007.
b. Is it possible that the population mean is $300 000? Explain.

72. Refer to the International data, which reports demographic and economic information on 46 countries.
a. Develop a 90 percent confidence interval for the mean percent of the population over 65 years old.
b. Develop a 90 percent confidence interval for the mean GDP per capita.
c. Develop a 90 percent confidence interval for the mean imports.

exercises.com

Additional exercises that require you to access information at related Internet sites are available on the CD-ROM included with this text.

Answers to Self-Reviews

8–1 **(a)** \$2000. This is called the point estimate.

(b) $\$2000 \pm 2.58\frac{\$300}{\sqrt{40}} = \$2000 \pm 122.$

(c) The endpoints of the confidence interval are \$1878 and \$2122. About 99 percent of the intervals similarly constructed would include the population mean.

8–2 **(a)** $\bar{X} = \frac{18}{10} = 1.8 \quad s = \sqrt{\frac{44 - \frac{(18)^2}{10}}{10-1}} = 1.1353.$

(b) The population mean is not known. The best estimate is the sample mean, 1.8 days.

(c) $1.80 \pm 2.262\frac{1.1353}{\sqrt{10}} = 1.80 \pm 0.81 = 0.99 \text{ to } 2.61.$

(d) t is used because the standard deviation of the population is unknown but the population is assumed to be normally distributed.

(e) The value of 0 is not in the interval. It is unreasonable to conclude that the mean number of days of work missed is 0 per employee.

8–3 **(a)** $p = \frac{420}{1400} = .30.$

(b) $s_p = \sqrt{\frac{.30(1-.30)}{1400}} = .0122.$

(c) $.30 \pm 2.58(.0122) = .30 \pm .03.$

(d) The interval is between .27 and .33. About 99 percent of the similarly constructed intervals would include the population mean.

8–4 $.375 \pm 1.96\sqrt{\frac{.375(1-.375)}{40}}\sqrt{\frac{250-40}{250-1}}$

$= .375 \pm 1.96(.0765)(.9184)$

$= .375 \pm .138$

$= .237 \text{ to } .513.$

The correction factor should be applied because 40/240 > .05.

8–5 $n = \left(\frac{2.58(.279)}{.05}\right)^2 = 207.26.$

The sample should be rounded to 208.

chapter 9

One-Sample Tests of a Hypothesis

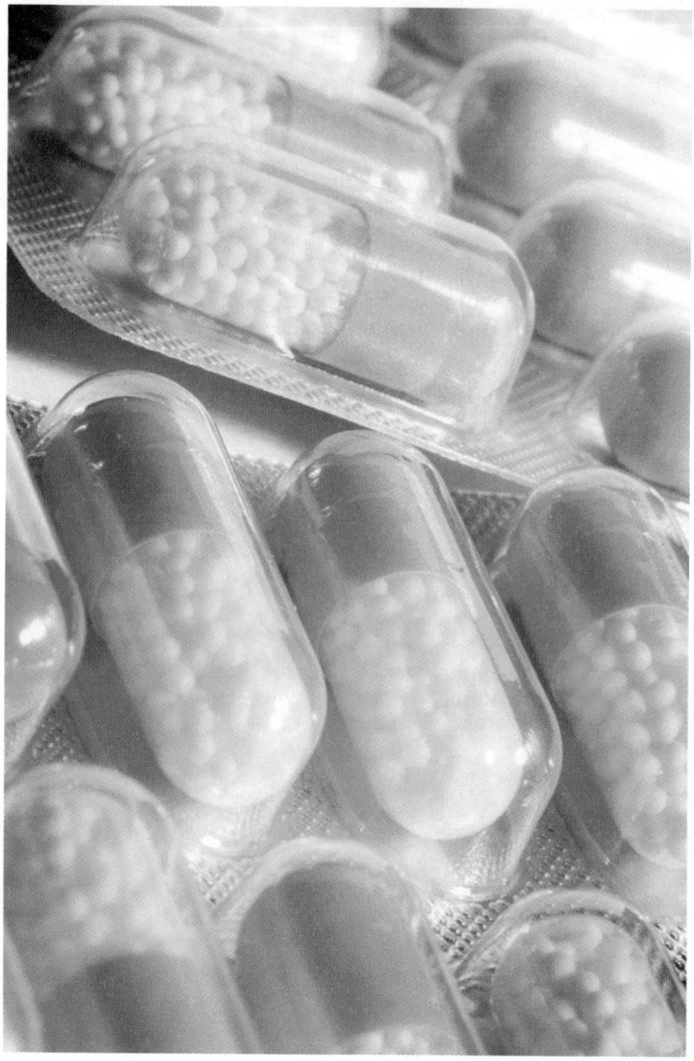

LEARNING GOALS

When you have completed this chapter, you will be able to:

1. Define a *hypothesis* and *hypothesis testing*.
2. Describe the five-step hypothesis testing procedure.
3. Define *Type I* and *Type II* errors.
4. Distinguish between a *one-tailed* and a *two-tailed test of hypothesis*.
5. Conduct a test of hypothesis about a population mean.
6. Describe and interpret a *p*-value.
7. Conduct a test of hypothesis about a population proportion.

Introduction

Chapter 7 began our study of statistical inference. We described how we could select a random sample and from this sample estimate the value of a population parameter. For example, we selected a sample of five employees at Spence Sprockets, found the number of years of service for each sampled employee, computed the mean years of service, and used the sample mean to estimate the mean years of service for all employees. In other words, we estimated a population parameter from a sample statistic.

1 **Define a *hypothesis* and *hypothesis testing*.**

Chapter 8 continued the study of statistical inference by developing a confidence interval. A confidence interval is a range of values within which we expect the population parameter to occur. In this chapter, rather than develop a range of values within which we expect the population parameter to occur, we develop a procedure to test the validity of a statement about a population parameter. Some examples of statements we can test are:

A hypothesis is a statement about a population parameter.

- The mean number of kilometres driven by those leasing a Chevy TrailBlazer for three years is 51 500 km.
- The mean time a Canadian family lives in a particular single-family dwelling is 11.8 years.
- The mean starting salary for graduates of business schools is $2900 per month.
- Eighty percent of those who play the lotteries regularly never win more than $100 in any one play.

hypothesis A statement about a population parameter subject to verification.

This chapter and several of the following chapters describe statistical hypothesis testing. We begin by defining what we mean by a statistical hypothesis and statistical hypothesis testing. Next, we outline the steps in statistical hypothesis testing. Then we conduct tests of hypothesis for means and proportions. In the last section of the chapter, we describe possible errors due to sampling in hypothesis testing.

Statistics in Action

LASIK is a 15-minute surgical procedure that uses a laser to reshape an eye's cornea with the goal of improving eyesight. Research shows that about 5 percent of all surgeries involve complications such as glare, corneal haze, overcorrection or undercorrection of vision, and loss of vision. In a statistical sense, the research tests a Null Hypothesis that the surgery will not improve eyesight with the Alternative Hypothesis that the surgery will improve eyesight. The sample data of LASIK surgery shows that 5 percent of all cases result in complications. The 5 percent represents a Type I error rate. When a person decides to have the surgery, he or she expects to reject the Null Hypothesis. In 5 percent of future cases, this expectation will not be met. (Source: *American Academy of Ophthalmology*, San Francisco, Vol. 16, no. 43.)

What Is a Hypothesis?

A **hypothesis** is a statement about a population. Data are then used to check the reasonableness of the statement. To begin we need to define the word *hypothesis*. In the Canadian legal system, a person is innocent until proven guilty. A jury hypothesizes that a person charged with a crime is innocent and subjects this hypothesis to verification by reviewing the evidence and hearing testimony before reaching a verdict. In a similar sense, a patient goes to a physician and reports various symptoms. Based on the symptoms, the physician will order certain diagnostic tests and then, according to the symptoms and the test results, determine the treatment to be followed.

In statistical analysis we make a claim, that is, state a hypothesis, collect data, then use the data to test the claim. In most cases the population is so large that it is not feasible to study all the items, objects, or persons in the population. For example, it would not be possible to contact every accountant in Canada to find his or her monthly income. Likewise, the quality control department cannot check the breaking strength of each wire produced to determine whether it is between 5 kg/m^2 and 20 kg/m^2.

As noted in Chapter 7, an alternative to measuring or interviewing the entire population is to take a sample from the population. We can, therefore, test a statement to determine whether the sample does or does not support the statement concerning the population.

What Is Hypothesis Testing?

The terms *hypothesis testing*, *significance testing*, and *testing a hypothesis* are used interchangeably. **Hypothesis testing** starts with a statement, or assumption, about a population parameter—such as the population mean. As noted, this statement is referred to as a *hypothesis*. A hypothesis might be that the mean monthly commission of sales associates in retail electronic stores, such as Computerland, is $3000. It would be too costly to contact all these sales associates to ascertain that the mean is in fact $3000. The cost of locating and interviewing every electronics sales associate would be exorbitant. To test the validity of the assumption (μ = $3000), we select a sample from the population of all electronics sales associates, calculate sample statistics, and based on specific decision rules accept or reject the hypothesis. A sample mean of $1500 for the electronic sales associate would certainly cause rejection of the hypothesis. However, suppose the sample mean is $2950. Is that close enough to $3000 for us to accept the assumption that the population mean is $3000? Can we attribute the difference of $50 between the two means to sampling error, or is that difference statistically significant?

hypothesis testing A procedure based on sample evidence and probability theory to determine whether the hypothesis is a reasonable statement.

2 Describe the five-step hypothesis testing procedure.

A systematic procedure

Five-Step Procedure for Testing a Hypothesis

There is a five-step procedure that systematizes hypothesis testing; when we get to step 5, we are ready to reject or not reject the hypothesis. However, hypothesis testing using sample statistics does not provide proof that something is true, in the manner in which a mathematician "proves" a statement. It does provide a kind of "proof beyond a reasonable doubt," in the manner of the court system. Hence, there are specific rules of evidence, or procedures, that are followed. The steps are shown in the following diagram. We will discuss in detail each of the steps.

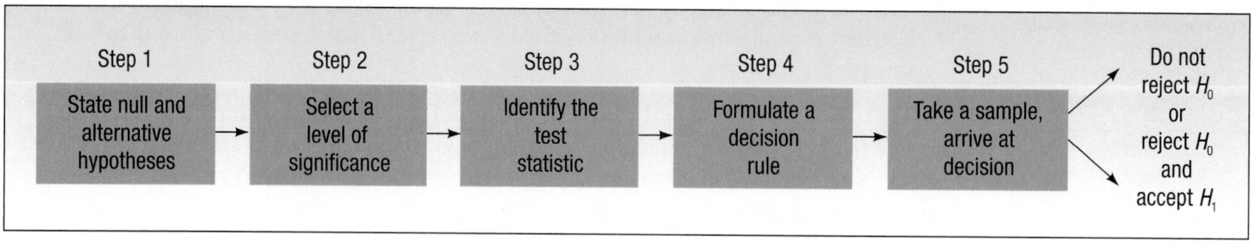

Step 1: State the Null Hypothesis (H_0) and the Alternative Hypothesis (H_1)

null hypothesis A statement about the value of a population parameter developed for the purpose of testing numerical evidence.

The first step is to state the hypothesis being tested. It is called the **null hypothesis**, designated H_0, and read "*H sub zero.*" The capital letter *H* stands for hypothesis, and the subscript zero implies "no difference." There is usually a "not" or a "no" term in the null hypothesis, meaning that there is "no change." For example, the null hypothesis is that the mean number of kilometres driven on the steel-belted tire is not different from 100 000. The null hypothesis would be written H_0: $\mu = 100\ 000$ km. Generally speaking, the null hypothesis is developed for the purpose of testing. We either reject or fail to reject the null hypothesis. The null hypothesis is a statement that is not rejected unless our sample data provide convincing evidence that it is false.

We should emphasize that if the null hypothesis is not rejected based on the sample data, we cannot say that the null hypothesis is true. To put it another way, failing to reject the null hypothesis does not prove that H_0 is true, it means we have *failed to disprove* H_0. To prove without any doubt the null hypothesis is true, the population parameter would have to be known. To actually determine it, we would have to test, survey, or count every item in the population. This is usually not feasible. The alternative is to take a sample from the population.

State the null hypothesis and the alternative hypothesis.

It should also be noted that we often begin the null hypothesis by stating, "There is no *significant* difference between . . . ," or "The mean impact strength of the glass is not *significantly* different from . . . ." When we select a sample from a population, the sample statistic is usually numerically different from the hypothesized population parameter. As an illustration, suppose the hypothesized impact strength of a glass plate is 500 kPa, and the mean impact strength of a sample of 12 glass plates is 495 kPa. We must make a decision about the difference of 5 kPa. Is it a true difference, that is, a significant difference, or is the difference between the sample statistic (495) and the hypothesized population parameter (500) due to chance (sampling)? As noted, to answer this question we conduct a test of significance, commonly referred to as a test of hypothesis.

alternative hypothesis A statement that is accepted if the sample data provide sufficient evidence that the null hypothesis is false.

The **alternative hypothesis** describes what you will conclude if you reject the null hypothesis. It is written H_1 and is read "*H sub one.*" It is also referred to as the research hypothesis. The alternative hypothesis is accepted if the sample data provide us with enough statistical evidence that the null hypothesis is false.

The following example will help clarify what is meant by the null hypothesis and the alternative hypothesis. A recent article indicated the mean number of pounds lost on the New Age diet is 15 lbs. To conduct a statistical test regarding this statement, the first step is to determine the null and the alternative hypotheses. The null hypothesis represents the current or reported condition. It is written H_0: $\mu = 15$. The alternative hypothesis is that the statement is not true, written as H_1: $\mu \neq 15$. It is important to remember that no matter how the problem is stated, *the null hypothesis will always contain the equal sign.* The equal sign (=) will never appear in the alternative hypothesis. Why? Because the null hypothesis is the statement being tested, and we need a specific value to include in our calculations. We turn to the alternative hypothesis only if we prove the null hypothesis to be untrue.

Select a level of significance or risk.

level of significance The probability of rejecting the null hypothesis when it is true.

Step 2: Select a Level of Significance

After setting up the null hypothesis and alternative hypothesis, the next step is to state the **level of significance.**

The level of significance is designated α, the Greek letter alpha. It is also sometimes called the level of risk. This may be a more appropriate term because it is the risk you take of rejecting the null hypothesis when it is really true.

There is no one level of significance that is applied to all tests. A decision is made to use the .05 level (often stated as the 5 percent level), the .01 level, the .10 level, or any other level between 0 and 1. Traditionally, the .05 level is selected for consumer research projects, .01 for quality control, and .10 for political polling. You, the researcher, must decide on the level of significance *before* formulating a decision rule and collecting sample data.

To illustrate how it is possible to reject a true hypothesis, suppose a firm manufacturing personal computers uses a large number of printed circuit boards. Suppliers bid on the boards, and the one with the lowest bid is awarded a sizable contract. Suppose the contract specifies that the computer manufacturer's quality control department will sample all incoming shipments of circuit boards. If more than 6 percent of the boards sampled fail to meet specifications, and hence are defective, the shipment will be rejected. The null hypothesis is that the incoming shipment of boards contains 6 percent or less defective boards. The alternative hypothesis is that more than 6 percent of the boards are defective.

A sample of 50 circuit boards received July 21 from Allied Electronics revealed that 4 boards, or 8 percent, were defective. The shipment was rejected because it exceeded the maximum of 6 percent defective circuit boards. However, suppose the 4 defective circuit boards selected in the sample of 50 were the only defective boards in the shipment of 4000 boards. Then only 1/10 of 1 percent were defective (4/4000 = .001). In that case, less than 6 percent of the entire shipment was defective and rejecting the shipment was an error. In terms of hypothesis testing, we rejected the null hypothesis that the shipment contained 6 percent defective circuit boards when we should have not rejected the null hypothesis. By rejecting a true null hypothesis, we commit a **Type I error**. The probability of committing a Type I error is α.

3 Define *Type I* and *Type II* errors.

Type I error Rejecting the null hypothesis, H_0, when it is true.

Type II error Not rejecting the null hypothesis when it is false.

The probability of committing another type of error, called a **Type II error**, is designated by the Greek letter beta (β).

The firm manufacturing personal computers would commit a Type II error if, unknown to the manufacturer, an incoming shipment of circuit boards from Allied Electronics contained 15 percent defective boards, yet the shipment was not rejected. How could this happen? Suppose 2 of the 50 boards in the sample (4 percent) tested were defective, and 48 of the 50 were good boards. According to the stated procedure, because the sample contained less than 6 percent defective boards, the shipment was accepted. It could be that *by chance* the 48 good boards selected in the sample were the only acceptable ones in the entire shipment of thousands of boards!

In retrospect, the researcher cannot study every item or individual in the population. Thus, there is a possibility of two types of error—a Type I error, wherein the null hypothesis is rejected when it should have not been rejected, and a Type II error, wherein the null hypothesis is not rejected when it should have been rejected.

We often refer to the probability of these two possible types of errors as *alpha*, α, and *beta*, β. Alpha (α) is the probability of making a Type I error, and beta (β) is the probability of making a Type II error. The following table summarizes the decisions the researcher could make and the possible consequences.

Null Hypothesis	Researcher: Not Rejecting H_0	Researcher: Rejects H_0
H_0 is true	Correct decision	Type I error
H_0 is false	Type II error	Correct decision

Step 3: Select the Test Statistic

test statistic A value, determined from sample information, used to determine whether to reject the null hypothesis.

There are many **test statistics**. In this chapter we use both z and t as the test statistic. In other chapters we will use such test statistics as F and χ^2, called chi-square.

In hypothesis testing for the mean (μ) when σ is known, the test statistic z is computed by:

z TEST STATISTIC
$$z = \frac{\bar{X} - \mu}{\sigma/\sqrt{n}} \qquad [9\text{–}1]$$

The z-value is based on the sampling distribution of $\bar{X}$ which follows the normal distribution with a mean ($\mu_{\bar{X}}$) equal to μ, and a standard deviation $\sigma_{\bar{X}}$, which is equal to $\sigma/\sqrt{n}$. We can thus determine whether the difference between $\bar{X}$ and μ is statistically significant by finding the number of standard deviations $\bar{X}$ is from μ using formula (9–1).

Step 4: Formulate the Decision Rule

The decision rule states the conditions when H_0 is rejected.

A decision rule is a statement under the specific conditions for which the null hypothesis is rejected and the conditions under which it is not rejected. The region or area of rejection defines the location of all those values that are so large or so small that the probability of their occurrence for a true null hypothesis is rather remote.

Chart 9–1 portrays the rejection region for a test of significance that will be conducted later in the chapter.

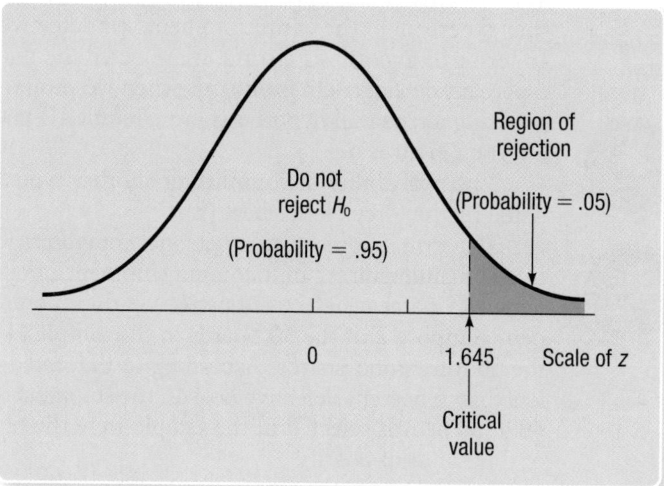

CHART 9–1 Sampling Distribution of the Statistic z, a Right-Tailed Test, .05 Level of Significance

Note in the chart that:

1. The area where the null hypothesis is not rejected is equal to or to the left of 1.645. We will explain how to get the 1.645 value shortly.
2. The area of rejection is to the right of 1.645.
3. A one-tailed test is being applied. (This will also be explained later.)
4. The .05 level of significance was chosen.

5. The sampling distribution of the statistic z is normally distributed.
6. The value 1.645 separates the regions where the null hypothesis is rejected and where it is not rejected.
7. The value 1.645 is the critical value.

Statistics in Action

During World War II, allied military planners needed estimates of the number of German tanks. The information provided by traditional spying methods was not reliable, but statistical methods proved to be valuable. For example, espionage and reconnaissance led analysts to estimate that 1550 tanks were produced during June of 1941. However, using the serial numbers of captured tanks and statistical analysis, military planners estimated 244. The actual number produced, as determined from German production records, was 271. The estimate using statistical analysis turned out to be much more accurate. A similar type of analysis was used to estimate the number of Iraqi tanks destroyed during Desert Storm.

Step 5: Make a Decision

The fifth and final step in hypothesis testing is computing the value of the test statistic, comparing it to the critical value, and making a decision to reject or not to reject the null hypothesis. Referring to Chart 9–1, if, based on sample information, z, the test statistic, is computed to be 2.34, the null hypothesis is rejected at the .05 level of significance. The decision to reject H_0 was made because 2.34 lies in the region of rejection, that is, beyond 1.645. We would reject the null hypothesis, reasoning that it is highly improbable that a computed z-value this large is due to sampling variation (chance).

Had the computed value been 1.645 or less, say 0.71, the null hypothesis would not be rejected. It would be reasoned that such a small computed value could be attributed to chance, that is, sampling error. As noted, only one of two decisions is possible in hypothesis testing—either accept or reject the null hypothesis. Instead of "accepting" the null hypothesis, H_0, some researchers prefer to phrase the decision as: "Do not reject H_0," "We fail to reject H_0," or "There is not enough evidence to reject H_0."

SUMMARY OF THE STEPS IN HYPOTHESIS TESTING

1. Establish the null hypothesis (H_0) and the alternative hypothesis (H_1).
2. Select the level of significance, that is α.
3. Select an appropriate test statistic.
4. Formulate a decision rule based on steps 1, 2, and 3 above.
5. Make a decision regarding the null hypothesis based on the sample information. Interpret the results.

It should be reemphasized that there is always a possibility that the null hypothesis is rejected when it should not be rejected (a Type I error). Also, there is a definable chance that the null hypothesis is accepted when it should be rejected (a Type II error).

Before actually conducting a test of hypothesis, we will differentiate between a one-tailed test of significance and a two-tailed test.

critical value The dividing point between the region where the null hypothesis is rejected and the region where it is not rejected.

4 Distinguish between a *one-tailed* and a *two-tailed test of hypothesis*.

One-Tailed and Two-Tailed Tests of Significance

Refer to Chart 9–1. It depicts a one-tailed test. The region of rejection is only in the right (upper) tail of the curve. To illustrate, suppose that the packaging department at Ralcorp Holdings Inc. is concerned that some boxes of Grape-Nuts are significantly overweight. The cereal is packaged in 453-gram boxes, so the null hypothesis is H_0: $\mu \leq 453$. This is read, "the population mean (μ) is equal to or less than 453." The alternative hypothesis is, therefore, H_1: $\mu > 453$. This is read, "μ is greater than 453." Note that the inequality sign in the alternative hypothesis ($>$) points to the region of rejection in the upper tail. (See Chart 9–1.) Also note the null hypothesis includes the equal sign. That is, H_0: $\mu \leq 453$. The equality condition always appears in H_0, never in H_1.

Chart 9–2 portrays a situation where the rejection region is in the left (lower) tail of the normal distribution. As an illustration, consider the problem of automobile manufacturers, large automobile leasing companies, and other organizations that purchase large quantities of tires. They want the tires to average, say, 100 000 km of wear under normal usage. They will, therefore, reject a shipment of tires if tests reveal that the mean life of the tires is significantly below 100 000 km on average. They gladly accept a shipment if the mean life is greater than 100 000 km! They are not concerned with this possibility, however. They are concerned only if they have sample evidence to conclude that the tires will average less than 100 000 km of useful life. Thus, the test is set up to satisfy the concern of the automobile manufacturers that *the mean life of the tires is no less than 100 000 km.* This statement appears in the alternate hypothesis. The null and alternative hypotheses in this case are written H_0: $\mu \geq 100\ 000$ and H_1: $\mu < 100\ 000$.

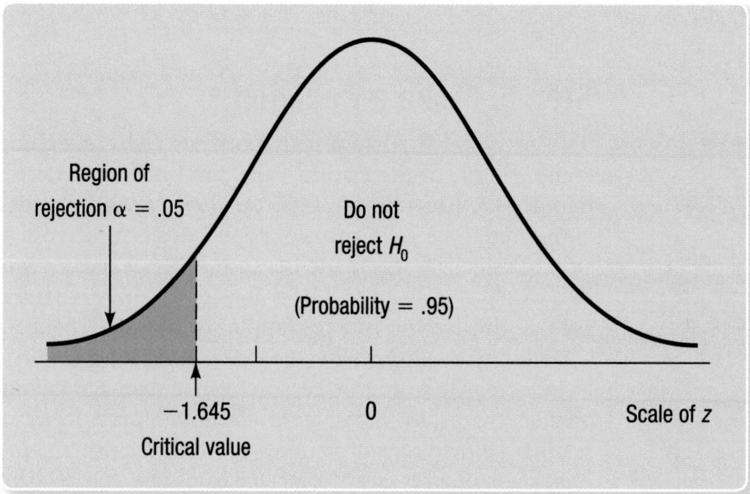

CHART 9–2 Sampling Distribution for the Statistic *z*, Left-Tailed Test, .05 Level of Significance

Test is one-tailed if H_1 states $\mu >$ or $\mu <$.

If H_1 states a direction, test is one-tailed.

One way to determine the location of the rejection region is to look at the direction in which the inequality sign in the alternative hypothesis is pointing (either < or >). In this problem it is pointing to the left, and the rejection region is therefore in the left tail.

In summary, a test is *one-tailed* when the alternative hypothesis, H_1, states a direction, such as:

> H_0: The mean income of female stockbrokers is less than or equal to \$85 000 per year.
> H_1: The mean income of female stockbrokers is *greater* than \$85 000 per year.

If no direction is specified in the alternative hypothesis, we use a *two-tailed* test. Changing the previous problem to illustrate:

> H_0: The mean income of female stockbrokers is \$85 000 per year.
> H_1: The mean income of female stockbrokers is *not equal to* \$85 000 per year.

If the null hypothesis is rejected and H_1 accepted in the two-tailed case, the mean income could be significantly greater than \$85 000 per year, or it could be significantly less than \$85 000 per year. To accommodate these two possibilities, the 5 percent area of rejection is divided equally into the two tails of the sampling distribution (2.5 percent each). Chart 9–3 shows the two probabilities and the critical values. Note that the total probability in the standard normal distribution is 1.0000, found by .9500 + .0250 + .0250.

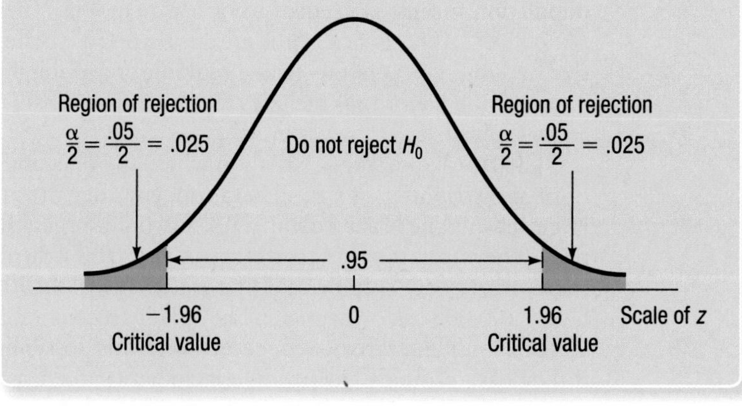

CHART 9–3 Regions of Nonrejection and Rejection for a Two-Tailed Test, .05 Level of Significance

5 Conduct a test of hypothesis about a population mean.

Testing for a Population Mean with a Known Population Standard Deviation

A Two-Tailed Test

An example will show the details of the five-step hypothesis testing procedure. We also wish to use a two-tailed test. That is, we are *not* concerned whether the sample results are larger or smaller than the proposed population mean. Rather, we are interested in whether it is *different from* the proposed value for the population mean. We begin, as we did in the previous chapter, with a situation in which we have historical information about the population and in fact know its standard deviation.

example

The Jamestown Steel Company manufactures and assembles desks and other office equipment at several plants. The weekly production of the Model A325 desk follows a normal probability distribution, with a mean of 200 and a standard deviation of 16. Recently, due to market expansion, new production methods have been introduced and new employees hired. The vice president of manufacturing would like to investigate whether there has been a change in the weekly production of the Model A325 desk. To put it another way, is the mean number of desks produced different from 200 at the .01 significance level?

solution

We use the statistical hypothesis testing procedure to investigate whether the production rate has changed from 200 per week.

Step 1: State the null hypothesis and the alternative hypothesis. The null hypothesis is "The population mean is 200." The alternative hypothesis is "The mean is different from 200" or "The mean is not 200." These two hypotheses are written:

$$H_0: \mu = 200$$
$$H_1: \mu \neq 200$$

This is a *two-tailed test* because the alternative hypothesis does not state a direction. In other words, it does not state whether the mean production is greater than 200 or less than 200. The vice president only wants to find out whether the production rate is different from 200.

Step 2: Select the level of significance. As noted, the .01 level of significance is used. This is α, the probability of committing a Type I error, and it is the probability of rejecting a true null hypothesis.

Step 3: Select the test statistic. The test statistic for a mean when σ is known is z. This was discussed at length in Chapter 6. Transforming the production data to standard units (z-values) permits their use not only in this problem but also in other hypothesis-testing problems. Formula (9–1) for z is repeated below with the various letters identified.

Formula for the test statistic

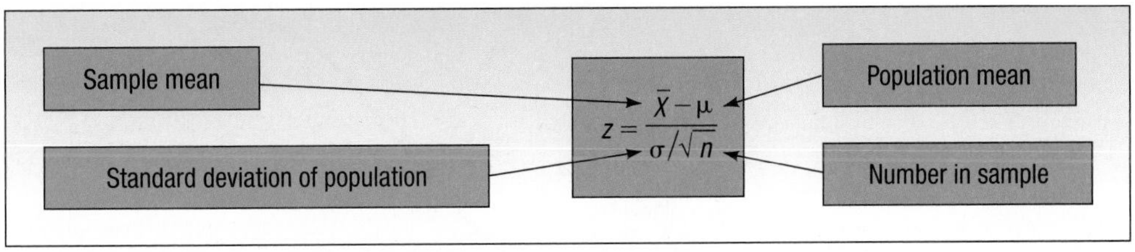

Step 4: Formulate the decision rule. The decision rule is formulated by finding the critical values of z from Appendix D. Since this is a two-tailed test, half of .01, or .005, is placed in each tail. The area where H_0 is not rejected, located between the two tails, is therefore .99. Appendix D is based on half of the area under the curve, or .5000. Then, .5000 − .005 is .4950, so .4950 is the area between 0 and

the critical value. Locate .4950 in the body of the table. The value nearest to .4950 is .4951. Then read the critical value in the row and column corresponding to .4951. It is 2.58.

All the details of this problem are shown in Chart 9–4.

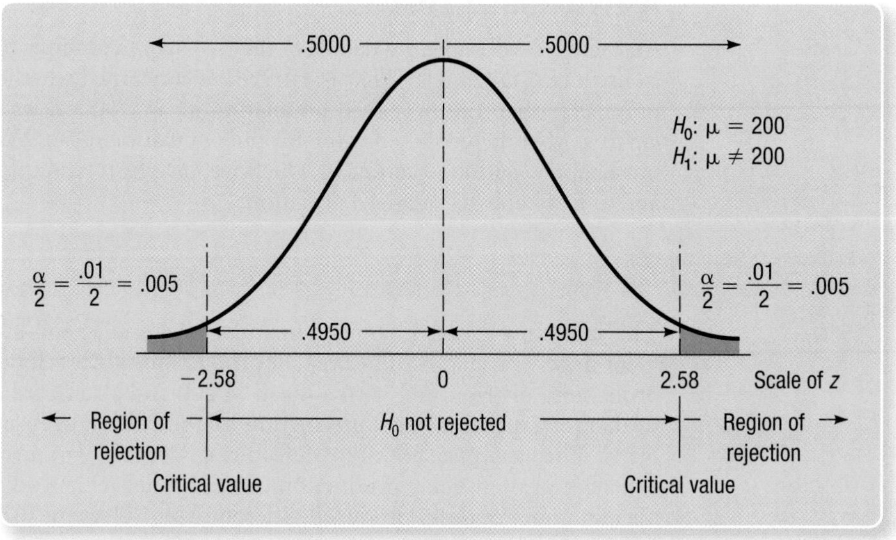

CHART 9–4 Decision Rule for the .01 Significance Level

The decision rule is, therefore: Reject the null hypothesis and accept the alternative hypothesis (which states that the population mean is not 200) if the computed value of z is not between −2.58 and +2.58. Do not reject the null hypothesis if z falls between −2.58 and +2.58.

Step 5: Make a decision. Take a sample from the population (weekly production), compute z, apply the decision rule, and arrive at a decision to reject H_0 or not to reject H_0. The mean number of desks produced last year (50 weeks, because the plant was shut down two weeks for vacation) is 203.5. The standard deviation of the population is 16 desks per week. Computing the z-value from formula (9–1):

$$z = \frac{\bar{X} - \mu}{\sigma/\sqrt{n}} = \frac{203.5 - 200}{16/\sqrt{50}} = 1.55$$

Because 1.55 does not fall in the rejection region H_0 is not rejected. We conclude that the population mean is *not* different from 200. So we would report to the vice president of manufacturing that the sample evidence does not show that the production rate has changed from 200 per week. The difference of 3.5 units between the historical weekly production rate and that last year can reasonably be attributed to sampling error. This information is summarized in the following chart.

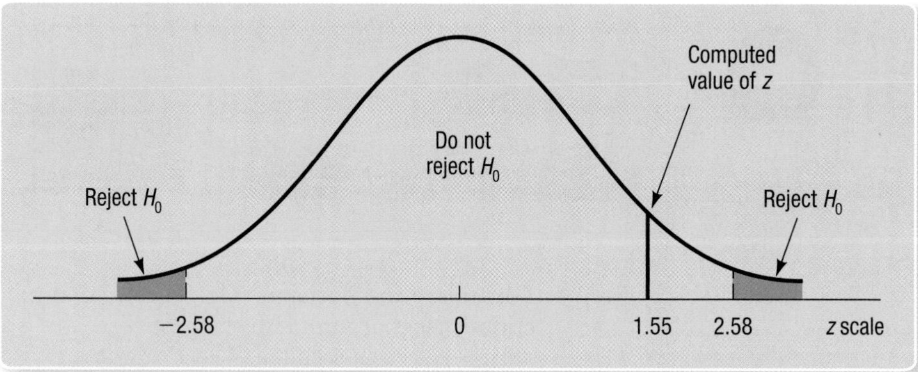

Did we prove that the assembly rate is still 200 per week? Not really. What we did, technically, was *fail to disprove the null hypothesis*. Failing to disprove the hypothesis that the population mean is 200 is not the same thing as proving it to be true. As we suggested in the chapter introduction, the conclusion is analogous to the Canadian judicial system. To explain, suppose a person is accused of a crime but is acquitted by a jury. If a person is acquitted of a crime, the conclusion is that there was not enough evidence to prove the person guilty. The trial did not prove that the individual was innocent, only that there was not enough evidence to prove the defendant guilty. That is what we do in statistical hypothesis testing when we do not reject the null hypothesis. The correct interpretation is that we have failed to disprove the null hypothesis.

We selected the significance level, .01 in this case, before setting up the decision rule and sampling the population. This is the appropriate strategy. The significance level should be set by the investigator, but it should be determined *before* gathering the sample evidence and not changed based on the sample evidence.

How does the hypothesis testing procedure just described compare with that of confidence intervals discussed in the previous chapter? When we conducted the test of hypothesis regarding the production of desks we changed the units from desks per week to a z-value. Then we compared the computed value of the test statistic (1.55) to that of the critical values (-2.58 and 2.58). Because the computed value was in the region where the null hypothesis was not rejected, we concluded that the population mean could be 200. To use the confidence interval approach, on the other hand, we would develop a confidence interval, based on formula (8–1). The interval would be from 197.66 to 209.34, found by $203.5 \pm 2.58(16/\sqrt{50})$. Note that the hypothesized population parameter, 200, is within this interval. Hence, we would conclude that the population mean could reasonably be 200.

In general, H_0 is rejected if the confidence interval does not include the hypothesized value. If the confidence interval includes the hypothesized value, then H_0 is not rejected. So, the "do not reject region" for a test of hypothesis is equivalent to the proposed population value occurring in the confidence interval. The primary difference between a confidence interval and the "do not reject" region for a hypothesis test is whether the interval is centred around the sample statistic, such as $\bar{X}$, as in the confidence interval, or around 0, as in the test of hypothesis.

The MegaStat steps and commands follow.

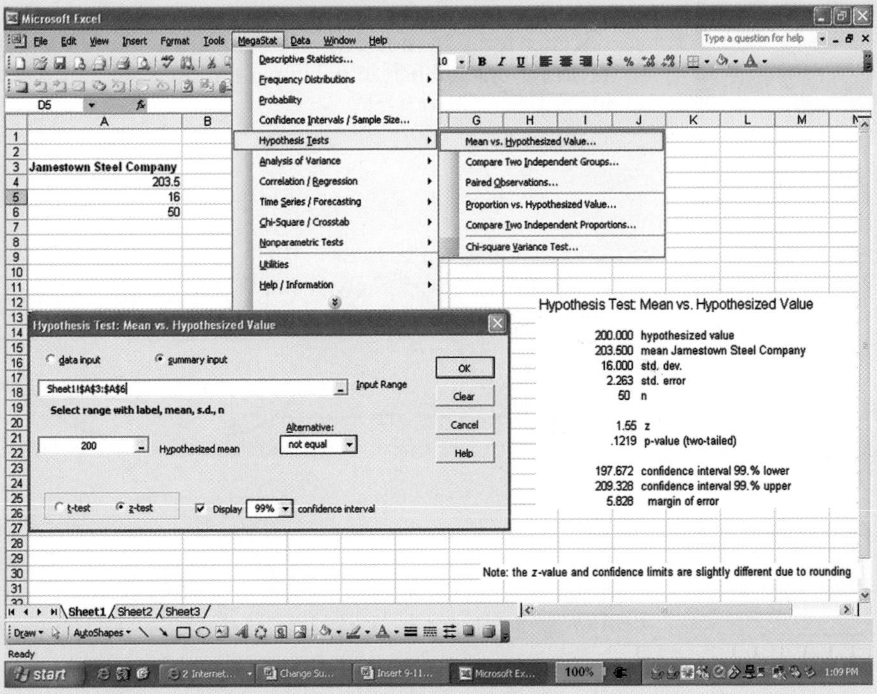

Note: the z-value and confidence limits are slightly different due to rounding.

self-review 9–1

The mean annual turnover rate of the 200-count bottle of Bayer Aspirin is 6.0 with a standard deviation of 0.50. (This indicates that the stock of Bayer Aspirin turns over on the pharmacy shelves an average of six times per year.) It is suspected that the mean turnover has changed and is not 6.0. Use the .05 significance level.

(a) State the null hypothesis and the alternative hypothesis.
(b) What is the probability of a Type I error?
(c) Give the formula for the test statistic.
(d) State the decision rule.
(e) A random sample of 64 bottles of the 200-count size Bayer Aspirin showed a mean of 5.84. Shall we reject the hypothesis that the population mean is 6.0? State your conclusion.

A One-Tailed Test

In the previous example, we emphasized that we were only concerned with reporting to the vice president whether there had been a change in the mean number of desks assembled. We were not concerned with whether the change was an increase or a decrease in the production.

To illustrate a one-tailed test, let's change the problem. Suppose the vice president wants to know whether there has been an *increase* in the number of units assembled. To put it another way, can we conclude, because of the improved production methods, that the mean number of desks assembled in the last 50 weeks was more than 200? Look at the difference in the way the problem is formulated. In the first case we wanted to know whether there was a *difference* in the mean number assembled, but now we want to know whether there has been an *increase*. Because we are investigating different questions, we will set our hypotheses differently. The biggest difference occurs in the alternative hypothesis. Before, we stated the alternative hypothesis as "different from"; now we want to state it as "greater than." In symbols:

A two-tailed test:	A one-tailed test:
$H_0: \mu = 200$	$H_0: \mu \leq 200$
$H_1: \mu \neq 200$	$H_1: \mu > 200$

Statistics in Action

There is a difference between statistically significant and practically significant. To explain, suppose we develop a new diet pill and test it on 100 000 people. We conclude that the typical person taking the pill for two years lost one pound. Do you think many people would be interested in taking the pill to lose one pound? The results of using the new pill were statistically significant but not practically significant.

The critical values for a one-tailed test are different from a two-tailed test at the same significance level. In the previous example, we split the significance level in half and put half in the lower tail and half in the upper tail. In a one-tailed test we put all the rejection region in one tail. See Chart 9–5.

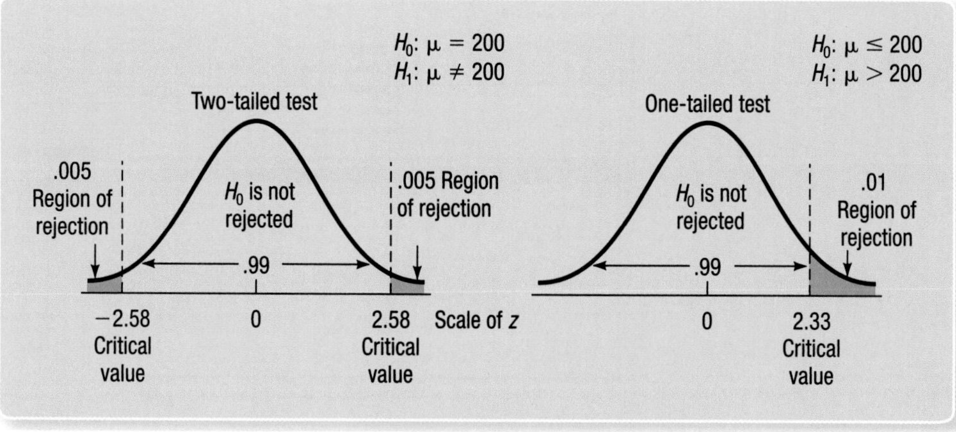

CHART 9–5 Rejection Regions for Two-Tailed and One-Tailed Tests, $\alpha = .01$

For the one-tailed test, the critical value is 2.33, found by: (1) subtracting .01 from .5000 and (2) finding the z-value corresponding to .4900.

The following table summarizes common z-values used in hypothesis testing.

Significance Level	Two-tailed Test	One-tailed Test
.01	2.58	2.33
.02	2.33	2.05
.05	1.96	1.645
.10	1.645	1.28

6 Describe and interpret a p-value.

p-Value in Hypothesis Testing

In testing a hypothesis, we compared the test statistic to a critical value. A decision is made to either reject the null hypothesis or not to reject it. So, for example, if the critical value is 1.96 and the computed value of the test statistic is 2.19, the decision is to reject the null hypothesis.

In recent years, spurred by the availability of computer software, additional information is often reported on the strength of the rejection or acceptance. That is, how confident are we in rejecting the null hypothesis? This approach reports the probability (assuming that the null hypothesis is true) of getting a value of the test statistic at least as extreme as the value actually obtained. This process compares the probability, called the **p-value**, with the significance level. If the p-value is smaller than the significance level, H_0 is rejected. If it is larger than the significance level, H_0 is not rejected.

p-value The probability of observing a sample value as extreme as, or more extreme than, the value observed, when the null hypothesis is true.

Determining the p-value not only results in a decision regarding H_0, but it gives us additional insight into the strength of the decision. A very small p-value, such as .0001, indicates that there is little likelihood the H_0 is true. On the other hand, a p-value of .2033 means that H_0 is not rejected, and there is little likelihood that it is false.

How do we compute the p-value? To illustrate, we use the example in which we tested the null hypothesis that the mean number of desks produced per week was 200. We did not reject the null hypothesis, because the value of 1.55 fell in the region between -2.58 and 2.58. We agreed not to reject the null hypothesis if the computed value of z fell in this region. The probability of finding a z-value of 1.55 or more is .0606, found by $.5000 - .4394$. In other words, the probability of obtaining an $\bar{X}$ greater than 203.5 if $\mu = 200$ is .0606. To compute the p-value, we need to be concerned with the region less than -1.55 as well as the values greater than 1.55 (because the rejection region is in both tails). The two-tailed p-value is .1212, found by 2(.0606). The p-value of .1212 is greater than the significance level of .01 decided upon initially, so H_0 is not rejected. The details are shown in the following graph.

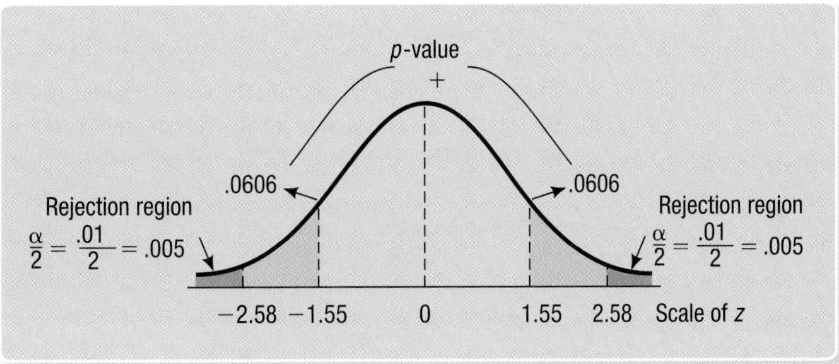

In general, the area is doubled in a two-tailed test. Then, the p-value can easily be compared with the significance level. The same decision rule is used as in the one-sided test.

A p-value is a way to express the likelihood that H_0 is false. But how do we interpret a p-value? We have already said that if the p-value is less than the significance level, then we reject H_0; if it is greater than the significance level, then we do not reject H_0. Also, if the p-value is very large, then it is likely that H_0 is true. If the p-value is small, then it is likely that H_0 is not true. The following box will help to interpret p-values.

INTERPRETING THE WEIGHT OF EVIDENCE AGAINST H_0

If the p-value is less than

(a) .10, we have *some evidence* that H_0 is not true.
(b) .05, we have *strong evidence* that H_0 is not true.
(c) .01, we have *very strong evidence* that H_0 is not true.
(d) .001, we have *extremely strong evidence* that H_0 is not true.

self-review 9–2

Refer to self-review 9–1.

(a) Suppose the hypothesis situation was changed to read: Does this evidence suggest that the mean annual turnover rate is less than 6.0? State the null hypothesis and the alternative hypothesis under these conditions.
(b) What is the decision rule under the new conditions stated in part (a)? Show the decision rule graphically. Show the rejection region and indicate the critical value.
(c) What is the p-value? What is your decision regarding the null hypothesis based on the p-value?

Exercises

1. For each of the following, state the null hypothesis and the alternative hypothesis.
  a. A new cash register has been installed at the Stop One Convenience store. The manager wants to see if the new register has made a difference in the average amount of time a customer takes to be served. The previous mean time for a customer to be served was two minutes.
  b. The shipping dock receives 40 kg bags of flour to use in the production of the baked goods produced by Little Cakes Inc. A sample of 25 bags is taken from each shipment and weighed to ensure that the average weight is at least 40 kg. If not, the shipment is returned to the supplier.
  c. An insurance company states that its average claim is \$1750. However, the company auditor feels that the average amount is actually higher than \$1750, and takes a sample of 60 recent claims to test his theory.
  d. The college cafeteria claims that the average amount spent by a student per visit is \$3.25. A random sample of 200 students is taken to see if this claim can be verified.

2. For each of the following, state the null hypothesis and the alternative hypothesis.
  a. The publisher of *Celebrity Living* claims that the mean sales for personality magazines featuring people such as Angelina Jolie or Paris Hilton is at least 1.5 million per week. A sample of 10 comparable titles shows that the mean weekly sales last week was 1.3 million. The publisher's claim is to be verified.
  b. The manager of Little Cakes Inc. states that an average of 1500 muffins is sold each week in the retail store. One of the bakers feels that the average is less than 1500, and decides to test this claim.
  c. For the past three years, an insurance company has stated that its average claim amount is \$2000. The manager feels that this amount should be updated and takes a sample of 55 claims to see if there is a difference in the average claim amount.
  d. A machine on a production line is set to automatically fill each bottle with 500 ml of water. The quality control manager regularly takes random samples of the bottles from the production line to ensure that the machine is filling the bottles correctly. If not, the machine will need adjusting.

For Exercises 3–6 answer the questions: (a) Is this a one- or two-tailed test? (b) What is the decision rule? (c) What is the value of the test statistic? (d) What is your decision regarding H_0? (e) What is the p-value? Interpret it.

3. The following information is available.

$$H_0: \mu = 50$$
$$H_1: \mu \neq 50$$

The sample mean is 49, and the sample size is 36. The population standard deviation is 5. Use the .05 significance level.

4. The following information is available.

$$H_0: \mu \leq 10$$
$$H_1: \mu > 10$$

The sample mean is 12 for a sample of 36. The population standard deviation is 3. Use the .02 significance level.

5. A sample of 36 observations is selected from a normal population. The sample mean is 21, and the population standard deviation is 5. Conduct the following test of hypothesis using the .05 significance level.

$$H_0: \mu \leq 20$$
$$H_1: \mu > 20$$

6. A sample of 64 observations is selected from a normal sample. The sample mean is 215, and the population standard deviation is 15. Conduct the following test of hypothesis using the .03 significance level.

$$H_0: \mu \geq 220$$
$$H_1: \mu < 220$$

For Exercises 7–10: (a) State the null hypothesis and the alternative hypothesis. (b) State the decision rule. (c) Compute the value of the test statistic. (d) What is your decision regarding H_0? (e) What is the p-value? Interpret it.

7. The manufacturer of the X-15 steel-belted radial truck tire claims that the mean mileage the tire can be driven before the tread wears out is 96 600 km. The population standard deviation of the mileage is 8050 km. The Crosset Truck Company bought 48 tires and found that the mean mileage for its trucks is 95 795 km. Is Crosset's experience different from that claimed by the manufacturer? Use $\alpha = .05$.
8. The MacBurger restaurant chain claims that the waiting time of customers for service is normally distributed, with a mean of 3 minutes and a standard deviation of 1 minute. The quality control department found in a sample of 50 customers at the Warren Road MacBurger that the mean waiting time was 2.75 minutes. Can we conclude that the mean waiting time is less than 3 minutes? Use $\alpha = .05$.
9. A recent national survey found that high school students watched an average (mean) of 6.8 DVDs per month. A random sample of 36 college students revealed that the mean number of DVDs watched last month was 6.2, with a population standard deviation of 0.5. Can we conclude that college students watch fewer DVDs per month than high school students? Use $\alpha = .01$.
10. At the time she was hired as a server at the Grumney Family Restaurant, Beth Brigden was told, "You can average more than $80 a day in tips." Assume the standard deviation of the population is $3.24. Over the first 35 days she was employed at the restaurant, the mean daily amount of her tips was $84.65. At the .01 significance level, can Ms. Brigden conclude that she is earning an average of more than $80 in tips?

Testing for a Population Mean: Population Standard Deviation (σ) Unknown

In the preceding example, we knew σ, the population standard deviation, and that the population followed the normal distribution. In most cases, however, the population standard deviation is unknown. Thus, σ must be based on prior studies or estimated by the sample standard deviation, s. The population standard deviation in the following example is not known, so the sample standard deviation is used to estimate σ. To find the value of the test statistic, we use the t distribution and revise formula (9–1) as follows:

TESTING A MEAN, σ UNKNOWN

$$t = \frac{\bar{X} - \mu}{s/\sqrt{n}} \quad [9\text{–}2]$$

with $n - 1$ degrees of freedom, where:

$\bar{X}$ is the sample mean
μ is the hypothesized population mean

s is the sample standard deviation
n is the number of observations in the sample

We encountered this same situation when constructing confidence intervals in the previous chapter, Chapter 8. We summarized this problem in Chart 8–3. Under these conditions, the correct statistical procedure is to replace the standard normal distribution with the t distribution. To review, the major characteristics of the t distribution are:

1. It is a continuous distribution.
2. It is bell-shaped and symmetrical.
3. There is a family of t distributions. Each time the degrees of freedom change, a new distribution is created.
4. As the number of degrees of freedom increases, the shape of the t distribution approaches that of the standard normal distribution.
5. The t distribution is more spread out than the standard normal distribution.

The following example shows the details.

example

The McFarland Insurance Company Claims Department reports that the mean cost to process a claim is \$60. An industry comparison showed this amount to be larger than most other insurance companies, so it instituted cost-cutting measures. To evaluate the effect of the cost-cutting measures, McFarland selected a random sample of 26 claims processed last month and determined the cost to process these selected claims. The sample information is reported below.

\$45	49	62	40	43	61
48	53	67	63	78	64
48	54	51	56	63	69
58	51	58	59	56	57
38	76				

At the .01 significance level, is it reasonable to conclude that the mean cost to produce a claim is now less than \$60?

solution

We will use the five-step hypothesis testing procedure.

Step 1: State the Null Hypothesis and the Alternative Hypothesis. The null hypothesis is that the population mean is at least \$60. The alternative hypothesis is that the population mean is less than \$60. We can express the null and alternative hypotheses as follows:

$$H_0: \mu \geq \$60$$
$$H_1: \mu < \$60$$

The test is *one*-tailed because we want to determine if there has been a *reduction* in the cost. The inequality in the alternative hypothesis points to the region of rejection in the left tail of the distribution.

Step 2: Select the Level of Significance. We decided on the .01 significance level.

Step 3: Select the Test Statistic. The test statistic in this situation is the t distribution. Why? First it is reasonable to conclude that the distribution of the cost per claim follows the normal distribution. We can confirm this from the following histogram and from the normal curve superimposed on the chart.

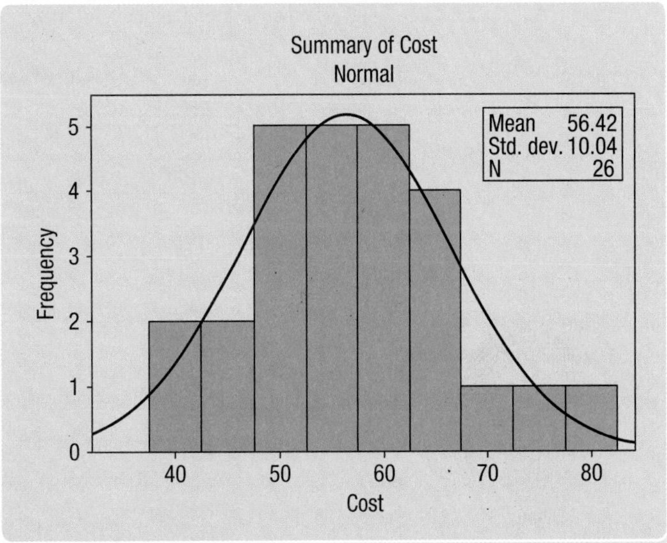

We do not know the standard deviation of the population, so we substitute the sample standard deviation. The value of the test statistic is computed using formula (9–2).

$$t = \frac{\bar{X} - \mu}{s/\sqrt{n}}$$

Step 4: Formulate the Decision Rule. The critical values of t are given in Appendix F, a portion of which is shown in Table 9–1. The far left column of the table is labelled "Degrees of Freedom, *df*." The number of degrees of freedom is the total number of observations in the sample minus the number of samples, written $n - 1$. In this case, the number of observations in the sample is 26, so there are $26 - 1 = 25$ degrees of freedom. To find the critical value, first locate the row with the appropriate degrees of freedom. This row is shaded in Table 9–1. Next, determine whether the test is one-tailed or two-tailed. In this case, we have a one-tailed test, so find the portion of the table that is labelled "one-tailed." Locate the column with the selected significance level. In this example, the significance level is .01. Move down the column labelled "0.01" until it intersects the row with 25 degrees of freedom. The value is 2.485. Because this is a one-tailed test and the rejection region is in the left tail, the critical value is negative. The decision rule is to reject H_0 if the value of t is less than −2.485.

Step 5: Make a Decision. In this problem, we find the following:

$\bar{X}$ = \$56.42, the sample mean.
μ = \$60, the hypothesized population mean.
s = \$10.04, the sample standard deviation.
n = 26, the number of observations in the sample.

Using formula (9–2):

$$t = \frac{\bar{X} - \mu}{s/\sqrt{n}} = \frac{\$56.42 - \$60}{\$10.04/\sqrt{26}} = -1.818$$

Because −1.818 lies in the region to the right of the critical value of −2.485, the null hypothesis is not rejected at the .01 significance level. We have not shown that the cost-cutting measures reduced the mean cost per claim to less than \$60. The difference of \$3.58 (\$56.42 − \$60) between the sample mean and the population mean could be due to sampling error. The computed value of t is shown in Chart 9–6. It is in the region where the null hypothesis is not rejected.

TABLE 9–1 A Portion of the *t* Distribution Table

	Confidence Intervals					
	80%	90%	95%	98%	99%	99.9%
	Level of Significance for One-Tailed Test					
df	0.100	0.050	0.025	0.010	0.005	0.0005
	Level of Significance for Two-Tailed Test					
	0.20	0.10	0.05	0.02	0.01	0.001
⋮	⋮	⋮	⋮	⋮	⋮	⋮
21	1.323	1.721	2.080	2.518	2.831	3.819
22	1.321	1.717	2.074	2.508	2.819	3.792
23	1.319	1.714	2.069	2.500	2.807	3.768
24	1.318	1.711	2.064	2.492	2.797	3.745
25	1.316	1.708	2.060	2.485	2.787	3.725
26	1.315	1.706	2.056	2.479	2.779	3.707
27	1.314	1.703	2.052	2.473	2.771	3.690
28	1.313	1.701	2.048	2.467	2.763	3.674
29	1.311	1.699	2.045	2.462	2.756	3.659
30	1.310	1.697	2.042	2.457	2.750	3.646

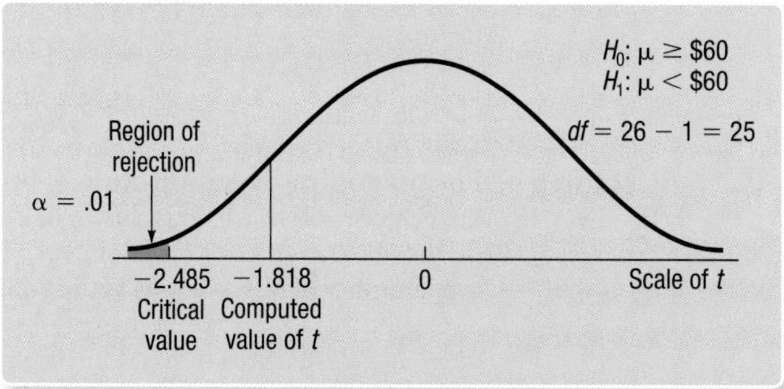

CHART 9–6 Rejection Region, *t* Distribution, .01 Significance Level

The MegaStat commands for the above exercise follow.

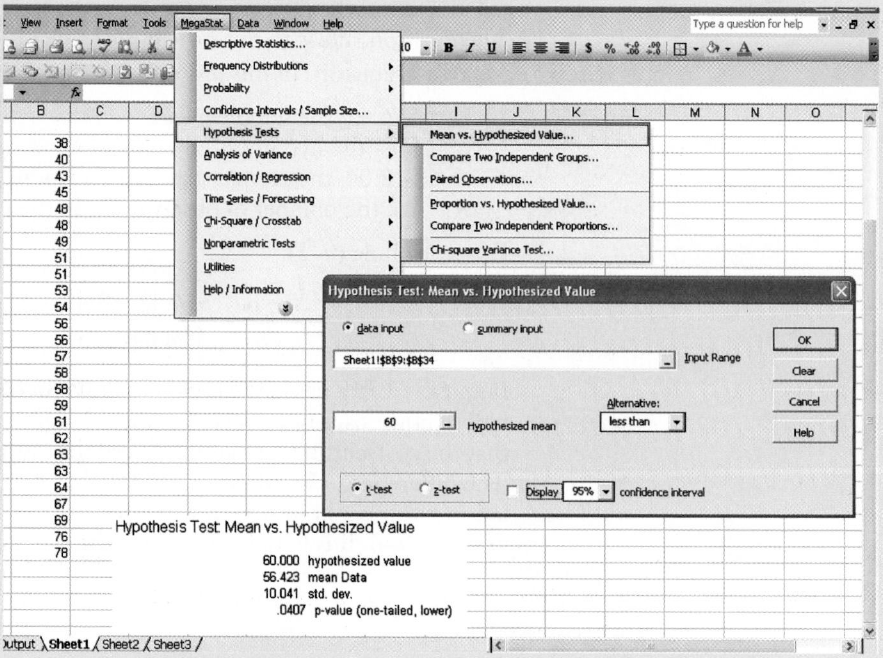

A portion of the MegaStat output is shown above. Note the p-value of .0407, which is greater than the significance level of .01. Therefore, there is not enough evidence to reject the null hypothesis.

In the following example we will review the use of a confidence interval and p-value in hypothesis testing.

example

The mean length of a small counterbalance bar is 43 mm. The production supervisor is concerned that the adjustments of the machine producing the bars have changed. He asks the engineering department to investigate. Engineering selects a random sample of 12 bars and measures each. The results are reported below in millimetres.

42	39	42	45	43	40	39	41	40	42	43	42

Is it reasonable to conclude that there has been a change in the mean length of the bars? Use the .02 significance level.

solution

We begin by stating the null hypothesis and the alternative hypothesis.

$$H_0: \mu = 43$$
$$H_1: \mu \neq 43$$

The alternative hypothesis does not state a direction, so this is a two-tailed test. There are 11 degrees of freedom, found by $n - 1 = 12 - 1 = 11$. The t-value is 2.718, found by referring to Appendix F for a two-tailed test, using the .02 significance level, with 11 degrees of freedom. The decision rule is: Reject the null hypothesis if the computed t is to the left of -2.718 or to the right of 2.718. This information is summarized in Chart 9–7.

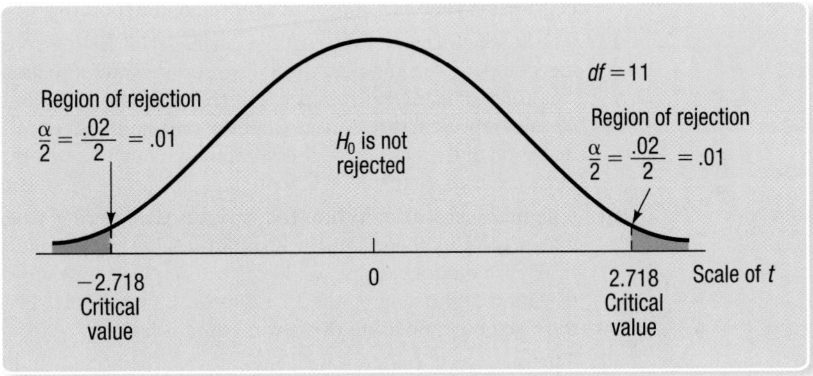

CHART 9–7 Regions of Rejection, Two-Tailed Test, Student's t Distribution, $\alpha = .02$

The mean and the standard deviation of the sample can be determined by calculator, formula (see Chapter 3), or computer software.

The mean, $\bar{X}$, is 41.5 mm, and the standard deviation, s, is 1.78 mm.

Now we are ready to compute the value of t, using formula (9–2).

$$t = \frac{\bar{X} - \mu}{s/\sqrt{n}} = \frac{41.5 - 43.0}{1.78/\sqrt{12}} = -2.92$$

The null hypothesis that the population mean is 43 mm is rejected because the computed t of -2.92 lies in the area to the left of -2.718. We accept the alternative hypothesis and conclude that the population mean is not 43 mm. The machine is out of control and needs adjustment.

self-review 9–3

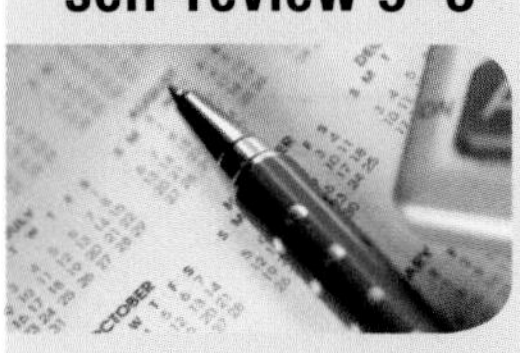

The mean life of a battery used in a digital clock is 305 days. The lives of the batteries follow the normal distribution. The battery was recently modified to last longer. A sample of 20 of the modified batteries had a mean life of 311 days with a standard deviation of 12 days. Did the modification increase the mean life of the battery?

(a) State the null hypothesis and the alternative hypothesis.
(b) Show the decision rule graphically. Use the .05 significance level.
(c) Compute the value of t. What is your decision regarding the null hypothesis? Briefly summarize your results.
(d) Determine or estimate the p-value and interpret.

Exercises

11. Given the following hypotheses:

$$H_0: \mu \leq 10$$
$$H_1: \mu > 10$$

For a random sample of 10 observations, the sample mean was 12 and the sample standard deviation 3. Using the .05 significance level:

a. State the decision rule.
b. Compute the value of the test statistic.
c. What is your decision regarding the null hypothesis?

12. Given the following hypotheses:

$$H_0: \mu = 400$$
$$H_1: \mu \neq 400$$

For a random sample of 12 observations, the sample mean was 407 and the sample standard deviation 6. Using the .01 significance level:

a. State the decision rule.
b. Compute the value of the test statistic.
c. What is your decision regarding the null hypothesis?

13. The Rocky Mountain district sales manager of Rath Publishing Inc., a college textbook publishing company, claims that the sales representatives make an average of 40 sales calls per week on professors. Several reps say that this estimate is too low. To investigate, a random sample of 28 sales representatives reveals that the mean number of calls made last week was 42. The standard deviation of the sample is 2.1 calls. Can we conclude that the mean number of calls per salesperson per week is more than 40? Choose an appropriate significance level.

14. The management of White Industries is considering a new method of assembling its golf cart. The present method requires 42.3 minutes, on the average, to assemble a cart. The mean assembly time for a random sample of 24 carts, using the new method, was 40.6 minutes, and the standard deviation of the sample was 2.7 minutes. Using the .10 level of significance, can we conclude that the assembly time using the new method is faster?

15. The records of Yellowstone Trucks reveal that the mean life of a set of spark plugs is 35 600 km. The distribution of the life of the plugs is approximately normal. A spark plug manufacturer claimed that its plugs have a mean life in excess of 35 600 km. The fleet owner purchased a large number of sets. A sample of 18 sets revealed that the mean life was 37 675 km and the standard deviation was 2415 km. Is there enough evidence to substantiate the manufacturer's claim at the .05 significance level?

16. Most air travelers now use e-tickets. Electronic ticketing allows passengers to not worry about a paper ticket, and it costs the airline companies less to handle than paper ticketing. However, in recent times, the airlines have received complaints from passengers regarding their e-tickets, particularly when connecting flights and a change of airlines were involved. To investigate the problem, an independent agency contacted a random sample of 20 airports and collected information on the number of complaints the airport had with e-tickets for the month of March. The information is reported below.

14	14	16	12	12	14	13	16	15	14
12	15	15	14	13	13	12	13	10	13

At the .05 significance level, can the agency conclude the mean number of complaints per airport is less than 15 per month?

a. What assumption is necessary before conducting a test of hypothesis?
b. Plot the number of complaints per airport in a frequency distribution. Is it reasonable to conclude that the population follows a normal distribution?
c. Conduct a test of hypothesis and interpret the results.

How can we estimate a *p*-value without a computer? To illustrate, recall that in the example regarding the length of a counterbalance, we rejected the null hypothesis that $\mu = 43$ and accepted the alternative hypothesis that $\mu \neq 43$. The significance level was .02, so logically the *p*-value is less than .02. To estimate the *p*-value more accurately, go to Appendix F and find the row with 11 degrees of freedom. The computed *t*-value of 2.91 is between 2.718 and 3.106. (A portion of Appendix F is reproduced as Table 9–2.) The two-tailed significance level corresponding to 2.718 is .02, and for 3.106 it is .01. Therefore, the *p*-value is between .01 and .02. The usual practice is to report that the *p*-value is *less* than the larger of the two significance levels. So we would report, "the *p*-value is less than .02."

TABLE 9–2 A Portion of Student's *t* Distribution

	Confidence Intervals					
	80%	90%	95%	98%	99%	99.9%
	Level of Significance for One-Tailed Test					
df	0.100	0.050	0.025	0.010	0.005	0.0005
	Level of Significance for Two-Tailed Test					
	0.20	0.10	0.05	0.02	0.01	0.001
⋮	⋮	⋮	⋮	⋮	⋮	⋮
9	1.383	1.833	2.262	2.821	3.250	4.781
10	1.372	1.812	2.228	2.764	3.169	4.587
11	1.363	1.796	2.201	2.718	3.106	4.437
12	1.356	1.782	2.179	2.681	3.055	4.318
13	1.350	1.771	2.160	2.650	3.012	4.221
14	1.345	1.761	2.145	2.624	2.977	4.140
15	1.341	1.753	2.131	2.602	2.947	4.073

We will use MegaStat to compute the confidence interval and exact *p*-value.

excel

minitab

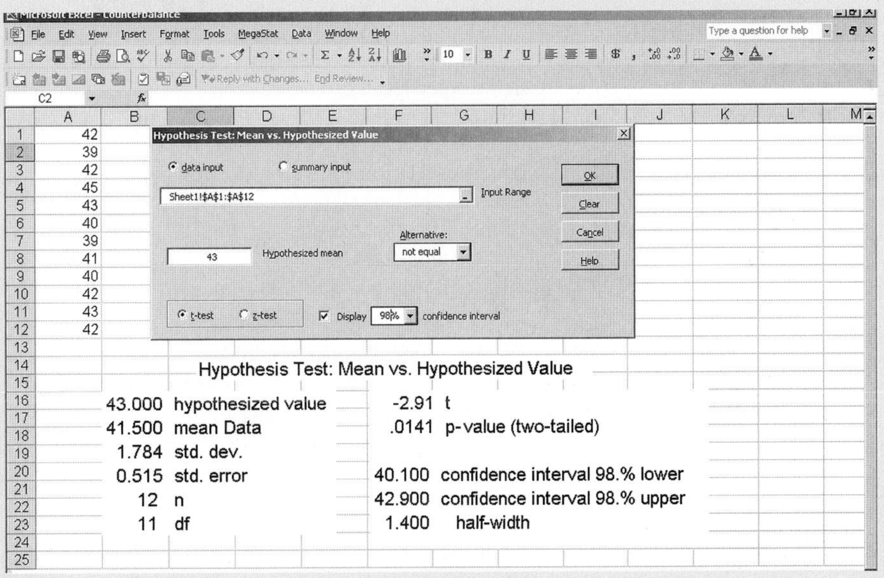

The 98 percent confidence interval is from 40.100 to 42.900. The hypothesized value of 43 mm is to the right of the upper limit of the confidence interval, and so, we reject H_0 and conclude that the population mean is not 43.

In addition, the p-value is .0141, which is less than the significance level of .02, and so, we reject H_0 and conclude that the population mean is not 43.

self-review 9–4

A machine is set to fill a small bottle with 9.0 g of medicine. A sample of eight bottles revealed the following amounts (grams) in each bottle.

9.2	8.7	8.9	8.6	8.8	8.5	8.7	9.0

At the .01 significance level, can we conclude that the mean weight is less than 9.0 g?

(a) State the null hypothesis and the alternative hypothesis.
(b) How many degrees of freedom are there?
(c) Give the decision rule.
(d) Compute the value of t. What is your decision regarding the null hypothesis?
(e) Determine or estimate the p-value. Interpret the p-value.

Exercises

17. Given the following hypotheses:

$$H_0: \mu \geq 20$$
$$H_1: \mu < 20$$

A random sample of five resulted in the following values: 18, 15, 12, 19, and 21. Using the .01 significance level, can we conclude the population mean is less than 20?

a. State the decision rule.
b. Compute the value of the test statistic.
c. What is your decision regarding the null hypothesis?
d. Estimate the p-value.

18. Given the following hypotheses:

$$H_0: \mu = 100$$
$$H_1: \mu \neq 100$$

A random sample of six resulted in the following values: 118, 105, 112, 119, 105, and 111. Using the .05 significance level, can we conclude the mean is different from 100?

a. State the decision rule.
b. Compute the value of the test statistic.
c. What is your decision regarding the null hypothesis?
d. Estimate the p-value.
e. Construct a 95 percent confidence interval. Use the results of the confidence interval to support your decision in part (c).

19. The mean mass of the puppies at five months is 4.35 kg. The masses follow the normal distribution. In an effort to increase their mass, a supplement is added to their daily meals. The subsequent masses of a sample of five-month-old puppies were (in kg):

4.41	4.37	4.33	4.35	4.30	4.39	4.36	4.38	4.40	4.39

At the .01 level, has the supplement increased the mean mass of the puppies? Estimate the p-value.

20. The liquid chlorine added to swimming pools to combat algae has a relatively short shelf life before it loses its effectiveness. Records indicate that the mean shelf life of a 4.5 L jug of chlorine is 2160 hours (90 days). As an experiment, Holdlonger was added to the chlorine to find whether it would increase the shelf life. A sample of nine jugs of chlorine had these shelf lives (in hours):

2159	2170	2180	2179	2160	2167	2171	2181	2185

At the .025 level, has Holdlonger increased the shelf life of the chlorine? Estimate the p-value.

21. A college states that the mean number of km per day that students travel for classes is 4.0. A study is done each year to verify the statement. The study for 2008 was done in the fall semester. The results were: 4, 4, 3, 2, 6, 8, 7, 1, 9, 3, 1, and 6. At the .05 level, can we conclude that the mean number of km travelled is greater than 4.0? Estimate the p-value.

22. Hugger Polls contends that an agent conducts a mean of 53 in-depth home surveys every week. A streamlined survey form has been introduced, and Hugger wants to evaluate its effectiveness. The number of in-depth surveys conducted during a week by a random sample of agents are:

53	57	50	55	58	54	60	52	59	62	60	60	51	59	56

At the .05 level of significance, can we conclude that the mean number of interviews conducted by the agents is more than 53 per week? Estimate or calculate the p-value.

a. Suppose the hypothesis situation was changed to read: Does this evidence suggest that the mean annual turnover rate is less than 6.0? State the null hypothesis and the alternative hypothesis under these conditions.
b. What is the decision rule under the new conditions stated in part (a)? Show the decision rule graphically. Show the rejection region and indicate the critical value.
c. What is the p-value? What is your decision regarding the null hypothesis based on the p-value?

7 Conduct a test of hypothesis about a population proportion.

Tests Concerning Proportions

In the previous chapter we discussed confidence intervals for proportions. We can also conduct a test of hypothesis for a proportion. Recall that a proportion is the ratio of the number of successes to the number of observations. We let X refer to the number of successes and n the number of observations, so the proportion of success in a fixed number of trials is X/n. Thus, the formula for computing a sample proportion, $\bar{p}$, is $\bar{p} = X/n$. Consider the following potential hypothesis testing situations.

- Historically, General Motors reports that 70 percent of leased vehicles are returned with less than 58 000 km. A recent sample of 200 vehicles returned at the end of their lease showed 158 had less than 58 000 km. Has the proportion increased?
- Able Moving and Storage Inc. advises its clients for long distance residential moves that their household goods will be delivered in three to five days from the time they are picked up. Able's records show that it is successful 90 percent of the time with this claim. A recent audit revealed it was successful 190 times out of 200. Can it conclude that its success rate has increased?

np and $n(1 - p)$ must be at least 5.

Some assumptions must be made and conditions met before testing a population proportion. To test a hypothesis about a population proportion, a random sample is chosen from the population. First we must meet the binomial assumptions discussed in Chapter 5. These assumptions are: (1) the sample data collected are the result of counts; (2) the outcome of an experiment is classified into one of two mutually exclusive categories—a "success" or a "failure"; (3) the probability of a success is the same for each trial; and (4) the trials are independent, meaning the outcome of one trial does not affect the outcome of any other trial. A test of proportions is appropriate when both np and $n(1 - p)$ are at least 5, where n is the sample size, and p is the population proportion. It uses the fact that a binomial distribution can be approximated by a normal distribution.

example

Prior elections indicate it is necessary for a candidate to receive at least 80 percent of the vote in the northern section of the province to be elected. The incumbent member of parliament is interested in assessing his chances of returning to office and plans to conduct a survey of 2000 registered voters in the northern section of the province.

Using the hypothesis testing procedure, assess the incumbent's chances of re-election.

solution

This situation meets the binomial conditions.

- There are only two possible outcomes. That is, a sampled voter will either vote or not vote for the member of parliament.
- The probability of success is the same for each trial. In this case, the likelihood a particular sampled voter will support re-election is .80.
- The trials are independent. This means, for example, the likelihood the 23rd voter sampled will support re-election is not affected by what the 22nd or 55th voter does.
- The sampled data is the result of counts. We are going to count the number of voters who support re-election in the sample of 2000.

We can use the normal approximation to the binomial distribution when both np and $n(1 - p)$ exceed 5. In this case, $n = 2000$ and $p = .80$ (p is the proportion of the vote in the northern part of the province, or 80 percent, needed for this incumbent to be re-elected). Thus, $np = 2000(.80) = 1600$ and $n(1 - p) = 2000(1 - .80) = 400$. Both 1600 and 400 are greater than 5.

Step 1: State the null hypothesis and the alternative hypothesis. The null hypothesis, H_0, is that the population proportion, p, is .80 or larger. The alternative hypothesis, H_1, is that the proportion is less than .80. From a practical standpoint, the incumbent is concerned only when the proportion is less than .80. If it is equal to or greater than .80, he will have no problem; that is, the sample data would indicate he will probably be re-elected. These hypotheses are written symbolically as:

$$H_0: p \geq .80$$
$$H_1: p < .80$$

H_1 states a direction. Thus, as noted previously, the test is one-tailed with the inequality sign pointing to the tail of the distribution containing the region of rejection.

Step 2: Select the level of significance. The level of significance is .05. This is the likelihood that a true hypothesis will be rejected.

Step 3: Select the test statistic. z is the appropriate statistic, found by:

TEST OF HYPOTHESIS, ONE PROPORTION

$$z = \frac{\bar{p} - p}{\sigma_p} \quad \textbf{[9–3]}$$

where:

p is the hypothesized population proportion parameter.
$\bar{p}$ is the sample proportion.
n is the sample size.
σ_p is the standard error of the population proportion. It is computed by $\sqrt{p(1-p)/n}$, so the formula for z becomes:

TEST OF HYPOTHESIS, ONE PROPORTION

$$z = \frac{\bar{p} - p}{\sqrt{\frac{p(1-p)}{n}}} \quad \textbf{[9–4]}$$

Finding the Critical Value

Step 4: State the decision rule. The critical value or values of z form the dividing point or points between the regions where H_0 is rejected and where it is not rejected. Since the alternative hypothesis states a direction, this is a one-tailed test. The sign of the inequality points to the left, so we use only the left side of the distribution. See Chart 9–8. The significance level was given as .05 in step 2. This probability is in the left tail and determines the region of rejection. The area between zero and the critical value is .4500, found by .5000 − .0500. Referring to Appendix D and searching for .4500, we find the critical value of z is 1.645 (or use the table of common z-values). The decision rule is, therefore: Reject the null hypothesis and accept the alternative hypothesis if the computed value of z falls to the left of −1.645; otherwise, do not reject H_0.

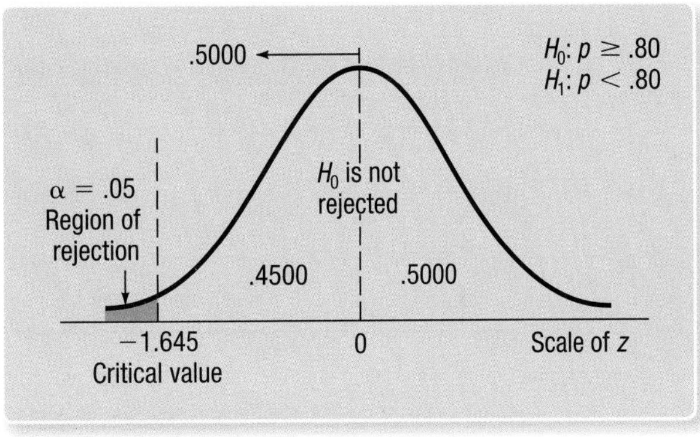

CHART 9–8 Rejection Region for the .05 Level of Significance, One-Tailed Test

Step 5: Make a decision. Select a sample and make a decision about H_0. A sample survey of 2000 potential voters in the northern part of the province revealed that 1550 planned to vote for the incumbent. Is the sample proportion of .775 (found by 1550/2000) close enough to .80 to conclude that the difference is due to chance? In this case:

- $\bar{p}$ is .775, the proportion in the sample who plan to vote for the incumbent.
- n is 2000, the number of voters surveyed.
- p is .80, the hypothesized population proportion.
- z is a normally distributed test statistic when the hypothesis is true and the other assumptions are true.

Using formula (9–4) and computing z:

$$z = \frac{\bar{p} - p}{\sqrt{\frac{p(1-p)}{n}}} = \frac{\frac{1550}{2000} - .80}{\sqrt{\frac{.80(1-.80)}{2000}}} = \frac{.775 - .80}{\sqrt{.00008}} = -2.80$$

The computed value of z (−2.80) is in the rejection region, so the null hypothesis is rejected at the .05 level. The difference of 2.5 percentage points between the sample percent (77.5 percent) and the hypothesized population percent in the northern part of the province necessary to carry the province (80 percent) is statistically significant. It is probably not due to sampling variation. To put it another way, the evidence at this point does not support the claim that the incumbent will return to office.

The p-value is the probability of finding a z-value less than −2.80. From Appendix D, the probability of a z-value between 0 and −2.80 is .4974. So the p-value is .0026, found by .5000 − .4974. The incumbent cannot be confident of re-election, as the p-value is less than the significance level.

MegaStat steps and commands follow.

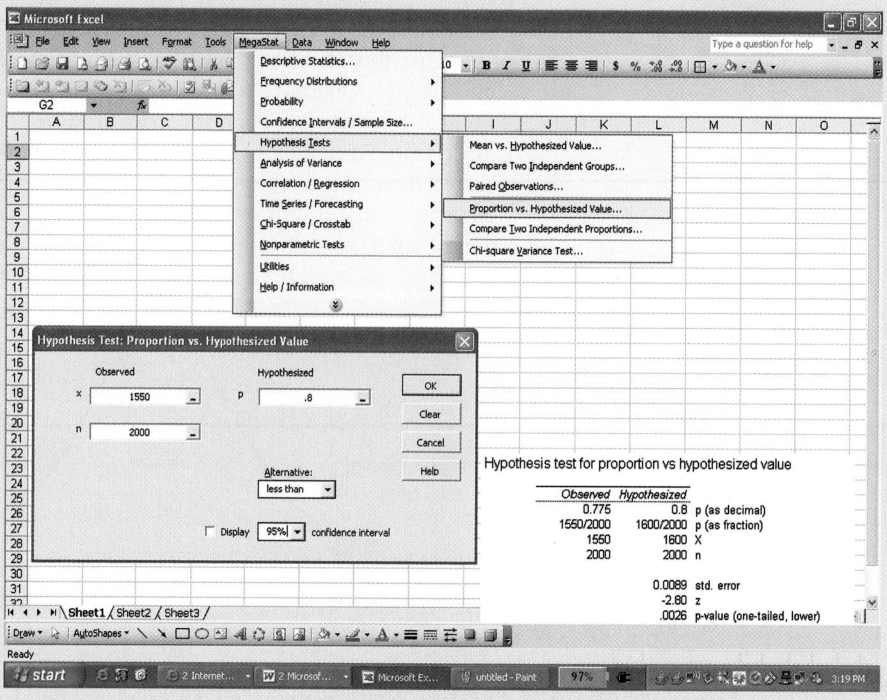

Note that the p-value is .0026, which is smaller than our significance level of .05, and is also smaller than a significance level of .01. This tells us that we have enough evidence to reject the null hypothesis and so we conclude that the proportion of the vote for the incumbent in the northern section of the province will be less than 80 percent.

self-review 9–5

A recent insurance industry report indicated that 40 percent of those persons involved in minor traffic accidents this year have been involved in at least one other traffic accident in the last five years. An advisory group decided to investigate this claim, believing it was too large. A sample of 200 traffic accidents this year showed 74 persons were also involved in another accident within the last five years. Use the .01 significance level.

(a) Can we use z as the test statistic? Tell why or why not.
(b) State the null hypothesis and the alternative hypothesis.
(c) Show the decision rule graphically.
(d) Compute the value of z and state your decision regarding the null hypothesis.
(e) Determine and interpret the p-value.

Exercises

23. The following hypotheses are given.

$$H_0: p \leq .70$$
$$H_1: p > .70$$

A sample of 100 observations revealed that $\overline{p} = .75$. At the .05 significance level, can the null hypothesis be rejected?

a. State the decision rule.
b. Compute the value of the test statistic.
c. What is your decision regarding the null hypothesis?

24. The following hypotheses are given.

$$H_0: p = .40$$
$$H_1: p \neq .40$$

A sample of 120 observations revealed that $\bar{p} = .30$. At the .05 significance level, can the null hypothesis be rejected?

a. State the decision rule.
b. Compute the value of the test statistic.
c. What is your decision regarding the null hypothesis?

Note: It is recommended that you use the five-step hypothesis testing procedure in solving the following problems.

25. An Ontario safety council reported that 52 percent of highway drivers are men. A sample of 300 cars travelling southbound on Highway 400 yesterday revealed that 170 were driven by men. Can we conclude that a larger proportion of men were driving on Highway 400 than the provincial figures indicate? Use a significance level of .01.

26. A recent article in a magazine reported that a job awaits only one in three new college graduates. The major reasons given were an overabundance of college graduates and a weak economy. A survey of 200 recent graduates revealed that 80 students had jobs. At the .02 significance level, can we conclude that a larger proportion of students have jobs?

27. Chicken Delight claims that 90 percent of its orders are delivered within 10 minutes of the time the order is placed. A sample of 100 orders revealed that 82 were delivered within the promised time. At the .01 significance level, can we conclude that less than 90 percent of the orders are delivered in less than 10 minutes?

28. Research at a university indicates that 50 percent of the students change their major area of study after their first year in a program. A random sample of 100 students in business revealed that 48 had changed their major area of study after their first year of the program. Has there been a significant decrease in the proportion of students who change their major after the first year in this program? Choose an appropriate level of significance.

Chapter Summary

I. The objective of hypothesis testing is to check the validity of a statement about a population parameter.

II. The steps in conducting a test of hypothesis are:

A. State the null hypothesis (H_0) and the alternative hypothesis (H_1).

B. Select the level of significance.
1. The level of significance is the likelihood of rejecting a true null hypothesis.
2. The most frequently used significance levels are .01, .05, and .10, but any value between 0 and 1.00 is possible.

C. Select the test statistic.
1. A test statistic is a value calculated from sample information used to determine whether to reject the null hypothesis.
2. Two test statistics were considered in this chapter.
   a. The standard normal distribution is used when the population follows a normal distribution and the population standard deviation is known.
   b. The *t* distribution is used when the population follows a normal distribution and the population standard deviation is unknown.

D. State the decision rule.
1. The decision rule indicates the condition or conditions when the null hypothesis is rejected.
2. In a two-tailed test, the rejection region is evenly split between the upper and lower tails.
3. In a one-tailed test, all of the rejection region is in either the upper or the lower tail.

E. Select a sample, compute the value of the test statistic, make a decision regarding the null hypothesis, and interpret the results.

III. A *p*-value is the probability that the value of the test statistic is as extreme as the value computed, when the null hypothesis is true.

IV. Testing a hypothesis about a population mean.

A. If the population standard deviation, σ, is known, the test statistic is the standard normal distribution and is determined from:

$$z = \frac{\bar{X} - \mu}{\sigma/\sqrt{n}} \quad [9\text{–}1]$$

B. If the population standard deviation is not known, s is substituted for σ.

C. When σ is unknown, the test statistic is the t distribution, and its value is determined from:

$$t = \frac{\bar{X} - \mu}{s/\sqrt{n}} \quad [9\text{–}2]$$

D. The major characteristics of the t distribution are:

1. It is a continuous distribution.
2. It is mound-shaped and symmetrical.
3. It is flatter, or more spread out, than the standard normal distribution.
4. There is a family of t distributions, depending on the number of degrees of freedom.

V. Testing about a population proportion.

A. The binomial conditions must be met.

B. Both np and $n(1 - p) \geq 5$.

C. The test statistic is

$$z = \frac{\bar{p} - p}{\sqrt{\frac{p(1-p)}{n}}} \quad [9\text{–}4]$$

Pronunciation Key

SYMBOL	MEANING	PRONUNCIATION
H_0	Null hypothesis	*H sub zero*
H_1	Alternative hypothesis	*H sub one*

Chapter Exercises

29. A new weight-watching company, Weight Reducers International, advertises that those who join will lose, on the average, 10 pounds the first two weeks. The population standard deviation is 2.8 pounds. A random sample of 50 people who joined the new weight reduction program revealed the mean loss to be 9 pounds. At the .05 level of significance, can we conclude that those joining Weight Reducers on average will lose less than 10 pounds? Determine the p-value.

30. Dole Pineapple Inc. is concerned that the 450 ml can of sliced pineapple is being overfilled. The population standard deviation is 0.85 ml. The quality control department took a random sample of 50 cans and found that the arithmetic mean volume was 451.4 ml. At the 5 percent level of significance, can we conclude that the mean volume is greater than 450 ml? Determine the p-value.

31. A recent survey states that the typical adult gets a mean of seven hours sleep per night. A random sample of 50 university students found that the mean number of hours slept last night was 6 hours and 48 minutes (6.8 hours). The standard deviation of the sample was 0.9 hours. Is it reasonable to conclude that university students sleep less than the typical adult? Compute the p-value and use the information in your answer.

32. A real estate sales agency specializes in selling vacation property. Its records indicate that the mean selling time of vacation property is 90 days. Because of recent hurricane conditions, it believes that the mean selling time is now greater than 90 days. A survey of 100 properties sold recently revealed that the mean selling time was 94 days, with a standard deviation of 22 days. At the .10 significance level, has there been an increase in selling time?

33. According to the local union president, the mean gross income of plumbers is normally distributed, with a mean of \$60 000 and a standard deviation of \$6000. An investigative reporter for the local television station recently found, for a sample of 120 plumbers, the mean gross income was \$62 500. At the .10 significance level, is it reasonable to conclude that the mean income is not equal to \$60 000? Determine the p-value and the 90 percent confidence interval. Use this information to support your decision.

34. A recent article in *Vitality* magazine reported that the mean amount of leisure time per week for men is 40.0 hours. You believe this figure is too large and decide to conduct your own test. In a random sample of 60 men, you find that the mean is 37.8 hours of leisure per week and that the standard deviation of the sample is 12.2 hours. Can you conclude that the information in the article is untrue? Use the .05 significance level. Determine the p-value and explain its meaning.

35. Global TV news, in a segment on the price of gasoline, reported last evening that the mean price nationwide is \$1.25 per litre for self-serve regular unleaded. A random sample of 35 stations in Edmonton revealed that the mean price was \$1.27 per litre and that the standard deviation was \$0.05 per litre. At the .05 significance level, can we conclude that the price of gasoline is higher in this city? Determine the p-value.

36. The Rutter Distribution Company claims that its average shipment is 50 kg. From a long history, the shipping department reports that the distribution of the bag masses follows a normal distribution and the standard deviation of this process is 3 kg per bag. At the end of each day, Jeff Rutter, the production manager, selects 10 bags and computes the mean mass of the sample. Below are the masses of 10 bags from today's production.

45.6	47.7	47.6	46.3	46.2	47.4	49.2	55.8	47.5	48.5

a. Can Mr. Rutter conclude that the mean mass of the bags is less than 50 kg? Use the .01 significance level.
b. In a brief report, tell why Mr. Rutter can use the z distribution as the test statistic.
c. Compute the p-value.

37. Tina Dennis is the comptroller for Meek Industries. She believes that the current cash-flow problem at Meek is due to the slow collection of accounts receivable. She believes that more than 60 percent of the accounts are in arrears more than three months. A random sample of 200 accounts showed that 140 were more than three months old. At the .01 significance level, can she conclude that more than 60 percent of the accounts are in arrears for more than three months?

38. The policy of the Suburban Transit Authority is to add a bus route if more than 55 percent of the potential commuters indicate they would use the particular route. A sample of 70 commuters revealed that 42 would use a proposed route from Bowman Park to the downtown area. Does the Bowman-to-downtown route meet the STA criterion? Use the .05 significance level.

39. Past experience at the Crowder Travel Agency indicated that 44 percent of those persons who wanted the agency to plan a vacation for them wanted to go to Europe. During the most recent busy season, a sampling of 1000 plans was selected at random from the files. It was found that 480 persons wanted to go to Europe on vacation. Has there been a significant shift upward in the percentage of persons who want to go to Europe? Test at the .05 significance level.

40. From past experience a television manufacturer found that 10 percent or less of its sets needed any type of repair in the first two years of operation. In a sample of 50 sets manufactured two years ago, 9 needed repair. At the .05 significance level, has the percent of sets needing repair increased? Determine the p-value.

41. An urban planner claims that, nationally, 20 percent of all families renting condominiums move during a given year. A random sample of 200 families renting condominiums in Vancouver revealed that 56 had moved during the past year. At the .01 significance level, does this evidence suggest that a larger proportion of condominium owners moved in the Vancouver area? Determine the p-value.

42. The cost of weddings has skyrocketed in recent years. As a result, many couples are opting to have their weddings in the Caribbean. A Caribbean vacation resort recently advertised that the cost of a Caribbean wedding was less than \$10 000. Listed below is the total cost (in \$ thousands) for a sample of eight Caribbean weddings.

\$9.7	9.4	11.7	9.0	9.1	10.5	9.1	9.8

At the .05 significance level is it reasonable to conclude the mean wedding cost is less than $10 000 as advertised?

43. The Myers Summer Casual Furniture Store tells customers that a special order will take six weeks (42 days). During recent months, the owner has received several complaints that the special orders are taking longer than 42 days. A sample of 12 special orders delivered in the last month showed that the mean waiting time was 51 days, with a standard deviation of 8 days. At the .05 significance level, are customers waiting an average of more than 42 days? Estimate the *p*-value.

44. A fast food restaurant chain claims that lunch will be served within nine minutes of placing your order, or it is free. A sample of eight customers revealed the following waiting times in minutes:

10.1	9.3	9.2	10.2	9.3	9.6	9.4	8.8

At the .01 significance level, can we conclude that the waiting time for lunch exceeds nine minutes? Estimate the *p*-value.

45. It is estimated that a typical college student drinks about 23 L of water per year, or 1.92 L per month. A sample of 12 college students revealed the following amounts of water consumed last month.

1.75	1.96	1.57	1.82	1.85	1.82	2.43	2.65	2.60	2.24	1.69	2.66

At the .05 significance level, is there a significant difference between the average amount consumed at the college surveyed and the national average? Construct a 95 percent confidence interval. Use the results of the confidence interval to support your decision.

46. In recent years, the interest rates on home mortgages has declined to less than 6.0 percent. However, a recent study shows that the rate charged on credit card debt is more than 14 percent. A sample of 10 credit cards showed that the mean rate charged is 15.64 percent with a standard deviation of 1.561 percent. Is it reasonable to conclude the mean rate charged is greater than 14 percent? Use the .01 significance level.

47. The 30-year mortgage rate is now less than 6.0 percent. A sample of eight financial institutions in Canada showed the mean mortgage rate to be 5.6375 percent with a standard deviation of 0.6346 percent. At the .01 significance level, can we conclude that the 30-year mortgage rate is less than 6.0 percent? Determine or estimate the *p*-value. Interpret the *p*-value.

48. The postanesthesia care area (recovery room) at St. Luke's Hospital was recently enlarged. The hope was that with the enlargement the mean number of patients per day would be more than 25. A random sample of 15 days revealed the following numbers of patients.

25	27	25	26	25	28	28	27	24	26	25	29	25	27	24

At the .01 significance level, can we conclude that the mean number of patients per day is more than 25? Estimate the *p*-value and interpret it.

49. The company *egolf.com* receives an average of 6.5 returns per day from online shoppers. For a sample of 12 days, it received the following number of returns.

0	4	3	4	9	4	5	9	1	6	7	10

At the .01 significance level, can we conclude the mean number of returns is less than 6.5?

50. During recent seasons, Major League Baseball has been criticized for the length of games. A report indicated that the average game lasts 3 hours and 30 minutes. A sample of 17 games revealed the following times to completion. (Note that the minutes have been changed to fractions of hours, so that a game that lasted 2 hours and 24 minutes is reported at 2.40 hours.)

2.98	2.40	2.70	2.25	3.23	3.17	2.93	3.18	2.80
2.38	3.75	3.20	3.27	2.52	2.58	4.45	2.45	

Can we conclude that the mean time for a game is less than 3.50 hours? Use the .05 significance level.

51. The Watch Corporation of Switzerland claims that its watches on average will neither gain nor lose time during a week. A sample of 18 watches provided the following gains (+) or losses (−) in seconds per week.

−0.38	−0.20	−0.38	−0.32	+0.32	−0.23	+0.30	+0.25	−0.10
−0.37	−0.61	−0.48	−0.47	−0.64	−0.04	−0.20	−0.68	+0.05

Is it reasonable to conclude that the mean gain or loss in time for the watches is 0? Use the .05 significance level. Determine or estimate the p-value. Interpret the p-value.

52. Listed below is the rate of return for one year (reported in percent) for a sample of 12 mutual funds that are classified as taxable money market funds.

4.63	4.15	4.76	4.70	4.65	4.52	4.70	5.06	4.42	4.51	4.24	4.52

Using the .05 significance level, is it reasonable to conclude that the mean rate of return is more than 4.50 percent?

53. A national grocer's magazine reports the typical shopper spends eight minutes in line waiting to check out. A sample of 24 shoppers at the local No Frills showed a mean of 7.5 minutes with a standard deviation of 3.2 minutes. Is the waiting time at the local No Frills less than that reported in the national magazine? Use the .05 significance level.

54. The campus bookstore reported that students paid an average of $267 per semester for textbooks. To verify this statement, the student union decided to select a random sample of students, and found the following amounts, in dollars, spent for textbooks:

$321	286	290	330	310	250	270	280	299	265	291	275	281

At the .01 significance level, can we conclude that the average amount spent on textbooks per semester has increased? What is the p-value?

55. A shopping centre wants to examine the amount of space required for parking. Studies indicated that 50 percent of staff and shoppers use public transportation. A survey of 1002 was taken, and 483 responded that they used public transportation. Is it reasonable to conclude that the survey results indicate a change? Use the .05 significance level.

56. Many grocery stores and large retailers such as Loblaws and Wal-Mart have installed self-checkout systems so shoppers can scan their own items and cash out themselves. How do customers like this service and how often do they use it? The results of a sample of the number of customers using the self-checkout system over a period of 15 days are listed below.

120	108	120	114	118	91	118	92
112	97	118	108	117	104	104	

Is it reasonable to conclude that the mean number of customers using the self-checkout system is more than 100 per day? Use the .05 significance level.

Data Set Exercises

57. Refer to the CREA (Canadian Real Estate Association) data on the CD-ROM, which reports information on average house prices nationally and in a selection of cities across Canada. Note: Select the cities only.

a. Develop a 95 percent confidence interval for the mean list price for January 2008.

b. Is it possible that the population mean is $350 000? Test at the .02 significance level.

c. Is it possible that the population mean is $275 000? Use the results in part (a) to test at the .05 significance level.

d. What is the p-value? Use the p-value to support your answer in part (c).

58. Refer to the real estate data, from the south-east area of Edmonton, on the CD-ROM, which reports information on listed homes.
   a. A recent article indicated that the mean list price of the homes is more than \$400 000. Can we conclude that the mean list price is more than \$400 000? Use the .01 significance level. What is the *p*-value? Interpret the *p*-value.
   b. The same article reported the mean size was more than 2100 square feet. Can we conclude that the mean size of homes listed is more than 2100 square feet? Use the .01 significance level. What is the *p*-value? Interpret the *p*-value.
   c. Determine the proportion of homes that are two-storey. At the .05 significance level, can we conclude that more than 50 percent of the homes listed are two-storey? What is the *p*-value? Interpret the *p*-value.
   d. Determine the proportion of homes with more than two bedrooms. At the .05 significance level, can we conclude that more than 60 percent of the homes listed have more than two bedrooms? What is the *p*-value? Interpret the *p*-value.

59. Refer to the International data, which reports demographic and economic information on 46 countries.
   a. Conduct a test of hypothesis to determine if the mean number of cell phones is greater than 4.0. Use the .05 significance level. What is the *p*-value?
   b. Conduct a test of hypothesis to determine if the mean size of the labor force is below 50. Use the .01 significance level. What is the *p*-value?

60. Refer to the CREA (Canadian Real Estate Association) data on the CD-ROM, which reports information on average house prices nationally and in a selection of cities across Canada. Note: Select the cities only.
   a. Develop a 98 percent confidence interval for the mean list price for January 2007.
   b. Is it possible that the population mean is \$250 000? Test at the .05 significance level.
   c. Is it possible that the population mean is \$400 000? Use the results in part (a) to test at the .02 significance level.
   d. What is the *p*-value? Use this result to support your answers.

exercises.com

Additional exercises that require you to access information at related Internet sites are available on the CD-ROM included with this text.

Answers to Self-Reviews

9–1 **(a)** H_0: $\mu = 6.0$; H_1: $\mu \neq 6.0$.
(b) .05.
(c) $z = \dfrac{\bar{X} - \mu}{\sigma/\sqrt{n}}$.
(d) Do not reject the null hypothesis if the computed z-value falls between −1.96 and +1.96.
(e) Yes. Computed $z = -2.56$, found by:

$$z = \frac{5.84 - 6.0}{0.5/\sqrt{64}} = \frac{-0.16}{.0625} = -2.56.$$

Reject H_0 at the .05 level of significance and conclude that the mean turnover rate is not equal to 6.0.

9–2 **(a)** H_0: $\mu \geq 6.0$;
H_1: $\mu < 6.0$.
Note that the inequality sign (<) in the alternative hypothesis points in the direction of the region of rejection. To determine the critical value: .5000 − .05 = .4500. The z-value from Appendix D is about −1.645.

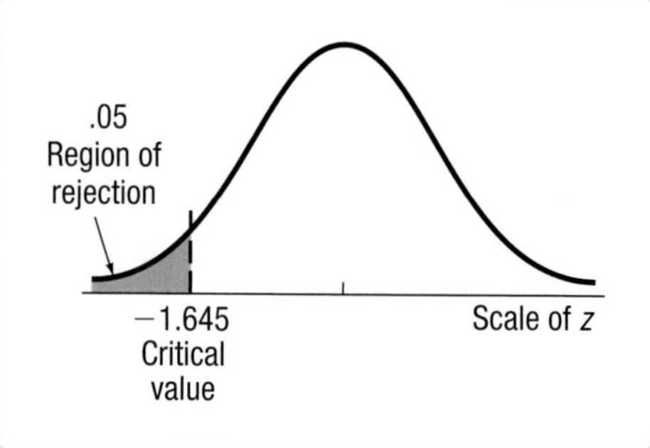

(c) Using Appendix D, the p-value is (.5 − .4948) = .0052. The p-value is less than the significance level of .05, so we reject H_0 and conclude that the mean is less than 6.0.

9–3 **(a)** H_0: $\mu \le 305$; H_1: $\mu > 305$.
(b) $df = n - 1 = 20 - 1 = 19$.

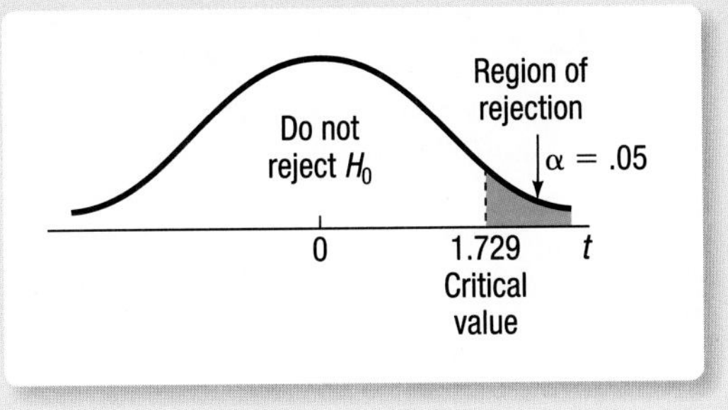

(c) $t = \dfrac{\bar{X} - \mu}{s/\sqrt{n}} = \dfrac{311 - 305}{12/\sqrt{20}} = 2.236.$

Reject H_0 because $2.236 > 1.729$. The modification increased the mean battery life to more than 305 days.

(d) The p-value is .0188, which is less than the significance level of .05, so we reject H_0 and conclude that mean battery life has increased.

9–4 **(a)** H_0: $\mu \ge 9.0$; H_1: $\mu < 9.0$.
(b) 7, found by $n - 1 = 8 - 1 = 7$.
(c) Reject H_0 if $t < -2.998$.

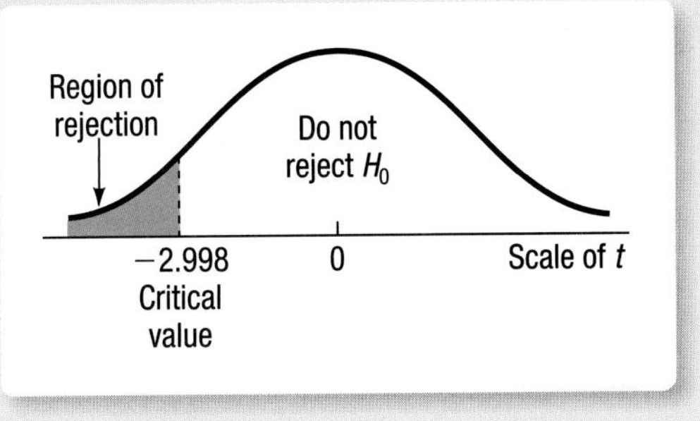

(d) $t = -2.494$, found by:

$$s = \sqrt{\frac{619.88 - \frac{(70.4)^2}{8}}{8 - 1}} = 0.2268.$$

$$\bar{X} = \frac{70.4}{8} = 8.8.$$

Then

$$t = \frac{8.8 - 9.0}{0.2268/\sqrt{8}} = -2.494.$$

Since -2.494 lies to the right of -2.998, H_0 is not rejected. We have not shown that the mean is less than 9.0.

(e) The p-value is .0207, which is greater than the significance level of .01, so there is not enough evidence to reject H_0. We conclude that the mean is at least 9.0.

9–5 **(a)** Yes, because both np and $n(1 - p)$ exceed 5: $np = 200(.40) = 80$, and $n(1 - p) = 200(.60) = 120$.
(b) H_0: $p \ge .40$.
H_1: $p < .40$.
(c)

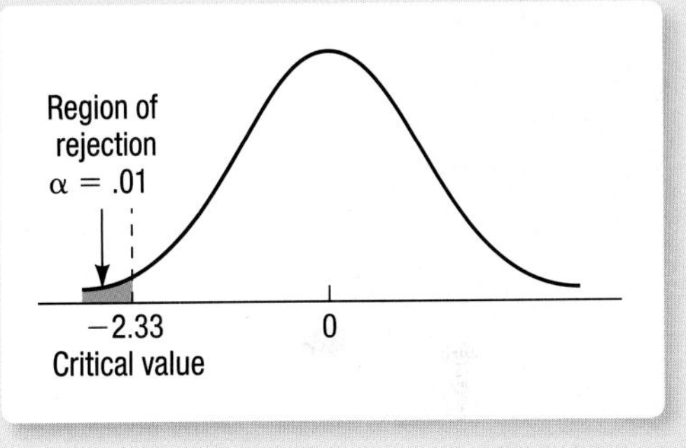

(d) $z = -0.87$, found by:

$$z = \frac{.37 - .40}{\sqrt{\frac{.40(1 - .40)}{200}}} = \frac{-.03}{\sqrt{.0012}} = -0.87.$$

Do not reject H_0.

(e) The p-value is .1922, found by $.5000 - .3078$. The p-value is greater than the significance level of .01, so we do not have enough evidence to reject H_0 and conclude that the population proportion is at least .40.

chapter 10

Two-Sample Tests of Hypothesis

See exercise 3.

LEARNING GOALS

When you have completed this chapter, you will be able to:

1. Conduct a test of a hypothesis about the difference between two independent population means.
2. Conduct a test of a hypothesis about the difference between two population proportions.
3. Conduct a test of a hypothesis about the mean difference between *paired* or *dependent observations*.
4. Understand the difference between *dependent* and *independent samples*.

Introduction

Chapter 9 began our study of hypothesis testing. We described the nature of hypothesis testing and conducted tests of a hypothesis in which we compared the results of a single sample to a population value. That is, we selected a random sample from a population and conducted a test of whether the proposed population value was reasonable. Recall, in Chapter 9 we selected a sample of weeks and found the number of desks assembled per week at the Jamestown Steel Company. We wished to determine whether there was a change in the production rate. Similarly, we sampled voters in one area of a particular province to determine whether the population proportion that would support the incumbent for re-election was less than .80. In both of these cases, we compared the results of a *single* sample statistic to a population parameter.

In this chapter we expand the idea of hypothesis testing to comparing populations. That is, we select random samples from two different populations to determine whether the population means or proportions are equal. Some questions we might want to test are:

1. Is there a difference in the mean value of residential real estate sold by male agents and female agents in Halifax?
2. Is there a difference in the mean number of defects produced on the day and the afternoon shifts at Kimble Products?
3. Is there a difference in the mean number of days absent between young workers (under 21 years of age) and older workers (more than 60 years of age) in the fast-food industry?
4. Is there an increase in the production rate if music is piped into the production area?

We begin this chapter with the case in which we select random samples from two independent populations and wish to investigate whether these populations have the same mean.

1 Conduct a test of a hypothesis about the difference between two independent population means.

Two-Sample Tests of Hypothesis: Independent Samples

A city planner in Winnipeg wishes to know whether there is a difference in the mean hourly wage rate of plumbers and electricians in the city. A financial accountant wishes to know whether the mean rate of return for high-yield mutual funds is different from the mean rate of return on global mutual funds. In each of these cases there are two independent populations. In the first case, the plumbers represent one population and the electricians the other. In the second case, high-yield mutual funds are one population and global mutual funds the other.

In each of these cases, to investigate the question, we would select a random sample from each population and compute the mean of the two samples. If the two population means are the same, that is, the mean hourly rate is the same for the plumbers and the electricians, we would expect the *difference* between the two sample means to be zero. But what if our sample results yield a difference other than zero? Is that difference due to chance or is it because there is a real difference in the hourly earnings? A two-sample test of means will help to answer this question.

We do need to return to the results of Chapter 7. Recall that we showed that a distribution of sample means would tend to approximate the normal distribution. We need to again assume that a distribution of sample means will follow the normal distribution. It can be shown mathematically that the distribution of the differences between sample means for two normal distributions is also normal.

We can illustrate this theory in terms of the city planner in Winnipeg. To begin, let's assume some information that is not usually available. Suppose that the population of wages of plumbers has a mean of \$30.00 per hour and a standard deviation of \$5.00 per hour. The population of wages of electricians has a mean of \$29.00 and a standard deviation of \$4.50. Now, from this information it is clear that the two population means are not the same. The plumbers actually earn \$1.00 per hour more than the electricians. But, we cannot expect to uncover this difference each time we sample the two populations.

Suppose we select a random sample of 40 plumbers and a random sample of 35 electricians and compute the mean of each sample. Then, we determine the difference between the sample means. It is this difference between the sample means that holds our interest. If the populations have the same mean, then we would expect the difference between the two sample means to be zero. If there is a difference between the population means, then we expect to find a difference between the sample means.

To understand the theory, we need to take several pairs of samples, compute the mean of each, determine the difference between the sample means, and study the distribution of the differences in the sample means. Because of our study of the distribution of sample means in Chapter 7, we know that the distribution of the sample means follows a normal distribution. If the two distributions of sample means follow a normal distribution, then we can reason that the distribution of their differences will also follow a normal distribution. This is the first hurdle.

The second hurdle refers to the mean of this distribution of differences. If we find the mean of this distribution is zero, that implies that there is no difference in the two populations. On the other hand, if the mean of the distribution of differences is equal to some value other than zero, either positive or negative, then we conclude that the two populations do not have the same mean.

To report some concrete results, let's return to the city planner. Table 10–1 shows the result of selecting 20 samples of 40 plumbers and 35 electricians, computing the mean of each sample, and finding the difference between the two sample means. In the first case, the sample of 40 plumbers has a mean of \$29.80, and for the 35 electricians the mean is \$28.76. The difference between the sample means is \$1.04. This process was repeated 19 more times. Observe that in 17 of the 20 cases the mean of the plumbers is larger than the mean of the electricians.

Statistics in Action

The U.S. Presidential Election of 2000 turned out to be one of the closest in history. The news media were unable to project a winner, and the final decision, including recounts and court decisions, took more than five weeks. This was not the only election in which there was controversy. Shortly before the 1936 presidential election, *The New York Times* carried the headline: "*Digest* Poll Gives Landon 32 States: Landon Leads 4–3." However, Alfred Landon of Kansas was not elected President. In fact, Roosevelt won by more than 11 million votes and received 523 Electoral College votes. How could the headline have been so wrong?

The *Literary Digest* collected a sample of voters from lists of telephone numbers, automobile registrations, and *Digest* readers. In 1936, not many people could afford a telephone or an automobile. In addition, those who read the *Digest* tended to be wealthier and voted Republican. Thus, the population that was sampled did not represent the population of voters. A second problem was with the nonresponses.

(Continued on Next Page)

(Continued)
More than 10 million people were sent surveys, and more than 2.3 million responded. However, no attempt was made to see whether those responding represented a cross-section of all the voters.

With modern computers and survey methods, samples are carefully selected and checked to ensure they are representative. What happened to the *Literary Digest*? It went out of business shortly after the 1936 election.

Our final hurdle is that we need to know something about the *variability* of the distribution of differences. To put it another way, what is the standard deviation of this distribution of differences? Statistical theory shows that when we have independent populations, such as the case here, the distribution of the differences has a variance (standard deviation squared) equal to the sum of the two individual variances. This means that we can add the variances of the two sampling distributions.

VARIANCE OF THE DISTRIBUTION OF DIFFERENCES IN MEANS

$$\sigma^2_{\bar{x}_1 - \bar{x}_2} = \frac{\sigma_1^2}{n_1} + \frac{\sigma_2^2}{n_2} \qquad [10\text{–}1]$$

TABLE 10–1 The Mean Wages of Random Samples of Plumbers and Electricians

Sample	Plumbers	Electricians	Difference
1	$29.80	$28.76	$1.04
2	30.32	29.40	0.92
3	30.57	29.94	0.63
4	30.04	28.93	1.11
5	30.09	29.78	0.31
6	30.02	28.66	1.36
7	29.60	29.13	0.47
8	29.63	29.42	0.21
9	30.17	29.29	0.88
10	30.81	29.75	1.06
11	30.09	28.05	2.04
12	29.35	29.07	0.28
13	29.42	28.79	0.63
14	29.78	29.54	0.24
15	29.60	29.60	0.00
16	30.60	30.19	0.41
17	30.79	28.65	2.14
18	29.14	29.95	−0.81
19	29.91	28.75	1.16
20	28.74	29.21	−0.47

The term $\sigma^2_{\bar{X}_1 - \bar{X}_2}$ looks complex but need not be difficult to interpret. The σ^2 portion reminds us that it is a population variance, and the subscript $\bar{X}_1 - \bar{X}_2$ that it is a distribution of differences in the sample means.

We can put this equation in more usable form by taking the square root, so that we have the standard deviation of the distribution or "standard error" of the differences. Finally, we standardize the distribution of the differences. The result is the following equation.

TWO-SAMPLE TEST OF MEANS—KNOWN σ

$$z = \frac{\bar{X}_1 - \bar{X}_2 - (\mu_1 - \mu_2)}{\sqrt{\dfrac{\sigma_1^2}{n_1} + \dfrac{\sigma_2^2}{n_2}}} \qquad [10\text{–}2]$$

Assumptions for large sample test

Before we present an example, let's review the assumptions necessary for using formula (10–2).

1. The two samples must be unrelated, that is, independent.
2. The standard deviations of both populations must be known.

The following example shows the details of the test of hypothesis for two population means.

example

Customers at FoodTown Super Marts now have a choice when paying for groceries. They may check out using the standard cashier-assisted checkout, or they may use the new U-Scan procedure. In the standard procedure, a FoodTown employee scans each item, puts it on a short conveyor where another employee puts it in a bag, and then into the grocery cart. In the U-Scan procedure, the customer scans each item, bags it, and places the bags in the cart. The U-Scan procedure is designed to reduce the time a customer spends in the checkout line.

The U-Scan facility was recently installed at the Lyons Road FoodTown location. The store manager would like to know if the mean checkout time using the standard checkout method is longer than using the U-Scan. She gathered the following sample information. The time is measured from when the customer enters the line until his or her bags are in the cart. Hence, the time includes both waiting in line and checking out. What is the *p*-value?

Customer Type	Sample Mean	Population Standard Deviation	Sample Size
Standard	5.50 minutes	0.40 minutes	50
U-Scan	5.30 minutes	0.30 minutes	100

solution

Statistics in Action

Do you live to work or work to live? A recent poll of 802 workers revealed that, among those who considered their work as a career, the mean number of hours worked per day was 8.7. Among those who considered their work a job, the mean number of hours worked per day was 7.6.

We use the five-step hypothesis testing procedure to investigate the question.

Step 1: State the null hypothesis and the alternative hypothesis. The null hypothesis is that there is no difference in the mean checkout times for the two groups. In other words, the difference of 0.20 minutes between the mean checkout time for the standard method and the mean checkout time for U-Scan is due to chance. The alternative hypothesis is that the mean checkout time is longer for those using the standard method. We will let μ_1 refer to the mean checkout time for the population of standard customers and μ_2 the mean checkout time for the U-Scan customers. The null and alternative hypotheses are:

$$H_0: \mu_1 - \mu_2 \leq 0$$
$$H_1: \mu_1 - \mu_2 > 0$$

Step 2: Select the level of significance. The significance level is the probability that we reject the null hypothesis when it is actually true. This likelihood is determined prior to selecting the sample or performing any calculations. The .05 and .01 significance levels are the most common, but other values, such as .02 and .10, are also used. In theory, we may select any value between 0 and 1 for the significance level. In this case we selected the .01 significance level.

Step 3: Determine the test statistic. In Chapter 9 we used the standard normal distribution (that is z) and t as test statistics. In this case, we use the z distribution as the test statistic because the standard deviations of both populations are known.

Step 4: Formulate a decision rule. The decision rule is based on the null and the alternative hypotheses (i.e., one-tailed or two-tailed test), the level of significance, and the test statistic used. We selected the .01 significance level, the z distribution as the test statistic, and we wish to determine whether the mean checkout time is longer using the standard method. We set the alternative hypothesis to indicate that the mean checkout time is longer for those using the standard method than the U-Scan method. Hence, the rejection region is in the upper tail of the standard normal distribution (a one-tailed test). To find the critical value, place .01 of the total area in the upper tail. This means that .4900 (.5000 − .0100) of the area is located between the z-value of 0 and the critical value. Next, we search the body of Appendix D for a value located near .4900. It is 2.33, so our decision rule is to reject H_0 if the value computed from the test statistic exceeds 2.33. Chart 10–1 depicts the decision rule.

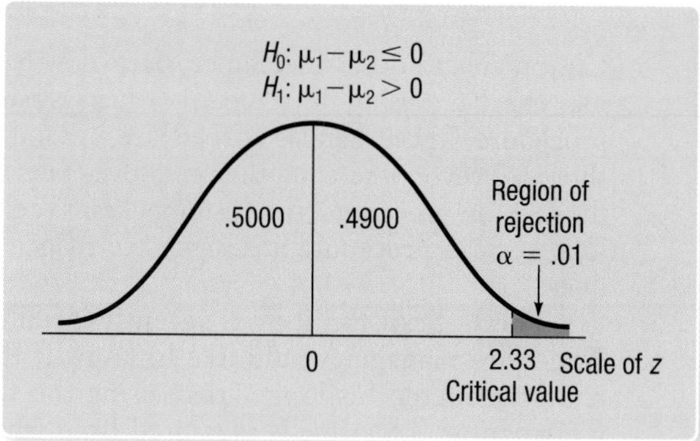

CHART 10–1 Decision Rule for One-Tailed Test at .01 Significance Level

Step 5: Make the decision regarding H_0 and interpret the result. We use formula (10–2) to compute the value of the test statistic.

$$z = \frac{\bar{X}_1 - \bar{X}_2 - (\mu_1 - \mu_2)}{\sqrt{\frac{\sigma_1^2}{n_1} + \frac{\sigma_2^2}{n_2}}} = \frac{5.5 - 5.3 - 0}{\sqrt{\frac{0.40^2}{50} + \frac{0.30^2}{100}}} = \frac{0.2}{0.064} = 3.13$$

The computed value of 3.13 is larger than the critical value of 2.33. Our decision is to reject the null hypothesis and accept the alternative hypothesis. The difference of 0.20 minutes between the mean checkout time using the standard method is too large to have occurred by chance. To put it another way, we conclude that the U-Scan method is faster.

What is the p-value for the test statistic? Recall that the p-value is the probability of finding a value of the test statistic this extreme when the null hypothesis is true. To calculate the p-value we need the probability of a z-value larger than 3.13. From Appendix D we cannot find the probability associated with 3.13. The largest value available is 3.09. The area corresponding to 3.09 is .4990. In this case we can report that the p-value is less than .0010, found by .5000 − .4990. We conclude that there is very little likelihood that the null hypothesis is true! Note that the p-value is less than the significance level, α = .01, so the test statistic lies in the rejection region.

excel

The MegaStat steps and commands follow. Results may differ slightly due to rounding.

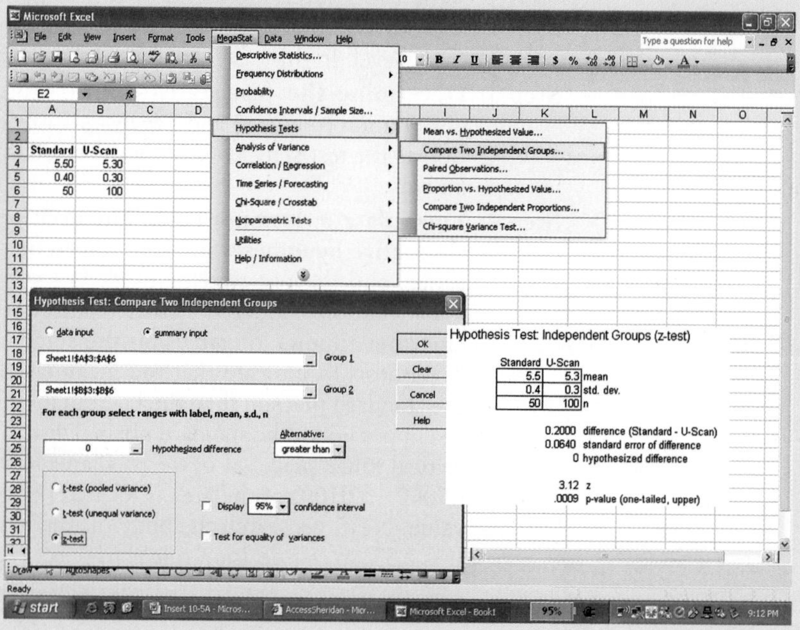

In summary, the criteria for using formula (10–2) are:

1. *The samples are from independent populations.* This means, for example, that the checkout time for the U-Scan customers is unrelated to the checkout time for the other customers. For example, Mr. Smith's checkout time does not affect any other customer's checkout time.
2. *Both population standard deviations are known.* In the FoodTown example, the population standard deviation of the U-Scan times was 0.30 minutes. The standard deviation of the standard checkout times was 0.40 minutes. We use formula (10–2) to find the value of the test statistic.

self-review 10–1

Tom Sevits is the owner of the Appliance Patch. Recently, Tom observed a difference in the dollar value of sales between the men and women he employs as sales associates. A sample of 40 days revealed the men sold a mean of \$1400 worth of appliances per day. For a sample of 50 days, the women sold a mean of \$1500 worth of appliances per day. Assume the population standard deviation for men is \$200 and for women \$250. At the .05 significance level, can Mr. Sevits conclude that the mean amount sold per day is larger for the women?

(a) State the null hypothesis and the alternative hypothesis.
(b) What is the decision rule?
(c) What is the value of the test statistic?
(d) What is your decision regarding the null hypothesis?
(e) What is the p-value?
(f) Interpret the result.

Exercises

1. A sample of 40 observations is selected from one population with a population standard deviation of 5. The sample mean is 102. A sample of 50 observations is selected from a second population with a population standard deviation of 6. The sample mean is 99. Conduct the following test of hypothesis using the .04 significance level.

$$H_0: \mu_1 - \mu_2 = 0$$
$$H_1: \mu_1 - \mu_2 \neq 0$$

   a. Is this a one-tailed or a two-tailed test?
   b. State the decision rule.
   c. Compute the value of the test statistic.
   d. What is your decision regarding H_0?
   e. What is the p-value? Interpret the p-value.

2. A sample of 65 observations is selected from one population with a population standard deviation of 0.75. The sample mean is 2.67. A sample of 50 observations is selected from a second population with a population standard deviation of 0.66. The sample mean is 2.59. Conduct the following test of hypothesis using the .08 significance level.

$$H_0: \mu_1 - \mu_2 \leq 0$$
$$H_1: \mu_1 - \mu_2 > 0$$

   a. Is this a one-tailed or a two-tailed test?
   b. State the decision rule.
   c. Compute the value of the test statistic.
   d. What is your decision regarding H_0?
   e. What is the p-value? Interpret the p-value.

Note: Use the five-step hypothesis testing procedure to solve the following exercises.

3. The Gibbs Baby Food Company wishes to compare the weight gain of infants using its brand versus its competitor's. A sample of 40 babies using the Gibbs products revealed a mean weight gain of 3.5 kg in the first three months after birth. For the Gibbs brand, the standard deviation of the population is 1.05 kg. A sample of 55 babies using the competitor's brand revealed a mean increase in weight of 3.7 kg, with a standard deviation of 1.3 kg. Can we conclude that babies using the Gibbs brand gained less weight? Choose an appropriate significance level. Compute the p-value and interpret it.

4. As part of a study of corporate employees, the director of human resources for PNC Inc. wants to compare the distance travelled to work by employees at its downtown and midtown offices. A sample of 35 downtown employees showed they travel a mean of 595 km per month. A sample of 40 midtown employees showed they travel a mean of 610 km per month. The population standard deviations for the downtown and midtown offices are 48 km and 42 km, respectively. Is there a difference in the mean distance travelled per month between downtown and midtown employees? Use the five-step hypothesis testing procedure. Choose an appropriate significance level.
5. A financial analyst wants to compare the turnover rates, in percent, for shares of oil-related stocks versus other stocks, such as GE and IBM. She selected 32 oil-related stocks and 49 other stocks. The mean turnover rate of oil-related stocks is 31.4 percent and the population standard deviation is 5.1 percent. For the other stocks, the mean rate was computed to be 34.9 percent and the population standard deviation is 6.7 percent. Is there a significant difference in the turnover rates of the two types of stock? Use the .01 significance level. Compute the p-value and interpret it.
6. Mary Jo Fitzpatrick is the vice president for nursing services at St. Luke's Memorial Hospital. Recently she noticed in the job postings for nurses that those that are unionized seem to offer higher wages. She decided to investigate and gathered the following sample information.

Group	Mean Wage	Population Standard Deviation	Sample Size
Union	$20.75	$2.25	40
Nonunion	$19.80	$1.90	45

Would it be reasonable for her to conclude that union nurses earn more? Use the .02 significance level. What is the p-value? What conclusions can you make given the p-value?

2 **Conduct a test of a hypothesis about the difference between two population proportions.**

Two-Sample Tests about Proportions

In the previous section, we considered a test involving population means. However, we are often interested in whether two sample proportions come from populations that are equal. Here are several examples.

- The vice president of human resources wishes to know whether there is a difference in the proportion of hourly employees who miss more than five days of work per year at the Sudbury and the Hamilton plants.
- General Motors is considering a new design for the Pontiac G6. The design is shown to a group of potential buyers under 30 years of age and to another group over 60 years of age. Pontiac wishes to know whether there is a difference in the proportion of the two groups who like the new design.
- A consultant in the airline industry is investigating the fear of flying among adults. Specifically, she wishes to know whether there is a difference in the proportion of men versus women who are fearful of flying.

In the above cases, each sampled item or individual can be classified as a "success" or a "failure." That is, in the Pontiac G6 example, each potential buyer is classified as "liking the new design" or "not liking the new design." We then compare the proportion in the under-30 group with the proportion in the over-60 group who indicated they liked the new design. Can we conclude that the differences are due to chance? In this study there is no measurement obtained, only classifying the individuals or objects. Then we assume the nominal scale of measurement.

To conduct the test, we assume each sample is large enough that the normal distribution will serve as a good approximation of the binomial distribution. The test statistic follows the standard normal distribution. We compute the value of z from the following formula:

TWO-SAMPLE TEST OF PROPORTIONS

$$z = \frac{\bar{p}_1 - \bar{p}_2 - (p_1 - p_2)}{\sqrt{\dfrac{p_c(1-p_c)}{n_1} + \dfrac{p_c(1-p_c)}{n_2}}} \qquad [10\text{-}3]$$

Formula (10–3) is formula (10–2) with the respective sample proportions replacing the sample means and $p_c(1 - p_c)$ replacing the two variances. In addition:

n_1 is the number of observations in the first sample.
n_2 is the number of observations in the second sample.
$\bar{p}_1$ is the proportion in the first sample possessing the trait.
$\bar{p}_2$ is the proportion in the second sample possessing the trait.
p_c is the pooled proportion possessing the trait in the combined samples. It is called the pooled estimate of the population proportion and is computed from the following formula.

POOLED PROPORTION

$$p_c = \frac{X_1 + X_2}{n_1 + n_2} \quad [10\text{–}4]$$

where:

X_1 is the number possessing the trait in the first sample.
X_2 is the number possessing the trait in the second sample.

The following example will illustrate the two-sample test of proportions.

example

The Manelli Perfume Company recently developed a new fragrance that it plans to market under the name "Heavenly." A number of market studies indicate that Heavenly has very good market potential. The sales department at Manelli is particularly interested in whether there is a difference in the proportions of younger and older women who would purchase Heavenly if it were marketed. There are two independent populations, a population consisting of the younger women and a population consisting of the older women. Each sampled woman will be asked to smell Heavenly and indicate whether she likes the fragrance well enough to purchase a bottle.

solution

We will use the usual five-step hypothesis testing procedure.

Step 1: State H_0 and H_1. In this case the null hypothesis is: "There is no difference in the proportion of young women and older women who prefer Heavenly." We designate p_1 as the proportion of young women who would purchase Heavenly and p_2 as the proportion of older women who would purchase the fragrance. The alternative hypothesis is that the two proportions are not equal.

$$H_0: p_1 - p_2 = 0$$
$$H_1: p_1 - p_2 \neq 0$$

Step 2: Select the level of significance. We choose the .05 significance level in this example.

Step 3: Determine the test statistic. The test statistic follows the standard normal distribution. The value of the test statistic can be computed from formula (10–3).

Step 4: Formulate the decision rule. Recall that the alternative hypothesis from step 1 does not state a direction, so this is a two-tailed test. To determine the critical value, we divide the significance level in half and place this amount in each tail of the z distribution. Next, we subtract this amount from the total area to the right of zero. That is .5000 − .0250 = .4750. Finally, we search the body of the z table (Appendix D) for the closest value. It is 1.96. The critical values are −1.96 and +1.96. As before, if the computed z-value falls in the region between +1.96 and −1.96, the null hypothesis is not rejected. If that does occur, it is assumed that any difference between the two sample proportions is due to chance variation. This information is summarized in Chart 10–2.

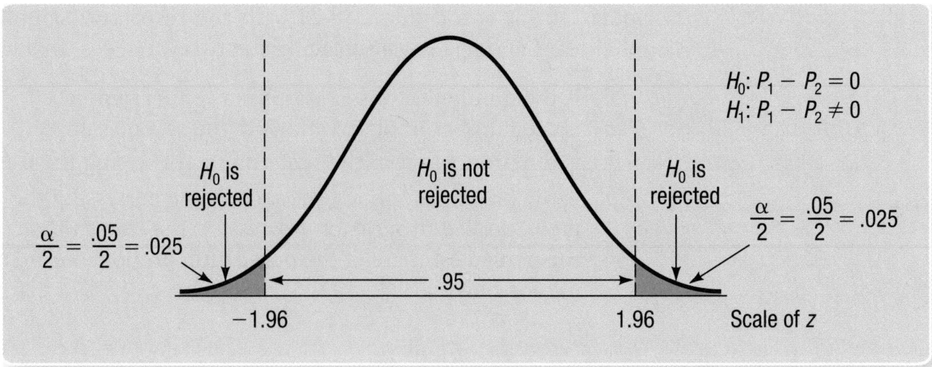

CHART 10–2 Decision Rules for Heavenly Fragrance Test, .05 Significance Level

Step 5: Select a sample and make a decision. A random sample of 100 young women revealed 19 liked the Heavenly fragrance well enough to purchase it. Similarly, a sample of 200 older women revealed 62 liked the fragrance well enough to make a purchase. We let $\bar{p}_1$ refer to the young women and $\bar{p}_2$ to the older women.

$$\bar{p}_1 = \frac{X_1}{n_1} = \frac{19}{100} = .19 \qquad \bar{p}_2 = \frac{X_2}{n_2} = \frac{62}{200} = .31$$

The research question is whether the difference of .12 in the two sample proportions is due to chance or whether there is a difference in the proportion of younger and older women who like the Heavenly fragrance.

Next, we combine or pool the sample proportions. We use formula (10–4).

$$p_c = \frac{X_1 + X_2}{n_1 + n_2} = \frac{19 + 62}{100 + 200} = \frac{81}{300} = .27$$

Note that the pooled proportion is closer to .31 than to .19 because more older women than younger women were sampled.

We use formula (10–3) to find the value of the test statistic.

$$z = \frac{\bar{p}_1 - \bar{p}_2 - (p_1 - p_2)}{\sqrt{\frac{p_c(1 - p_c)}{n_1} + \frac{p_c(1 - p_c)}{n_2}}} = \frac{.19 - .31 - 0}{\sqrt{\frac{.27(1 - .27)}{100} + \frac{.27(1 - .27)}{200}}} = -2.21$$

The computed value of −2.21 is in the area of rejection; that is, it is to the left of −1.96. Therefore, the null hypothesis is rejected at the .05 significance level. To put it another way, we reject the null hypothesis that the proportion of young women who would purchase Heavenly is equal to the proportion of older women who would purchase Heavenly. It is unlikely that the difference between the two sample proportions is due to chance. To find the p-value, we go to Appendix D and look for the likelihood of finding a z-value less than −2.21 or greater than 2.21. The z-value corresponding to 2.21 is 0.4864, so the likelihood of finding the value of the test statistic to be less than −2.21 or greater than 2.21 is:

$$p\text{-value} = 2(.5000 - .4864) = .0272$$

The p-value of .0272 is less than the significance level of .05, so our decision is to reject the null hypothesis. Again, we conclude that there is a difference in the proportion of younger and older women who would purchase the fragrance Heavenly.

The MegaStat steps and commands follow.

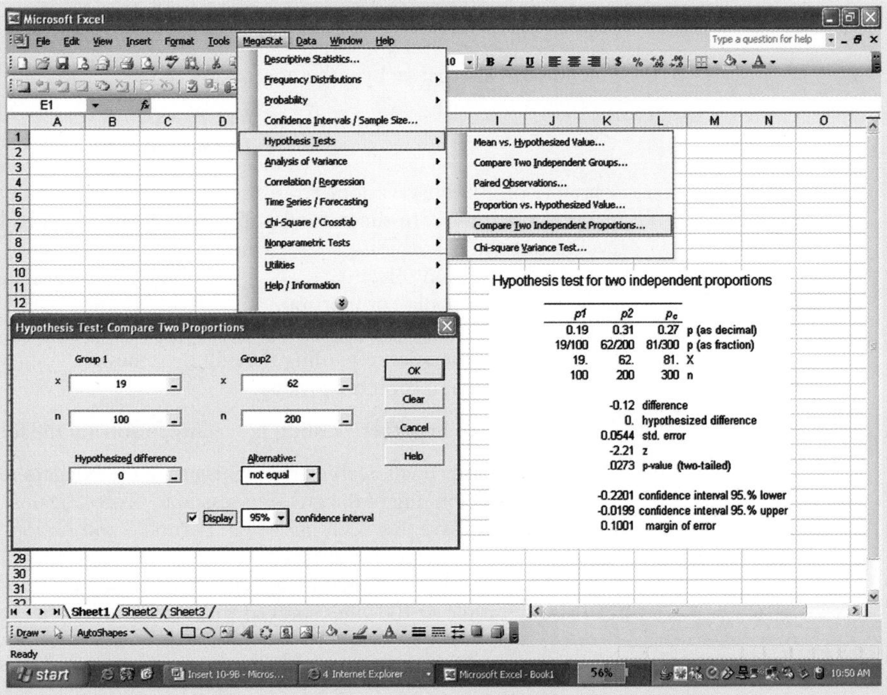

To interpret the MegaStat output, we see a p-value of .0273. The slight difference in the value is due to rounding. Also note the 95 percent confidence level, which ranges from -0.2201 to -0.0199. As the confidence interval does not contain the hypothesized value of zero, the null hypothesis should be rejected.

self-review 10–2

Of 150 adults who tried a new peach-flavoured peppermint patty, 87 rated it excellent. Of 200 children sampled, 123 rated it excellent. Using the .10 level of significance, can we conclude that there is a significant difference in the proportion of adults and the proportion of children who rate the new flavour excellent?

(a) State the null hypothesis and the alternative hypothesis.
(b) What is the probability of a Type I error?
(c) Is this a one-tailed or a two-tailed test?
(d) What is the decision rule?
(e) What is the value of the test statistic?
(f) What is your decision regarding the null hypothesis?
(g) What is the p-value? Explain what it means in terms of this problem.

Exercises

7. The null and alternative hypotheses are:

$$H_0: p_1 - p_2 \leq 0$$
$$H_1: p_1 - p_2 > 0$$

A sample of 100 observations from the first population indicated that X_1 is 70. A sample of 150 observations from the second population revealed X_2 to be 90. Use the .05 significance level to test the hypothesis.

a. State the decision rule.
b. Compute the pooled proportion.
c. Compute the value of the test statistic.
d. What is your decision regarding the null hypothesis?
e. Calculate and interpret the p-value.

8. The null and alternative hypotheses are:

$$H_0: p_1 - p_2 = 0$$
$$H_1: p_1 - p_2 \neq 0$$

A sample of 200 observations from the first population indicated that X_1 is 170. A sample of 150 observations from the second population revealed X_2 to be 110. Use the .05 significance level to test the hypothesis.
a. State the decision rule.
b. Compute the pooled proportion.
c. Compute the value of the test statistic.
d. What is your decision regarding the null hypothesis?
e. Calculate and interpret the p-value.

Note: Use the five-step hypothesis testing procedure in solving the following exercises.

9. The Damon family owns a large grape vineyard in the Niagara Peninsula. The grapevines must be sprayed at the beginning of the growing season to protect against various insects and diseases. Two new insecticides have just been marketed: Pernod 5 and Action. To test their effectiveness, three long rows were selected and sprayed with Pernod 5, and three others were sprayed with Action. When the grapes ripened, 400 of the vines treated with Pernod 5 were checked for infestation. Likewise, a sample of 400 vines sprayed with Action were checked. The results are:

Insecticide	Number of Vines Checked (sample size)	Number of Infested Vines
Pernod 5	400	24
Action	400	40

Can we conclude that there is a difference in the proportion of vines infested using Pernod 5 as opposed to Action? Test at the .05 significance level. Calculate and interpret the p-value.

10. The Roper Organization conducted identical surveys five years apart. One question asked women was, "Are most men basically kind, gentle, and thoughtful"? The earlier survey revealed that, of the 3000 women surveyed, 2010 said that they were. In the later survey, 1530 of the 3000 women surveyed thought that men were kind, gentle, and thoughtful. Can we conclude that women think men are less kind, gentle, and thoughtful in the later survey compared with the earlier one? Choose an appropriate significance level. Calculate and interpret the p-value.

11. A nationwide sample of influential Liberals and Conservatives was asked as a part of a comprehensive survey whether they favoured lowering environmental standards so that high-sulphur coal could be burned in coal-fired power plants. The results were:

	Liberals	Conservatives
Number sampled	1000	800
Number in favour	200	168

At the .02 level of significance, can we conclude that there is a larger proportion of Conservatives in favour of lowering the standards? Calculate and interpret the p-value.

12. The research department at the home office of Superior Insurance conducts ongoing research on the causes of automobile accidents, the characteristics of the drivers, and so on. A random sample of 400 policies written on single persons revealed 120 had at least one accident in the previous three-year period. Similarly, a sample of 600 policies written on married persons revealed that 150 had been in at least one accident. At the .05 significance level, is there a significant difference in the proportions of single and married persons having an accident during a three-year period? Calculate and interpret the p-value.

Comparing Population Means with Unknown Population Standard Deviations (the Pooled *t*-test)

In the previous two sections, we described conditions where the standard normal distribution, that is z, is used as the test statistic. In one case, we were working with a variable (calculating the mean) and in the second attribute (calculating a proportion). In the first case, we wished to compare two sample means from independent populations to determine if they came from the same or equal populations. In that instance, we assumed the population followed the normal probability distribution and that we knew the standard deviation of the population. In many cases, in fact in most cases, we do not know the population standard deviation. We can overcome this problem, as we did in the one sample case in the previous chapter, by substituting the sample standard deviation (s) for the population standard deviation (σ). See formula (9–2).

This section describes another method for comparing the sample means of two independent populations to determine if the sampled populations could reasonably have the same mean. The method described does *not* require that we know the standard deviations of the populations. This gives us a great deal more flexibility when investigating the difference in sample means. There are two major differences in this test and the previous test described earlier in this chapter.

Assumptions for small sample test of means

1. We assume the sampled populations have equal but unknown standard deviations. Because of this assumption we combine or 'pool' the sample standard deviations.
2. We use the t distribution as the test statistic.

The formula for computing the test statistic t is similar to (10–2), but an additional calculation is necessary. The two sample standard deviations are pooled to form a single estimate of the unknown population standard deviation. In essence, we compute a weighted mean of the two sample standard deviations and use this value as an estimate of the population standard deviation. The weights are the degrees of freedom that each sample provides. Why do we need to pool the standard deviations? Because we assume that the two populations have equal standard deviations, the best estimate we can make of that value is to combine or pool all the information we have about the value of the population standard deviation.

The following formula is used to pool the sample variances. Notice that two factors are involved: the number of observations in each sample and the sample standard deviations themselves.

POOLED SAMPLE VARIANCE

$$s_p^2 = \frac{(n_1 - 1)s_1^2 + (n_2 - 1)s_2^2}{n_1 + n_2 - 2} \qquad \textbf{[10–5]}$$

where:

s_1^2 is the variance (standard deviation squared) of the first sample.

s_2^2 the variance of the second sample.

The value of t is computed from the following equation.

TWO-SAMPLE TEST OF MEANS—UNKNOWN σ

$$t = \frac{\bar{X}_1 - \bar{X}_2 - (\mu_1 - \mu_2)}{\sqrt{s_p^2\left(\frac{1}{n_1} + \frac{1}{n_2}\right)}} \qquad \textbf{[10–6]}$$

where:

$\bar{X}_1$ is the mean of the first sample.

$\bar{X}_2$ is the mean of the second sample.

n_1 is the number of observations in the first sample.
n_2 is the number of observations in the second sample.
s_p^2 is the pooled estimate of the population variance.

The number of degrees of freedom in the test is the total number of items sampled minus the total number of samples. Because there are two samples, there are $n_1 + n_2 - 2$ degrees of freedom.

To summarize, there are three requirements or assumptions for the test:

1. Each population follows a normal distribution.
2. The sampled populations are independent.
3. The standard deviations of the two populations are equal.

The following example explains the details of the test.

example

Owens Lawn Care Inc. manufactures and assembles lawnmowers that are shipped to dealers throughout the United States and Canada. Two different procedures have been proposed for mounting the engine on the frame of the lawnmower. The question is: Is there a difference in the mean time to mount the engines on the frames of the lawnmowers? The first procedure was developed by longtime Owens employee Herb Welles, and the other procedure was developed by Owens Vice-President of Engineering William Atkins. To evaluate the two methods, it was decided to conduct a time and motion study. A sample of five employees was timed using the Welles method and six using the Atkins method. The results, in minutes, are shown below. Is there a difference in the mean mounting times? Use the .10 significance level.

Welles (minutes)	Atkins (minutes)
2	3
4	7
9	5
3	8
2	4
	3

solution

Following the five steps to test a hypothesis, the null hypothesis states that there is no difference in mean mounting times between the two procedures. The alternative hypothesis indicates that there is a difference.

$$H_0: \mu_1 - \mu_2 = 0$$
$$H_1: \mu_1 - \mu_2 \neq 0$$

The required assumptions are:

1. The observations in the Welles sample are *independent* of the observations in the Atkins sample and of each other.
2. The two populations follow a normal distribution.
3. The two populations have equal standard deviations.

Is there a difference between the mean assembly times using the Welles and the Atkins methods? The degrees of freedom are equal to the total number of items sampled minus the number of samples. In this case, that is $n_1 + n_2 - 2$. Five assemblers used the Welles method and six the Atkins method. Thus, there are 9 degrees of freedom, found by $5 + 6 - 2$. The critical values of t, from Appendix F for $df = 9$, a two-tailed test, and the .10 significance level, are -1.833 and 1.833. The decision rule is portrayed graphically in Chart 10–3. We do not reject the null hypothesis if the computed value of t falls between -1.833 and 1.833.

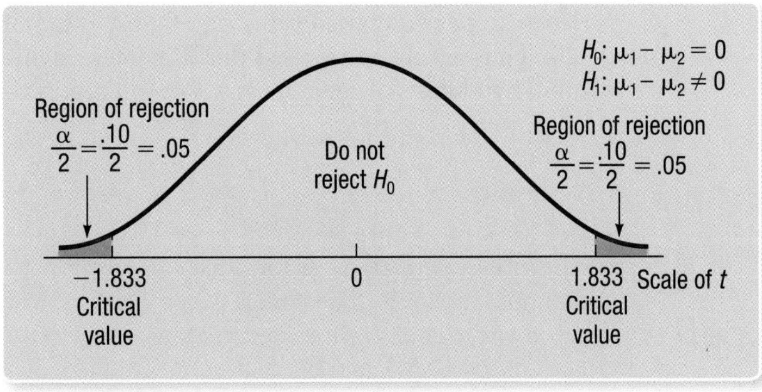

CHART 10–3 Regions of Rejection, Two-Tailed Test, $df = 9$, and .10 Significance Level

We use three steps to compute the value of t.

1: Calculate the Sample Standard Deviations. See the details below.

Welles Method		Atkins Method	
X_1	X_1^2	X_2	X_2^2
2	4	3	9
4	16	7	49
9	81	5	25
3	9	8	64
2	4	4	16
20	114	3	9
		30	172

$$s_1 = \sqrt{\frac{\Sigma X_1^2 - \frac{(\Sigma X_1)^2}{n_1}}{n_1 - 1}} = \sqrt{\frac{114 - \frac{(20)^2}{5}}{5 - 1}} = 2.9155$$

$$s_2 = \sqrt{\frac{\Sigma X_2^2 - \frac{(\Sigma X_2)^2}{n_2}}{n_2 - 1}} = \sqrt{\frac{172 - \frac{(30)^2}{6}}{6 - 1}} = 2.0976$$

2: Pool the Sample Variances. We use formula (10–5) to pool the sample variances (standard deviations squared).

$$s_p^2 = \frac{(n_1 - 1)s_1^2 + (n_2 - 1)s_2^2}{n_1 + n_2 - 2} = \frac{(5-1)(2.9155)^2 + (6-1)(2.0976)^2}{5 + 6 - 2} = 6.2222$$

3: Determine the value of *t*. The mean mounting time for procedure 1 is 4.00 minutes, found by $\bar{X}_1 = 20/5$. The mean mounting time for procedure 2 is 5.00 minutes, found by $\bar{X}_2 = 30/6$. We use formula (10–6) to calculate the value of t.

$$t = \frac{\bar{X}_1 - \bar{X}_2 - (\mu_1 - \mu_2)}{\sqrt{s_p^2\left(\frac{1}{n_1} + \frac{1}{n_2}\right)}} = \frac{4.00 - 5.00 - 0}{\sqrt{6.2222\left(\frac{1}{5} + \frac{1}{6}\right)}} = -0.662$$

The decision is not to reject the null hypothesis, because −.662 falls in the region between −1.833 and 1.833. We conclude that there is no difference in the mean times to mount the engine on the frame using the two methods.

We can also estimate the p-value using Appendix F. Locate the row with 9 degrees of freedom, and use the two-tailed test column. Find the t-value, without regard to the sign, which is closest to our computed value of −0.662. It is 1.383, corresponding to a significance level of .20. Thus, even had we used the 20 percent significance level, we would not have rejected the null hypothesis of equal means. We can report that the p-value is greater than .20.

Excel has a procedure called "t-Test: Two-Sample Assuming Equal Variances" that will perform the calculations of formulas (10–5) and (10–6) as well as find the sample means and sample variances. The data are input in the first two columns of the **Excel** spreadsheet. They are labelled "Welles" and "Atkins." The output follows. The value of t, called the "t Stat," is −0.66205, and the two-tailed p-value is .52453. As we would expect, the p-value is larger than the significance level of .10. The conclusion is not to reject the null hypothesis.

Excel steps and output follow.

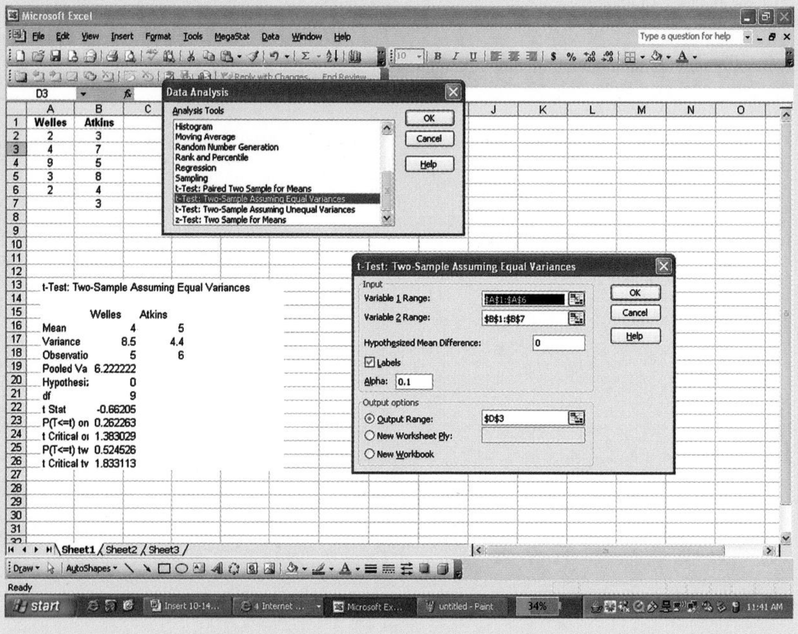

MegaStat steps and output follow.

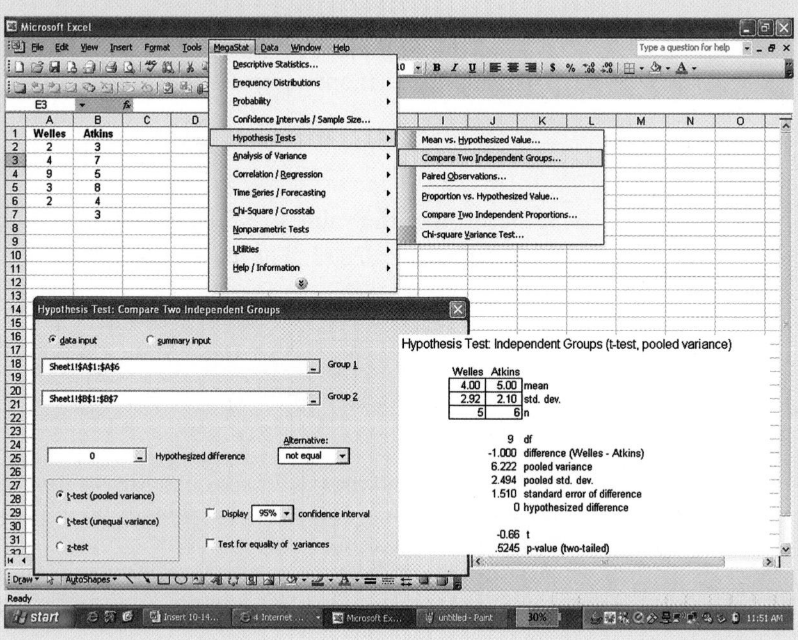

self-review 10–3

The production manager at Bellevue Steel, a manufacturer of wheelchairs, wants to compare the number of defective wheelchairs produced on the day shift with the number on the afternoon shift. A sample of the production from six day shifts and eight afternoon shifts revealed the following number of defects.

Day	5	8	7	6	9	7		
Afternoon	8	10	7	11	9	12	14	9

Is there a difference in the mean number of defects per shift? Choose an appropriate significance level.

(a) State the null hypothesis and the alternative hypothesis.
(b) What is the decision rule?
(c) What is the value of the test statistic?
(d) What is your decision regarding the null hypothesis?
(e) What is the *p*-value?
(f) Interpret the result.
(g) What assumptions are necessary for this test?

Exercises

For Exercises 13 and 14: (a) state the decision rule, (b) compute the pooled estimate of the population variance, (c) compute the test statistic, (d) state your decision about the null hypothesis, and (e) estimate the *p*-value.

13. The null and alternative hypotheses are:

$$H_0: \mu_1 - \mu_2 = 0$$
$$H_1: \mu_1 - \mu_2 \neq 0$$

A random sample of 10 observations from one population revealed a sample mean of 23 and a sample deviation of 4. A random sample of 8 observations from another population revealed a sample mean of 26 and a sample standard deviation of 5. At the .05 significance level, is there a difference between the population means?

14. The null and alternative hypotheses are:

$$H_0: \mu_1 - \mu_2 = 0$$
$$H_1: \mu_1 - \mu_2 \neq 0$$

A random sample of 15 observations from the first population revealed a sample mean of 350 and a sample standard deviation of 12. A random sample of 17 observations from the second population revealed a sample mean of 342 and a sample standard deviation of 15. At the .10 significance level, is there a difference in the population means?

Note: Use the five-step hypothesis testing procedure for the following exercises.

15. A sample of scores on an examination given in Statistics 201 are:

Men	72	69	98	66	85	76	79	80	77
Women	81	67	90	78	81	80	76		

At the .01 significance level, is the mean grade of the women higher than that of the men? Calculate and interpret the *p*-value.

16. A recent study compared the time spent together by single- and dual-earner couples. According to the records kept by the wives during the study, the mean amount of time spent together watching television among the single-earner couples was 61 minutes per day, with a standard deviation of 15.5 minutes. For the dual-earner couples, the mean number of minutes spent watching television was 48.4 minutes, with a standard deviation of 18.1 minutes. At the .01 significance level, can we conclude that the single-earner couples on average spend more time watching television together? There were 15 single-earner and 12 dual-earner couples studied. Estimate and interpret the *p*-value.

17. Ms. Lisa Monnin is the budget director for the New Process Company. She would like to compare the daily travel expenses for the sales staff and the audit staff. She collected the following sample information.

Sales ($)	131	135	146	165	136	142	
Audit ($)	130	102	129	143	149	120	139

At the .10 significance level, can she conclude that the mean daily expenses are greater for the sales staff than the audit staff? What is the *p*-value? Interpret the *p*-value.

18. The Milton Area Chamber of Commerce wanted to know whether the mean weekly salary of nurses was larger than that of school teachers. To investigate, it collected the following information on the amounts earned last week by a sample of school teachers and nurses.

School teachers ($)	845	826	827	875	784	809	802	820	829	830	842	832
Nurses ($)	841	890	821	771	850	859	825	829				

Is it reasonable to conclude that the mean weekly salary of nurses is higher? Use the .01 significance level. What is the *p*-value? Interpret the *p*-value.

3 Conduct a test of a hypothesis about the mean difference between *paired* or *dependent observations*.

Two-Sample Tests of Hypothesis: Dependent Samples

Previously in this chapter, we tested the difference between the means from two independent samples. We compared the mean time required to mount an engine using the Welles method to the time to mount the engine using the Atkins method. The samples were *independent*, meaning that the sample of assembly times using the Welles method was in no way related to the sample of assembly times using the Atkins method.

There are situations, however, in which the samples are not independent. To put it another way, the samples are **dependent** or related. As an example, Nickel Savings and Loan employs two firms, Schadek Appraisals and Bowyer Real Estate, to appraise the value of the real estate properties on which it makes loans. It is important that these two firms be similar in their appraisal values. To review the consistency of the two appraisal firms, Nickel Savings randomly selects 10 homes and has both Schadek Appraisals and Bowyer Real Estate appraise the value of the selected homes. For each home, there will be a pair of appraisal values. That is, for each home there will be an appraised value from both Schadek Appraisals and Bowyer Real Estate. The appraised values depend on, or are related to, the home selected. This is also referred to as a **paired sample**.

For hypothesis testing, we are interested in the distribution of the *differences* in the appraised value of each home. Hence, there is only one sample. To put it more formally, we are investigating whether the mean of the distribution of differences in the appraised values is 0. The sample is made up of the *differences* between the appraised values determined by Schadek Appraisals and the values from Bowyer Real Estate. If the two appraisal firms are reporting similar estimates, then sometimes Schadek Appraisals will be the higher value and sometimes Bowyer Real Estate will have the higher value. However, the mean of the distribution of differences will be 0. On the other hand, if one of the firms consistently reports the larger appraisal values, then the mean of the distribution of the differences will not be 0.

We will use the symbol μ_d to indicate the population mean of the distribution of differences. We assume the distribution of the population of differences follows the normal distribution. The test statistic follows the *t* distribution and we calculate its value from the following formula:

PAIRED *t* TEST

$$t = \frac{\bar{d} - \mu_d}{s_d / \sqrt{n}} \qquad \text{[10-7]}$$

There are $n - 1$ degrees of freedom and

- $\bar{d}$ is the mean of the difference between the paired or related observations.
- s_d is the sample standard deviation of the differences between the paired or related observations.
- n is the number of paired observations.

The standard deviation of the differences is computed by the direct formula for the standard deviation, except d is substituted for X. The formula is:

$$s_d = \sqrt{\frac{\Sigma d^2 - \frac{(\Sigma d)^2}{n}}{n-1}}$$

The following example illustrates this test.

example

Recall that Nickel Savings and Loan wishes to compare the two companies it uses to appraise the value of residential homes. Nickel Savings selected a sample of 10 residential properties and scheduled both firms for an appraisal. The results, reported in thousands of dollars, ($000) are:

Home	Schadek ($ thousands)	Bowyer ($ thousands)
1	$235	$228
2	210	205
3	231	219
4	242	240
5	205	198
6	230	223
7	231	227
8	210	215
9	225	222
10	249	245

At the .05 significance level, can we conclude there is a difference in the mean appraised values of the homes?

solution

The first step is to state the null and the alternative hypotheses. In this case, a two-tailed alternative is appropriate because we are interested in determining whether there is a *difference* in the appraised values. We are not interested in showing whether one particular firm appraises property at a higher value than the other. The question is whether the sample differences in the appraised values could have come from a population with a mean of 0. If the population mean of the differences is 0, then we conclude that there is no difference in the appraised values. The null and alternative hypotheses are:

$$H_0: \mu_d = 0$$
$$H_1: \mu_d \neq 0$$

There are 10 homes appraised by both firms, so $n = 10$, and $df = n - 1 = 10 - 1 = 9$. We have a two-tailed test, and the significance level is .05. To determine the critical value, go to Appendix F, move across the row with 9 degrees of freedom to the column for a two-tailed test and the .05 significance level. The value at the intersection is 2.262. This value appears in the box in Table 10–2 which is on the following page. The decision rule is to reject the null hypothesis if the computed value of t is less than -2.262 or greater than 2.262. Here are the computational details.

Home	Schadek ($ thousands)	Bowyer ($ thousands)	Difference, d	Difference Squared, d^2
1	$235	$228	7	49
2	210	205	5	25
3	231	219	12	144
4	242	240	2	4
5	205	198	7	49
6	230	223	7	49
7	231	227	4	16
8	210	215	−5	25
9	225	222	3	9
10	249	245	4	16
			46	386

$$\bar{d} = \frac{\Sigma d}{n} = \frac{46}{10} = 4.60$$

$$s_d = \sqrt{\frac{\Sigma d^2 - \frac{(\Sigma d)^2}{n}}{n-1}} = \sqrt{\frac{386 - \frac{(46)^2}{10}}{10-1}} = 4.402$$

Using formula (10–7), the value of the test statistic is 3.305, found by

$$t = \frac{\bar{d} - \mu_d}{s_d/\sqrt{n}} = \frac{4.6 - 0}{4.402/\sqrt{10}} = 3.305$$

Because the computed t falls in the rejection region, the null hypothesis is rejected. The population distribution of differences does not have a mean of 0. We conclude that there is a difference in the mean appraised values of the homes. The largest difference of $12 000 is for Home 3. Perhaps that would be an appropriate place to begin a more detailed review.

To find the p-value, we use Appendix F and the section for a two-tailed test. Move along the row with 9 degrees of freedom and find the values of t that are closest to our calculated value. For a .01 significance level, the value of t is 3.250. The computed value is larger than this value, but smaller than the value of 4.781 corresponding to the .001 significance level. Hence, the p-value is less than .01. Since the p-value is less than the level of significance $\alpha = .01$, the test statistic lies in the rejection region. A portion of the t distribution table from Appendix F is highlighted in Table 10–2 below.

TABLE 10–2 A Portion of the t Distribution from Appendix F

	Confidence Intervals					
	80%	90%	95%	98%	99%	99.9%
	Level of Significance for One-Tailed Test					
df	0.100	0.050	0.025	0.010	0.005	0.0005
	Level of Significance for Two-Tailed Test					
	0.20	0.10	0.05	0.02	0.01	0.001
1	3.078	6.314	12.706	31.821	63.657	636.619
2	1.886	2.920	4.303	6.965	9.925	31.599
3	1.638	2.353	3.182	4.541	5.841	12.924
4	1.533	2.132	2.776	3.747	4.604	8.610
5	1.476	2.015	2.571	3.365	4.032	6.869
6	1.440	1.943	2.447	3.143	3.707	5.959
7	1.415	1.895	2.365	2.998	3.499	5.408
8	1.397	1.860	2.306	2.896	3.355	5.041
9	1.383	1.833	2.262	2.821	3.250	4.781
10	1.372	1.812	2.228	2.764	3.169	4.587

excel

Excel has a procedure called "t-Test: Paired Two-Sample for Means" that will perform the calculations of formula (10–7). The output from this procedure follows below.

The computed value of t is 3.3045, and the two-tailed p-value is .00916. Because the p-value is less than .05, we reject the hypothesis that the mean of the distribution of the differences between the appraised values is zero. In fact, this p-value is less than 1.0 percent. There is very little likelihood that the null hypothesis is true. The **Excel** commands and output follow.

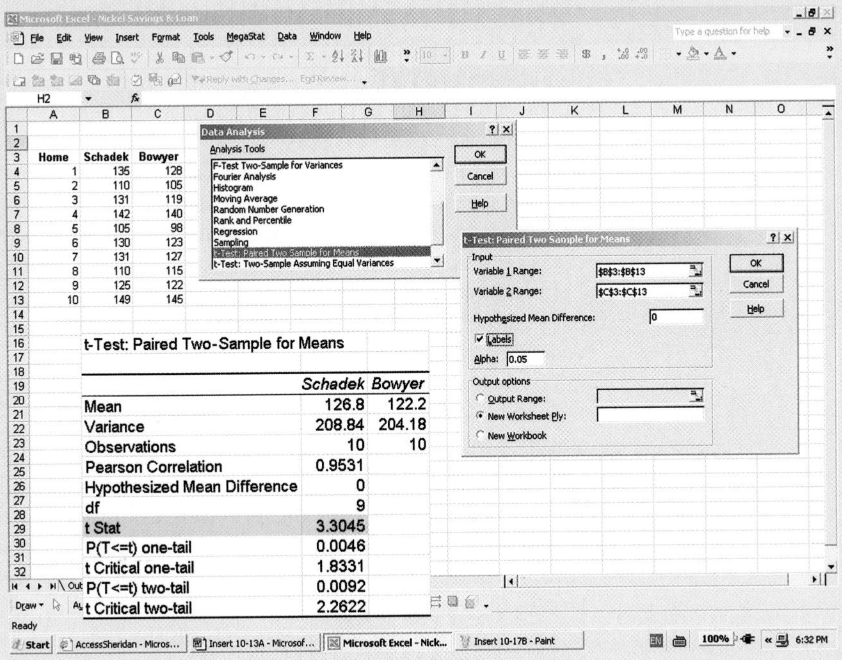

excel

MegaStat steps and output follow.

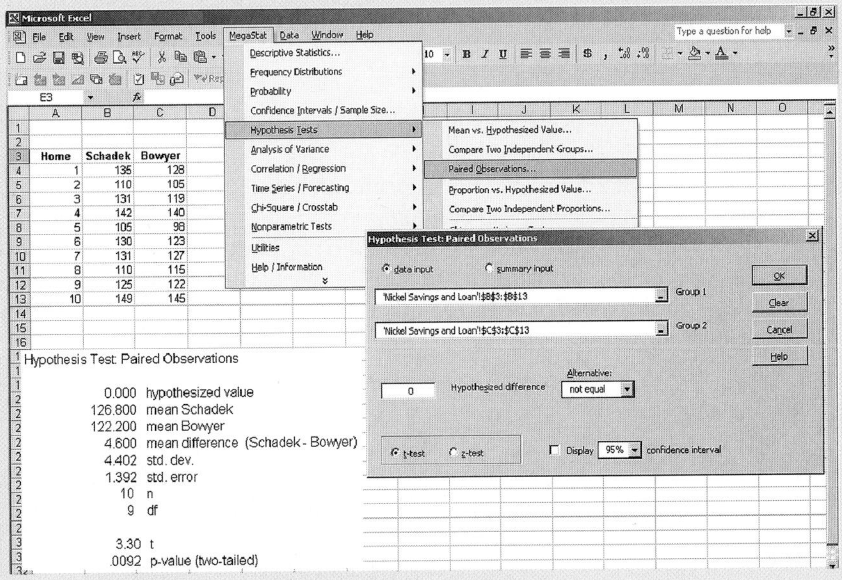

4 Understand the difference between *dependent* and *independent samples*.

Comparing Dependent and Independent Samples

Students are often confused by the difference between tests for independent samples (formula 10–6) and tests for dependent samples (formula 10–7). How do we tell the difference between dependent and independent samples? There are two types of dependent samples: (1) those characterized by a measurement, an intervention of some type, and then another measurement; and (2) a matching or pairing of the observations. To explain further:

1. The first type of dependent sample is characterized by a measurement followed by an intervention of some kind and then another measurement. This could be called a "before" and "after" study. Two examples will help to clarify. Suppose we want to show that, by placing speakers in the production area and playing soothing music, we are able to increase production. We begin by selecting a sample of workers and measuring their output under the current conditions. The speakers are then installed in the production area, and we again measure the output of the same workers. There are two measurements, before placing the speakers in the production area, and after. The intervention is placing speakers in the production area.

   A second example involves an educational firm that offers courses designed to increase test scores and reading ability. Suppose the firm wants to offer a course that will help high school students increase their SAT scores. To begin, each student takes the SAT in the second year of high school. During the summer between the second and third year, they participate in the course that gives them tips on taking tests. Finally, during the fall of their third year of high school, they retake the SAT. Again, the procedure is characterized by a measurement (taking the SAT as a second year student), an intervention (the summer workshops), and another measurement (taking the SAT during their third year).
2. The second type of dependent sample is characterized by matching or pairing observations. Nickel Savings, in the previous example, is a dependent sample of this type. It selected a property for appraisal and then had two appraisals on the same property. As a second example, suppose an industrial psychologist wishes to study the intellectual similarities of newly married couples. She selects a sample of newlyweds. Next, she administers a standard intelligence test to both the man and woman to determine the difference in the scores. Notice the matching that occurred: comparing the scores that are paired or matched by marriage.

Why do we prefer dependent samples to independent samples? By using dependent samples, we are able to reduce the variation in the sampling distribution. To illustrate, we will use the Nickel Savings and Loan example just completed. Suppose we assume that we have two independent samples of real estate property for appraisal and conduct the following test of hypothesis, using formula (10–6). The null and alternative hypotheses are:

$$H_0: \mu_1 - \mu_2 = 0$$
$$H_1: \mu_1 - \mu_2 \neq 0$$

There are now two independent samples of 10 each. So, the number of degrees of freedom is 10 + 10 − 2 = 18. From Appendix D, using the .05 significance level, H_0 is rejected if t is less than −2.101 or greater than 2.101.

The mean of the appraised value of the 10 properties by Schadek is \$226 800, and the standard deviation is \$14 450. For Bowyer Real Estate, the mean appraised value is \$222 200, and the standard deviation is \$14 290. To make the calculations easier, we use thousands of dollars instead of dollars. The value of the pooled estimate of the variance from formula (10–5) is

$$s_p^2 = \frac{(n_1 - 1)s_1^2 + (n_2 - 1)s_2^2}{n_1 + n_2 - 2} = \frac{(10 - 1)(14.45)^2 + (10 - 1)(14.29)^2}{10 + 10 - 2} = 206.50$$

Using formula (10–6), t is 0.716.

$$t = \frac{\bar{X}_1 - \bar{X}_2 - (\mu_1 - \mu_2)}{\sqrt{s_p^2\left(\frac{1}{n_1} + \frac{1}{n_2}\right)}} = \frac{226.8 - 222.2 - 0}{\sqrt{206.50\left(\frac{1}{10} + \frac{1}{10}\right)}} = \frac{4.6}{6.4265} = .716$$

The computed t (.716) is less than 2.101, so the null hypothesis is not rejected. We cannot show that there is a difference in the mean appraisal value. That is not the same conclusion that we got before! Why does this happen? The numerator is the same in the paired observations test (4.6). However, the denominator is smaller. In the paired test the denominator is 1.3920. In the case of the independent samples, the denominator is 6.4265. There is more variation or uncertainty. This accounts for the difference in the t-values and the difference in the statistical decisions. The denominator measures the standard error of the statistic. When the samples are *not* paired, two kinds of variation are present: differences between the two appraisal firms and the difference in the value of the real estate. Properties numbered 4 and 10 have relatively high values, whereas number 5 is relatively low. These data show how different the values of the property are, but we are really interested in the difference between the two appraisal firms.

The trick is to pair the values to reduce the variation among the properties. The paired test uses only the difference between the two appraisal firms for the same property. Thus, the paired or dependent statistic focuses on the variation between Schadek Appraisals and Bowyer Real Estate. Thus, its standard error is always smaller. That, in turn, leads to a larger test statistic and a greater chance of rejecting the null hypothesis. So, whenever possible you should pair the data.

There is a bit of bad news here. In the paired observations test, the degrees of freedom are half of what they are if the samples are not paired. For the real estate example, the degrees of freedom drop from 18 to 9 when the observations are paired. However, in most cases, this is a small price to pay for a better test.

self-review 10–4

Advertisements by Sylph Fitness Center claim that completing its course will result in losing weight. A random sample of eight recent participants showed the following weights before and after completing the course. At the .01 significance level, can we conclude the students lost weight?

Name	Before	After
Hunter	155	154
Cashman	228	207
Mervine	141	147
Massa	162	157
Creola	211	196
Perterson	164	150
Redding	184	170
Poust	172	165

(a) State the null hypothesis and the alternative hypothesis.
(b) What is the critical value of t?
(c) What is the computed value of t?
(d) Interpret the result. What is the p-value?
(e) What assumption needs to be made about the distribution of the differences?

Exercises

19. The null and alternative hypotheses are:

$$H_0: \mu_d \leq 0$$
$$H_1: \mu_d > 0$$

The following sample information shows the number of defective units produced on the day shift and the afternoon shift for a sample of four days last month.

	Day			
	1	2	3	4
Day shift	10	12	15	11
Afternoon shift	8	9	12	15

At the .05 significance level, can we conclude there are more defects produced on the afternoon shift?

20. The null and alternative hypotheses are:

$$H_0: \mu_d = 0$$
$$H_1: \mu_d \neq 0$$

The following paired observations show the number of traffic citations given for speeding by Officer Dhondt and Officer Meredith of the OPP for the last five months.

	May	June	July	August	September
Officer Dhondt	30	22	25	19	26
Officer Meredith	26	19	20	15	19

At the .05 significance level, is there a difference in the mean number of citations given by the two officers?

Note: Use the five-step hypothesis testing procedure to solve the following exercises.

21. The management of Discount Furniture designed an incentive plan for salespeople. To evaluate this innovative plan, 12 salespeople were selected at random, and their weekly incomes before and after the plan were recorded.

Salesperson	Before	After
Sid Mahone	\$320	\$340
Carol Quick	290	285
Tom Jackson	421	475
Andy Jones	510	510
Jean Sloan	210	210
Jack Walker	402	500
Peg Mancuso	625	631
Anita Loma	560	560
John Cuso	360	365
Carl Utz	431	431
A. S. Kushner	506	525
Fern Lawton	505	619

Was there a significant increase in the typical salesperson's weekly income due to the innovative incentive plan? Use the .05 significance level. Estimate the *p*-value, and interpret it.

22. The federal government recently granted funds for a special program designed to reduce crime in high-crime areas. A study of the results of the program in eight high-crime areas yielded the following results.

	Number of Crimes by Area							
	A	B	C	D	E	F	G	H
Before	14	7	4	5	17	12	8	9
After	2	7	3	6	8	13	3	5

Has there been a decrease in the number of crimes since the inauguration of the program? Use the .01 significance level. Estimate the *p*-value.

Chapter Summary

I. In comparing two population means we wish to know whether they could be equal.

A. We are investigating whether the distribution of the difference between the means could have a mean of 0.

B. The test statistic follows the standard normal distribution if the population standard deviations are known.

1. No assumption about the shape of either population is required.
2. The samples are from independent populations.
3. The formula to compute the value of z is

$$z = \frac{\bar{X}_1 - \bar{X}_2 - (\mu_1 - \mu_2)}{\sqrt{\frac{\sigma_1^2}{n_1} + \frac{\sigma_2^2}{n_2}}} \qquad [10\text{–}2]$$

II. We can also test whether two samples came from populations with an equal proportion of successes.

A. The two sample proportions are pooled using the following formula:

$$p_c = \frac{X_1 + X_2}{n_1 + n_2} \qquad [10\text{–}4]$$

B. We compute the value of the test statistic from the following formula:

$$z = \frac{\bar{p}_1 - \bar{p}_2 - (p_1 - p_2)}{\sqrt{\frac{p_c(1 - p_c)}{n_1} + \frac{p_c(1 - p_c)}{n_2}}} \qquad [10\text{–}3]$$

III. The test statistic to compare two means is the t distribution if the population standard deviations are not known.

A. Both populations must follow the normal distribution.

B. The populations must have equal standard deviations.

C. The samples are independent.

D. Finding the value of t requires two steps.

1. The first step is to pool the sample standard deviations according to the following formula:

$$s_p^2 = \frac{(n_1 - 1)s_1^2 + (n_2 - 1)s_2^2}{n_1 + n_2 - 2} \qquad [10\text{–}5]$$

2. The value of t is computed from the following formula:

$$t = \frac{\bar{X}_1 - \bar{X}_2 - (\mu_1 - \mu_2)}{\sqrt{s_p^2\left(\frac{1}{n_1} + \frac{1}{n_2}\right)}} \qquad [10\text{–}6]$$

3. The degrees of freedom for the test are $n_1 + n_2 - 2$.

IV. For dependent samples, we assume the distribution of the paired differences between the populations has a mean of 0.

A. We first compute the mean and the standard deviation of the sample differences.

B. The value of the test statistic is computed from the following formula:

$$t = \frac{\bar{d} - \mu_d}{s_d / \sqrt{n}} \qquad [10\text{–}7]$$

Pronunciation Key

SYMBOL	MEANING	PRONUNCIATION
p_c	Pooled proportion	*p sub c*
s_p^2	Pooled sample variance	*s sub p squared*
$\bar{X}_1$	Mean of the first sample	*X bar sub 1*

$\bar{X}_2$	Mean of the second sample	*X bar sub 2*
$\bar{d}$	Mean of the difference between dependent observations	*d bar*
s_d	Standard deviation of the difference between dependent observations	*s sub d*

Chapter Exercises

23. A recent study focused on the number of times men and women who live alone buy takeout dinners in a month. The information is summarized below.

Number of Dinners per Month

Statistic	Men	Women
Mean	24.51	22.69
Population standard deviation	4.48	3.86
Sample size	35	40

At the .01 significance level, is there a difference in the mean number of times men and women order takeout dinners in a month? Calculate and interpret the p-value.

24. The Simone Company is considering a new computer program to speed up the processing of its inventory. Two programs are being considered, Program A and Program B. To test the programs, 50 employees were divided into two groups of 25. The mean processing time of Program A was 30 seconds with a standard deviation of 5 seconds. The mean processing time of Program B was 28 seconds with a standard deviation of 3 seconds. Is there a difference in the speed of the two programs? Choose an appropriate significance level. Calculate and interpret the p-value.

25. An official of the Ministry of Transport wants to compare the useful life, in months, of two brands of paint used for striping roads. The mean number of months Cooper Paint lasted was 36.2. The official reviewed 35 road stripes. For King Paint, the mean number of months was 37.0. The official reviewed 40 road stripes. The population standard deviation for the Cooper Paint is 1.14 months and for the King Paint, 1.3 months. At the .01 significance level, is there a difference in the useful life of the two paints? Compute and interpret the p-value.

26. Clark Heter is an industrial engineer at Lyons Products. He would like to determine whether there are more units produced on the afternoon shift than on the day shift. A sample of 54 day-shift workers showed that the mean number of units produced was 345. A sample of 60 afternoon-shift workers showed that the mean number of units produced was 351, Assume the population standard deviation for the number of units produced on the day shift is 21 and on the night shift is 28. At the .05 significance level, is the number of units produced on the afternoon shift larger?

27. Fry Brothers Heating and Air Conditioning Inc. employs Larry Clark and George Murnen to make service calls to repair furnaces and air conditioning units in homes. Tom Fry, the owner, would like to know whether there is a difference in the mean number of service calls they make per day. A random sample of 40 days last year showed that Larry Clark made an average of 4.77 calls per day. For a sample of 50 days, George Murnen made an average of 5.02 calls per day. The population standard deviation for Larry Clark is 1.05 calls per day, and for George Murnen, it is 1.23 calls per day. At the .05 significance level, is there a difference in the mean number of calls per day between the two employees? Compute and interpret the p-value.

28. A coffee manufacturer is interested in whether the mean daily consumption of regular-coffee drinkers is less than that of decaffeinated-coffee drinkers. Assume the population standard deviation for those drinking regular coffee is 1.20 cups per day and for those drinking decaffeinated coffee is 1.36 cups per day. A random sample of 50 regular-coffee drinkers showed a mean of 4.35 cups per day. A sample of 40 decaffeinated-coffee drinkers showed a mean of 5.84 cups per day. Use the .01 significance level. Compute and interpret the p-value.

29. The manufacturer of Advil, a common headache remedy, recently developed a new formulation of the drug that is claimed to be more effective. To evaluate the new drug, a sample of 200 current users is asked to try it. After a one-month trial, 180 indicated the new drug was more effective in relieving a headache. At the same time, a sample of 300 current Advil users is given the current drug but told it is the new formulation. From this group, 261 said it was an improvement. At the .05 significance level can we conclude that the new drug is more effective?

30. Each month the National Association of Purchasing Managers publishes the NAPM index. One of the questions asked on the survey to purchasing agents is: Do you think the economy is expanding? Last month, of the 300 responses, 160 answered yes to the question. This month, 170 of the 290 responses indicated they felt the economy was expanding. At the .05 significance level, can we conclude that a larger proportion of the agents believe the economy is expanding this month?

31. As part of a recent survey among dual-wage-earner couples, an industrial psychologist found that 990 men out of the 1500 surveyed believed the division of household duties was fair. A sample of 1600 women found 970 believed the division of household duties was fair. At the .01 significance level, is it reasonable to conclude that the proportion of men who believe the division of household duties is fair is larger? Calculate and interpret the *p*-value.

32. Two major Internet providers want to investigate whether there is a difference in the proportion of times a customer is able to access the Internet. During a one-week period, 500 calls were placed at random times throughout the day and night to the first provider. A connection was made to the Internet on 450 occasions. A similar one-week study with the second provider showed the Internet to be available on 352 of 400 trials. At the .01 significance level, is there a difference in the percent of time that access to the Internet is successful? Calculate and interpret the *p*-value.

33. The owner of Bun 'N' Run Hamburger wishes to compare the sales per day at two locations. The mean number sold for 10 randomly selected days at the Northside site was 83.55, and the standard deviation was 10.50. For a random sample of 12 days at the Southside location, the mean number sold was 78.80 and the standard deviation was 14.25. At the .05 significance level, is there a difference in the mean number of hamburgers sold at the two locations? Calculate and interpret the *p*-value.

34. A cell phone company offers two plans to its subscribers. At the time new subscribers sign up, they are asked to provide some demographic information. The mean yearly income for a sample of 40 subscribers to Plan A is $57 000 with a standard deviation of $9200. This distribution is positively skewed; the coefficient of skewness is 2.11. For a sample of 30 subscribers to Plan B, the mean income is $61 000 with a standard deviation of $7100. The distribution of Plan B subscribers is also positively skewed, but not as severely. The coefficient of skewness is 1.54. At the .05 significance level, is it reasonable to conclude the mean income of those selecting Plan B is larger? What is the *p*-value? Do the coefficients of skewness affect the results of the hypothesis test? Explain.

35. A computer manufacturer offers a help line that purchasers can call for help 24 hours a day, 7 days a week. Clearing these calls for help in a timely fashion is important to the company's image. After telling the caller that resolution of the problem is important, the caller is asked whether the issue is "software" or "hardware" related. The mean time it takes a technician to resolve a software issue is 18 minutes with a standard deviation of 4.2 minutes. This information was obtained from a sample of 35 monitored calls. For a study of 45 hardware issues, the mean time for the technician to resolve the problem was 15.5 minutes with a standard deviation of 3.9 minutes. This information was also obtained from monitored calls. At the .05 significance level, is it reasonable to conclude that it takes longer to resolve software issues? Calculate and interpret the *p*-value.

36. The engineering department at Sims Software Inc. recently developed two chemical solutions designed to increase the usable life of computer disks. A sample of disks treated with the first solution lasted 86, 78, 66, 83, 84, 81, 84, 109, 65, and 102 hours. Those treated with the second solution lasted 91, 71, 75, 76, 87, 79, 73, 76, 79, 78, 87, 90, 76, and 72 hours. At the .10 significance level, can we conclude that there is a difference in the length of time the two types of treatment lasted?

37. The Willow Run Outlet Mall has two Haggar Outlet Stores, one located on Peach Street and the other on Plum Street. The two stores are laid out differently, but both store managers claim their layout maximizes the amounts customers will purchase on impulse. A sample of 10 customers at the Peach Street store revealed they spent the following amounts more than planned: $17.58, $19.73, $12.61, $17.79, $16.22, $15.82, $15.40, $15.86, $11.82, and $15.85. A sample of 14 customers at the Plum Street store revealed they spent the following amounts more than they planned: $18.19, $20.22, $17.38, $17.96, $23.92, $15.87, $16.47, $15.96, $16.79, $16.74, $21.40, $20.57, $19.79, and $14.83. At the .01 significance level, is there a difference in the mean amounts purchased on impulse at the two stores?

38. The Grand Strand Family Medical Centre is specifically set up to treat minor medical emergencies for visitors. There are two facilities, one in the Little River Area and the other in Murrells Inlet. The quality control department wishes to compare the mean waiting time for patients at the two locations. Samples of the waiting times, reported in minutes, follow:

Location	Waiting Time											
Little River	31.73	28.77	29.53	22.08	29.47	18.60	32.94	25.18	29.82	26.49		
Murrells Inlet	22.93	23.92	26.92	27.20	26.44	25.62	30.61	29.44	23.09	23.10	26.69	22.31

At the .05 significance level, is there a difference in the mean waiting time?

www.mcgrawhill.ca/olc/lind

39. The Commercial Bank and Trust Company is studying the use of its automatic teller machines (ATMs). Of particular interest is whether young adults (under 25 years old) use the machines more than senior citizens. To investigate further, samples of customers under 25 years of age and customers over 60 years of age were selected. The number of ATM transactions last month was determined for each selected individual, and the results are shown below. At the .01 significance level, can bank management conclude that younger customers use the ATMs more?

Under 25	10	10	11	15	7	11	10	9			
Over 60	4	8	7	7	4	5	1	7	4	10	5

40. Two horses, *Rocky* and *Duke*, are competing in the Coliseum Grand Prize horse race next month. To decide which is faster, they race over a part of the course several times. Below are the sample times in minutes. At the .05 significance level, can we conclude that there is a difference in their mean times?

Horse	Times (minutes)											
Rocky	12.9	12.5	11.0	13.3	11.2	11.4	11.6	12.3	14.2	11.3		
Duke	14.1	14.1	14.2	17.4	15.8	16.7	16.1	13.3	13.4	13.6	10.8	19.0

41. The manufacturer of an MP3 player wanted to know whether a 10 percent reduction in price is enough to increase the sales of its product. To investigate, the owner randomly selected eight outlets and sold the MP3 player at the reduced price. At seven randomly selected outlets, the MP3 player was sold at the regular price. Reported below is the number of units sold last month at the sampled outlets. At the .01 significance level, can the manufacturer conclude that the price reduction resulted in an increase in sales?

Regular price	138	121	88	115	141	125	96	
Reduced price	128	134	152	135	114	106	112	120

42. A number of minor automobile accidents occur at various high-risk intersections despite traffic lights. The traffic department claims that a modification in the type of light will reduce these accidents. The traffic commissioners have agreed to a proposed experiment. Eight intersections were chosen at random, and the lights at those intersections were modified. The numbers of minor accidents during a six-month period before and after the modifications were:

	Number of Accidents							
	A	**B**	**C**	**D**	**E**	**F**	**G**	**H**
Before modification	5	7	6	4	8	9	8	10
After modification	3	7	7	0	4	6	8	2

At the .01 significance level is it reasonable to conclude that the modification reduced the number of traffic accidents?

43. Lester Hollar is vice president for human resources for a large manufacturing company. In recent years he has noticed an increase in absenteeism that he thinks is related to the general health of the employees. Four years ago, in an attempt to improve the situation, he began a fitness program in which employees exercise during their lunch hour. To evaluate the program, he selected a random sample of eight participants and found the number of days each was absent in the six months before the exercise program began and in the last six months. Below are the results. At the .05 significance level, can he conclude that the number of absences has declined? Estimate the *p*-value.

Employee	Before	After
1	6	5
2	6	2
3	7	1
4	7	3
5	4	3
6	3	6
7	5	3
8	6	7

44. The president of an insurance company wants to compare the yearly costs of auto insurance offered by two leading competitors. He selects a sample of 15 families, some with only a single insured driver, others with several teenage drivers, and pays each family a stipend to contact the two competitors and ask for a price quote. To make the data comparable, certain features, such as the amount deductible and limits of liability, are standardized. The sample information is reported below. At the .10 significance level, can we conclude that there is a difference in the amounts quoted?

Family	Competitor A	Competitor B
Becker	$2090	$1610
Berry	1683	1247
Cobb	1402	2327
Debuck	1830	1367
DuBrul	930	1461
Eckroate	697	1789
German	1741	1621
Glasson	1129	1914
King	1018	1956
Kucic	1881	1772
Meredith	1571	1375
Obeid	874	1527
Price	1579	1767
Phillips	1577	1636
Tresize	860	1188

45. Fairfield Homes is developing two parcels of land near White Pigeon. In order to test different advertising approaches, it uses different media to reach potential buyers. The mean annual family income for 75 people making inquiries at the first development is \$150 000, with a standard deviation of \$40 000. A corresponding sample of 120 people at the second development had a mean income of \$180 000, with a standard deviation of \$30 000. At the .05 significance level, can Fairfield conclude that the population means are different?

46. The following data resulted from a taste test of two different chocolate bars. The first number is a rating of the taste, which could range from 0 to 5, with a 5 indicating the person liked the taste. The second number indicates whether a "secret ingredient" was present. If the ingredient was present, a code of "1" was used and, if not, a "0" otherwise. At the .05 significance level, does this data show a difference in the taste ratings?

Rating	"With/Without"	Rating	"With/Without"
3	1	1	1
1	1	4	0
0	0	4	0
2	1	2	1
3	1	3	0
1	1	4	0

47. An investigation of the effectiveness of an antibacterial soap in reducing operating room contamination resulted in the accompanying table. The new soap was tested in a sample of eight operating rooms in the Cambridge area during the last year.

	Operating Room							
	A	B	C	D	E	F	G	H
Before	6.6	6.5	9.0	10.3	11.2	8.1	6.3	11.6
After	6.8	2.4	7.4	8.5	8.1	6.1	3.4	2.0

At the .05 significance level, can we conclude the contamination measurements are lower after use of the new soap?

48. The following data on annual rates of return were collected from five stocks listed on the New York Stock Exchange (the "Big Board") and five stocks listed on NASDAQ. At the .10 significance level, can we conclude that the annual rates of return are higher on the Big Board?

NYSE	NASDAQ
17.16	15.80
17.08	16.28
15.51	16.21
8.43	17.97
25.15	7.77

Data Set Exercises

49. Refer to the real estate data, from the south-east area of Edmonton on the CD-ROM, which reports information on listed homes.
    a. At the .05 significance level, can we conclude that there is a difference in the mean list price of homes with up to and including 2000 square feet compared to those with more than 2000 square feet? Compute and interpret the p-value.
    b. At the .01 significance level, can we conclude that there is a difference in the mean list price of homes with more than three bedrooms? Compute and interpret the p-value.
50. Refer to the CREA (Canadian Real Estate Association) data on the CD-ROM, which reports information on average house prices nationally and in a selection of cities across Canada. Select the cities only.
    a. At the .05 significance level, can we conclude that the mean list price for July 2008 is less than July 2007?
    b. What is the p-value? Use this result to support your answer.
51. Refer to the Average retail prices for gasoline and fuel oil, by urban centre, computed annual average (cents per litre) data on the CD-ROM (found in the file named Gasoline Prices).
    a. Using the data from June 2004 to June 2008, compare the gasoline prices for Winnipeg and Calgary. At the .05 significance level, can we conclude that there is a difference in the average gasoline price? Compute and interpret the p-value.
    b. Using the data from June 2004 to June 2008, compare the gasoline prices for Halifax, Nova Scotia and Saint John, New Brunswick. At the .01 significance level, can we conclude that there is a difference in the average gasoline price? Compute and interpret the p-value.
    c. Using the data from June 2004 to June 2008, compare the gasoline prices for Toronto and Montreal. At the .05 significance level, can we conclude that the gasoline prices in Toronto are less than the gasoline prices in Montreal? Compute and interpret the p-value.
52. Refer to the International data, which reports demographic and economic information on 46 countries. Conduct a test of hypothesis to determine whether the mean percent of the population over 65 years of age in G-20 countries is different from those that are not G-20 members. Use the .05 significance level.

exercises.com

Additional exercises that require you to access information at related Internet sites are available on the CD-ROM included with this text.

Answers to Self-Reviews

10–1 (a) H_0: $\mu_1 - \mu_2 \leq 0$.
H_1: $\mu_1 - \mu_2 > 0$.
The subscript 1 refers to the women and 2 to the men.

(b) Reject H_0 if $z > 1.645$.

(c) $$z = \frac{\$1500 - \$1400 - 0}{\sqrt{\dfrac{(\$250)^2}{50} + \dfrac{(\$200)^2}{40}}} = 2.11.$$

(d) Reject the null hypothesis.

(e) p-value = .5000 − .4826 = .0174.

(f) The p-value is less than the significance level, α = .05, so the test statistic lies in the rejection region. We conclude that the mean amount sold per day is larger for women.

10–2 (a) H_0: $p_1 - p_2 = 0$.
H_1: $p_1 - p_2 \neq 0$.

(b) .10.

(c) Two-tailed.
(d) Reject H_0 if z is less than −1.645 or greater than 1.645.

(e) $$p_c = \frac{87+123}{150+200} = \frac{210}{350} = .60.$$

$$\bar{p}_1 = \frac{87}{150} = .58 \quad \bar{p}_2 = \frac{123}{200} = .615.$$

$$z = \frac{.58 - .615 - 0}{\sqrt{\frac{.60(.40)}{150} + \frac{.60(.40)}{200}}} = -0.66.$$

(f) Do not reject H_0.
(g) p-value = 2(.5000 − .2454) = .5092.

The p-value is greater than the significance level, α = .10, so the test statistic lies in the acceptance region. There is not enough evidence to reject H_0 and so we conclude that there is no difference in the proportion of adults and children that liked the proposed flavour.

10–3 (a) H_0: $\mu_1 - \mu_2 = 0$.
H_1: $\mu_1 - \mu_2 \neq 0$.

(b) df = 6 + 8 − 2 = 12.
An appropriate significance level is α = .05. Reject H_0 if t is less than −2.179 or t is greater than 2.179.

(c) $$\bar{X}_1 = \frac{42}{6} = 7.00. \quad s_1 = \sqrt{\frac{304 - \frac{42^2}{6}}{6-1}} = 1.4142.$$

$$\bar{X}_2 = \frac{80}{8} = 10.00. \quad s_2 = \sqrt{\frac{836 - \frac{80^2}{8}}{8-1}} = 2.2678.$$

$$s_p^2 = \frac{(6-1)(1.4142)^2 + (8-1)(2.2678)^2}{6+8-2}$$

$$= 3.8333.$$

$$t = \frac{7.00 - 10.00 - 0}{\sqrt{3.8333\left(\frac{1}{6} + \frac{1}{8}\right)}} = -2.837.$$

(d) Reject H_0 because −2.837 is less than the critical value.
(e) The p-value is less than .02.
(f) The p-value is less than the significance level, so the test statistic lies in the rejection region. Reject H_0, and conclude that the mean number of defects is not the same on the two shifts.
(g) Independent populations; populations follow the normal distribution; populations have equal standard deviations.

10–4 (a) H_0: $\mu_d \leq 0$, H_1: $\mu_d > 0$.
(b) Reject H_0 if $t > 2.998$.
(c)

Name	Before	After	d	d^2
Hunter	155	154	1	1
Cashman	228	207	21	441
Mervine	141	147	−6	36
Massa	162	157	5	25
Creola	211	196	15	225
Peterson	164	150	14	196
Redding	184	170	14	196
Poust	172	165	7	49
			71	1169

$$\bar{d} = \frac{71}{8} = 8.875.$$

$$s_d = \sqrt{\frac{1169 - \frac{(71)^2}{8}}{8-1}} = 8.774.$$

$$t = \frac{8.875}{8.774/\sqrt{8}} = 2.861.$$

(d) Do not reject H_0. We cannot conclude that the students lost weight. The p-value is greater than the significance level of .01.
(e) The distribution of the differences must follow a normal distribution.

chapter 11

Analysis of Variance

LEARNING GOALS

When you have completed this chapter, you will be able to:

1. List the characteristics of the *F distribution*.
2. Conduct a test of hypothesis to determine whether the variances of two populations are equal.
3. Discuss the general idea of *analysis of variance*.
4. Conduct a test of hypothesis among three or more treatment means.
5. Organize data into a *one-way ANOVA table*.
6. Develop confidence intervals for the difference in treatment means.

Introduction

In this chapter we continue our discussion of hypothesis testing. Recall that in Chapters 9 and 10 we examined the general theory of hypothesis testing. We described the case where a large sample was selected from the population. We used the z distribution (the standard normal distribution) or the t distribution to determine whether it was reasonable to conclude that the population mean was equal to a specified value. We tested whether two population means are the same. We also conducted both one- and two-sample tests for population proportions, using the standard normal distribution as the distribution of the test statistic. In this chapter we expand further our idea of hypothesis tests. We describe a test for variances and then a test that simultaneously compares several means to determine if they came from equal populations.

1 List the characteristics of the *F distribution*.

The *F* Distribution

The probability distribution used in this chapter is the F distribution. It was named to honour Sir Ronald Fisher, one of the founders of modern-day statistics. This probability distribution is used as the test statistic for several situations. It is used to test whether two samples are from populations having equal variances, and it is also applied when we want to compare several population means simultaneously. The simultaneous comparison of several population means is called **analysis of variance (ANOVA)**. In both of these situations, the populations must be normal, and the data must be at least interval-scale.

What are the characteristics of the *F* distribution?

Characteristics of the *F* distribution.

1. **There is a "family" of *F* distributions.** A particular member of the family is determined by two parameters: the degrees of freedom in the numerator and the degrees of freedom in the denominator. The shape of the distribution is illustrated by the following graph. There is one *F* distribution for the combination of 29 degrees of freedom in the numerator and 28 degrees of freedom in the denominator. There is another *F* distribution for 19 degrees of freedom in the numerator and 6 degrees of freedom in the denominator. The final distribution shown has 6 degrees of freedom in the numerator and 6 degrees of freedom in the denominator. We will describe the concept of degrees of freedom later in the chapter. Note that the shapes of the curves change as the degrees of freedom change.

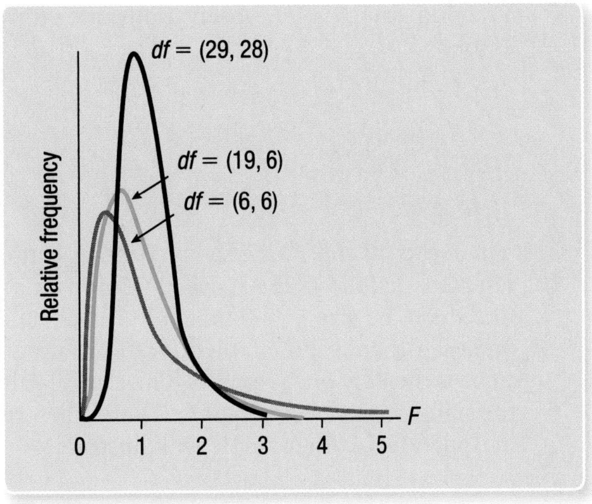

2. **The *F* distribution is continuous.** This means that it can assume an infinite number of values between 0 and positive infinity.
3. **The *F* distribution cannot be negative.** The smallest value *F* can assume is 0.
4. **It is positively skewed.** The long tail of the distribution is to the right-hand side. As the number of degrees of freedom increases in both the numerator and denominator, the distribution approaches a normal distribution.
5. **It is asymptotic.** As the values of *X* increase, the *F* curve approaches the *X*-axis but never touches it. This is similar to the behaviour of the normal distribution, described in Chapter 6.

2 Conduct a test of hypothesis to determine whether the variances of two populations are equal.

Comparing Two Population Variances

The *F* distribution is used to test the hypothesis that the variance of one normal population equals the variance of another normal population. The following examples will show the use of the test:

- Two Barth shearing machines are set to produce steel bars of the same length. The bars, therefore, should have the same mean length. We want to ensure that in addition to having the same mean length, they also have similar variation.
- The mean rate of return on two types of common stock may be the same, but there may be more variation in the rate of return in one than the other. A sample of 10 technology stocks and 10 utility stocks shows the same mean rate of return, but there is likely more variation in the technology stocks.
- A study by the marketing department for a large newspaper found that men and women spent about the same amount of time per day surfing the Internet. However, the same report indicated there was nearly twice as much variation among the men than the women.

The *F* distribution is also used to test assumptions for some statistical tests. Recall that in the previous chapter, we used the *t* test to investigate whether the means of two independent populations differed. To employ that test, we sometimes assume that the variances of two normal populations are the same. The F distribution provides a way to conduct a test comparing the variances of two normal populations.

Regardless of whether we want to determine if one population has more variation than another population or validate an assumption for a statistical test, we first state the null hypothesis. The null hypothesis is that the variance of one normal population, σ_1^2, equals the variance of the other normal population, σ_2^2. The alternative hypothesis could be that the variances differ. In this instance, the null hypothesis and the alternative hypothesis are:

$$H_0: \sigma_1^2 - \sigma_2^2 = 0$$
$$H_1: \sigma_1^2 - \sigma_2^2 \neq 0$$

To conduct the test, we select a random sample of n_1 observations from one population, and a random sample of n_2 observations from the second population. The test statistic is defined as follows.

TEST STATISTIC FOR COMPARING TWO VARIANCES

$$F = \frac{s_1^2}{s_2^2}, s_1^2 > s_2^2 \qquad \textbf{[11–1]}$$

The terms s_1^2 and s_2^2 are the respective sample variances. If the null hypothesis is true, the test statistic follows the F distribution with $n_1 - 1$ and $n_2 - 1$ degrees of freedom. In order to reduce the size of the table of critical values, the *larger* sample variance is placed in the numerator; hence, the tabled F ratio is always larger than 1.00. Thus, the right-tail critical value is the only one required. The critical value of F for a two-tailed test is found by dividing the significance level in half ($\alpha/2$) and then referring to the appropriate degrees of freedom in Appendix G. An example will illustrate.

example

Luxury Limos offers limousine service from the city hall in Toronto, Ontario, to the Toronto International Airport. Sean Lammers, president of the company, is considering two routes. One is via Highway 427 and the other via Avenue Road. He wants to study the time it takes to drive to the airport using each route and then compare the results. He collected the following sample data, which is reported in minutes. Using the .10 significance level, is there a difference in the variation in the driving times using the two routes?

Avenue Road	Highway 427
52	59
67	60
56	61
45	51
70	56
54	63
64	57
	65

solution

The mean driving times along the two routes are nearly the same. The mean time is 58.29 minutes for the Avenue Road route and 59.0 minutes along the Highway 427 route. However, in evaluating travel times, Mr. Lammers is also concerned about the variation in the travel times. The first step is to compute the two sample variances. We'll use formula (3–12) to compute the sample standard deviations. To obtain the sample variances, we can compute the variances directly or square the standard deviations.

Avenue Road

$$\bar{X} = \frac{\Sigma X}{n} = \frac{408}{7} = 58.29 \qquad s = \sqrt{\frac{\Sigma X^2 - \frac{(\Sigma X)^2}{n}}{n-1}} = \sqrt{\frac{24\,266 - \frac{(408)^2}{7}}{7-1}} = 8.9947$$

Highway 427

$$\bar{X} = \frac{\Sigma X}{n} = \frac{472}{8} = 59.00 \qquad s = \sqrt{\frac{\Sigma X^2 - \frac{(\Sigma X)^2}{n}}{n-1}} = \sqrt{\frac{27\,982 - \frac{(472)^2}{8}}{8-1}} = 4.3753$$

There is more variation, as measured by the standard deviation, in the Avenue Road route than in the Highway 427 route. This is somewhat consistent with his knowledge of the two routes; the Avenue Road route contains more traffic lights, whereas Highway 427 is a limited-access highway. However, to access the highway, the driver must first go south to the QEW, west on the QEW, and then north on Highway 427. It is important that the service offered be both timely and consistent, so he decides to conduct a statistical test to determine whether there really is a difference in the variation of the two routes.

The usual five-step hypothesis testing procedure will be employed.

Step 1: We begin by stating the null hypothesis and the alternative hypothesis. The test is two-tailed because we are looking for a difference in the variation of the two routes. We are *not* trying to show that one route has more variation than the other.

$$H_0 : \sigma_1^2 - \sigma_2^2 = 0$$
$$H_1 : \sigma_1^2 - \sigma_2^2 \neq 0$$

Step 2: We select the .10 significance level.

Step 3: The appropriate test statistic follows the F distribution.

Step 4: The critical value is obtained from Appendix G, a portion of which is reproduced as Table 11–1. Because we are conducting a two-tailed test, the tabled significance level is .05, found by $\alpha/2 = .10/2 = .05$. There are $n_1 - 1 = 7 - 1 = 6$ degrees of freedom in the numerator, and $n_2 - 1 = 8 - 1 = 7$ degrees of freedom in the denominator. To find the critical value, move horizontally across the top portion of the F table (Table 11–1 or Appendix G) for the .05 significance level to 6 degrees of freedom in the numerator. Then move down that column to the critical value opposite 7 degrees of freedom in the denominator. The critical value is 3.87. Thus, the decision rule is: Reject the null hypothesis if the ratio of the sample variances exceeds 3.87.

Step 5: The final step is to take the ratio of the two sample variances, determine the value of the test statistic, and make a decision regarding the null hypothesis. Note that formula (11–1) refers to the sample *variances* but we calculated the sample *standard deviations*. We need to square the standard deviations to determine the variances.

TABLE 11–1 Critical Values of the *F* Distribution, $\alpha = .05$

Degrees of Freedom for Denominator	Degrees of Freedom for Numerator			
	5	6	7	8
1	230	234	237	239
2	19.3	19.3	19.4	19.4
3	9.01	8.94	8.89	8.85
4	6.26	6.16	6.09	6.04
5	5.05	4.95	4.88	4.82
6	4.39	4.28	4.21	4.15
7	3.97	3.87	3.79	3.73
8	3.69	3.58	3.50	3.44
9	3.48	3.37	3.29	3.23
10	3.33	3.22	3.14	3.07

$$F = \frac{s_1^2}{s_2^2} = \frac{(8.9947)^2}{(4.3753)^2} = 4.23$$

The decision is to reject the null hypothesis, because the computed F value (4.23) is larger than the critical value (3.87). We conclude that there is a difference in the variation of the travel times along the two routes.

As noted, the usual practice is to determine the F ratio by putting the larger of the two sample variances in the numerator. This will force the F ratio to be at least 1.00. This allows us to always use the right tail of the F distribution, thus avoiding the need for more extensive F tables.

A logical question arises regarding one-tailed tests. For example, suppose in the previous example we suspected that the variance of the times using the Avenue Road route was *larger* than the variance of the times along the Highway 427 route. We would state the null and the alternative hypothesis as

$$H_0: \sigma_1^2 - \sigma_2^2 \leq 0$$
$$H_1: \sigma_1^2 - \sigma_2^2 > 0$$

The test statistic is computed as s_1^2/s_2^2. Notice that we labelled the population with the suspected larger variance as population 1. So, s_1^2 appears in the numerator. The F ratio will be larger than 1.00, so we can use the upper tail of the F distribution. Under these conditions, it is not necessary to divide the significance level in half. Because Appendix G gives us only the .05 and .01 significance levels, we are restricted to these levels for one-tailed tests and .10 and .02 for two-tailed tests, unless we consult a more complete table or use a statistical software package to compute the F statistic.

excel

Excel has a procedure to perform a test of variances. The output follows. The computed value of F is the same as determined using formula (11–1).

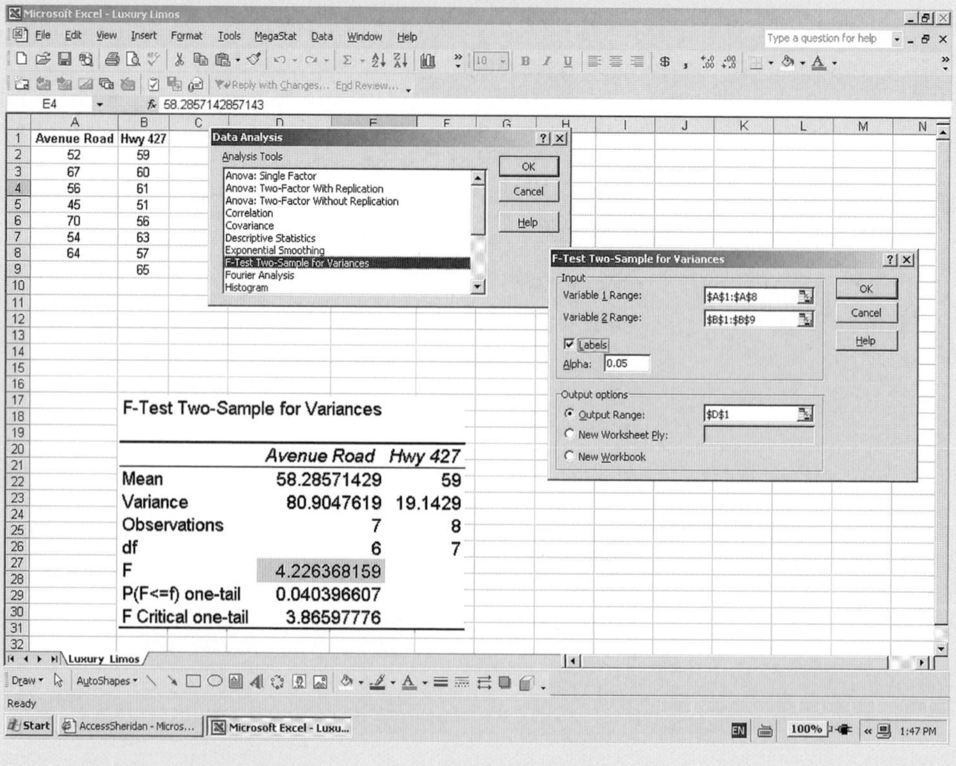

In addition, **Excel** has an FTEST function that will return a p-value for a two-tailed test.

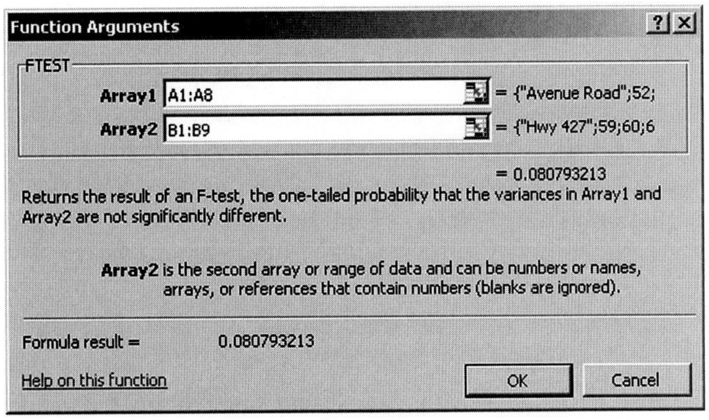

Note the p-value result = .08079.

Note: Since the p-value (.081) < the significance level (.10), the decision is to reject the null hypothesis.

self-review 11–1

Steele Electric Products Inc. assembles electrical components for stereo equipment. For the last 10 days Mark Nagy has averaged nine rejects, with a standard deviation of two rejects per day. Debbie Richmond averaged 8.5 rejects, with a standard deviation of 1.5 rejects, over the same period. At the .05 significance level, can we conclude that there is more variation in the number of rejects per day attributed to Mark?

Exercises

1. What is the critical F value for a sample of six observations in the numerator and four in the denominator? Use a two-tailed test and the .10 significance level.
2. What is the critical F value for a sample of four observations in the numerator and seven in the denominator? Use a one-tailed test and the .01 significance level.
3. The following hypotheses are given.

$$H_0: \sigma_1^2 - \sigma_2^2 = 0$$
$$H_1: \sigma_1^2 - \sigma_2^2 \neq 0$$

A random sample of eight observations from the first population resulted in a standard deviation of 10. A random sample of six observations from the second population resulted in a standard deviation of 7. At the .02 significance level, is there a difference in the variation of the two populations?

4. The following hypotheses are given.

$$H_0: \sigma_1^2 - \sigma_2^2 \leq 0$$
$$H_1: \sigma_1^2 - \sigma_2^2 > 0$$

A random sample of five observations from the first population resulted in a standard deviation of 12. A random sample of seven observations from the second population showed a standard deviation of 7. At the .01 significance level, is there more variation in the first population?

5. Stargell Research Associates conducted a study of the iPod listening habits of men and women. One facet of the study involved the mean listening time. It was discovered that the mean listening time for men was 35 minutes per day. The standard deviation of the sample of the 10 men studied was 10 minutes per day. The mean listening time for the 12 women studied was also 35 minutes, but the standard deviation of the sample was 12 minutes. At the .10 significance level, can we conclude that there is a difference in the variation in the listening times for men and women?
6. A stockbroker at Critical Securities reported that the mean rate of return on a sample of 10 oil stocks was 12.6 percent with a standard deviation of 3.9 percent. The mean rate of return on a sample of eight utility stocks was 10.9 percent with a standard deviation of 3.5 percent. At the .05 significance level, can we conclude that there is more variation in the oil stocks?

3 Discuss the general idea of *analysis of variance.*

ANOVA Assumptions

Another use of the F distribution is the analysis of variance (ANOVA) technique in which we compare three or more population means to determine whether they could be equal. To use ANOVA, we assume the following:

1. The populations follow a normal distribution.
2. The populations have equal standard deviations (σ).
3. The populations are independent.

When these conditions are met, F is used as the distribution of the test statistic.

Why do we need to study ANOVA? Why can't we just use the test of differences in population means discussed in the previous chapter? We could compare the means two at a time. The major reason is the unsatisfactory buildup of Type I error. To explain further, suppose we have four different methods (A, B, C, and D) of training new recruits to be firefighters. We randomly assign each of the 40 recruits in this year's class to one of the four methods. At the end of the training program, we administer to the four groups a common test to measure understanding of firefighting techniques. The question is: Is there a difference in the mean test scores among the four groups? An answer to this question will allow us to compare the four training methods.

Using the t distribution leads to a buildup of Type I error.

Using the t distribution to compare the four population means, we would have to conduct six different t tests. That is, we would need to compare the mean scores for the four methods as follows: A versus B, A versus C, A versus D, B versus C, B versus D, and C versus D. If we set the significance level at .05, the probability of a single correct statistical decision is .95, found by 1 − .05. Because we conduct six separate tests, the probability that we do *not* make an incorrect decision due to sampling in any of the six tests is:

$$P(\textit{All correct}) = (.95)(.95)(.95)(.95)(.95)(.95) = .735$$

To find the probability of a least one error due to sampling, we subtract this result from 1. Thus, the probability of at least one incorrect decision due to sampling is 1 − .735 = .265. To summarize, if we conduct six independent tests using the t distribution, the likelihood of rejecting a true null hypothesis because of sampling error is increased from .05 to an unsatisfactory level of .265. It is obvious that we need a better method than conducting six t tests. ANOVA will allow us to compare the treatment means simultaneously and avoid the buildup of Type I error.

ANOVA was developed for applications in agriculture, and many of the terms related to that context remain. In particular, the term *treatment* is used to identify the different populations being examined. For example, treatment refers to how a plot of ground was treated with a particular type of fertilizer. The following illustration will clarify the term *treatment* and demonstrate an application of ANOVA.

example

Joyce Kuhlman manages a regional financial centre. She wishes to compare the productivity, as measured by the number of customers served, among three employees. Four days are randomly selected and the number of customers served by each employee is recorded. The results are:

Wolfe	White	Korosa
55	66	47
54	76	51
59	67	46
56	71	48

solution

Is there a difference in the mean number of customers served? Chart 11–1 illustrates how the populations would appear if there was a difference in the treatment means. Note that the populations follow the normal distribution and the variation in each population is the same, but the means are *not* the same.

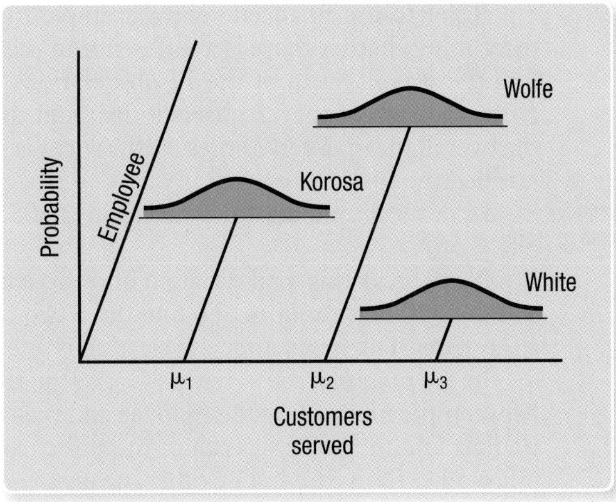

CHART 11–1 Case Where Treatment Means Are Different

Suppose the populations are the same. That is, there is no difference in the (treatment) means. This is shown in Chart 11–2. This would indicate that the population means are the same. Note again that the populations follow the normal distribution and the variation in each of the populations is the same.

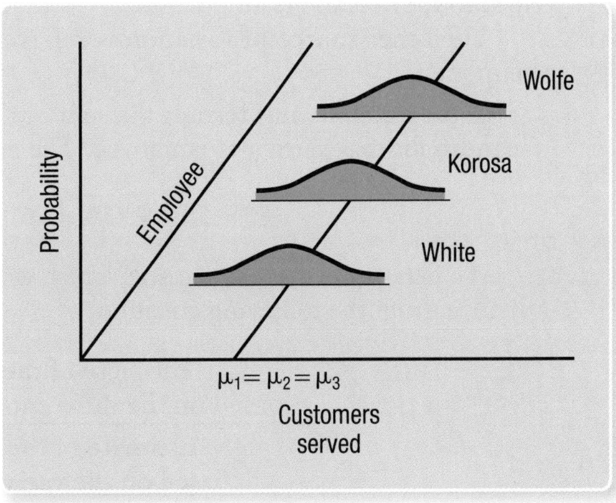

CHART 11–2 Case Where Treatment Means Are the Same

4 Conduct a test of hypothesis among three or more treatment means.

The ANOVA Test

How does the ANOVA test work? Recall that we want to determine whether the various sample means came from a single population or populations with different means. We actually compare these sample means through their variances. To explain, recall that we listed the assumptions required for ANOVA. One of those assumptions was that the standard deviations of the various normal populations had to be the same. We take advantage of this requirement in the ANOVA test. The underlying strategy is to estimate the population variance (standard deviation squared) two ways and then find the ratio of these two estimates. If this ratio is about 1, then logically the two estimates are the same, and we conclude that the population means are the same. If the ratio is quite different from 1, then we conclude that the population means are not the same. The F distribution serves as a referee by indicating when the ratio of the sample variances is too much greater than 1 to have occurred by chance.

Refer to the financial centre example in the previous section. The manager wants to determine whether there is a difference in the mean number of customers served. To begin, find the overall mean of the 12 observations. It is 58, found by $(55 + 54 + \cdots + 48)/12$. Next, for each of the 12 observations, find the difference between the particular value and the overall mean. Each of these differences is squared and these squares summed. This term is called the **total variation**.

total variation The sum of the squared differences between each observation and the overall mean.

In our example the total variation is 1082, found by $(55 - 58)^2 + (54 - 58)^2 + \cdots + (48 - 58)^2$.

Next, break this total variation into two components: that which is due to the **treatments**, and that which is **random**. To find these two components, determine the mean of each of the treatments. The first source of variation is due to the treatments.

treatment variation The sum of the squared differences between each treatment mean and the overall mean.

In the example, the variation due to the treatments is the sum of the squared differences between the mean of each employee and the overall mean. This term is 992. To calculate it, we first find the mean of each of the three treatments. The mean for Wolfe is 56, found by $(55 + 54 + 59 + 56)/4$. The other means are 70 and 48, respectively. The sum of the squares due to the treatments is:

$$(56-58)^2 + (56-58)^2 + \cdots + (48-58)^2 = 4(56-58)^2 + 4(70-58)^2 + 4(48-58)^2 = 992$$

If there is considerable variation among the treatment means, it is logical that this term will be large. If the treatment means are similar, this term will be a small value. The smallest possible value would be zero. This would occur when all the treatment means are the same and equal to the overall mean.

The other source of variation is referred to as the **random** component, or the error component.

random variation The sum of the squared differences between each observation and its treatment mean.

In the example, this term is the sum of the squared differences between each value and the mean for that particular employee. The error variation is 90.

$$(55-56)^2 + (54-56)^2 + \cdots + (48-48)^2 = 90$$

We determine the test statistic, which is the ratio of the two estimates of the population variance, from the following equation.

$$F = \frac{\text{Estimate of the population variance based on the differences among the sample means}}{\text{Estimate of the population variance based on the variation within the samples}}$$

Our first estimate of the population variance is based on the treatment variation, that is, the difference *between* the means. It is 992/2. Why did we divide by 2? Recall from Chapter 3, to find a sample variance (see formula 3–10), we divide by the number of observations minus 1. In this case there are three treatments, so we divide by 2. Our first estimate of the population variance is 992/2.

The variance estimate *within* the treatments is the random variation divided by the total number of observations less the number of treatments. That is $90/(12 - 3)$. Hence, our second estimate of the population variance is 90/9. This is actually a generalization of formula (10–5), where we pooled the sample variances from two populations.

The last step is to take the ratio of these two estimates.

$$F = \frac{992/2}{90/2} = 49.6$$

Because this ratio is quite different from 1, we can conclude that the population means are not the same. There is a difference in the mean number of customers served by the three employees.

Here is another example of the ANOVA technique that deals with samples of different sizes, which broadens the ANOVA applications.

example

Recently, airlines have cut services, such as meals and snacks during flights, and started to charge extra for some services such as overweight baggage and last minute flight changes. However, they are still very concerned about service. A group of four carriers (the names have been omitted for confidentiality) recently hired Muir Marketing Research Inc. to survey passengers regarding their level of satisfaction with a flight they just took.

The survey included questions on ticketing, boarding, in-flight service, baggage handling, cabin communication, and so forth. Twenty-five questions offered a range of possible answers: excellent, good, fair, or poor. A response of excellent was given a rating of 4, good a 3, fair a 2, and poor a 1. These responses were then totalled, so the total score was an indication of the satisfaction with the flight. The greater the rating, the higher the level of satisfaction with the service. The highest possible rating was 100.

Samantha Muir randomly selected and surveyed passengers from the four airlines. Below is the sample information. Is there a difference in the mean satisfaction level among the four airlines? Note: the airlines are labelled AirWaves, Belle Air, Cirrus Airlines, and Debonair. Use the .01 significance level.

Mean Satisfaction Level			
AirWaves	**Belle Air**	**Cirrus Airlines**	**Debonair**
94	75	70	68
90	68	73	70
85	77	76	72
80	83	78	65
	88	80	74
		68	65
		65	

solution

We will follow the usual five-step hypothesis testing procedure.

Step 1: State the null hypothesis and the alternative hypothesis. The null hypothesis is that the mean scores are the same for the four airlines. We can write this symbolically as:

$$H_0: \mu_1 = \mu_2 = \mu_3 = \mu_4$$

The alternative hypothesis is that the mean scores are not all the same for the four airlines.

H_1: The mean scores are not all equal.

We can also think of the alternative hypothesis as "at least two mean scores are not equal."

If the null hypothesis is not rejected, we conclude that there is no difference in the mean ratings for the four airlines. If H_0 is rejected, we conclude that there is a difference in at least one pair of mean ratings, but at this point we do not know which pair or how many pairs differ.

Step 2: Select the level of significance. We select the .01 significance level.

Step 3: Determine the test statistic. The test statistic follows the F distribution.

Step 4: Formulate the decision rule. To determine the decision rule, we need the critical value. The critical value for the F statistic is found in Appendix G. The critical values for the .05 significance level are found on the first page and the .01 significance level on the second page. To use this table, we need to know the degrees of freedom in the numerator and the denominator. The degrees of freedom in the numerator equals the number of treatments, designated as k, minus 1. The degrees of freedom in the denominator is the total number of observations, n, minus the number of treatments. For this problem, there are four treatments and a total of 22 observations.

Degrees of freedom in the numerator = $k - 1 = 4 - 1 = 3$
Degrees of freedom in the denominator = $n - k = 22 - 4 = 18$

Refer to Appendix G and the .01 significance level. Move horizontally across the top of the page to 3 degrees of freedom in the numerator. Then move down that column to the row with 18 degrees of freedom. The value at this intersection is 5.09. So, the decision rule is to reject H_0 if the computed value of F exceeds 5.09.

Step 5: Select the sample, perform the calculations, and make a decision. It is convenient to summarize the calculations of the F statistic in an **ANOVA table.** The format for an ANOVA table is as follows. Statistical software packages also use this format.

5 Organize data into a *one-way ANOVA table*.

ANOVA Table

Source of Variation	Sum of Squares	Degrees of Freedom	Mean Square	F
Treatments	SST	$k - 1$	MST = SST/(k − 1)	MST/MSE
Error	SSE	$n - k$	MSE = SSE/(n − k)	
Total	SS total	$n - 1$		

There are three values, or **sum of squares**, used to compute the test statistic, F. We can determine these values by finding SS total and SSE, then finding SST by subtraction. The SS total term is the total variation, SST is the variation due to the treatments, and SSE is the variation within the treatments, or the random error.

We usually start the process by finding SS total. This is the sum of the squared differences between each observation and the overall mean. The formula for finding SS total is

$$\text{SS total} = \Sigma(X - \bar{X}_G)^2 \qquad \textbf{[11–2]}$$

where:

X is each sample observation
$\bar{X}_G$ is the overall or grand mean. The subscript G refers to the "grand" mean.

Next, determine SSE or the sum of the squared errors. This is the sum of the squared differences between each observation and its respective treatment mean. The formula for finding SSE is:

$$\text{SSE} = \Sigma(X - \bar{X}_c)^2 \qquad \textbf{[11–3]}$$

where:

$\bar{X}_c$ is the sample mean for treatment c. The subscript c refers to the particular column.

The detailed calculations of SS total and SSE for this example follow. To determine the values of SS total and SSE, we start by calculating the overall or grand mean. There are 22 observations and the total is 1664, so the grand mean is 75.64.

$$\bar{X}_G = \frac{1664}{22} = 75.64$$

	AirWaves	Belle Air	Cirrus Airlines	Debonair	Total
	94	75	70	68	
	90	68	73	70	
	85	77	76	72	
	80	83	78	65	
		88	80	74	
			68	65	
			65		
Column Total	349	391	510	414	1664
n	4	5	7	6	22
Mean	87.25	78.20	72.86	69.00	75.64

Next, we find the deviation of each observation from the grand mean, square these deviations, and sum this result for all 22 observations. For example, the first sampled passenger had a score of 94 and the overall or grand mean is 75.64. So $(X - \bar{X}_G) = 94 - 75.64 = 18.36$. For the last passenger, $65 - 75.64 = -10.64$. The calculations for all other passengers follow.

AirWaves	Belle Air	Cirrus Airlines	Debonair
18.36	−0.64	−5.64	−7.64
14.36	−7.64	−2.64	−5.64
9.36	1.36	0.36	−3.64
4.36	7.36	2.36	−10.64
	12.36	4.36	−1.64
		−7.64	−10.64
		−10.64	

Then, square each of these differences and sum the values. Thus, for the first passenger:

$$(X - \bar{X}_G)^2 = (94 - 75.64)^2 = (18.36)^2 = 337.09$$

Finally, sum all the squared differences as formula (11–2) directs. Our SS total value is 1485.09.

Statistics in Action

Have you ever waited in line for a telephone and it seemed like the person using the phone talked on and on? There is evidence that people actually talk longer on public telephones when someone is waiting. In a recent survey, researchers measured the length of time that 56 shoppers in a mall spent on the phone (1) when they were alone, (2) when a person was using the adjacent phone, and (3) when a person was using an adjacent phone and someone was waiting to use the phone. The study, using the one-way ANOVA technique, showed that the mean time using the telephone was significantly less when the person was alone.

	AirWaves	Belle Air	Cirrus Airlines	Debonair	Total
	337.09	0.41	31.81	58.37	
	206.21	58.37	6.97	31.81	
	87.61	1.85	0.13	13.25	
	19.00	54.17	5.57	113.21	
		152.77	19.01	2.69	
			58.37	113.21	
			113.21		
Total	649.91	267.57	235.07	332.54	1485.09

To compute the term SSE, find the deviation between each observation and its treatment mean. In the example, the mean of the first treatment (that is, the passenger ratings for AirWaves) is 87.25, found by $\bar{X}_{AW} = 349/4$. The subscript AW refers to the first airline.

The first passenger rated AirWaves at 94, so $(X - \bar{X}_{AW}) = (94 - 87.25) = 6.75$.

The first passenger in Belle Air's group responded with a rating of 75, so $(X - \bar{X}_{BA}) = (75 - 78.20) = -3.20$. The details of each of these calculations follow.

AirWaves	Belle Air	Cirrus Airlines	Debonair
6.75	−3.2	−2.86	−1
2.75	−10.2	0.14	1
−2.25	−1.2	3.14	3
−7.25	4.8	5.14	−4
	9.8	7.14	5
		−4.86	−4
		−7.86	

Each of these values is squared and then summed for all 22 observations. The values are shown in the following table.

	AirWaves	Belle Air	Cirrus Airlines	Debonair	Total
	45.5625	10.24	8.18	1	
	7.5625	104.04	0.02	1	
	5.0625	1.44	9.86	9	
	52.5625	23.04	26.42	16	
		96.04	50.98	25	
			23.62	16	
			61.78		
Total	110.7500	234.80	180.86	68	594.41

So, the SSE value is 594.41. That is, $\Sigma(X - \bar{X}_c)^2 = 594.41$.

Finally, we determine SST, the sum of the squares due to the treatments, by subtraction,

$$\text{SST} = \text{SS total} - \text{SSE} \qquad [11\text{–}4]$$

For this example:

$$\text{SST} = \text{SS total} - \text{SSE} = 1485.09 - 594.41 = 890.68$$

To find the computed value of F, work your way across the ANOVA table. The degrees of freedom for the numerator and the denominator are the same as in **step 4** above when we were finding the critical value of F. The term **mean square** is another expression for an estimate of the variance. The mean square for treatments is SST divided by its degrees of freedom. The result is the **mean square for treatments** and is written MST. Compute the **mean square error** in a similar fashion. To be precise, divide SSE by its degrees of freedom. To complete the process and find F, divide MST by MSE.

Insert the particular values of F into an ANOVA table and compute the value of F as follows.

Source of Variation	Sum of Squares	Degrees of Freedom	Mean Square	*F*
Treatments	890.68	3	296.89	8.99
Error	594.41	18	33.02	
Total	1485.09	21		

The computed value of F is 8.99, which is greater than the critical value of 5.09, so the null hypothesis is rejected. We conclude the population means are not all equal. The mean scores are not the same for the four airlines. It is likely that the passenger scores are related to the particular airline. At this point, we can only conclude there is a difference in the treatment means. We cannot determine which treatment groups differ or how many treatment groups differ.

As noted in the previous example, the calculations become very tedious if the number of observations in each treatment is large. There are many software packages that will output the results. Following is the **Excel** output in the form of an ANOVA table for the previous example involving airlines and passenger ratings. There are some slight differences between the **Excel** output and our calculations due to rounding.

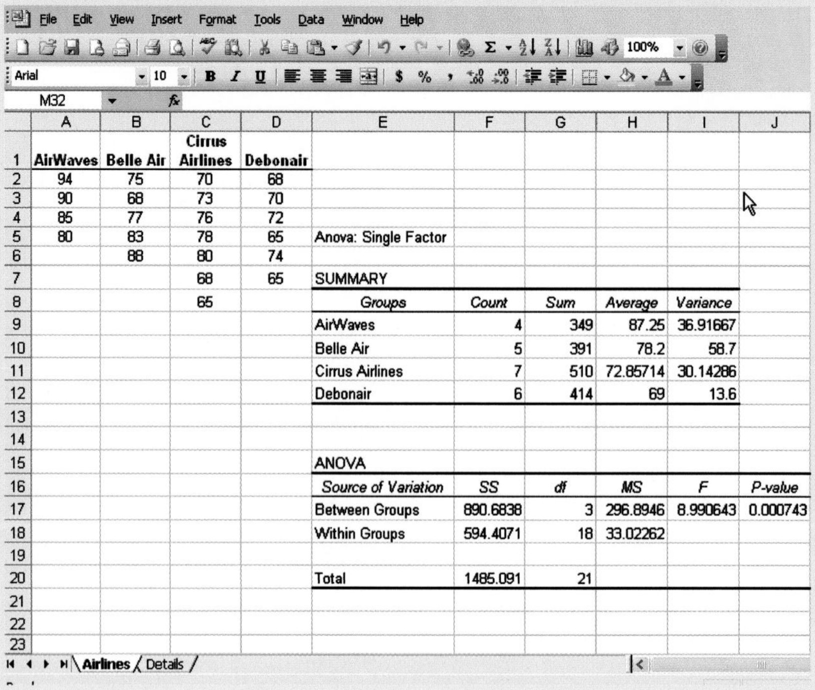

	A	B	C	D	E	F	G	H	I	J
1	AirWaves	Belle Air	Cirrus Airlines	Debonair						
2	94	75	70	68						
3	90	68	73	70						
4	85	77	76	72						
5	80	83	78	65	Anova: Single Factor					
6		88	80	74						
7			68	65	SUMMARY					
8			65		Groups	Count	Sum	Average	Variance	
9					AirWaves	4	349	87.25	36.91667	
10					Belle Air	5	391	78.2	58.7	
11					Cirrus Airlines	7	510	72.85714	30.14286	
12					Debonair	6	414	69	13.6	
13										
14										
15					ANOVA					
16					Source of Variation	SS	df	MS	F	P-value
17					Between Groups	890.6838	3	296.8946	8.990643	0.000743
18					Within Groups	594.4071	18	33.02262		
19										
20					Total	1485.091	21			
21										
22										
23										

Notice **Excel** uses the term "Between Groups" for "Treatments", and "Within Groups" for "Error." However, they have the same meanings. The p-value is .0007. This is the probability of finding a value of the test statistic this large or larger when the null hypothesis is true. To put it another way, it is the likelihood of calculating an F value larger than 8.99 with 3 degrees of freedom in the numerator and 18 degrees of freedom in the denominator. So, when we reject the null hypothesis in this instance there is a very small likelihood of committing a Type I error!

MegaStat steps and commands follow.

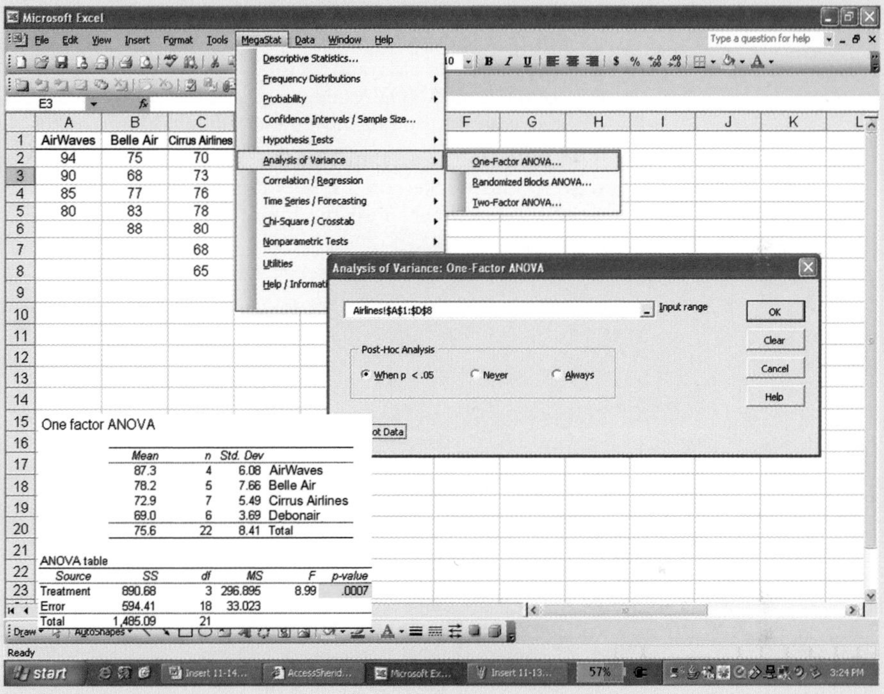

self-review 11–2

Clean All is a new all-purpose cleaner being test marketed by placing displays in three different locations within various supermarkets. The number of 950 ml bottles sold from each location within the supermarket is reported below.

Near the bread	20	15	24	18
Near the beer	12	18	10	15
With other cleaners	25	28	30	32

At the .05 significance level, is there a difference in the mean number of bottles sold at the three locations?

(a) State the null hypothesis and the alternative hypothesis.
(b) What is the decision rule?
(c) Compute the values of SS total, SST, and SSE.
(d) Develop an ANOVA table.
(e) What is your decision regarding the null hypothesis?

Exercises

7. We want to investigate whether there is a difference in the average amount ($00) spent on gardening supplies in the spring for households in various areas of Ottawa. A sample was taken in three communities. Let treatment 1 be the amount spent ($00) by households in Rockcliffe, treatment 2, the amount spent ($00) by households in Nepean, and treatment 3, the amount spent ($00) by households in Gloucester. Test the hypothesis that the treatment means are equal. Use the .05 significance level.

Treatment 1	Treatment 2	Treatment 3
$8	$3	$3
6	2	4
10	4	5
9	3	4

   a. State the null hypothesis and the alternative hypothesis.
   b. What is the decision rule?
   c. Compute SST, SSE, and SS total.
   d. Complete an ANOVA table.
   e. State your decision regarding the null hypothesis.

8. The following is a sample of the approximate hourly wages of servers, waiters, and head waiters who worked on a cruise ship travelling from Los Angeles to Mexico during the last week of December. Test the hypothesis at the .05 significance level that the hourly wages are equal.

Servers	Waiters	Head Waiters
$9	$13	$10
7	20	9
11	14	15
9	13	14
12		15
10		

   a. State the null hypothesis and the alternative hypothesis.
   b. What is the decision rule?
   c. Compute SST, SSE, and SS total.
   d. Complete an ANOVA table.
   e. State your decision regarding the null hypothesis.

9. A real estate developer is considering investing in a shopping mall. Three parcels of land are being evaluated. Of particular importance is the income in the area surrounding the proposed mall. A random sample of four families is selected near each proposed mall. Following are the sample results. At the .05 significance level, can the developer conclude there is a difference in the mean income? Use the usual five-step hypothesis testing procedure.

Area 1 ($ thousands)	Area 2 ($ thousands)	Area 3 ($ thousands)
$64	$74	$75
68	71	80
70	69	76
60	70	78

10. The manager of a computer software company wishes to study the number of hours top executives spend at their computer terminals by type of industry. The manager selected a sample of five executives from each of three industries. At the .05 significance level, can she conclude there is a difference in the mean number of hours spent at a terminal per week by industry?

Banking	Retail	Insurance
12	8	10
10	8	8
10	6	6
12	8	8
10	10	10

6 Develop confidence intervals for the difference in treatment means.

Inferences about Pairs of Treatment Means

Suppose we carry out the ANOVA procedure and make the decision to reject the null hypothesis. This allows us to conclude that two or more treatment means are not the same. Sometimes we may be satisfied with this conclusion, but in other instances we may want to know which treatment means differ. This section provides the details for such a test.

Recall that in the example regarding the airlines there was a difference in the treatment means. That is, the null hypothesis was rejected and the alternative hypothesis accepted. If the passenger ratings do differ, the question is: Between which groups do the treatment means differ?

Several procedures are available to answer this question. The simplest is through the use of confidence intervals, that is, formula (8–2). From the computer output of the previous example, note that the sample mean score for AirWaves is 87.25, and for Debonair is 69.00. Is there enough disparity to justify the conclusion that there is a significant difference in the mean satisfaction scores of the two airlines?

The t distribution, described in Chapters 8, 9, and 10, is used as the basis for this test. Recall that one of the assumptions of ANOVA is that the population variances are the same for all treatments. This common population value is the **mean square error**, or MSE, and is determined by SSE/$(n - k)$. A confidence interval for the difference between two populations is found by:

CONFIDENCE INTERVAL FOR THE DIFFERENCE IN TREATMENT MEANS

$$(\bar{X}_1 - \bar{X}_2) \pm t\sqrt{\text{MSE}\left(\frac{1}{n_1} + \frac{1}{n_2}\right)} \qquad \textbf{[11–5]}$$

where:

$\bar{X}_1$ is the mean of the first sample.
$\bar{X}_2$ is the mean of the second sample.
t is obtained from Appendix F. The degrees of freedom is equal to $n - k$.
MSE is the mean square error term obtained from the ANOVA table [SSE/$(n - k)$].
n_1 is the number of observations in the first sample.
n_2 is the number of observations in the second sample.

How do we decide whether there is a difference in the treatment means? If the confidence interval includes zero, there is *not* a difference between the treatment means. For example, if the left endpoint of the confidence interval has a negative sign and the right endpoint has a positive sign, the interval includes zero and the two means do not differ. So, if we develop a confidence interval from formula (11–5) and find the difference in the sample means was 5.00, the confidence interval would range from −7.00 up to 17, that is, if

$$\bar{X}_1 - \bar{X}_2 = 5 \text{ and } t\sqrt{\text{MSE}\left(\frac{1}{n_1} + \frac{1}{n_2}\right)} = 12$$

To put it in symbols:

$$(\bar{X}_1 - \bar{X}_2) \pm t\sqrt{\text{MSE}\left(\frac{1}{n_1} + \frac{1}{n_2}\right)} = 5.00 \pm 12.00 = -7.00 \text{ up to } 17.00$$

Note that zero is included in this interval. Therefore, we conclude that there is no significant difference in the selected treatment means.

On the other hand, if the endpoints of the confidence interval have the same sign, this indicates that the treatment means differ. For example, the confidence interval would range from −0.60 up to −0.10, if,

$$\bar{X}_1 - \bar{X}_2 = -0.35 \text{ and } t\sqrt{\text{MSE}\left(\frac{1}{n_1} + \frac{1}{n_2}\right)} = 0.25$$

Because −0.60 and −0.10 have the same sign, both negative, we conclude that these treatment means differ.

Using the previous airline example, let us compute the confidence interval for the difference between the mean scores of passengers on AirWaves and Debonair airlines. With a 95 percent level of confidence, the endpoints of the confidence interval are 10.46 and 26.04.

$$(\bar{X}_1 - \bar{X}_4) \pm t\sqrt{\text{MSE}\left(\frac{1}{n_1} + \frac{1}{n_4}\right)} = (87.25 - 69.00) \pm 2.101\sqrt{33.0\left(\frac{1}{4} + \frac{1}{6}\right)}$$
$$= 18.25 \pm 7.79$$

where:

$\bar{X}_1$ is 87.25.
$\bar{X}_4$ is 69.00.
t is 2.101: from Appendix F with $(n - k) = 22 - 4 = 18$ degrees of freedom.
MSE is 33.0: from the ANOVA table with $\text{SSE}/(n - k) = 594.4/18$.
n_1 is 4.
n_4 is 6.

The 95 percent confidence interval ranges from 10.46 up to 26.04. Both endpoints are positive; hence, we can conclude these treatment means differ significantly. That is, passengers on AirWaves rated service significantly different from those on Debonair. Approximate results can also be obtained directly from MINITAB. The output follows.

On the left side is number of observations, the mean, and the standard deviation for each treatment. On the right side are the confidence intervals for each treatment mean. We can get an idea of where the treatment means differ by examining the confidence intervals. The asterisk (*) indicates the location of the treatment mean and the open and close parantheses are the endpoints of the confidence intervals. Where the intervals overlap, the treatment means may not differ. If there is no common area in the confidence intervals, that pair of means likely differs.

```
                        Individual 95% CIs For Mean Based on Pooled St Dev

Level         N    Mean    StDev     +---------+---------+---------+---------
AirWaves      4   87.250   6.076                          (-------*-------)
Belle Air     5   78.200   7.662                 (-------*------)
Cirrus        7   72.857   5.490           (-----*-----)
Debonair      4   69.000   3.688     (-----*------)
                                     +---------+---------+---------+---------
                                    64.0      72.0      80.0      88.0

Pooled StDev = 5.747
```

The endpoints of the 95 percent confidence interval for the mean passenger scores for Cirrus Airlines are about 69 and 77. For Debonair the endpoints of the 95 percent confidence interval for the mean passenger score are about 64 and 73. There is a common area between these points, so we can conclude that this pair probably does not differ. In other words, there is no significant difference between the mean passenger ratings for Cirrus Airlines and Debonair. The differences in the mean scores are due to chance.

There appear to be two pairs of means that differ. The mean scores of passengers on AirWaves are significantly different from the mean of ratings of passengers on Cirrus Airlines and Debonair. There is no common area between these two pairs of confidence intervals.

self-review 11–3

The following data are the tuition charges in thousands of dollars for a sample of private high schools in various regions of Canada. At the .05 significance level, can we conclude there is a difference in the mean tuition rates for the various regions?

East ($ thousands)	Central ($ thousands)	West ($ thousands)
$20	$18	$17
21	19	18
22	20	16
20	18	17
22		16

(a) State the null and the alternative hypotheses.
(b) What is the decision rule?
(c) Develop an ANOVA table. What is the value of the test statistic?
(d) What is your decision regarding the null hypothesis?
(e) Could there be a significant difference between the mean tuition in the East and that of the West? If so, develop a 95 percent confidence interval for that difference.

Exercises

11. Given the following sample information, test the hypothesis that the treatment means are equal at the .05 significance level.

Treatment 1	Treatment 2	Treatment 3
8	3	3
11	2	4
10	1	5
	3	4
	2	

a. State the null hypothesis and the alternative hypothesis.
b. What is the decision rule?
c. Compute SST, SSE, and SS total.
d. Complete an ANOVA table.
e. State your decision regarding the null hypothesis.
f. If H_0 is rejected, can we conclude that treatment 1 and treatment 2 differ? Use the 95 percent level of confidence.

12. Given the following sample information, test the hypothesis that the treatment means are equal at the .05 significance level.

Treatment 1	Treatment 2	Treatment 3
3	9	6
2	6	3
5	5	5
1	6	5
3	8	5
1	5	4
	4	1
	7	5
	6	
	4	

a. State the null hypothesis and the alternative hypothesis.
b. What is the decision rule?
c. Compute SST, SSE, and SS total.
d. Complete an ANOVA table.

e. State your decision regarding the null hypothesis.
f. If H_0 is rejected, can we conclude that treatment 2 and treatment 3 differ? Use the 95 percent level of confidence.

13. A senior accounting major has job offers from four CGA firms. To explore the offers further, she asked a sample of recent trainees how many months each worked for the firm before receiving a raise in salary. The sample information follows:

Analysis of Variance

Source	DF	SS	MS	F	P
Factor	3	32.33	10.78	2.36	0.133
Error	10	45.67	4.57		
Total	13	78.00			

At the .05 level of significance, is there a difference in the mean number of months before a raise was granted among the four CGA firms?

14. A stock analyst wants to determine whether there is a difference in the mean rate of return for three types of stock: utility, retail, and banking stocks. The following output is obtained:

Analysis of Variance

Source	DF	SS	MS	F	P
Factor	2	86.49	43.25	13.09	0.001
Error	13	42.95	3.30		
Total	15	129.44			

a. Using the .05 level of significance, is there a difference in the mean rate of return among the three types of stock?
b. Suppose the null hypothesis is rejected. Can the analyst conclude there is a difference between the mean rates of return for the utility and the retail stocks? Explain.

Chapter Summary

I. The characteristics of the F distribution are:
- **A.** It is continuous.
- **B.** Its values cannot be negative.
- **C.** It is positively skewed.
- **D.** There is a family of F distributions. Each time the degrees of freedom in either the numerator or the denominator changes, a new distribution is created.

II. The F distribution is used to test whether two population variances are the same.
- **A.** The sampled populations must be normal.
- **B.** The larger of the two sample variances is placed in the numerator, forcing the ratio to be at least 1.00.
- **C.** The value of F is computed using the following equation:

$$F = \frac{s_1^2}{s_2^2}, \; s_1^2 > s_2^2 \qquad [11\text{–}1]$$

III. A one-way ANOVA is used to compare several treatment means.
- **A.** A treatment is a source of variation.
- **B.** The assumptions underlying ANOVA are:
  1. The samples are from populations that follow a normal distribution.
  2. The populations have equal standard deviations.
  3. The samples are from independent populations.
- **C.** The information for finding the value of F is summarized in an ANOVA table.
  1. The formula for SS total, the sum of squares total, is:

$$\text{SS total} = \Sigma(X - \bar{X}_G)^2 \qquad [11\text{–}2]$$

2. The SSE, the sum of squares error, is:

$$\text{SSE} = \Sigma(X - \bar{X}_c)^2 \quad [11\text{–}3]$$

3. The formula for the SST, the sum of squares treatment, is:

$$\text{SST} = \text{SS total} - \text{SSE} \quad [11\text{–}4]$$

4. This information is summarized in the following table and the value of F determined.

Source of Variation	Sum of Squares	Degrees of Freedom	Mean Square	F
Treatments	SST	$k - 1$	MST = SST/(k − 1)	MST/MSE
Error	SSE	$n - k$	MSE = SSE/(n − k)	
Total	SS total	$n - 1$		

IV. If a null hypothesis of equal treatment means is rejected, we can identify the pairs that differ from the following confidence interval.

$$(\bar{X}_1 - \bar{X}_2) \pm t\sqrt{\text{MSE}\left(\frac{1}{n_1} + \frac{1}{n_2}\right)} \quad [11\text{–}5]$$

Pronunciation Key

SYMBOL	MEANING	PRONUNCIATION
SS total	Sum of squares total	*S S total*
SST	Sum of squares treatment	*S S T*
SSE	Sum of squares error	*S S E*
T_c^2	Column totals squared	*T sub c squared*
n_c	Number of observations in each treatment	*n sub c*
MSE	Mean square error	*M S E*

Chapter Exercises

15. A real estate agent in Northern Ontario wants to compare the variation in the selling price of homes on waterfronts with those one to three blocks from the water. A sample of 21 waterfront homes sold within the last year revealed the standard deviation of the selling prices was \$45 600. A sample of 18 homes, also sold within the last year, that were one to three blocks from the water, revealed that the standard deviation was \$21 330. At the .01 significance level, can we conclude that there is more variation in the selling prices of the waterfront homes?

16. A computer manufacturer is about to unveil a new, faster personal computer. The new machine clearly is faster, but initial tests indicate there is more variation in the processing time. The processing time depends on the particular program being run, the amount of input data, and the amount of output. A sample of 16 computer runs, covering a range of production jobs, showed that the standard deviation of the processing time was 22 (hundredths of a second) for the new machine and 12 (hundredths of a second) for the current machine. At the .05 significance level, can we conclude that there is more variation in the processing time of the new machine?

17. There are two Chevrolet dealers in Jamestown. The mean weekly sales at Sharkey Chevy and Dave White Chevrolet are about the same. However, Tom Sharkey, the owner of Sharkey Chevy, believes his sales are more consistent. Below is the number of new cars sold at Sharkey in the last seven months and for the last eight months at Dave White. Do you agree with Mr. Sharkey? Use the .01 significance level.

Sharkey	98	78	54	57	68	64	70	
Dave White	75	81	81	30	82	46	58	101

18. Random samples of five were selected from each of three populations. The sum of squares total was 100. The sum of squares due to the treatments was 40.
   a. Set up the null hypothesis and the alternative hypothesis.
   b. What is the decision rule? Use the .05 significance level.
   c. Complete the ANOVA table. What is the value of F?
   d. What is your decision regarding the null hypothesis?

19. In an ANOVA table, MSE was equal to 10. Random samples of six were selected from each of four populations, where the sum of squares total was 250.
   a. Set up the null hypothesis and the alternative hypothesis.
   b. What is the decision rule? Use the .05 significance level.
   c. Complete the ANOVA table. What is the value of F?
   d. What is your decision regarding the null hypothesis?

20. The following is a partial ANOVA table.

Source	Sum of Squares	*df*	Mean Square	*F*
Treatment		2		
Error			20	
Total	500	11		

Complete the table and answer the following questions. Use the .05 significance level.
   a. How many treatments are there?
   b. What is the total sample size?
   c. What is the critical value of F?
   d. Write out the null and alternative hypotheses.
   e. What is your conclusion regarding the null hypothesis?

21. A consumer organization wants to know whether there is a difference in the price of a particular toy at three different types of stores. The price of the toy was checked in a sample of five discount stores, five variety stores, and five department stores. The results are shown below. Use the .05 significance level.

Discount	Variety	Department
$12	$15	$19
13	17	17
14	14	16
12	18	20
15	17	19

22. A physician who specializes in weight control has three different diets she recommends. As an experiment, she randomly selected 15 patients and then assigned 5 to each diet. After three months the following weight losses, in kg, were noted. At the .05 significance level, can she conclude that there is a difference in the mean amount of weight loss among the three diets?

Plan A	Plan B	Plan C
5	6	7
7	7	8
4	7	9
5	5	8
4	6	9

23. The City of Maumee comprises four districts. Chief of Police Andy North wants to determine whether there is a difference in the mean number of crimes committed among the four districts. He recorded the number of crimes reported in each district for a sample of six days. At the .05 significance level, can the chief of police conclude there is a difference in the mean number of crimes?

Number of Crimes			
Rec Centre	**Key Street**	**Monclova**	**Whitehouse**
13	21	12	16
15	13	14	17
14	18	15	18
15	19	13	15
14	18	12	20
15	19	15	18

24. A study of the effect of television commercials on 12-year-old children measured their attention span, in seconds. The commercials were for clothes, food, and toys. At the .05 significance level, is there a difference in the mean attention span of the children for the various commercials? Are there significant differences between pairs of means? Would you recommend dropping one of the three commercial types?

Clothes	Food	Toys
26	45	60
21	48	51
43	43	43
35	53	54
28	47	63
31	42	53
17	34	48
31	43	58
20	57	47
	47	51
	44	51
	54	

a. At the .05 level, can it be concluded that there is a difference in the three mean scores?
b. If the null hypothesis is rejected, can you state that the mean score of those with a rural background is different from the score of those with a large-city background?

25. It can be shown that when only two treatments are involved, ANOVA and the Student t test (Chapter 9) result in the same conclusions. Also, $t^2 = F$. As an example, suppose that 14 randomly selected college students were divided into two groups, one consisting of six students and the other of eight. One group was taught using a combination of lecture and programmed instruction, the other using a combination of lecture and television. At the end of the course, each group was given a 50-item test. The following is a list of the number correct for each of the two groups.

Lecture and Programmed Instruction	Lecture and Television
19	32
17	28
23	31
22	26
17	23
16	24
	27
	25

a. Using analysis of variance techniques, test H_0 that the two mean test scores are equal; $\alpha = .05$.
b. Using the t test from Chapter 9, compute t.
c. Interpret the results.

26. One reads that a business school graduate with a college diploma or an undergraduate degree earns more than a high school graduate with no additional education, and a person with a master's degree or a doctorate earns even more. To test this, a random sample of 25 executives from companies with assets over $1 million was selected. Their incomes, classified by highest level of education, follow.

Income ($ thousands)		
High School or Less	College Diploma or Undergraduate Degree	Master's Degree or More
$45	$49	$51
47	57	73
53	85	82
62	73	59
39	81	94
43	84	89
54	89	89
	92	95
	62	73

Test at the .05 level of significance that there is no difference in the arithmetic mean salaries of the three groups. If the null hypothesis is rejected, conduct further tests to determine which groups differ.

27. There are four auto body shops in Shell River, Manitoba and all claim to promptly serve customers. To check if there is any difference in service, customers are randomly selected from each repair shop and their waiting times in days are recorded. The output from a statistical software package is:

Summary

Groups	Count	Sum	Average	Variance
Body Shop A	3	15.4	5.133333	0.323333
Body Shop B	4	32	8	1.433333
Body Shop C	5	25.2	5.04	0.748
Body Shop D	4	25.9	6.475	0.595833

ANOVA

Source of Variation	SS	*df*	MS	*F*	*p*-value
Between Groups	23.37321	3	7.791069	9.612506	0.001632
Within Groups	9.726167	12	0.810514		
Total	33.09938	15			

Is there evidence to suggest a difference in the mean waiting times at the four body shops? Use the .05 significance level.

28. The fuel efficiencies for a sample of 27 compact, midsize, and large cars are entered into a statistical software package. In order to test whether there is a difference among the mean fuel efficiencies for the three car types, an analysis of variance is computed. What do you conclude? Use the .01 significance level.

Summary

Groups	Count	Sum	Average	Variance
Compact	12	268.3	22.35833	9.388106
Midsize	9	172.4	19.15556	7.315278
Large	6	100.5	16.75	7.303

ANOVA

Source of Variation	SS	*df*	MS	*F*	*p*-value
Between Groups	136.4803	2	68.24014	8.258752	0.001866
Within Groups	198.3064	24	8.262766		
Total	334.7867	26			

29. Three assembly lines are used to produce a certain component for an airliner. To examine the production rate, a random sample of six hourly periods is chosen for each assembly line and the number of components produced during these periods for each line is recorded. The output from a statistical software package is:

Summary

Groups	Count	Sum	Average	Variance
Line A	6	250	41.66667	0.266667
Line B	6	260	43.33333	0.666667
Line C	6	249	41.5	0.7

ANOVA

Source of Variation	SS	*df*	MS	*F*	*p*-value
Between Groups	12.33333	2	6.166667	11.32653	0.001005
Within Groups	8.166667	15	0.544444		
Total	20.5	17			

a. Use a .01 level of significance to test if there is a difference in the mean production of the three assembly lines.
b. Develop a 99 percent confidence interval for the difference in the means between Line B and Line C.

30. A grocery store wants to monitor the amount of withdrawals that its customers make from automatic teller machines (ATMs) located within its stores. It samples 10 withdrawals from each location and the output from a statistical software package is:

Summary

Groups	Count	Sum	Average	Variance
Location X	10	825	82.5	1808.056
Location Y	10	540	54	921.1111
Location Z	10	382	38.2	1703.733

ANOVA

Source of Variation	SS	*df*	MS	*F*	*p*-value
Between Groups	10081.27	2	5040.633	3.411288	0.047766
Within Groups	39896.1	27	1477.633		
Total	49977.37	29			

a. Use a .01 level of significance to test if there is a difference in the mean amount of money withdrawn.
b. Develop a 90 percent confidence interval for the difference in the means between Location X and Location Z.

31. Listed below are the masses (in grams) of a sample of M&M's Plain candies, classified according to colour. Use statistical software to determine whether there is a difference in the mean masses of candies of different colours. Use the .05 significance level.

Red	Orange	Yellow	Brown	Tan	Green
0.946	0.902	0.929	0.896	0.845	0.935
1.107	0.943	0.960	0.888	0.909	0.903
0.913	0.916	0.938	0.906	0.873	0.865
0.904	0.910	0.933	0.941	0.902	0.822
0.926	0.903	0.932	0.838	0.956	0.871
0.926	0.901	0.899	0.892	0.959	0.905
1.006	0.919	0.907	0.905	0.916	0.905
0.914	0.901	0.906	0.824	0.822	0.852
0.922	0.930	0.930	0.908		0.965
1.052	0.883	0.952	0.833		0.898
0.903		0.939			
0.895		0.940			
		0.882			
		0.906			

32. There are four radio stations in Midland. The stations have different formats (hard rock, classical, country/western, and easy listening), but each is concerned with the number of minutes of music played per hour. From a sample of 10 hours from each station, the following sample means were offered.

$$\bar{X}_1 = 51.43 \quad \bar{X}_2 = 44.64 \quad \bar{X}_3 = 47.2 \quad \bar{X}_4 = 50.85$$

$$\text{SS total} = 650.75$$

a. Determine SST.
b. Determine SSE.
c. Complete an ANOVA table.
d. At the .05 significance level, is there a difference in the treatment means?
e. Is there a difference in the mean amount of music time between station 1 and station 4? Use the .05 significance level.

Data Set Exercises

33. Refer to the real estate data, from the south-east area of Edmonton, on the CD-ROM, which reports information on listed homes, January 2008.
   a. At the .05 significance level, is there a difference in the variability of the mean list prices of the homes that are bungalows, two storeys, bi-levels, four level splits, or 2½ storeys?
   b. At the .05 significance level, is there a difference in the variability of the mean list prices of the homes with more than three bedrooms?
   c. At the .05 significance level, is there a difference in the variability of list price of the homes with less than 1500 square feet?

34. Refer to the CREA (Canadian Real Estate Association) data on the CD-ROM, which reports information on average house prices nationally and in a selection of cities across Canada. At the .05 significance level, is there a difference in the variation in the list prices between July 2008 and July 2007? Select the cities only.

35. Refer to the data found on the CD-ROM in the file Gasoline Prices.
   a. Using the data from June 2004 to June 2008, compare the gasoline prices for Winnipeg, Calgary, and Saskatoon. At the .05 significance level, can we conclude that there is a difference in the average gasoline prices?
   b. Using the data from June 2004 to June 2008, compare the gasoline prices for Halifax, Nova Scotia; Calgary, Alberta; and Saint John, New Brunswick. At the .01 significance level, can we conclude that there is a difference in the average gasoline prices?
   c. Using the data from June 2004 to June 2008, compare the gasoline prices for Toronto, Vancouver and Montreal. At the .05 significance level, can we conclude that gasoline prices are different in the three cities?

36. Refer to the International data, which reports demographic and economic information on 46 countries. Conduct a test of hypothesis to determine whether the mean percent of the population over 65 years of age in G-20 countries is different from those that are not G-20 countries.

exercises.com

Additional exercises that require you to access information at related Internet sites are available on the CD-ROM included with this text.

Answers to Self-Reviews

11–1 Let Mark's assemblies be population 1, then $H_0: \sigma_1^2 \leq \sigma_2^2$; $H_1: \sigma_1^2 > \sigma_2^2$; $df_1 = 10 - 1 = 9$; and df_2 also equals 9. H_0 is rejected if $F > 3.18$.

$$F = \frac{(2.0)^2}{(1.5)^2} = 1.78.$$

H_0 is not rejected. The variation is the same for both employees.

11–2 (a) H_0: $\mu_1 = \mu_2 = \mu_3$.
H_1: At least one treatment mean is different.

(b) Reject H_0 if $F > 4.26$.

(c) $\text{SS total} = 5651 - \frac{(247)^2}{12} = 566.92.$

$\text{SST} = \frac{(77)^2}{4} + \frac{(55)^2}{4} + \frac{(115)^2}{4} - \frac{(247)^2}{12}$

$= 460.67.$

$\text{SSE} = 566.92 - 460.67 = 106.25.$

(d)

Source	Sum of Squares	Degrees of Freedom	Mean Square	F
Treatment	460.67	2	230.335	19.510
Error	106.25	9	11.806	

(e) H_0 is rejected. There is a difference in the mean number of bottles sold at the various locations.

11–3 (a) H_0: $\mu_1 = \mu_2 = \mu_3$.

H_1: Not all means are equal.

(b) H_0 is rejected if $F > 3.98$.

(c) $\text{SS total} = 5032 - \frac{(264)^2}{14} = 53.71.$

$\text{SST} = \frac{(105)^2}{5} + \frac{(75)^2}{4} + \frac{(84)^2}{5}$

$- \frac{(264)^2}{14} = 44.16.$

$\text{SSE} = 53.71 - 44.16 = 9.55.$

Source	Sum of Squares	df	Mean Square	F
Treatment	44.16	2	22.08	25.43
Error	9.55	11	0.8682	
Total	53.71	13		

(d) H_0 is rejected. The treatment means differ.

(e) $(21.0 - 16.8) \pm 2.201\sqrt{0.8682\left(\frac{1}{5} + \frac{1}{5}\right)}$

$= 4.2 \pm 1.30 = 2.90$ and 5.50.

These treatment means differ because both endpoints of the confidence interval are of the same sign—positive in this problem.

chapter 12

Linear Regression and Correlation

LEARNING GOALS

When you have completed this chapter, you will be able to:

1. Draw a *scatter diagram*.
2. Understand and interpret the terms *dependent variable* and *independent variable*.
3. Calculate a least squares regression line.
4. Construct and interpret confidence intervals and prediction intervals for the dependent variable.
5. Calculate and interpret the *coefficient of correlation*, the *coefficient of determination*, and the *standard error of estimate*.
6. Conduct a test of hypothesis to determine whether the coefficient of correlation in the population is zero.
7. Interpret an ANOVA table.

Introduction

Chapters 2 and 3 dealt with *descriptive statistics*. We organized raw data into a frequency distribution and computed several measures of location and measures of dispersion to describe the major characteristics of the data. Chapter 4 started the study of *statistical inference*. The main emphasis was on inferring something about a population parameter, such as the population mean on the basis of a sample. We tested for the reasonableness of a population mean or a population proportion, the difference between two population means, or whether several population means were equal. All of these tests involved just *one* interval- or ratio-level variable, such as the mean cost to process a claim, the income of female stockbrokers, or the difference in checkout time between customers using standard checkouts or a self-checkout system.

In this chapter, we shift our emphasis to the study of two variables. That is, we develop numerical measures to express the relationship between the two variables. Is the relationship strong or weak, is it direct or inverse? In addition, we develop an equation to express the relationship between the variables. This equation will allow us to estimate one variable on the basis of the other. Here are some examples:

- Is there a strong relationship between the amount The Bay spends per month on advertising and the sales in the month?
- Can we estimate the cost to heat a home in January based on the number of square feet in the home?
- Is there a relationship between the number of hours that a student studied for an exam and the score earned?

Note in each of these cases there are two variables observed for each sampled observation. For the last example, we find, for each student selected for the sample, the hours studied and the score earned.

We begin this chapter by looking at a chart designed to portray the relationship between two variables: a **scatter diagram**. We continue our study by developing a mathematical equation that will allow us to estimate the value of one variable based on the value of another. This is called **regression analysis**. We will (1) determine the equation of the line that best fits the data, (2) estimate the value of one variable based on another, (3) measure the error in our estimate, and (4) establish confidence and prediction intervals for our estimate. Then, we examine the meaning and purpose of **correlation analysis**.

1 Draw a *scatter diagram*.

Describing the Relationship between Two Variables

As we discussed earlier, there are situations where we wish to study and visually portray the relationship between two variables. When we study the relationship between two variables we refer to the data as **bivariate**. One graphical technique we use to show this relationship is called a scatter diagram.

scatter diagram A chart that portrays the relationship between two variables.

To draw a scatter diagram we need two variables. We scale one variable along the horizontal axis (X-axis) of a graph and the other variable along the vertical (Y-axis). Determining the variables is based on a hunch that one variable depends to some degree on the other. In our first example, it is very likely that the monthly sales of a company depends on advertising. So, we would scale the amount spent on advertising on the horizontal axis and that of sales on the vertical axis.

Following are three scatter diagrams (Chart 12–1). The one on the left shows a rather strong positive relationship between the age in years and the maintenance cost last year for a sample of 10 buses owned by the city of Miramichi. Note that as the age of the bus increases, generally, the yearly maintenance cost also increases. The example in the centre, for a sample of 20 vehicles, shows a rather strong indirect (inverse) relationship between the odometer reading and the selling price of the car. That is, as the number of kilometres driven increases, generally, the selling price decreases. The example on the right depicts the relationship between the height and yearly salary for a sample of 15 shift supervisors. This graph indicates there is little, if any, relationship between their height and yearly salary.

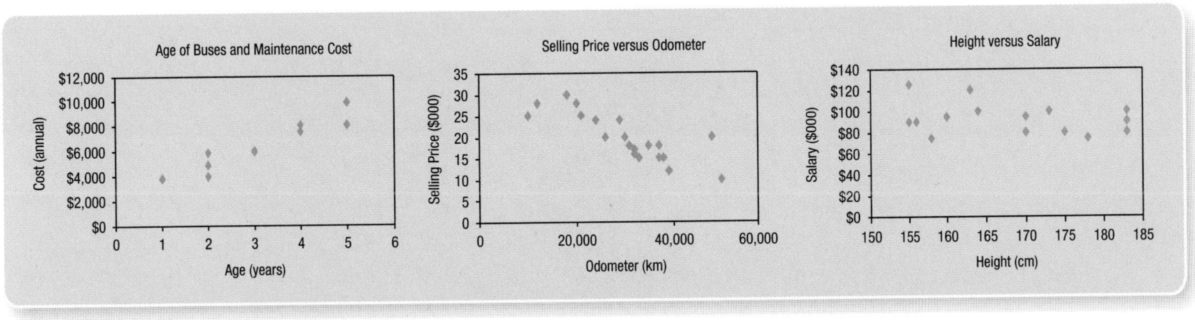

CHART 12–1 Three Examples of Scatter Diagrams

An example will show how a scatter diagram is used.

example

Copier Sales Inc. sells copiers to businesses of all sizes. Ms. Marcy Bancer was recently promoted to the position of national sales manager. At the upcoming sales meeting, the sales representatives from all over the country will be in attendance. She would like to impress upon them the importance of making that extra sales call each day. She decides to gather some information on the relationship between the number of sales calls and the number of copiers sold. She selects a random sample of 10 sales representatives and determines the number of sales calls they made last month and the number of copiers they sold. The sample information is reported in Table 12–1. What observations can you make about the relationship between the number of sales calls and the number of copiers sold? Develop a scatter diagram to display the information.

TABLE 12–1 Sales Calls and Copiers Sold for 10 Sales Representatives

Sales Representative	Number of Sales Calls	Number of Copiers Sold
Tom Keller	20	30
Jeff Hall	40	60
Brian Virost	20	40
Greg Fish	30	60
Susan Welch	10	30
Carlos Ramirez	10	40
Rich Niles	20	40
Mike Kiel	20	50
Mark Reynolds	20	30
Soni Jones	30	70

solution

2 Understand and interpret the terms *dependent variable* and *independent variable*.

independent variable A variable that provides the basis for estimation. It is the predictor variable.

dependent variable The variable that is being predicted or estimated.

Based on the information in Table 12–1, Ms. Bancer suspects there is a relationship between the number of sales calls made in a month and the number of copiers sold. Soni Jones sold the most copiers last month, and she was one of three representatives making 30 or more sales calls. On the other hand, Susan Welch and Carlos Ramirez made only 10 sales calls last month. Ms. Welch was tied with two other individuals for the lowest number of copiers sold among the sampled representatives.

The implication is that the number of copiers sold is related to the number of sales calls made. As the number of sales calls increases, the number of copiers sold also increases. We refer to number of sales calls as the **independent variable** and number of copiers sold as the **dependent variable**.

We will scale the dependent variable (copiers sold) on the vertical or Y-axis and the independent variable (number of sales calls) on the horizontal or X-axis. To develop the scatter diagram of the Copier Sales Inc. sales information, we begin with the first sales representative, Tom Keller. Tom made 20 sales calls last month and sold 30 copiers, so $X = 20$ and $Y = 30$. To plot this point, move along the horizontal axis to $X = 20$, then go vertically to $Y = 30$ and place a dot at the intersection. This process is continued until all the paired data are plotted, as shown in Chart 12–2. Note: only 8 data points show on the graph as 2 sets of data are the same.

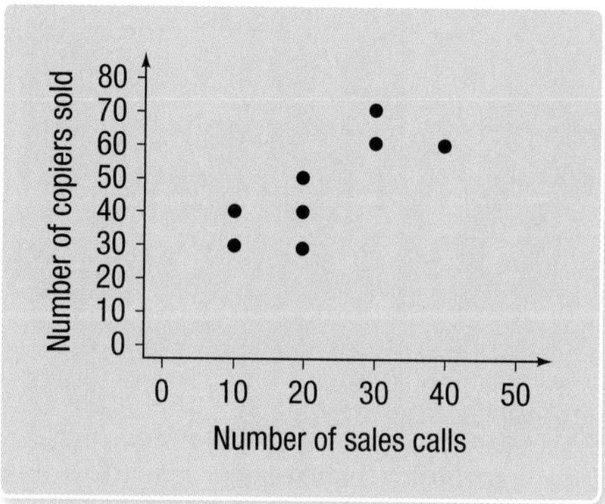

CHART 12–2 Scatter Diagram Showing Sales Calls and Copiers Sold

The scatter diagram shows graphically that the sales representatives who make more calls tend to sell more copiers. It is reasonable for Ms. Bancer, the national sales manager at Copier Sales Inc., to tell her sales representatives that the more sales calls they make, the more copiers they can expect to sell. Note that while there appears to be a positive relationship between the two variables, all the points do not fall on a line. In the following section you will develop an equation to express the relationship between two variables.

self-review 12–1

Reliable Furniture is a family business that has been selling to retail customers in the Oakville area for many years. It advertises extensively on radio and TV, emphasizing its low prices and easy credit terms. The owner would like to review the relationship between sales and the amount spent on advertising. Below is information on sales and advertising expense for the last four months.

Month	Advertising Expense ($ thousands)	Sales Revenue ($ thousands)
July	$2	$7
August	1	3
September	3	8
October	4	10

(a) The owner wants to forecast sales based on advertising expense. Which variable is the dependent variable? Which variable is the independent variable?
(b) Draw a scatter diagram.

Regression Analysis

In the previous section we developed a scatter diagram to depict the relationship between two variables. In this section we wish to develop an equation to express the *linear* (straight line) relationship between two variables. In addition, we want to be able to estimate the value of the dependent variable, Y, based on a selected value of the independent variable, X. The technique used to develop the equation and provide the estimates is called **regression analysis.**

In Table 12–1 we reported the number of sales calls and the number of units sold for a sample of 10 sales representatives employed by Copier Sales Inc. Chart 12–2 portrayed this information in a scatter diagram. The scatter diagram showed that there is a linear relationship between the two variables. Now we want to develop a linear equation that expresses the relationship between the number of sales calls and the number of units sold. The equation for the line used to estimate Y based on X is referred to as the **regression equation.**

regression equation
An equation that defines the linear relationship between two variables.

The scatter diagram in Chart 12–2 is reproduced in Chart 12–3, with a line drawn with a ruler through the dots to illustrate that a straight line would probably fit the data. However, the line drawn using a straight edge has one disadvantage: Its position is based in part on the judgment of the person drawing the line. The hand-drawn lines in Chart 12–4 represent the judgments of four people. All the lines except line A seem to be reasonable. However, each would result in a different estimate of units sold for a particular number of sales calls.

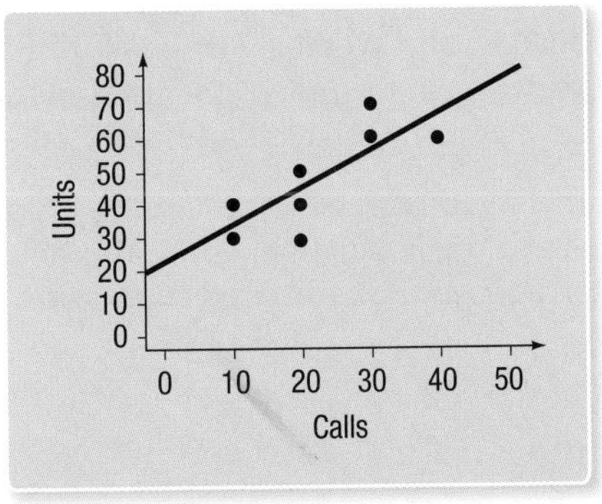

CHART 12–3 Sales Calls and Copiers Sold for 10 Sales Representatives

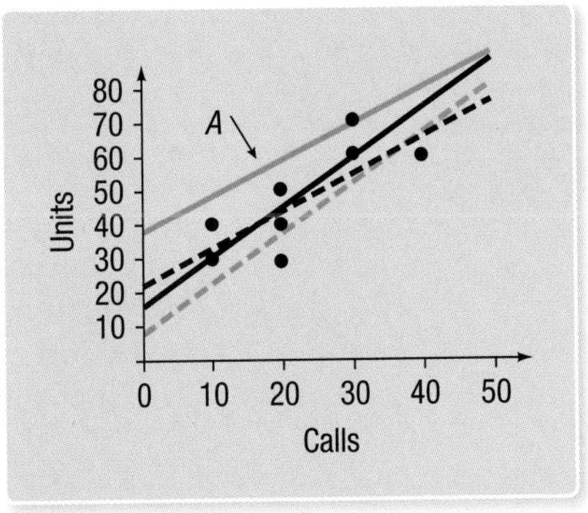

CHART 12–4 Four Lines Superimposed on the Scatter Diagram

3 Calculate a least squares regression line.

Least squares line gives "best" fit; subjective method is unreliable.

least squares principle Determining a regression equation by minimizing the sum of the squares of the vertical distances between the actual Y values and the predicted values of Y.

Least Squares Principle

Judgment is eliminated by determining the regression line using a mathematical method called the **least squares principle**. This method gives what is commonly referred to as the "best-fitting" line.

To illustrate this concept, the same data are plotted in the three charts that follow. The regression line in Chart 12–5 was determined using the least squares method. It is the best-fitting line because the sum of the squares of the vertical deviations about it is at a minimum. The first point ($X = 3$, $Y = 8$) deviates by 2 from the line, found by 10−8. The deviation squared is 4. The squared deviation for the point $X = 4$, $Y = 18$ is 16. The squared deviation for the point $X = 5$, $Y = 16$ is 4. The sum of the squared deviations is 24, found by 4 + 16 + 4.

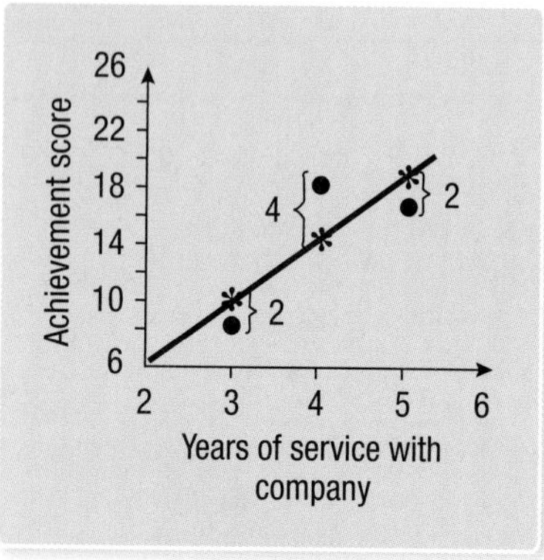

CHART 12–5 The Least Squares Line

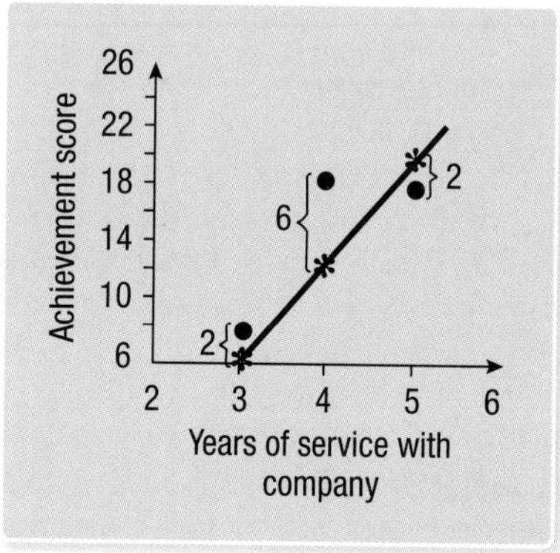

CHART 12–6 Line Drawn Using a Straight Edge

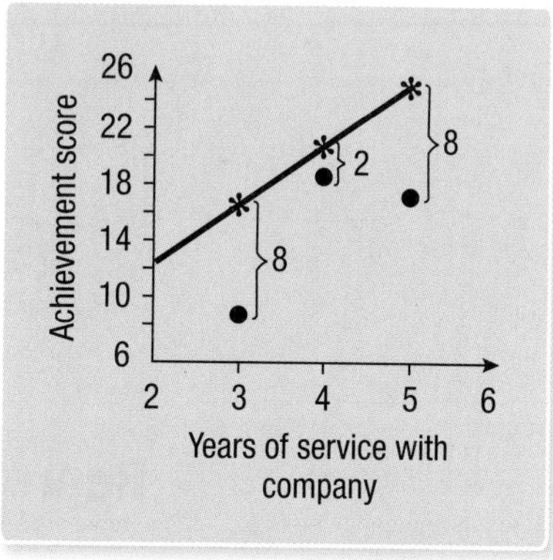

CHART 12–7 Line Drawn Using a Straight Edge

Statistics in Action

Sir Francis Galton compared the heights of parents with the heights of their children. He converted the heights of parents and their children to z-values and noted that the children's z-value deviated less from the mean than did the value for their parents. He called this "regression" toward the mean. This discovery formed the basis of regression analysis.

Assume that the lines in Charts 12–6 and 12–7 were drawn using a straight edge. The sum of the squared vertical deviations in Chart 12–6 is 44. For Chart 12–7 it is 132. Both sums are greater than the sum for the line in Chart 12–5, found using the least squares method.

The equation of a straight line has the form:

GENERAL FORM OF LINEAR REGRESSION EQUATION
$$Y' = a + bX \quad [12\text{–}1]$$

where:

- Y' read Y prime, is the predicted value of the Y variable for a selected X value.
- a is the Y-intercept. It is the estimated value of Y when $X = 0$. Another way to put it is: a is the estimated value of Y where the regression line crosses the Y-axis when X is zero.
- b is the slope of the line, or the average change in Y' for each change of one unit (either increase or decrease) in the independent variable, X.
- X is any value of the independent variable that is selected.

It should be noted that the linear regression equation is just an estimate of the relationship between the two variables in the population. Thus, the values of a and b in the regression equation are usually referred to as the **estimated regression coefficients**, or simply the **regression coefficients**.

The formulas for b and a are:

SLOPE OF THE REGRESSION LINE
$$b = \frac{n(\Sigma XY) - (\Sigma X)(\Sigma Y)}{n(\Sigma X^2) - (\Sigma X)^2} \quad [12\text{–}2]$$

Y-INTERCEPT

$$a = \frac{\Sigma Y}{n} - b\frac{\Sigma X}{n} \qquad [12\text{–}3]$$

where:

ΣX is the sum of the values of the independent variable.
ΣY is the sum of the values of the dependent variable.
n is the number of items in the sample.
ΣXY is the sum of the products of the two variables.
ΣX^2 is the sum of the squares of the independent variable.

example

Recall the example involving Copier Sales Inc. The sales manager gathered information on the number of sales calls made and the number of copiers sold for a random sample of 10 sales representatives. As a part of her presentation at the upcoming sales meeting, Ms. Bancer, the sales manager, would like to offer specific information about the relationship between the number of sales calls and the number of copiers sold. Use the least squares method to determine a linear equation to express the relationship between the two variables. What is the expected number of copiers sold by a representative who makes 20 calls?

solution

Statistics in Action

In finance, investors are interested in the trade-off between returns and risk. One technique to quantify risk is a regression analysis of a company's stock price (dependent variable) and an average measure of the stock market (independent variable). Often the Standard and Poor's (S&P) 500 Index is used to estimate the market. The regression coefficient, called "beta" in finance, shows the change in a company's stock price for a one-unit change in the S&P Index. For example, if a stock has a beta of 1.5, when the S&P index increases by 1 percent, the stock price will increase by 1.5 percent. The opposite is also true. If the S&P decreases by 1 percent, the stock price will increase by 1.5 percent. If the beta is 1.0, then a 1 percent change in the index should show a 1 percent change in a stock price. If the beta is less than 1.0, then a 1 percent change in the index shows less than a 1 percent change in the stock price.

TABLE 12–2 Calculations Needed for Determining the Least Squares Regression Equation

Sales Representative	Sales Calls (X)	Copiers Sold (Y)	X^2	Y^2	XY
Tom Keller	20	30	400	900	600
Jeff Hall	40	60	1600	3600	2400
Brian Virost	20	40	400	1600	800
Greg Fish	30	60	900	3600	1800
Susan Welch	10	30	100	900	300
Carlos Ramirez	10	40	100	1600	400
Rich Niles	20	40	400	1600	800
Mike Kiel	20	50	400	2500	1000
Mark Reynolds	20	30	400	900	600
Soni Jones	30	70	900	4900	2100
Total	220	450	5600	22 100	10 800

Table 12–2 repeats the sample information from Table 12–1. It also includes the sums needed in formulas (12–2) and (12–3) to calculate the regression equation.

The calculations necessary to determine the regression equation are as follows:

$$b = \frac{n(\Sigma XY) - \Sigma X \Sigma Y}{n\Sigma X^2 - n(\Sigma X)^2} = \frac{10(10\,800) - (220)(450)}{10(5600) - (220)^2} = 1.1842$$

$$a = \frac{\Sigma Y}{n} - b\frac{\Sigma X}{n} = \frac{450}{10} - (1.1842)\frac{220}{10} = 18.9476$$

Thus, the regression equation is $Y' = 18.9476 + 1.1842X$. So, if a sales representative makes 20 calls, he or she can expect to sell 42.6316 copiers, found by $Y' = 18.9476 + 1.1842X = 18.9476 + 1.1842(20)$. The b value of 1.1842 means that for each additional sales call made, the sales representative can expect to increase the number of copiers sold by about 1.2. To put it another way, five additional sales calls in a month will result in about six more copiers being sold 1.1842(5) = 5.921.

The a value of 18.9476 is the point where the equation crosses the Y-axis. A literal translation is that if no sales calls are made, that is, $X = 0$, 18.9476 copiers will be sold. Note that $X = 0$ is outside the range of values included in the sample and, therefore, should not be used to estimate the number of copiers sold. The sales calls ranged from 10 to 40, so estimates should be made within that range.

Note that calculators and computer software will provide the regression equation coefficients, *a* and *b*, directly from data.

Drawing the Regression Line

The least squares equation, $Y' = 18.9476 + 1.1842X$, can be drawn on the scatter diagram. The first sales representative in the sample is Tom Keller. He made 20 calls. His estimated number of copiers sold is $Y' = 18.9476 + 1.1842(20) = 42.6316$. The point $X = 20$ and $Y = 42.6316$ is located by moving to 20 on the X-axis and then going vertically to 42.6316. The other points on the regression equation can be determined by substituting the particular value of X into the regression equation.

Sales Representative	Sales Calls (X)	Estimated Sales (Y')	Sales Representative	Sales Calls (X)	Estimated Sales (Y')
Tom Keller	20	42.6316	Carlos Ramirez	10	30.7896
Jeff Hall	40	66.3156	Rich Niles	20	42.6316
Brian Virost	20	42.6316	Mike Kiel	20	42.6316
Greg Fish	30	54.4736	Mark Reynolds	20	42.6316
Susan Welch	10	30.7896	Soni Jones	30	54.4736

All the other points are connected to draw the line. See Chart 12–8.

This line has some interesting features. As we have discussed, there is no other line through the data for which the sum of the squared deviations is smaller. In addition, this line will pass through the points represented by the mean of the X values and the mean of the Y values, that is, $\bar{X}$ and $\bar{Y}$. In this example, $\bar{X} = 22.0$ and $\bar{Y} = 45.0$.

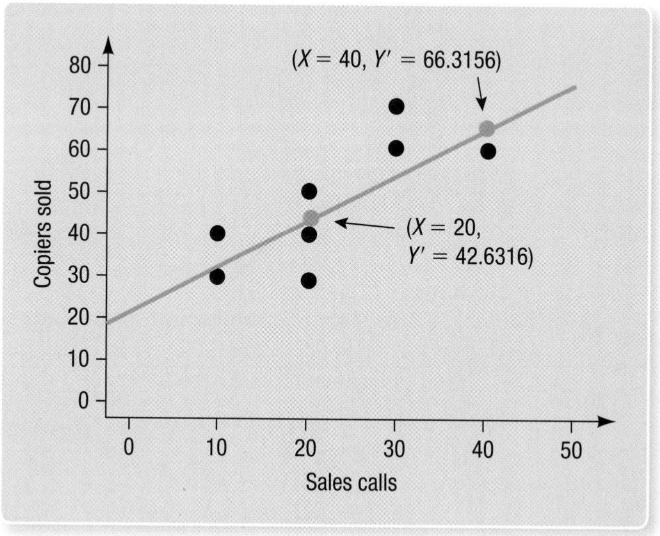

CHART 12–8 The Line of Regression Drawn on the Scatter Diagram

The least squares regression line has some interesting and unique features. First, it will always pass through the point $(\bar{X}, \bar{Y})$. To show this is true, we can use the mean number of sales calls to predict the number of copiers sold. In this example, the mean number of sales calls is 22.0, found by $\bar{X} = \Sigma X/10 = 220/10 = 22.0$. The mean number of copiers sold is 45.0, found by $\bar{Y} = \Sigma Y/10 = 450/10 = 45.0$. If we let $X = 22$ and then use the regression equation to find the estimated value for Y', the result is:

$$Y' = 18.9476 + (1.1842 \times 22) = 45$$

The estimated number of copiers sold is exactly equal to the mean number of copiers sold. This simple example shows the regression line will pass through the point represented by the two means. In this case, the regression equation will pass through the point $\bar{X} = 22$ and $\bar{Y} = 45$.

Second, as we discussed earlier in this section, there is no other line through the data where the sum of the squared deviations is smaller. To put it another way, the term $\Sigma(Y - Y')^2$ is smaller for the least squares regression equation than for any other equation.

Sales Representative	Sales Calls	Units Sold	Estimated Sales	$(Y - Y')$	$(Y - Y')^2$
Tom Keller	20	30	42.6316	−12.6316	159.5573
Jeff Hall	40	60	66.3156	−6.3156	39.8868
Brian Virost	20	40	42.6316	−2.6316	6.9253
Greg Fish	30	60	54.4736	5.5264	30.5411
Susan Welch	10	30	30.7896	−0.7896	0.6235
Carlos Ramirez	10	40	30.7896	9.2104	84.8315
Rich Niles	20	40	42.6316	−2.6316	6.9253
Mike Kiel	20	50	42.6316	7.3684	54.2933
Mark Reynolds	20	30	42.6316	−12.6316	159.5573
Soni Jones	30	70	54.4736	15.5264	241.0691
					784.2105

In the column $(Y - Y')$ above, we calculated the **residuals,** or error values. This is the difference between the actual values and the predicted values. For the last sales representative, Soni Jones, the actual number of units sold is 70. The predicted number of units sold is 54.4736, found by substituting the number of calls (30) into the regression equation as follows:

$$Y' = 18.9476 + (1.1842 \times 30) = 54.4736$$

The residual, or error estimate, is then $(Y - Y') = 15.5264$ $(70 - 54.4736)$. This value reflects the amount the predicted value of sales is "off" from the actual sales value.

The next column squares the residuals for each of the sales representatives and then totals the result. The total is 784.2105. This is the sum of the squared differences or the least squares value. There is no other line through these 10 data points where the sum of the squared differences is smaller.

Excel Paste Function commands to find the slope and y-intercept follow.

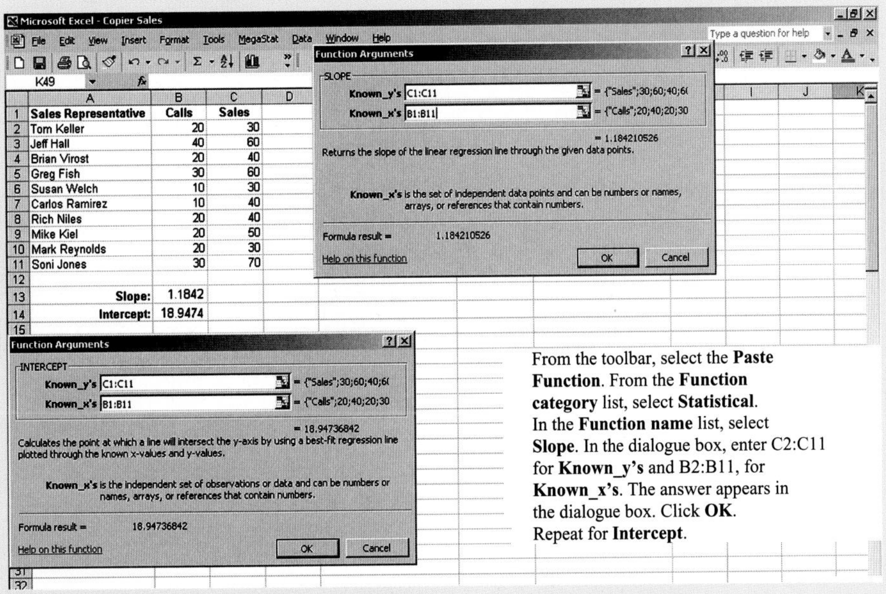

From the toolbar, select the **Paste Function**. From the **Function category** list, select **Statistical**. In the **Function name** list, select **Slope**. In the dialogue box, enter C2:C11 for **Known_y's** and B2:B11, for **Known_x's**. The answer appears in the dialogue box. Click **OK**. Repeat for **Intercept**.

Note: the computer values may be slightly different due to rounding.

Excel commands to create the graph and regression equation follow:

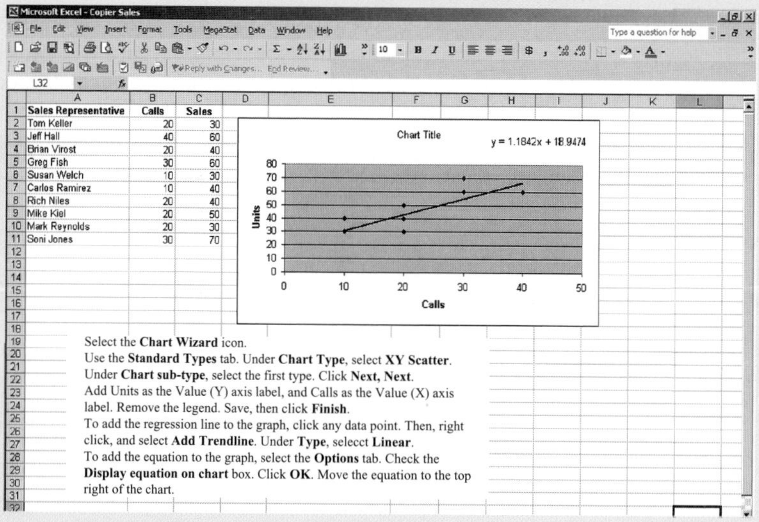

MegaStat steps and output follow.

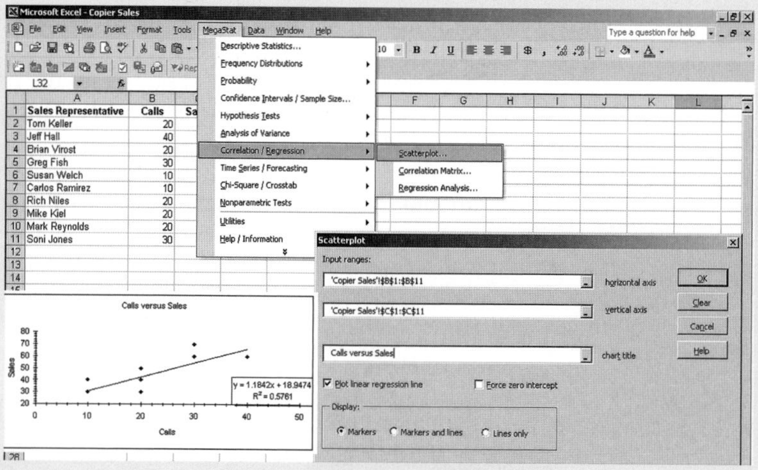

self-review 12–2

Refer to self-review 12–1, where the owner of the Reliable Furniture Company was studying the relationship between sales and the amount spent on advertising. The sales information for the last four months is repeated below.

Month	Advertising Expense ($ thousands)	Sales Revenue ($ thousands)
July	$2	$7
August	1	3
September	3	8
October	4	10

(a) Determine the regression equation.
(b) Interpret the values of a and b.
(c) Estimate sales when $3000 is spent on advertising.

Exercises

Note: It is suggested that you save your values, as these exercises will be referred to later in the chapter.

1. The following sample observations were randomly selected.

X:	4	5	3	6	10
Y:	4	6	5	7	7

   a. Draw a scatter diagram.
   b. Determine the regression equation.
   c. Determine the value of Y' when X is 7.

2. The following sample observations were randomly selected.

X:	5	3	6	3	4	4	6	8
Y:	13	15	7	12	13	11	9	5

   a. Draw a scatter diagram.
   b. Determine the regression equation.
   c. Determine the value of Y' when X is 7.

3. The Bradford Electric Illuminating Company is studying the relationship between kilowatt-hours (thousands) used and the number of rooms in a private single-family residence. A random sample of 10 homes yielded the following.

Number of Rooms	Kilowatt-Hours (thousands)	Number of Rooms	Kilowatt-Hours (thousands)
12	9	8	6
9	7	10	8
14	10	10	10
6	5	5	4
10	8	7	7

   a. Draw a scatter diagram.
   b. Determine the regression equation.
   c. Determine the number of kilowatt-hours, in thousands, for a six-room house.

4. Mr. James McWhinney, president of Daniel-James Financial Services, believes there is a relationship between the number of client contacts and the dollar amount of sales. To document this assertion, Mr. McWhinney gathered the following sample information. The X column indicates the number of client contacts last month, and the Y column shows the value of sales ($ thousands) last month for each client sampled.

Number of Contacts, X	Sales ($ thousands), Y	Number of Contacts, X	Sales ($ thousands), Y
14	$24	23	$30
12	14	48	90
20	28	50	85
16	30	55	120
46	80	50	110

   a. Draw a scatter diagram.
   b. Determine the regression equation.
   c. Determine the estimated sales if 40 contacts are made.

5. In a recent poll concerning sales, earnings, and job creation, 12 companies responded with the following information:

Company	Sales ($ thousands)	Earnings ($ thousands)	Company	Sales ($ thousands)	Earnings ($ thousands)
M Studios	$89.2	$4.9	Armstrong Aircraft	$17.5	$2.6
Marika's Kitchen	18.6	4.4	WWW Snow Removal	11.9	1.7
ABC Tutoring Services	18.2	1.3	Ice Skaters Group	19.6	3.5
Larry's Motorcycles	71.7	8.0	The Knitting Club	51.2	8.2
Comeau Karts	58.6	6.6	Summer Games	28.6	6.0
Marion Florence Jewelry	46.8	4.1	Skiing with Marilyn	69.2	12.8

Let sales be the independent variable and earnings be the dependent variable.
a. Draw a scatter diagram.
b. Determine the regression equation.
c. For a small company with $50.0 thousand in sales, estimate the earnings.

6. We are studying mutual bond funds for the purpose of investing in several funds. For this particular study, we want to focus on the assets of a fund and its five-year performance. The question is: Can the five-year rate of return be estimated based on the assets of the fund? Nine mutual funds were selected at random, and their assets and rates of return are shown below.

Fund	Assets ($ millions)	Return (%)	Fund	Assets ($ millions)	Return (%)
AARP High Quality Bond	$622.2	10.8%	MFS Bond A	$494.5	11.6%
Babson Bond L	160.4	11.3	Nichols Income	158.3	9.5
Compass Capital Fixed Income	275.7	11.4	T. Raive Price Short-term	681.0	8.2
Galaxy Bond Retail	433.2	9.1	Thompson Income B	241.3	6.8
Keystone Custodian B-1	437.9	9.2			

a. Draw a scatter diagram.
b. Determine the regression equation. Use assets as the independent variable.
c. For a fund with $400.0 million in sales, determine the five-year rate of return (in percent).

7. The city council of Pine Bluffs is considering increasing the number of police in an effort to reduce crime. Before making a final decision, the council asks the chief of police to survey other cities of similar size to determine the relationship between the number of police and the number of crimes reported. The chief gathered the following sample information.

City	Police	Number of Crimes	City	Police	Number of Crimes
Oxford	15	17	Holgate	17	7
Starksville	17	13	Carey	12	21
Danville	25	5	Whistler	11	19
Athens	27	7	Woodville	22	6

a. If we went to estimate crimes based on the number of police, which variable is the dependent variable and which is the independent variable?
b. Draw a scatter diagram.
c. Determine the regression equation.
d. Estimate the number of crimes for a city with 20 police.
e. Interpret the regression equation.

8. The owner of Maumee Motors wants to study the relationship between the age of a car and its selling price. Listed below is a random sample of 12 used cars sold at Maumee Motors during the last year.

Car	Age (years)	Selling Price ($ thousands)	Car	Age (years)	Selling Price ($ thousands)
1	9	$8.1	7	8	$7.6
2	7	6.0	8	11	8.0
3	11	3.6	9	10	8.0
4	12	4.0	10	12	6.0
5	8	5.0	11	6	8.6
6	7	10.0	12	6	8.0

a. If we want to estimate selling price based on the age of the car, which variable is the dependent variable and which is the independent variable?
b. Draw a scatter diagram.

c. Determine the regression equation.
d. Estimate the selling price of a 10-year-old car.
e. Interpret the regression equation.

The Standard Error of Estimate

Note in the preceding scatter diagram (Chart 12–8) that all of the points do not lie exactly on the regression line. If they all were on the line, there would be no error in estimating the number of units sold. To put it another way, if all the points were on the regression line, units sold could be predicted with 100 percent accuracy. Thus, there would be no error in predicting the Y variable based on an X variable. This is true in the following hypothetical case (see Chart 12–9). Theoretically, if $X = 4$, then an exact Y of 100 could be predicted with 100 percent confidence. Or if $X = 12$, then $Y = 300$. Because there is no difference between the observed values and the predicted values, there is no error in this estimate.

Perfect prediction unrealistic in business

Perfect prediction in economics and business is practically impossible. For example, the revenue for the year from gasoline sales (Y) based on the number of automobile registrations (X) as of a certain date could no doubt be closely approximated, but the prediction would not be exact to the nearest dollar, or probably even to the nearest thousand dollars. Even predictions of tensile strength of steel wires based on the outside diameters of the wires are not always exact due to slight differences in the composition of the steel.

standard error of estimate A measure of the scatter, or dispersion, of the observed values around the line of regression.

What is needed, then, is a measure that describes how precise the prediction of Y is based on X or, conversely, how inaccurate the estimate might be. This measure is called the **standard error of estimate**. The standard error of estimate, symbolized by S_e, is the same concept as the standard deviation discussed in Chapter 3. The standard deviation measures the dispersion around the mean. The standard error of estimate measures the dispersion about the regression line.

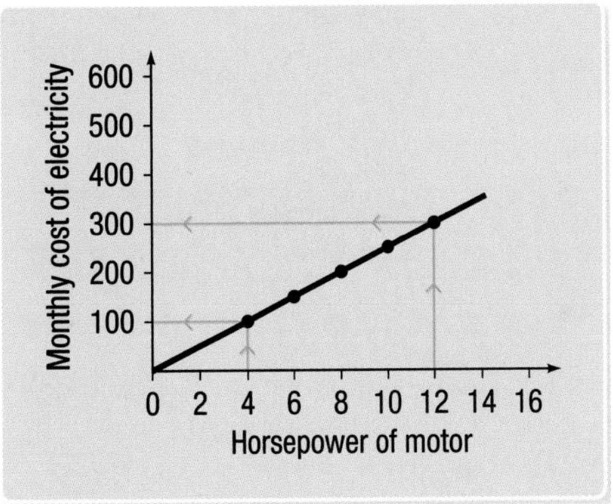

CHART 12–9 Example of Perfect Prediction: Horsepower and Cost of Electricity

The standard error of estimate is found by the following formula (12–4). Note the following important features:

1. It is similar to the standard deviation in that it is based on squared deviations. The numerator of the standard deviation is based on squared deviations from the mean. The numerator of the standard error is based on squared deviations from the regression line.
2. The sum of the squared deviations is the least square value used to find the best fitting regression line. Recall in the previous section we described how to find the least squares value.
3. The denominator of the equation is $n - 2$. As usual, n is the number of sample observations. We lose two degrees of freedom because we are estimating two parameters. So the values of b, the slope of the line, and a, the Y-intercept, are sample values we use to estimate their corresponding population values. We are sampling from a population and are estimating the slope of the line and the intercept with the Y-axis. Hence, the denominator is $n - 2$.

STANDARD ERROR OF ESTIMATE

$$S_e = \sqrt{\frac{\Sigma(Y - Y')^2}{n - 2}} \qquad [12\text{–}4]$$

If S_e is small, this means that the data are relatively close to the regression line and the regression equation can be used to predict Y with little error. If S_e is large, this means that the data are widely scattered around the regression line and the regression equation will not provide a precise estimate Y.

example

Recall the example involving Copier Sales Inc. The sales manager determined the least squares regression equation to be $Y' = 18.9476 + 1.1842X$, where Y' refers to the number of copiers sold and X the number of sales calls made. Determine the standard error of estimate as a measure of how well the values fit the regression line.

solution

To find the standard error, we begin by finding the difference between the value, Y, and the value estimated from the regression equation, Y'. Next we square this difference, that is, $(Y - Y')^2$. We do this for each of the n observations and sum the results. That is, we compute $\Sigma(Y - Y')^2$, which is the numerator of formula (12–4). Finally, we divide by the number of observations minus 2. The details of the calculations are summarized in Table 12–3.

Statistics in Action

Studies indicate that for both men and women, those who are considered good-looking earn higher wages than those who are not. In addition, for men there is a correlation between height and salary. For each additional inch of height, a man can expect to earn an additional \$250 per year. So a man 6′6″ tall receives a \$3000 "stature" bonus over his 5′6″ counterpart. Being overweight or underweight is also related to earnings, particularly among women. A study of young women showed the heaviest 10 percent earned about 6 percent less than their lighter counterparts.

TABLE 12–3 Computations Needed for the Standard Error of Estimate

Sales Representative	Actual Sales (Y)	Estimated Sales (Y')	Deviation ($Y - Y'$)	Deviation Squared ($(Y - Y')^2$)
Tom Keller	30	42.6316	−12.6316	159.557
Jeff Hall	60	66.3156	−6.3156	39.887
Brian Virost	40	42.6316	−2.6316	6.925
Greg Fish	60	54.4736	5.5264	30.541
Susan Welch	30	30.7896	−0.7896	0.623
Carlos Ramirez	40	30.7896	9.2104	84.831
Rich Niles	40	42.6316	−2.6316	6.925
Mike Kiel	50	42.6316	7.3684	54.293
Mark Reynolds	30	42.6316	−12.6316	159.557
Soni Jones	70	54.4736	15.5264	241.069
			0.0000	784.208

The standard error of estimate is 9.901, found by using formula (12–4).

$$S_e = \sqrt{\frac{\Sigma(Y - Y')^2}{n - 2}} = \sqrt{\frac{784.208}{10 - 2}} = 9.901$$

The deviations $(Y - Y')$ are the vertical deviations from the regression line. To illustrate, the 10 deviations from Table 12–3 are shown in Chart 12–10. Note in Table 12–3 that the sum of the signed deviations is zero. This indicates that the positive deviations (above the regression line) are offset by the negative deviations (below the regression line).

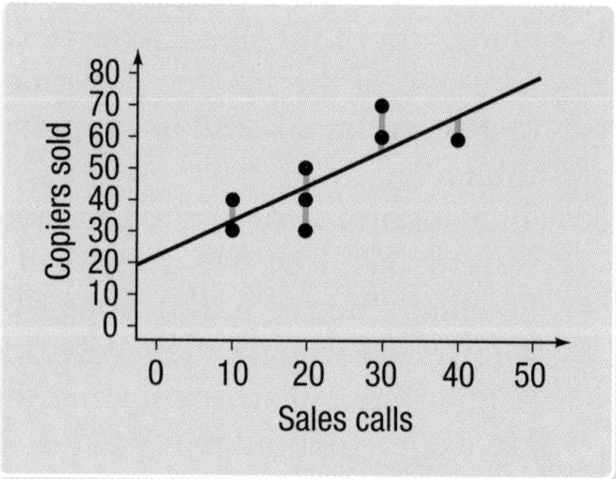

CHART 12–10 Sales Calls and Copiers Sold for 10 Sales Representatives

Formula (12–4) for the standard error of estimate was applied to show the similarity in concept and computation between the standard deviation and the standard error of estimate. Suppose a large number of observations are being studied, and the numbers are large. Computing each Y' point on the regression line and then squaring the differences—that is, $(Y - Y')^2$—would be rather tedious. The following formula is algebraically equivalent to formula (12–4) but is much easier to use.

COMPUTATION FORMULA FOR THE STANDARD ERROR OF ESTIMATE

$$S_e = \sqrt{\frac{\Sigma Y^2 - a(\Sigma Y) - b(\Sigma XY)}{n - 2}} \quad \textbf{[12–5]}$$

The squares, sums, and other numbers for the Copier Sales Inc. example were calculated in Table 12–2. Inserting these values into the formula:

$$S_e = \sqrt{\frac{22\,100 - 18.9476(450) - 1.1842(10\,800)}{10 - 2}}$$

$$= 9.901$$

This is the same standard error of estimate as computed previously. How do we interpret 9.901? Think of it as the typical vertical distance of the observation from the regression line.

Statistical Software eases computation when finding the least squares regression line, calculating fitted values, or finding the standard error of the estimate. The **Excel** output from the Copier Sales Inc. example is included below. The slope and intercept are in the column "Coefficients" (cells F17 and F18). The fitted values for each sales representative are the column "Predicted Sales" (cells F23:F32). The "Residuals" or differences between the actual and the estimated values are in the next column (cells G23:G32). The standard error of estimate is in cell F7. All of these values are shown below.

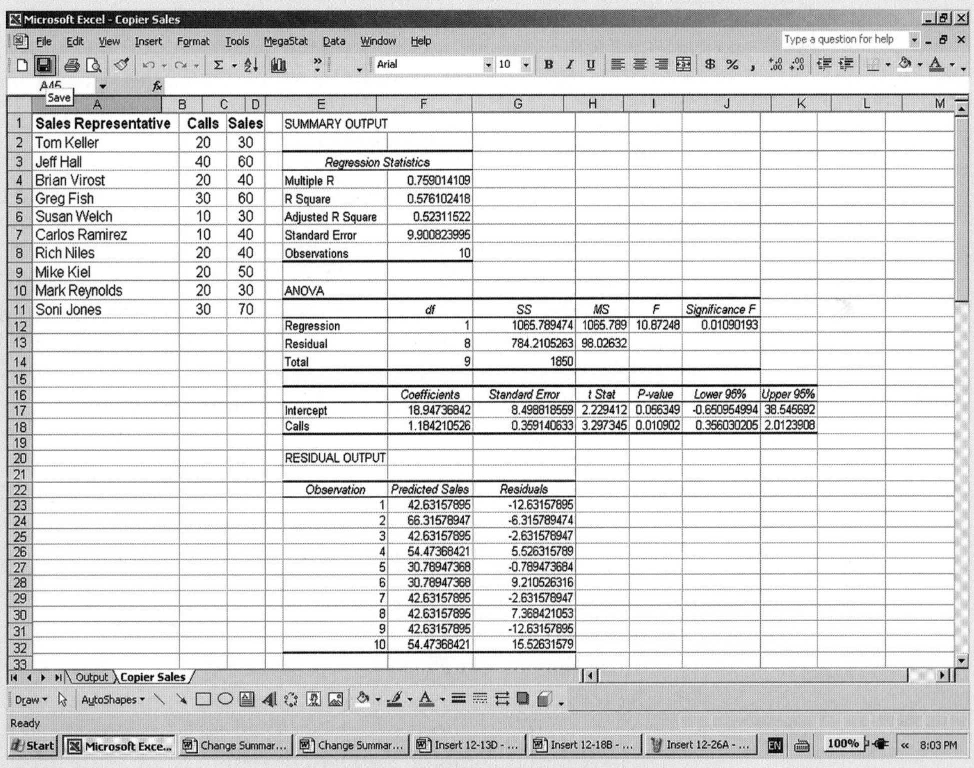

	A	B	C	D	E	F	G	H	I	J	K	L	M
1	**Sales Representative**	**Calls**	**Sales**		SUMMARY OUTPUT								
2	Tom Keller	20	30										
3	Jeff Hall	40	60		*Regression Statistics*								
4	Brian Virost	20	40		Multiple R	0.759014109							
5	Greg Fish	30	60		R Square	0.576102418							
6	Susan Welch	10	30		Adjusted R Square	0.52311522							
7	Carlos Ramirez	10	40		Standard Error	9.900823995							
8	Rich Niles	20	40		Observations	10							
9	Mike Kiel	20	50										
10	Mark Reynolds	20	30		ANOVA								
11	Soni Jones	30	70			*df*	*SS*	*MS*	*F*	*Significance F*			
12					Regression	1	1065.789474	1065.789	10.87248	0.01090193			
13					Residual	8	784.2105263	98.02632					
14					Total	9	1850						
15													
16						*Coefficients*	*Standard Error*	*t Stat*	*P-value*	*Lower 95%*	*Upper 95%*		
17					Intercept	18.94736842	8.498818559	2.229412	0.056349	-0.650954994	38.545692		
18					Calls	1.184210526	0.359140633	3.297345	0.010902	0.356030205	2.0123908		
19													
20					RESIDUAL OUTPUT								
21													
22					*Observation*	*Predicted Sales*	*Residuals*						
23					1	42.63157895	-12.63157895						
24					2	66.31578947	-6.315789474						
25					3	42.63157895	-2.631578947						
26					4	54.47368421	5.526315789						
27					5	30.78947368	-0.789473684						
28					6	30.78947368	9.210526316						
29					7	42.63157895	-2.631578947						
30					8	42.63157895	7.368421053						
31					9	42.63157895	-12.63157895						
32					10	54.47368421	15.52631579						
33													

Excel commands to create the regression statistics follow.

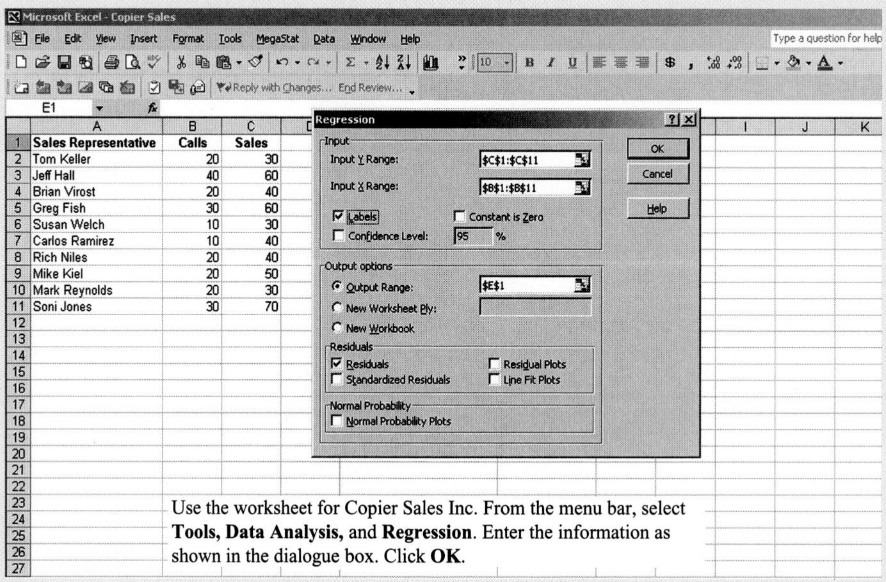

Thus far we have presented linear regression only as a descriptive tool. In other words, it is a simple summary ($Y' = a + bX$) of the relationship between the dependent Y variable and the independent X variable. When our data are a sample taken from a population, we are doing inferential statistics. Then we need to recall the distinction between population parameters and sample statistics. In this case, we "model" the linear relationship in the population by the equation:

$$Y = \alpha + \beta X$$

where:

- Y is any value of the dependent variable.
- α is the Y-intercept (the value of Y when $X = 0$) in the population.
- β is the slope (the amount by which Y changes when X increases by one unit) of the population values.
- X is any value of the independent variable.

Now α and β are population parameters and a and b, respectively, are estimates of those parameters. They are computed from a particular sample taken from the population. Fortunately, the formulas given earlier in the chapter for a and b do not change when we move from using regression as a descriptive tool to regression in statistical inference. It should be noted that the linear regression equation for the sample of sales representatives is only an estimate of the relationship between two variables for the population. Thus, the values of a and b in the regression equation are usually referred to as the **estimated regression coefficients**, or simply the **regression coefficients**.

Assumptions Underlying Linear Regression

To properly apply linear regression, several assumptions must be met. Chart 12–11 illustrates these assumptions.

1. For each value of X, there are corresponding Y values. These Y values follow the normal distribution.
2. The means of these normal distributions lie on the regression line.
3. The standard deviations of these normal distributions are all the same. The best estimate we have of this common standard deviation is the standard error of estimate (S_e).

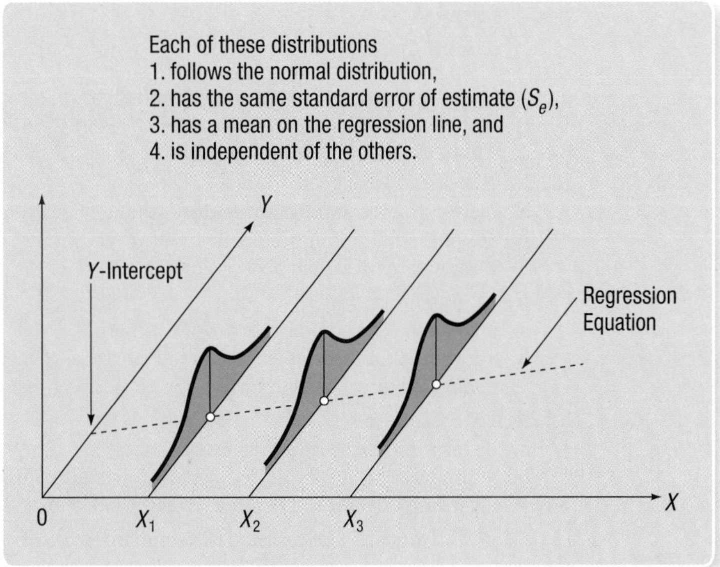

CHART 12–11 Regression Assumptions Shown Graphically

4. The Y values are statistically independent. This means that in selecting a sample a particular X does not depend on any other value of X. This assumption is particularly important when data are collected over a period of time. In such situations, the errors for a particular time period are often correlated with those of other time periods.

Recall from Chapter 6 that if the values follow a normal distribution, then the mean plus or minus 1 standard deviation will encompass about 68 percent of the observations, the mean plus or minus 2 standard deviations will encompass about 95 percent of the observations, and the mean plus or minus 3 standard deviations will encompass virtually all of the observations. The same relationship exists between the predicted values Y' and the standard error of estimate (S_e).

1. $Y' \pm S_e$ will include the middle 68 percent of the observations.
2. $Y' \pm 2S_e$ will include the middle 95 percent of the observations.
3. $Y' \pm 3S_e$ will include virtually all the observations.

We can now relate these assumptions to Copier Sales Inc., where we studied the relationship between the number of sales calls and the number of copiers sold. Assume that we took a much larger sample than $n = 10$, but that the standard error of estimate were still 9.901. If we drew a parallel line 9.901 units above the regression line and another 9.901 units below the regression line, about 68 percent of the points would fall between the two lines. Similarly, a line 19.802 [$2S_e = 2(9.901)$] units above the regression line and another 19.802 units below the regression line should include about 95 percent of the data values.

As a rough check, refer to the second column from the right in Table 12–3, i.e., the column headed "Deviation." Three of the 10 deviations exceed one standard error of estimate. That is, the deviation of −12.6316 for Tom Keller, −12.6316 for Mark Reynolds, and +15.5264 for Soni Jones all exceed the value of 9.901, which is 1 standard error from the regression line. All of the values are within 19.802 units of the regression line. To put it another way, 7 of the 10 deviations in the sample are within 1 standard error of the regression line and all are within 2—a good result for a relatively small sample.

self-review 12–3

Refer to self-reviews 12–1 and 12–2, where the owner of Reliable Furniture was studying the relationship between sales and the amount spent on advertising. Determine the standard error of estimate.

Exercises

9. Refer to Exercise 1.
   a. Determine the standard error of estimate.
   b. Suppose a large sample is selected (instead of just five). About 68 percent of the predictions would be between what two values?

10. Refer to Exercise 2.
   a. Determine the standard error of estimate.
   b. Suppose a large sample is selected (instead of just eight). About 95 percent of the predictions would be between what two values?

11. Refer to Exercise 3.
   a. Determine the standard error of estimate.
   b. Suppose a large sample is selected (instead of just 10). About 95 percent of the predictions regarding kilowatt-hours would occur between what two values?

12. Refer to Exercise 4.
   a. Determine the standard error of estimate.
   b. Suppose a large sample is selected (instead of just 10). About 95 percent of the predictions regarding sales would occur between what two values?

13. Refer to Exercise 7. Determine the standard error of estimate.

14. Refer to Exercise 8. Determine the standard error of estimate.

4 Construct and interpret confidence intervals and prediction intervals for the dependent variable.

Confidence Intervals and Prediction Intervals

The standard error of estimate is also used to establish confidence intervals when the sample size is large and the scatter around the regression line approximates a normal distribution. In our example involving the number of sales calls and the number of copiers sold, the sample size is small; hence, we need a correction factor to account for the size of the sample. In addition, when we move away from the mean of the independent variable, our estimates are subject to more variation, and we also need to adjust for this.

We are interested in providing interval estimates of two types. The first, which is called a **confidence interval**, reports the *mean* value of Y for a given X. The second type of estimate is called a **prediction interval**, and it reports the *range of values* of Y for a *particular* value of X. To explain further, suppose we estimate the salary of executives in the retail industry based on their years of experience. If we want an interval estimate of the mean salary of *all* retail executives with 20 years of experience, we calculate a confidence interval. If we want an estimate of the salary of Curtis Bender, a particular retail executive with 20 years of experience, we calculate a prediction interval.

To determine the confidence interval for the mean value of Y for a given X, the formula is:

CONFIDENCE INTERVAL FOR THE MEAN OF *Y*, GIVEN *X*.

$$Y' \pm tS_e\sqrt{\frac{1}{n}+\frac{(X-\bar{X})^2}{\Sigma(X-\bar{X})^2}} \qquad [12\text{–}6]$$

where:

Y' is the predicted value for any selected independent variable, X.
X is any selected value of X.
$\bar{X}$ is the mean of the X-values, found by $\Sigma X/n$.
n is the number of observations.
S_e is the standard error of estimate.
t is the value of t from Appendix F with $n - 2$ degrees of freedom.

We first described the t distribution in Chapter 8. The concept of t was developed by William Gosset in the early 1900s. He noticed that $\bar{X} \pm z(s)$ was not precisely correct for small samples. He observed, for example, for samples of size 120, that 95 percent of the items fell within $\bar{X} \pm 1.98s$ instead of $\bar{X} \pm 1.96s$. This difference is not too critical, but note what happens as the sample size becomes smaller:

df	*t*
120	1.980
60	2.000
21	2.080
10	2.228
3	3.182

This is logical. The smaller the sample, the larger the possible error. The increase in the *t*-value compensates for this possibility.

example

We return to the Copier Sales Inc. illustration. Determine a 95 percent confidence interval for all sales representatives who make 25 calls and for Sheila Baker, a West Coast sales representative who made 25 calls.

solution

We use formula (12–6) to determine a confidence interval. Table 12–4 includes the necessary totals.

TABLE 12–4 Calculations Needed for Determining the Confidence Interval and Prediction Interval

Sales Representative	Sales Calls (X)	Copiers Sold (Y)	X^2	$(X - \bar{X})$	$(X - \bar{X})^2$
Tom Keller	20	30	400	−2	4
Jeff Hall	40	60	1600	18	324
Brian Virost	20	40	400	−2	4
Greg Fish	30	60	900	8	64
Susan Welch	10	30	100	−12	144
Carlos Ramirez	10	40	100	−12	144
Rich Niles	20	40	400	−2	4
Mike Kiel	20	50	400	−2	4
Mark Reynolds	20	30	400	−2	4
Soni Jones	30	70	900	8	64
Total	220	450	5600	0	760

The first step is to determine the number of copiers we expect a sales representative to sell if he or she makes 25 calls. It is 48.5526, found by $Y' = 18.9476 + 1.1842X = 18.9476 + 1.1842(25)$.

To find the *t*-value, we need to first know the number of degrees of freedom. In this case the degrees of freedom is $n - 2 = 10 - 2 = 8$. We set the confidence level at 95 percent. To find the value of *t*, move down the left-hand column to 8 degrees of freedom, then move across to the column with the 95 percent level of confidence. The value of *t* is 2.306.

In the previous section we calculated the standard error of estimate to be 9.901, $X = 25$, and from Table 12–4, $\Sigma X = 220$ and $\Sigma X^2 = 5600$. In addition $\bar{X} = \Sigma X/n = 220/10 = 22$. Inserting these values in formula (12–6), we can determine the confidence interval.

$$\textbf{Confidence interval} = Y' \pm tS_e\sqrt{\frac{1}{n} + \frac{(X - \bar{X})^2}{\Sigma(X - \bar{X})^2}}$$

$$= 48.5526 \pm 2.306(9.901)\sqrt{\frac{1}{10} + \frac{(25 - 22)^2}{760}}$$

$$= 48.5526 \pm 7.6356$$

Thus, the 95 percent confidence interval of copiers sold for all sales representatives who make 25 calls is from 40.9170 up to 56.1882. To interpret, let's round the values. If a sales representative makes 25 calls, he or she can expect to sell 48.6 copiers. It is likely that copiers sold will range from 40.9 to 56.2 copiers.

To determine the prediction interval for a particular value of Y for a given X, formula (12–6) is modified slightly: A "1" is added under the radical. The formula becomes:

PREDICTION INTERVAL FOR Y, GIVEN X

$$Y' \pm tS_e\sqrt{1+\frac{1}{n}+\frac{(X-\bar{X})^2}{\Sigma(X-\bar{X})^2}} \qquad [12\text{–}7]$$

Suppose we want to estimate the number of copiers sold by Sheila Baker, who made 25 sales calls. The 95 percent prediction interval is determined as follows:

$$\textbf{Prediction interval} = Y' \pm tS_e\sqrt{1+\frac{1}{n}+\frac{(X-\bar{X})^2}{\Sigma(X-\bar{X})^2}}$$

$$= 48.5526 \pm 2.306(9.901)\sqrt{1+\frac{1}{10}+\frac{(25-22)^2}{760}}$$

$$= 48.5526 \pm 24.0746$$

Thus, the interval is from 24.478 up to 72.627 copiers. We conclude that the number of copiers sold will be between about 24 and 73 for a particular sales representative who makes 25 calls. This interval is quite large. It is much larger than the confidence interval for the mean of all sales representatives who made 25 calls. It is logical, however, that there should be more variation in the sales estimate for an individual than for the mean of a group.

The following MINITAB graph shows the relationship between the regression line (in the centre), the confidence interval (green dashed lines), and the prediction interval (black dashed lines). The bands for the prediction interval are always further from the regression line than for the confidence interval. Also, as the values of X move away from the mean number of calls (22) in either the positive or the negative direction, the confidence interval and prediction interval bands widen. This is caused by the numerator of the right-hand term in formulas (12–6) and (12–7). That is, as the term $(X-\bar{X})^2$ increases, the widths of the confidence interval and prediction interval also increase. To put it another way, there is less precision in our estimates as we move away, in either direction, from the mean of the independent variable.

minitab

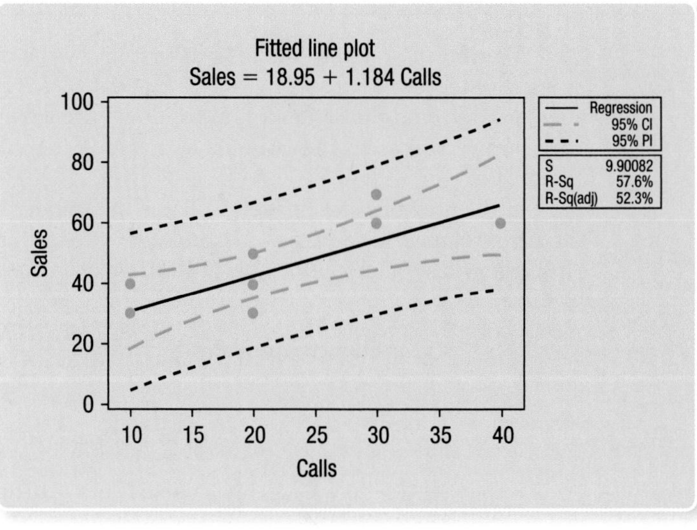

We wish to emphasize again the distinction between a confidence interval and a prediction interval. A confidence interval refers to the mean of all observations for a given value of X and is computed using formula (12–6). A prediction interval refers to a particular observation for a given value of X and is computed using formula (12–7). The prediction interval will always be wider because of the extra "1" under the radical in the second equation.

self-review 12–4

Refer to the sample data in self-reviews 12–1, 12–2, and 12–3, where the owner of Reliable Furniture was studying the relationship between sales and the amount spent on advertising. The sales information for the last four months is repeated below.

Month	Advertising Expense ($ thousands)	Sales Revenue ($ thousands)
July	$2	$7
August	1	3
September	3	8
October	4	10

The regression equation was computed to be $Y' = 1.5 + 2.2X$, and the standard error is 0.9487. Both variables are reported in thousands of dollars. Determine the 90 percent confidence interval for the typical month in which $3 thousand was spent on advertising.

Exercises

15. Refer to Exercise 1.
  a. Determine the 95 percent confidence interval for the mean predicted when $X = 7$.
  b. Determine the 95 percent prediction interval for an individual predicted when $X = 7$.

16. Refer to Exercise 2.
  a. Determine the 95 percent confidence interval for the mean predicted when $X = 7$.
  b. Determine the 95 percent prediction interval for an individual predicted when $X = 7$.

17. Refer to Exercise 3.
  a. Determine the 90 percent confidence interval, in thousands of kilowatt-hours, for the mean of all six-room homes.
  b. Determine the 90 percent prediction interval, in thousands of kilowatt-hours, for a particular six-room home.

18. Refer to Exercise 4.
  a. Determine the 98 percent confidence interval, in thousands of dollars, for the mean of all sales personnel who make 40 contacts.
  b. Determine the 98 percent prediction interval, in thousands of dollars, for a particular sales person who makes 40 contacts.

5 Calculate and interpret the *coefficient of correlation*, the *coefficient of determination*, and the *standard error of estimate*.

What Is Correlation Analysis?

In the previous section we developed an equation to express the linear relationship between two variables. In this section we will investigate how to measure the strength and direction of the linear relationship between variables. Correlation analysis is the study of this relationship. To explain, we will again use the example of Copier Sales Inc. The sales manager of Copier Sales Inc., which has a large sales force throughout Canada and the United States, wants to determine whether there is a relationship between the number of sales calls made in a month and the number of copiers sold that month. The manager selects a random sample of 10 representatives and determines the number of sales calls each representative made last month and the number of copiers sold. The sample information is repeated below in Table 12–5.

Statistics in Action

The space shuttle *Challenger* exploded on January 28, 1986. An investigation of the cause examined four contractors: Rockwell International for the shuttle and engines, Lockheed for ground support, Martin Marietta for the external fuel tanks, and Morton Thiokol for the solid fuel booster rockets. After several months, the investigation blamed the explosion on defective O-rings produced by Morton Thiokol. A study of the contractor's stock prices showed an interesting situation. On the day of the crash, Morton Thiokol stock was down 11.86 percent and the stock of the other three lost only 2 to 3 percent. Can we conclude that financial markets predicted the outcome of the investigation?

TABLE 12–5 Sales Calls and Copiers Sold for 10 Sales Representatives

Sales Representative	Number of Sales Calls	Number of Copiers Sold
Tom Keller	20	30
Jeff Hall	40	60
Brian Virost	20	40
Greg Fish	30	60
Susan Welch	10	30
Carlos Ramirez	10	40
Rich Niles	20	40
Mike Kiel	20	50
Mark Reynolds	20	30
Soni Jones	30	70

By reviewing the data, we observe that there does seem to be some relationship between the number of sales calls and the number of units sold. That is, the sales representatives who made the most sales calls sold the most units. However, the relationship is not "perfect" or exact. For example, Soni Jones made fewer sales calls than Jeff Hall, but she sold more units.

Instead of talking in generalities, as we have been doing up to this point, we will develop some statistical measures to portray more precisely the relationship between the two variables, sales calls and copiers sold. This group of statistical techniques is called **correlation analysis.**

The basic idea of correlation analysis is to report the strength of the association between two variables.

The Coefficient of Correlation

correlation analysis A group of techniques to measure the strength of the association between two variables.

Interval- or ratio-level data are required.

Characteristics of r

Originated by Karl Pearson about 1900, the **coefficient of correlation** describes the strength of the linear relationship between two sets of interval-scaled or ratio-scaled variables. Designated r, it is often referred to as *Pearson's r* and as the *Pearson product-moment correlation coefficient.* It can assume any value from -1.00 to $+1.00$ inclusive. A correlation coefficient of -1.00 or $+1.00$ indicates *perfect correlation.* For example, a correlation coefficient for the preceding example computed to be $+1.00$ would indicate that the number of sales calls and the number of copiers sold are perfectly related in a positive linear sense. A computed value of -1.00 reveals that sales calls and the number of copiers sold are perfectly related in a negative linear sense. How the scatter diagram would appear if the relationship between the two sets of data were linear and perfect is shown in Chart 12–12.

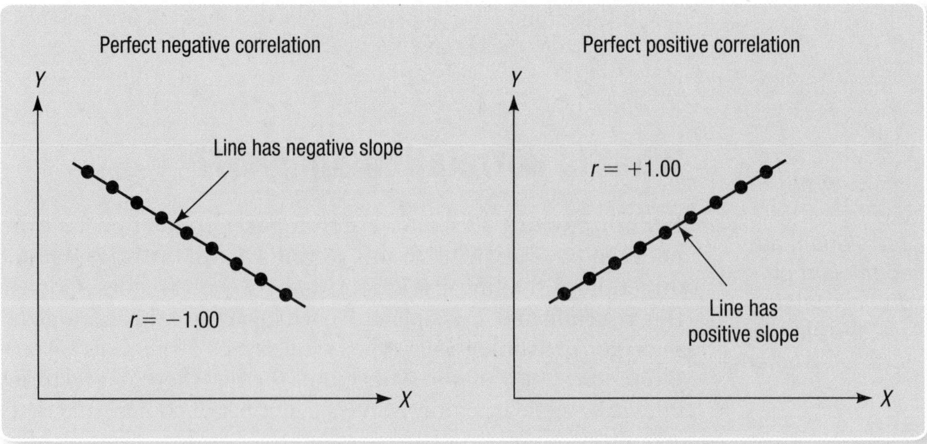

CHART 12–12 Scatter Diagrams Showing Perfect Negative Correlation and Perfect Positive Correlation

If there is absolutely no relationship between the two sets of variables, Pearson's r is 0. A coefficient of correlation r close to 0 (say, .08) shows that the relationship is quite weak. The same conclusion is drawn if $r = -.08$. Coefficients of $-.91$ and $+.91$ have equal strength; both indicate very strong correlation between the two variables. Thus, *the strength of the correlation does not depend on the direction (either − or +).*

Scatter diagrams for $r = 0$, a weak r (say, $-.23$), and a strong r (say, $+.87$) are shown in Chart 12–13. Note that if the correlation is weak, there is considerable scatter about a line drawn through the centre of the data. For the scatter diagram representing a strong relationship, there is very little scatter about the line. This indicates, in the example shown on the chart, that hours studied is a good predictor of exam score.

Examples of degrees of correlation

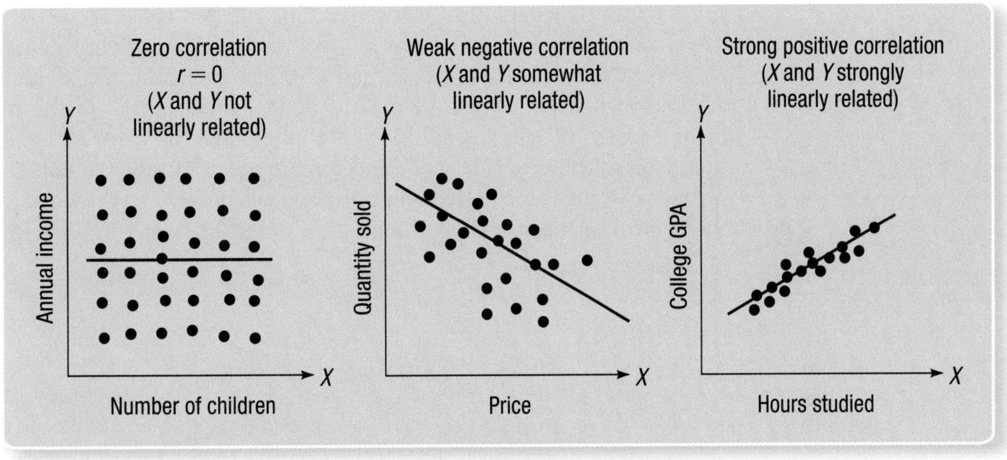

CHART 12–13 Scatter Diagrams Depicting Zero, Weak, and Strong Correlation

The following drawing summarizes the strength and direction of the coefficient of correlation.

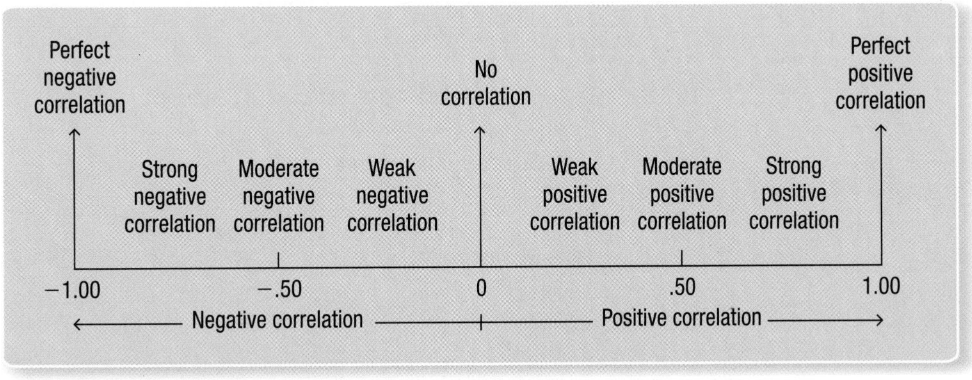

coefficient of correlation A measure of the strength of the linear relationship between two variables.

The characteristics of the **coefficient of correlation** are summarized below.

CHARACTERISTICS OF THE COEFFICIENT OF CORRELATION

1. The sample coefficient of correlation is identified by the lowercase letter r.
2. It shows the direction and strength of the linear (straight line) relationship between two interval- or ratio- scale variables.
3. It ranges from –1 up to and including +1.
4. A value near 0 indicates there is little association between the variables.
5. A value near 1 indicates a direct or positive association between the variables.
6. A value near –1 indicates inverse or negative association between the variables.

How is the value of the coefficient of correlation determined? We will use the Copier Sales Inc. data, which are reported in Table 12–1, as an example. We begin with a scatter diagram, similar to Chart 12–2. Draw a vertical line through the data values at the mean of the X-values and a horizontal line at the mean of the Y-values. In Chart 12–14 we've added a vertical line at 22.0 calls ($\bar{X} = \Sigma X / n = 220/10 = 22$) and a horizontal line at 45.0 copiers ($\bar{Y} = \Sigma X / n = 450/10 = 45.0$). These lines pass through the "centre" of the data and divide the scatter diagram into four quadrants. Think of moving the origin from (0, 0) to (22, 45).

The two variables are positively related because the number of copiers sold is above the mean and the number of sales calls is also above the mean. These points appear in the upper-right quadrant (labelled Quadrant I) of Chart 12–14. Similarly, when the number of copiers sold is less than the mean, so is the number of sales calls; these points fall in the lower-left quadrant (labelled Quadrant III). For example, the last person on the list in Table 12–6, Soni Jones, made 30 sales calls and sold 70 copiers. These values are above their respective means, so this point is located in Quadrant I. She made 8 ($X - \bar{X} = 30 - 22$) more sales calls than the mean and sold 25 ($Y - \bar{Y} = 70 - 45$) more copiers than the mean. Tom Keller, the first name on the list in Table 12–1, made 20 sales calls and sold 30 copiers. Both of these values are less than their respective means; hence, this point is in the lower-left quadrant. Tom made 2 less sales calls and sold 15 less copiers than the respective means. The deviations from the mean number of sales calls and for the mean number of copiers sold are summarized in Table 12–6 for the 10 sales representatives. The sum of the products of the deviations from the respective means is 900. That is, the term $\Sigma(X - \bar{X})(Y - \bar{Y}) = 900$.

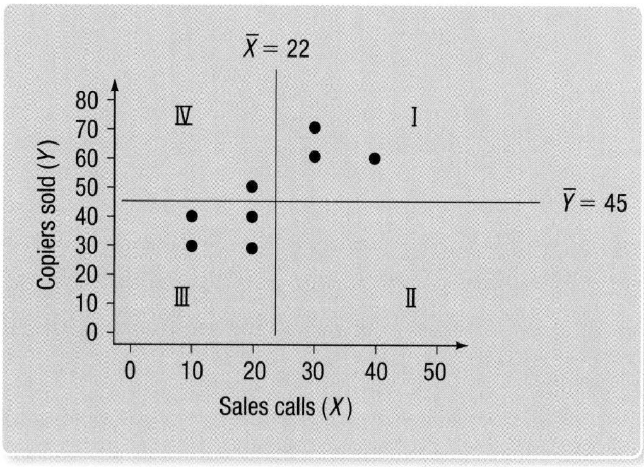

CHART 12–14 Computation of the Coefficient of Correlation.

TABLE 12–6 Deviations from the Mean and Their Products

Sales Representative	Calls Y	Sales X	$X - \bar{X}$	$Y - \bar{Y}$	$(X - \bar{X})(Y - \bar{Y})$
Tom Keller	20	30	−2	−15	30
Jeff Hall	40	60	18	15	270
Brian Virost	20	40	−2	−5	10
Greg Fish	30	60	8	15	120
Susan Welch	10	30	−12	−15	180
Carlos Ramirez	10	40	−12	−5	60
Rich Niles	20	40	−2	−5	10
Mike Kiel	20	50	−2	5	−10
Mark Reynolds	20	30	−2	−15	30
Soni Jones	30	70	8	25	200
					900

In both the upper-right and the lower-left quadrants, the product of $(X - \bar{X})(Y - \bar{Y})$ is positive because both of the factors have the same sign. In our example this happens for all sales representatives except Mike Kiel. We can therefore expect the coefficient of correlation to have a positive value.

If the two variables are inversely related, one variable will be above its mean and the other below its mean. Most of the points in this case occur in the upper-left and lower-right quadrants, that is, Quadrant IV and Quadrant II. Now $(X - \bar{X})$ and $(Y - \bar{Y})$ will have opposite signs, so their product is negative. The resulting correlation coefficient is negative.

What happens if there is no linear relationship between the two variables? The points in the scatter diagram will appear in all four quadrants. The negative products of $(X - \bar{X})(Y - \bar{Y})$ offset the positive products, so the sum is near zero. This leads to a correlation coefficient near zero.

The correlation coefficient also needs to be unaffected by the units of the two variables. For example, if we had used hundreds of copiers sold instead of the number sold, the coefficient of correlation would be the same. The coefficient of correlation is independent of the scale used if we divide the term $\Sigma(X - \bar{X})(Y - \bar{Y})$ by the sample standard deviations. It is also made independent of the sample size and bounded by the values +1.00 and −1.00 if we divide by $(n - 1)$.

This reasoning leads to the following formula:

CORRELATION COEFFICIENT—CONCEPTUAL FORM

$$r = \frac{\Sigma(X - \bar{X})(Y - \bar{Y})}{(n-1)s_x s_y} \quad [12\text{–}8]$$

To compute the coefficient of correlation, we use the standard deviations of the sample of 10 sales calls and 10 copiers sold. We could use formula (3–12) to calculate the sample standard deviations or we could use a software package. The following is the **Excel** output. The standard deviation of the number of sales calls is 9.189 and of the number of copiers sold 14.337.

excel

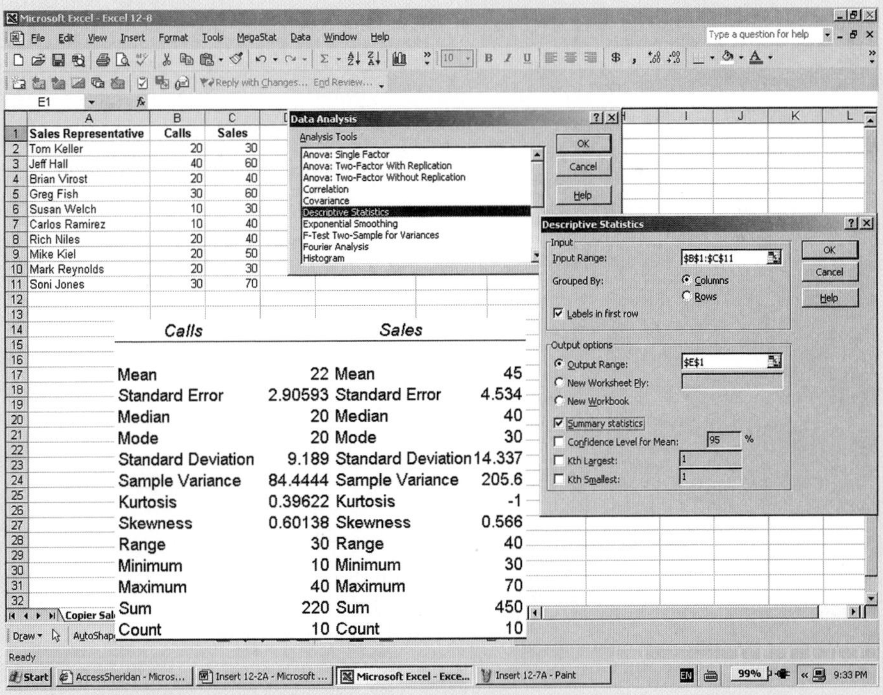

We now insert these values into formula (12–8) to determine the coefficient of correlation:

$$r = \frac{\Sigma(X - \bar{X})(Y - \bar{Y})}{(n-1)s_x s_y} = \frac{900}{(10-1)(9.189)(14.337)} = .759$$

The coefficient of correlation can also be determined from a computational formula based on the actual values of X and Y. The formula is:

CORRELATION COEFFICIENT
$$r = \frac{n(\Sigma XY) - (\Sigma X)(\Sigma Y)}{\sqrt{[n(\Sigma X^2) - (\Sigma X)^2][n(\Sigma Y^2) - (\Sigma Y)^2]}} \quad \textbf{[12–9]}$$

where:

- n is the number of paired observations.
- ΣX is the X variable summed.
- ΣY is the Y variable summed.
- (ΣX^2) is the X variable squared and the squares summed.
- $(\Sigma X)^2$ is the X variable summed and the sum squared.
- (ΣY^2) is the Y variable squared and the squares summed.
- $(\Sigma Y)^2$ is the Y variable summed and the sum squared.
- ΣXY is the sum of the products of X and Y.

Note: Calculators and computer software can provide the value of r directly from data.

example

Refer to the previous example where we developed a scatter diagram depicting the relationship between the number of sales calls and the number of copiers sold. Determine the coefficient of correlation and interpret its value.

solution

Table 12–2 repeats the information on the number of sales calls and the number of copiers sold. Also included are additional totals necessary to determine the coefficient of correlation.

The coefficient of correlation is .759, found by using formula (12–9).

$$r = \frac{n(\Sigma XY) - (\Sigma X)(\Sigma Y)}{\sqrt{[n(\Sigma X^2) - (\Sigma X)^2][n(\Sigma Y^2) - (\Sigma Y)^2]}}$$
$$= \frac{10(10\,800) - (220)(450)}{\sqrt{[10(5600) - (220)^2][10(22\,100) - (450)^2]}}$$
$$= .759$$

How do we interpret a correlation of .759? First, it is positive, so we see there is a direct relationship between the number of sales calls and the number of copiers sold. This confirms our reasoning based on the scatter diagram, Chart 12–2. The value of .759 is fairly close to 1.00, so we conclude that the association is strong. So, an increase in calls will likely lead to more sales.

The Coefficient of Determination

coefficient of determination
The proportion of the total variation in the dependent variable, Y, that is explained, or accounted for, by the variation in the independent variable, X.

In the previous example regarding the relationship between the number of sales calls and the units sold, the coefficient of correlation, .759, was interpreted as being "strong." Terms such as *weak*, *moderate*, and *strong*, however, do not have precise meaning. A measure that has a more easily interpreted meaning is the **coefficient of determination**. It is computed by squaring the coefficient of correlation. In the example, the coefficient of determination, r^2, is .576, found by $(.759)^2$. This is a proportion or a percent; we can say that 57.6 percent of the variation in the number of copiers sold is explained, or accounted for, by the variation in the number of sales calls.

Further discussion of the coefficient of determination is found later in the chapter.

Correlation and Cause

If there is a strong relationship (say, $r^2 = .91$) between two variables, we are tempted to assume that an increase or decrease in one variable *causes* a change in the other variable. For example, it can be shown that the consumption of peanuts and the consumption of aspirin have a strong correlation. However, this does not indicate that an increase in the consumption of peanuts *caused* the consumption of aspirin to increase. Likewise, the incomes of professors and the number of inmates in mental institutions have increased proportionately. Further, as the population of donkeys has decreased, there has been an increase in the number of doctoral degrees granted. Relationships such as these are called **spurious correlations**. What we can conclude when we find two variables with a strong correlation is that there is a relationship between the two variables, not that a change in one causes a change in the other.

The **Excel** Paste Function to find the coefficient of correlation follows.

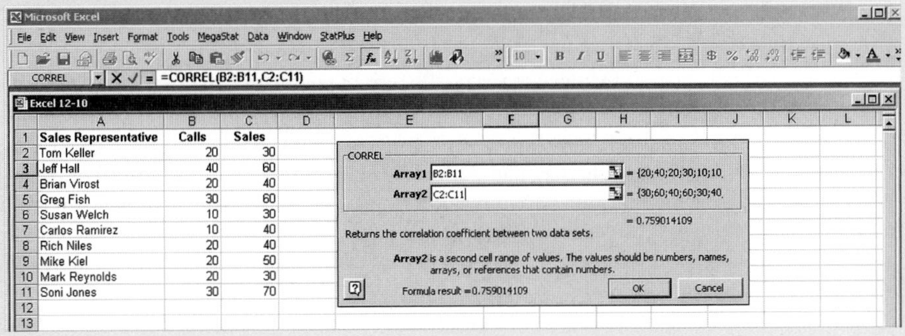

MegaStat steps and commands to find the coefficient of correlation follow.

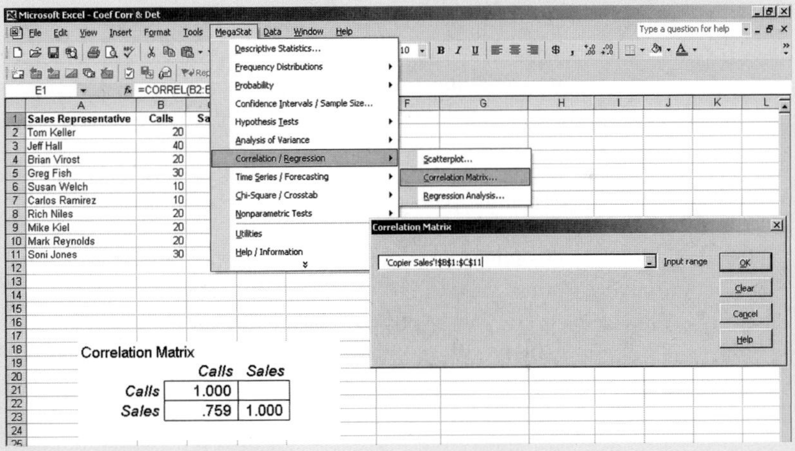

self-review 12–5

Refer to self-review 12–1 where the owner of Reliable Furniture was studying the relationship between sales and the amount spent on advertising. The information on sales and advertising for the last four months is repeated below.

Month	Advertising Expense ($ thousands)	Sales Revenue ($ thousands)
July	$2	$7
August	1	3
September	3	8
October	4	10

(a) Determine the coefficient of correlation.
(b) Interpret the strength of the correlation coefficient.
(c) Determine the coefficient of determination. Interpret.

Exercises

19. The following sample observations were randomly selected.

X:	4	5	3	6	10
Y:	4	6	5	7	7

Determine the coefficient of correlation and the coefficient of determination. Interpret.

20. The following sample observations were randomly selected.

X:	5	3	6	3	4	4	6	8
Y:	13	15	7	12	13	11	9	5

Determine the coefficient of correlation and the coefficient of determination. Interpret.

21. Bi-lo Appliance Super Store has outlets in several large Canadian cities. The general sales manager plans to air a commercial for a digital camera on selected TV stations prior to a sale starting on Saturday and ending Sunday. She plans to get the information for the Saturday–Sunday digital camera sales at the various outlets and pair them with the number of times the advertisement was shown on the local TV stations. The purpose is to find whether there is any relationship between the number of times the advertisement was aired and digital camera sales. The pairings are:

Location of TV Station	Number of Airings	Sales ($ thousands)
Calgary	4	$15
Edmonton	2	8
Quebec City	5	21
Halifax	6	24
St John's	3	17

a. Determine the coefficient of correlation.
b. Determine the coefficient of determination.
c. Interpret these statistical measures.

22. The production department of NDB Electronics wants to explore the relationship between the number of employees who assemble a subassembly and the number produced. As an experiment, two employees were assigned to assemble the subassemblies. They produced 15 during a one-hour period. Then, four employees assembled them. They produced 25 during a one-hour period. The complete set of paired observations follows.

Number of Assemblers	One-Hour Production (units)
2	15
4	25
1	10
5	40
3	30

The dependent variable is production; that is, it is assumed that the level of production depends upon the number of employees.
a. Compute the coefficient of correlation.
b. Evaluate the strength of the relationship by computing the coefficient of determination.

23. The city council of Pine Bluffs is considering increasing the number of police in an effort to reduce crime. Before making a final decision, the council asks the chief of police to survey other cities of similar size to determine the relationship between the number of police and the number of crimes reported. The chief gathered the following sample information.

City	Police	Number of Crimes	City	Police	Number of Crimes
Oxford	15	17	Holgate	17	7
Starksville	17	13	Carey	12	21
Danville	25	5	Whistler	11	19
Athens	27	7	Woodville	22	6

a. Determine the coefficient of correlation.
b. Determine the coefficient of determination.
c. Interpret these statistical measures. Does it surprise you that the relationship is inverse?

24. The owner of Maumee Motors wants to study the relationship between the age of a car and its selling price. Listed below is a random sample of 12 used cars sold at Maumee Motors during the last year.

Car	Age (years)	Selling Price ($ thousands)	Car	Age (years)	Selling Price ($ thousands)
1	9	$8.1	7	8	$7.6
2	7	6.0	8	11	8.0
3	11	3.6	9	10	8.0
4	12	4.0	10	12	6.0
5	8	5.0	11	6	8.6
6	7	10.0	12	6	8.0

a. Determine the coefficient of correlation.
b. Determine the coefficient of determination.
c. Interpret these statistical measures. Does it surprise you that the relationship is inverse?

6 Conduct a test of hypothesis to determine whether the coefficient of correlation in the population is zero.

Testing the Significance of the Correlation Coefficient

Recall that the sales manager of Copier Sales Inc. found the correlation between the number of sales calls and the number of copiers sold was .759. This indicated a strong association between the two variables. However, only 10 sales representatives were sampled. Could it be that the correlation in the population is actually 0? This would mean the correlation of .759 was due to chance. The population in this example is all the salespeople employed by the firm.

Resolving this dilemma requires a test to answer the question: Could there be zero correlation in the population from which the sample was selected? To put it another way, did the computed r come from a population of paired observations with zero correlation? To continue our convention of allowing Greek letters to represent a population parameter, we will let ρ represent the correlation in the population. It is pronounced "rho."

We will continue with the illustration involving sales calls and copiers sold by following the five-step procedure for hypothesis testing. **Step one** is to state H_0 and H_1. The null hypothesis and the alternative hypothesis are:

H_0: $\rho = 0$ (The correlation in the population is zero.)
H_1: $\rho \neq 0$ (The correlation in the population is different from zero.)

Step 2: Select a level of significance. We will use $\alpha = .05$.

Step 3: From the way H_1 is stated, we know that the test is two-tailed. It is a *t*-test. The formula for *t* is:

t TEST FOR THE COEFFICIENT OF CORRELATION

$$t = \frac{r\sqrt{n-2}}{\sqrt{1-r^2}} \quad \text{with } n - 2 \text{ degrees of freedom} \qquad [12\text{–}10]$$

Step 4: Using the .05 level of significance, the decision rule states that if the computed t falls in the area between plus 2.306 and minus 2.306, the null hypothesis is not rejected. To locate the critical value of 2.306, refer to Appendix F for $df = n - 2 = 10 - 2 = 8$. See Chart 12–15.

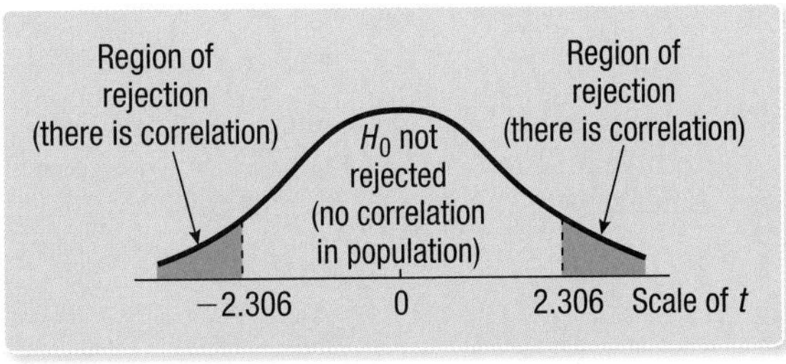

CHART 12–15 Decision Rule for Test of Hypothesis at .05 Significance Level and 8 *df*

Applying formula (12–10) to the example regarding the number of sales calls and units sold:

$$t = \frac{r\sqrt{n-2}}{\sqrt{1-r^2}} = \frac{.759\sqrt{10-2}}{\sqrt{1-.759^2}} = 3.297$$

Step 5: The computed t is in the rejection region. Thus, H_0 is rejected at the .05 significance level. This means the correlation in the population is not zero. From a practical standpoint, it indicates to the sales manager that there is a positive or direct correlation between the number of sales calls made and the number of copiers sold in the population of sales representatives.

We can also interpret the test of hypothesis in terms of p-values. A p-value is the likelihood of finding a value of the test statistic more extreme than the one computed, when H_0 is true. To determine the p-value, go to the t distribution in Appendix F and find the row for 8 degrees of freedom. The value of the test statistic is 3.297, so in the row for 8 degrees of freedom and a two-tailed test, find the value closest to 3.297. For a two-tailed test at the .02 significance level, the critical value is 2.896, and the critical value at the .01 significance level is 3.355. Because 3.297 is between 2.896 and 3.355 we conclude that the p-value is between (.01) and (.02), which is less than the significance level of .05. Therefore, the test statistic lies in the rejection region.

Both **MINITAB** and **Excel**/Megastat will report the correlation between two variables. In addition to the correlation, they also report the p-value for the test of hypothesis that the correlation in the population between the two variables is 0. MegaStat steps and partial output showing the results follow.

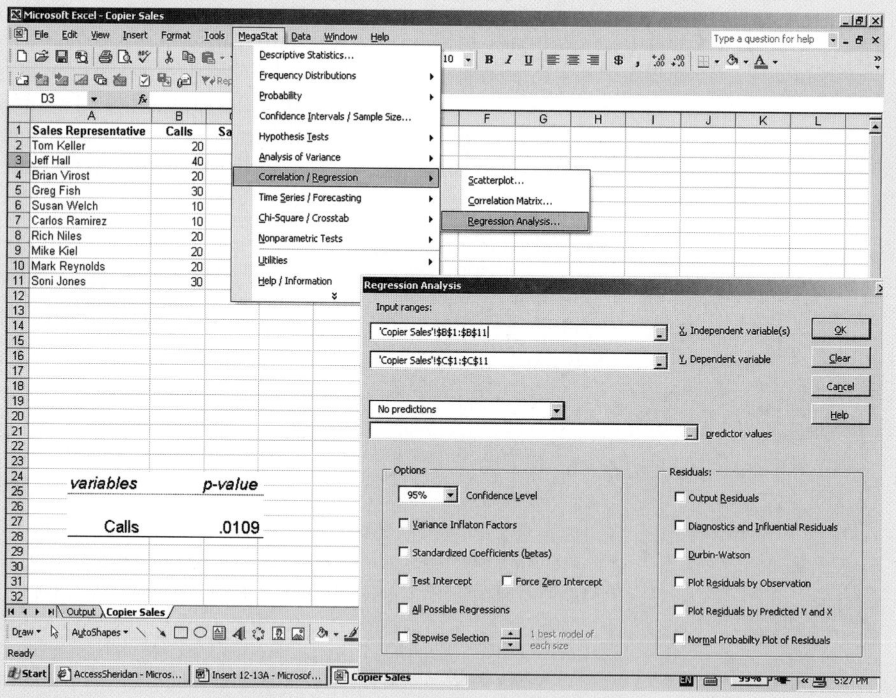

self-review 12–6

A sample of 25 mayoral campaigns in cities with populations larger than 50 000 showed that the correlation between the percent of the vote received and the amount spent on the campaign by the candidate was .43. At the .05 significance level, is there a positive association between the variables?

Exercises

25. The following hypotheses are given.

$$H_0: \rho \leq 0$$
$$H_1: \rho > 0$$

A random sample of 12 paired observations indicated a correlation of .32. Can we conclude that the correlation in the population is greater than zero? Use the .05 significance level.

26. The following hypotheses are given.

$$H_0: \rho \geq 0$$
$$H_1: \rho < 0$$

A random sample of 15 paired observations have a correlation of .246. Can we conclude that the correlation in the population is less than zero? Use the .05 significance level.

27. A refining company is studying the relationship between the pump price of gasoline and the number of litres sold. For a sample of 20 stations last Tuesday, the correlation was −.78. At the .01 significance level, is the correlation in the population less than zero?

28. A study of 20 worldwide financial institutions showed the correlation between their assets and pretax profit to be .86. At the .05 significance level, can we conclude that there is positive correlation in the population?

29. The Airline Passenger Association studied the relationship between the number of passengers on a particular flight and the cost of the flight. It seems logical that more passengers on the flight will result in more weight and more luggage which in turn will result in higher fuel costs. For a sample of 15 flights, the correlation between the number of passengers and total fuel cost was .667. Is it reasonable to conclude that there is positive association in the population between the two variables? Use the .01 significance level.

30. The SU (Student Union) Association at a local college wanted to demonstrate the relationship between the numbers of beers a student drinks and their blood alcohol content (BAC). A random sample of 18 students participated in the study in which each participating student was randomly assigned a number of 341 ml cans of beer to drink. Thirty minutes after consuming their assigned number of beers, a member of the local sheriff's office measured their blood alcohol content. The sample information is reported below.

Student	Beers	BAC	Student	Beers	BAC
1	6	0.10	10	3	0.07
2	7	0.09	11	3	0.05
3	7	0.09	12	7	0.08
4	4	0.10	13	1	0.04
5	5	0.10	14	4	0.07
6	3	0.07	15	2	0.06
7	3	0.10	16	7	0.12
8	6	0.12	17	2	0.05
9	6	0.09	18	1	0.02

a. Develop a scatter diagram for the number of beers consumed and the blood alcohol content. Comment on the relationship. Does it appear to be strong or weak? Does it appear to be direct or inverse?
b. Determine the coefficient of correlation.
c. Determine the coefficient of determination.
d. At the .01 significance level, is it reasonable to conclude that there is a positive relationship in the population between the number of beers consumed and the blood alcohol content? What is the p-value?

More on the Coefficient of Determination

Earlier in the chapter we defined the coefficient of determination as the percent of the variation in the dependent variable that is accounted for by the independent variable. We indicated it is the square of the coefficient of correlation and that it is written r^2.

To further examine the basic concept of the coefficient of determination, suppose there is interest in the relationship between years on the job, X, and weekly production, Y. Sample data revealed:

Employee	Years on Job, X	Weekly Production, Y
Gordon	14	6
James	7	5
Ford	3	3
Salter	15	9
Artes	11	7

The sample data were plotted in a scatter diagram. Since the relationship between X and Y appears to be linear, a line was drawn through the points (see Chart 12–16). The equation is $Y' = 2 + 0.4X$.

Note in Chart 12–16 that if we were to use that line to predict weekly production for an employee, in no case would our prediction be exact. That is, there would be some error in each of our predictions. As an example, for Gordon, who has been with the company 14 years, we would predict weekly production to be 7.6 units; however, he produces only 6 units.

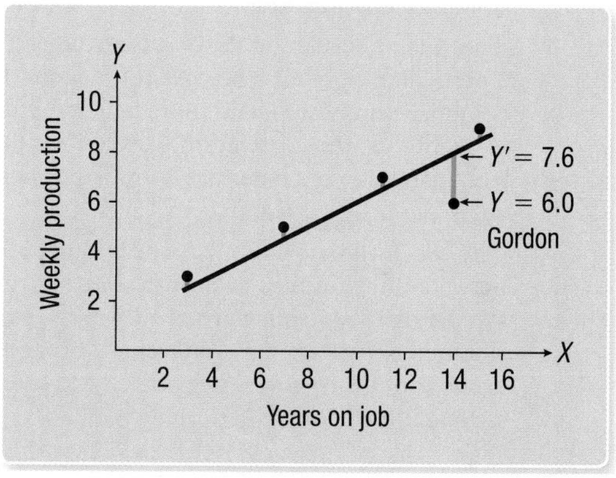

CHART 12–16 Observed Data and the Least Squares Line

Unexplained variation

To measure the overall error in our prediction, every deviation from the line is squared and the squares summed. The predicted point on the line is designated Y', read Y prime, and the observed point is designated Y. For Gordon, $(Y - Y')^2 = (6 - 7.6)^2 = (-1.6)^2 = 2.56$. Logically, this variation cannot be explained by the independent variable, so it is referred to as the *unexplained variation*. Specifically, we cannot explain why Gordon's production of 6 units is 1.6 units below his predicted production of 7.6 units, based on the number of years he has been on the job.

The sum of the squared deviations, $\Sigma(Y - Y')^2$, is 4.00. (See Table 12–7.) The term $\Sigma(Y - Y')^2 = 4.00$ is the variation in Y (production) that cannot be predicted from X. It is the "unexplained" variation in Y.

TABLE 12–7 Computations Needed for the Unexplained Variation and Explained Variation

	X	Y	Y'	$Y - Y'$	$(Y - Y')^2$	$Y' - \bar{Y}$	$(Y' - \bar{Y})^2$
Gordon	14	6	7.6	−1.6	2.56	1.6	2.56
James	7	5	4.8	0.2	0.04	−1.2	1.44
Ford	3	3	3.2	−0.2	0.04	−2.8	7.84
Salter	15	9	8.0	1.0	1.00	2.0	4.0
Artes	11	7	6.4	0.6	0.36	0.4	0.16
Total	50	30		0.0*	4.00	0.0	16.00

*Must be 0.

Now suppose *only* the Y values (weekly production, in this problem) are known and we want to predict production for every employee. The actual production figures for the employees are 6, 5, 3, 9, and 7 (from Table 12–7). To make these predictions, we could assign the mean weekly production (6 units, found by $\Sigma Y/n = 30/5 = 6$) to each employee. This would keep the sum of the squared prediction errors at a minimum. (Recall from Chapter 3 that the sum of the squared deviations from the arithmetic mean for a set of numbers is smaller than the sum of the squared deviations from any other value, such as the median.) Table 12–8 shows the necessary calculations. The sum of the squared deviations is 20, as shown in Table 12–8. The value 20 is referred to as the ***total variation in*** Y. What we did to arrive at the total variation in Y is shown diagrammatically in Chart 12–17.

Total variation in Y

Logically, the total variation in Y can be subdivided into unexplained variation and explained variation. To arrive at the explained variation, since we know the total variation and unexplained variation, we simply subtract: Explained variation = Total variation − Unexplained variation. Dividing the explained variation by the total variation gives the coefficient of determination, r^2, which is a proportion. In terms of a formula:

COEFFICIENT OF DETERMINATION

$$r^2 = \frac{\text{Explained variation}}{\text{Total variation}} = \frac{\Sigma(Y' - \bar{Y})^2}{\Sigma(Y - \bar{Y})^2} \qquad \textbf{[12–11]}$$

In this problem:

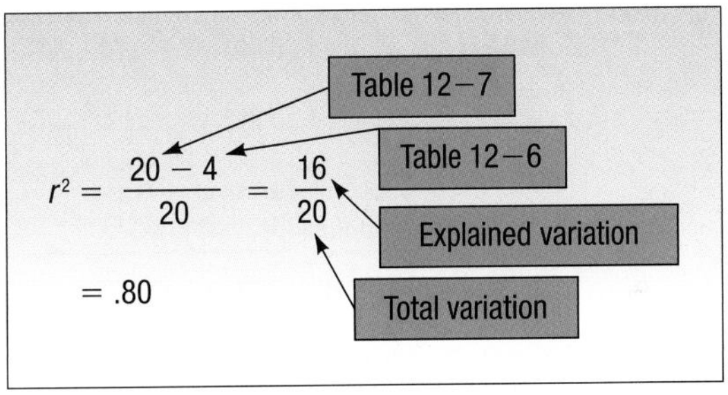

As mentioned, .80 is a proportion. We say that 80 percent of the variation in weekly production, Y, is determined, or accounted for, by its linear relationship with X (years on the job).

TABLE 12–8 Calculations Needed for the Total Variation in Y

Name	Weekly Production, Y	Mean Weekly Production, $\bar{Y}$	$Y - \bar{Y}$	$(Y - \bar{Y})^2$
Gordon	6	6	0	0
James	5	6	−1	1
Ford	3	6	−3	9
Salter	9	6	3	9
Artes	7	6	1	1
Total			0*	20

*Must be 0.

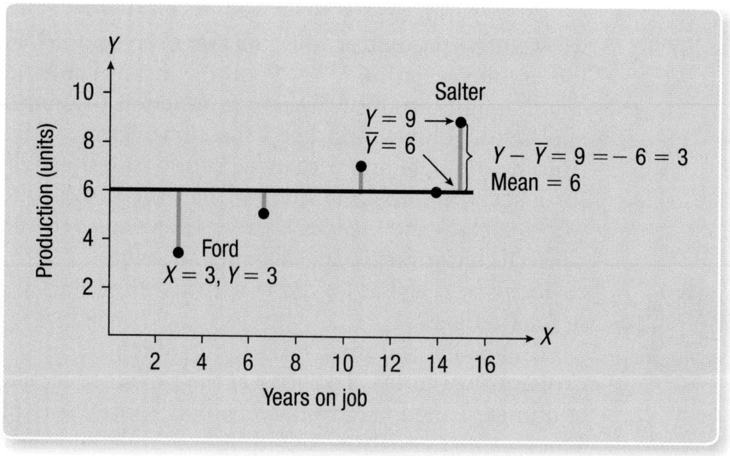

CHART 12–17 Deviations from the Mean of Y

As a check, the computational formula (12–1) for the coefficient of correlation could be used. Squaring r gives the coefficient of determination. Exercise 31 offers a check on the preceding problem.

Exercises

31. Using the preceding problem, involving years on the job and weekly production, verify that the coefficient of determination is in fact .80.

32. The number of shares of Icom Inc. turned over during a month and the prices at the end of the month are listed in the following table. Also, the Y' values on the line going through observed data are given.

Turnover (thousands of shares), X	Actual Price, Y	Estimated Price, Y'
4	$2	$2.7
1	1	0.6
5	4	3.4
3	2	2.0
2	1	1.3

a. Draw a scatter diagram. Plot a line through the dots.
b. Compute the coefficient of determination.
c. Interpret the coefficient of determination.

The Relationships among the Coefficient of Correlation, the Coefficient of Determination, and the Standard Error of Estimate

In an earlier section, we discussed the standard error of estimate, which measures how close the actual values are to the regression line. When the standard error is small, it indicates that the two variables are closely related. In the calculation of the standard error, the key term is $\Sigma(Y - Y')^2$. If the value of this term is small, then the standard error will also be small.

The correlation coefficient measures the strength of the association between two variables. When the points on the scatter diagram appear close to the line, we note that the correlation coefficient tends to be large. Thus, the standard error of estimate and the coefficient of correlation relate the same information but use a different scale to report the strength of the association. However, both measures involve the term $\Sigma(Y - Y')^2$.

We also noted that the square of the correlation coefficient is the coefficient of determination. The coefficient of determination measures the percent of the variation in Y that is explained by the variation in X.

7 Interpret an ANOVA table.

A convenient vehicle for showing the relationship among these three measures is an ANOVA table. This table is similar to the analysis of variance table developed in Chapter 11. In that chapter, the total variation was divided into two components: that due to the *treatments* and that due to *random error*. The concept is similar in regression analysis. The total variation, $\Sigma(Y - \bar{Y})^2$, is divided into two components: (1) that explained by the *regression* (explained by the independent variable) and (2) the *error*, or unexplained variation. These two categories are identified in the first column of the ANOVA table that follows. The column headed "*df*" refers to the degrees of freedom associated with each category. The total number of degrees of freedom is $n - 1$. The number of degrees of freedom in the regression is 1, since there is only one independent variable. The number of degrees of freedom associated with the error term is $n - 2$. The term "SS" located in the middle of the ANOVA table refers to the sum of squares—the variation. The terms are computed as follows:

$$\textbf{Regression} = \textbf{SSR} = \Sigma(Y' - \bar{Y})^2$$
$$\textbf{Error variation} = \textbf{SSE} = \Sigma(Y - Y')^2$$
$$\textbf{Total variation} = \textbf{SST} = \Sigma(Y - \bar{Y})^2$$

The format for the ANOVA table is:

Source	*df*	SS	MS
Regression	1	SSR	SSR/1
Error	$n - 2$	SSE	SSE/(n − 2)
Total	$n - 1$	SST*	

*SST = SSR + SSE.

The coefficient of determination, r^2, can be obtained directly from the ANOVA table by:

COEFFICIENT OF DETERMINATION

$$r^2 = \frac{\text{SSR}}{\text{SST}} = 1 - \frac{\text{SSE}}{\text{SST}} \qquad \textbf{[12–12]}$$

The term "SSR/SST" is the proportion of the variation in Y *explained* by the independent variable, X. Note the effect of the SSE term on r^2. As SSE decreases, r^2 will increase. Conversely, as the standard error increases, the r^2 term decreases.

The standard error of estimate can also be obtained from the ANOVA table using the following equation:

STANDARD ERROR OF ESTIMATE

$$S_e = \sqrt{\frac{\text{SSE}}{n - 2}} \qquad \textbf{[12–13]}$$

The Copier Sales Inc. example is used to illustrate the computations of the coefficient of determination and the standard error of estimate from an ANOVA table.

example

In the Copier Sales Inc. example we studied the relationship between the number of sales calls made and the number of copiers sold. Use a computer software package to determine the least squares regression equation and the ANOVA table. Identify the regression equation, the standard error of estimate, and the coefficient of determination on the computer output. From the ANOVA table on the computer output, determine the coefficient of determination and the standard error of estimate using formulas (12–12) and (12–13).

solution

Following is the output from **Excel**.

Sales Representative	Calls	Sales
Tom Keller	20	30
Jeff Hall	40	60
Brian Virost	20	40
Greg Fish	30	60
Susan Welch	10	30
Carlos Ramirez	10	40
Rich Niles	20	40
Mike Kiel	20	50
Mark Reynolds	20	30
Soni Jones	30	70

SUMMARY OUTPUT

Regression Statistics	
Multiple R	0.759014
R Square	0.576102
Adjusted R Square	0.523115
Standard Error	9.900824
Observations	10

ANOVA

	df	*SS*	*MS*	*F*	*Significance F*
Regression	1	1066	1066	10.87	0.01090193
Residual	8	784.2	98.03		
Total	9	1850			

Using formula (12–12) the coefficient of determination is .576, found by

$$r^2 = \frac{\text{SSR}}{\text{SST}} = \frac{1066}{1850} = .576$$

This is the same value we computed earlier in the chapter, when we found the coefficient of determination by squaring the coefficient of correlation. Again, the interpretation is that the independent variable, *Calls*, explains 57.6 percent of the variation in the number of copiers sold. If we needed the coefficient of correlation, we could find it by taking the square root of the coefficient of determination:

$$r = \sqrt{r^2} = \sqrt{.576} = .759$$

A problem does remain, and that involves the sign for the coefficient of correlation. Recall that the square root of a value could have either a positive or a negative sign. The sign of the coefficient of correlation will always be the same as that of the slope. That is, b and r will always have the same sign. In this case the sign is positive, so the coefficient of correlation is .759.

To find the standard error of estimate, we use formula (12–13):

$$S_e = \sqrt{\frac{\text{SSE}}{n-2}} = \sqrt{\frac{784.2}{10-2}} = 9.901$$

Again, this is the same value calculated earlier in the chapter. These values are identified on the **Excel** output.

MegaStat Steps and output follow.

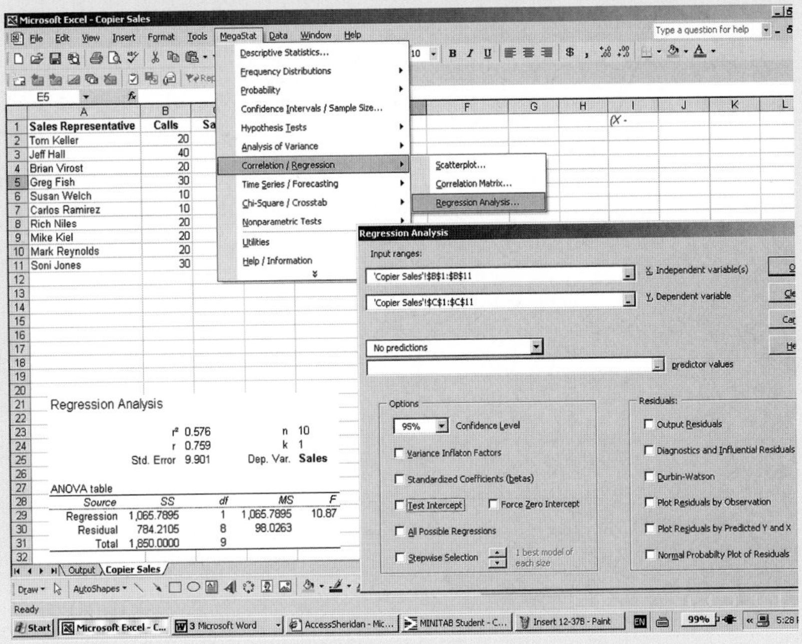

Exercises

33. Given the following ANOVA table:

SOURCE	DF	SS	MS	F
Regression	1	1000.0	1000.00	26.00
Error	13	500.0	38.46	
Total	14	1500.0		

a. Determine the coefficient of determination.

b. Assuming a direct relationship between the variables, what is the coefficient of correlation?

c. Determine the standard error of estimate.

34. On the first statistics exam, the coefficient of determination between the hours studied and the grade earned was 80 percent. The standard error of estimate was 10. There were 20 students in the class. Develop an ANOVA table.

Chapter Summary

I. A scatter diagram is a graphic tool to portray the relationship between two variables.

A. The dependent variable is scaled on the Y-axis and is the variable being estimated.

B. The independent variable is scaled on the X-axis and is the variable used as the estimator.

II. In regression analysis we estimate one variable based on another variable.

A. The variable being estimated is the dependent variable.

B. The variable used to make the estimate is the independent variable.

1. The relationship between the variables must be linear.
2. Both the independent and the dependent variable must be interval or ratio level.
3. The least squares criterion is used to determine the regression equation.

III. The least squares regression line is of the form $Y' = a + bX$.

A. Y' is the estimated value of Y for a selected value of X.

B. b is the slope of the line.
1. It shows the amount of change in Y' for a change of 1 in X.
2. A positive value for b indicates that if one variable increases so does the other, and a negative value indicates that if one variable increases the other decreases.
3. The sign of b and the sign of r, the coefficient of correlation, are always the same.
4. b is computed using the following equation.

$$b = \frac{n(\Sigma XY) - (\Sigma X)(\Sigma Y)}{n(\Sigma X^2) - (\Sigma X)^2} \quad [12\text{–}2]$$

C. a is the constant or intercept.
1. It is the value of Y' when $X = 0$.
2. a is computed using the following equation.

$$a = \frac{\Sigma Y}{n} - b\frac{\Sigma X}{n} \quad [12\text{–}3]$$

D. X is the value of the independent variable.

IV. The standard error of estimate measures the variation around the regression line.

A. It is in the same units as the dependent variable.

B. It is based on squared deviations from the regression line.

C. Small values indicate that the points cluster closely about the regression line.

D. It is computed using the following formula.

$$S_e = \sqrt{\frac{\Sigma(Y - Y')^2}{n - 2}} = \sqrt{\frac{\Sigma Y^2 - a(\Sigma Y) - b(\Sigma XY)}{n - 2}} \quad [12\text{–}4, 12\text{–}5]$$

V. Inference about linear regression is based on the following assumptions.

A. For a given value of X, the values of Y are normally distributed about the line of regression.

B. The standard deviation of each of the normal distributions is the same for all values of X and is estimated by the standard error of estimate.

C. The deviations from the regression line are independent, with no pattern to the size or direction.

VI. There are two types of interval estimates.

A. In a confidence interval the mean value of Y is estimated for a given value of X.
1. It is computed from the following formula.

$$Y' \pm tS_e = \sqrt{\frac{1}{n} + \frac{(X - \bar{X})^2}{\Sigma(X - \bar{X})^2}} \quad [12\text{–}6]$$

2. The width of the interval is affected by the level of confidence, the size of the standard error of estimate, and the size of the sample, as well as the value of the independent variable.

B. In a prediction interval the individual value of Y is estimated for a given value of X.
1. It is computed from the following formula.

$$Y' \pm tS_e = \sqrt{1 + \frac{1}{n} + \frac{(X - \bar{X})^2}{\Sigma(X - \bar{X})^2}} \quad [12\text{–}7]$$

2. The difference between formulas (12–6) and (12–7) is the 1 under the radical.
   a. The prediction interval will be wider than the confidence interval.
   b. The prediction interval is also based on the level of confidence, the size of the standard error of estimate, the size of the sample, and the value of the independent variable.

VII. The coefficient of correlation measures the strength of the association between two variables.

A. Both variables must be at least the interval level of measurement.

B. The coefficient of correlation can range from −1.00 up to 1.00.

C. If the correlation between two variables is 0, there is no association between them.

D. A value of 1.00 indicates perfect positive correlation, and −1.00 perfect negative correlation.

E. A positive sign means that if one variable increases so does the other, and a negative sign means that if one variable increases the other decreases.

F. It is designated by the letter r and found by the following equations:

$$r = \frac{\Sigma(X - \bar{X})(Y - \bar{Y})}{(n-1)s_x s_y} = \frac{n(\Sigma XY) - (\Sigma X)(\Sigma Y)}{\sqrt{[n(\Sigma X^2) - (\Sigma X^2)][n(\Sigma Y^2) - (\Sigma Y)^2]}} \quad [12\text{–}8, 12\text{–}9]$$

G. The following equation is used to determine whether the correlation in the population is different from 0.

$$t = \frac{r\sqrt{n-2}}{\sqrt{1-r^2}} \quad [12\text{–}10]$$

VIII. The coefficient of determination is the fraction of the variation in one variable that is explained by the variation in the other variable.

A. It ranges from 0 to 1.0.

B. It is the square of the coefficient of correlation.

Pronunciation Key

SYMBOL	MEANING	PRONUNCIATION
ΣXY	Sum of the products of X and Y	*Sum X Y*
ρ	Coefficient of correlation in the population	*Rho*
Y'	Estimated value of Y	*Y prime*
S_e	Standard error of estimate	*S sub e*
r^2	Coefficient of determination	*r square*

Chapter Exercises

35. A regional commuter airline selected a random sample of 25 flights and found that the correlation between the number of passengers and the total mass, in kilograms, of luggage stored in the luggage compartment is .94. Using the .05 significance level, can we conclude that there is a positive association between the two variables?

36. A sociologist claims that the success of students in college (measured by their GPA) is related to their family's income. For a sample of 20 students, the coefficient of correlation is .40. Using the .01 significance level, can we conclude that there is a positive correlation between the variables?

37. A CAA study of 12 automobiles revealed a correlation of .47 between the engine size and performance. At the .01 significance level, can we conclude that there is a positive association between these variables? What is the p-value? Interpret.

38. A study of college soccer games revealed the correlation between the number of shots attempted and the number of goals scored to be .21 for a sample of 20 games. Is it reasonable to conclude that there is a positive correlation between the two variables? Use the .05 significance level. Determine the p-value.

39. A sample of 30 used cars sold by Northcut Motors in 2009 revealed that the correlation between the selling price and the number of kilometres driven was −.45. At the .05 significance level, can we conclude that there is a negative association in the population between the two variables?

40. A sample of 15 financial executives in the pharmaceutical industry revealed the correlation between the number of fat grams an executive consumed the previous day and that executive's cholesterol level is .345.

a. Does cholesterol seem to increase for those who consumed more fat?

b. How much of the variation in cholesterol level is accounted for by the number of fat grams consumed?

c. At the .05 significance level is it reasonable to conclude there is a positive association between fat grams consumed and cholesterol level? What is the p-value?

41. A suburban hotel derives its gross income from its hotel and restaurant operations. The owners are interested in the relationship between the number of rooms occupied on a nightly basis and the revenue per day in the restaurant. Below is a sample of 25 days (Monday through Thursday) from last year showing the restaurant income at breakfast and number of rooms occupied.

Day	Income	Occupied	Day	Income	Occupied
1	$1452	23	14	$1425	27
2	1361	47	15	1445	34
3	1426	21	16	1439	15
4	1470	39	17	1348	19
5	1456	37	18	1450	38
6	1430	29	19	1431	44
7	1354	23	20	1446	47
8	1442	44	21	1485	43
9	1394	45	22	1405	38
10	1459	16	23	1461	51
11	1399	30	24	1490	61
12	1458	42	25	1426	39
13	1537	54			

a. Does the breakfast revenue seem to increase as the number of occupied rooms increases? Draw a scatter diagram to support your conclusions.
b. Determine the coefficient of correlation between the two variables. Interpret the value.
c. Is it reasonable to conclude that there is a positive relationship between revenue and occupied rooms? Use the .10 significance level.
d. What percent of the variation in revenue in the restaurant is accounted for by the number of rooms occupied?

42. Dr. Raymond Lim wants to investigate the relationship between stress and job satisfaction. To begin, he developed a profile for stress based on assigning points for events such as the death of a spouse, a change in sleeping habits, a change in eating habits, and the addition of a family member. The job satisfaction was also based on assigning points for salary, ability to get along with coworkers, and the job environment. Dr. Lim sampled 25 workers in the technology sector and found correlation between stress and job satisfaction is −.536.
a. Does job satisfaction seem to increase or decrease as stress increases?
b. How much of the variation in stress is accounted for by the variation in job satisfaction?
c. At the .05 significance level, is it reasonable to conclude there is negative association between stress and job satisfaction?

43. The following Regression Analysis and ANOVA table show the relationship between units sold and price.

Regression Analysis

ANOVA table

Source	SS	*df*	MS
Regression	3119.4256	1	3119.4256
Residual	840.5744	14	60.0410
Total	3960.0000	15	

Regression Output

Variables	Coefficients	Std. error	$t(df = 14)$
Intercept	51.0218	4.9740	10.258
Price	−0.5170	0.0717	−7.211

a. Do the units sold seem to increase as the price increases?
b. How much of the variation in the units sold is accounted for by price?
c. What is the coefficient of correlation? Describe the type and the strength of the relationship between units sold and price.
d. What is the estimated number of units sold for a price of $10? Is this value reasonable?

44. The following output shows the relationship between the number of hours studied and the final grade in a statistics course.

Regression Analysis

ANOVA table

Source	SS	*df*	MS
Regression	1569.0299	1	1569.0299
Residual	1163.9701	14	83.1407
Total	2733.0000	15	

Regression Output

Variables	Coefficients	Std. error	$t\,(df = 14)$
Intercept	60.1418	4.06725	14.787
Hours of Study	4.3284	0.9964	4.344

a. Does the final grade seem to increase as the number of hours studied increases?
b. How much of the variation in the final grade is accounted for by the hours studied?
c. What is the coefficient of correlation? Describe the type and the strength of the relationship between the final grade and hours studied.
d. What is the estimated final grade for five hours studied? Is this final grade reasonable?

45. What is the relationship between the amount spent per week on food and the size of the family? Do larger families spend more on food? A sample of 10 families revealed the following figures for family size and the amount spent on food per week.

Family Size	Amount Spent on Food ($)	Family Size	Amount Spent on Food ($)
3	$99	3	$111
6	104	4	74
5	151	4	91
6	129	5	119
6	142	3	91

a. Compute the coefficient of correlation.
b. Determine the coefficient of determination.
c. Can we conclude that there is a positive association between the amount spent on food and the family size? Use the .05 significance level.

46. A sample of 12 condominiums sold last week is selected. Can we conclude that as the number of bedrooms increases, the selling price (reported in $ thousands) also increases?

Number of Bedrooms	Selling Price ($ thousands)	Number of Bedrooms	Selling Price ($ thousands)
3	$200	2	$210
3	210	3	185
2	205	1	205
4	220	2	175
2	180	2	170
3	205	1	195

a. Compute the coefficient of correlation.
b. Determine the coefficient of determination.
c. Can we conclude that there is a positive association between the number of bedrooms and the selling price? Use the .05 significance level.

47. The manufacturer of Cardio Glide exercise equipment wants to study the relationship between the number of months since the glide was purchased and the length of time the equipment was used last week.

Person	Months Owned	Hours Exercised	Person	Months Owned	Hours Exercised
Rupple	12	4	Massa	2	8
Hall	2	10	Sass	8	3
Bennett	6	8	Karl	4	8
Longnecker	9	5	Malrooney	10	2
Phillips	7	5	Veights	5	5

a. Plot the information on a scatter diagram. Let hours of exercise be the dependent variable. Comment on the graph.
b. Determine the coefficient of correlation. Interpret.
c. At the .01 significance level, can we conclude that there is a negative association between the variables?

48. The following regression equation was computed from a sample of 20 observations:

$$Y' = 15 - 5X$$

SSE was found to be 100 and SS total 400.
a. Determine the standard error of estimate.
b. Determine the coefficient of determination.
c. Determine the coefficient of correlation. (Caution: Watch the sign!)

49. An ANOVA table is:

SOURCE	DF	SS	MS	F
Regression	1	50		
Error				
Total	24	500		

a. Complete the ANOVA table.
b. How large was the sample?
c. Determine the standard error of estimate.
d. Determine the coefficient of determination.

50. Following is a regression equation.

$$Y' = 17.08 = 0.16X$$

This information is also available: $S_e = 4.05$, $\Sigma X = 210$, $\Sigma X^2 = 9850$, and $n = 5$.
a. Estimate the value of Y' when $X = 50$.
b. Develop a 95 percent prediction interval for an individual value of Y for $X = 50$.

51. The relationship between the number of bidders on a highway project and the winning (lowest) bid for the project has been studied. Of particular interest is whether the number of bidders increases or decreases the amount of the winning bid.

Project	Number of Bidders, X	Winning Bid ($ millions), Y	Project	Number of Bidders, X	Winning Bid ($ millions), Y
1	9	$5.1	9	6	$10.3
2	9	8.0	10	6	8.0
3	3	9.7	11	4	8.8
4	10	7.8	12	7	9.4
5	5	7.7	13	7	8.6
6	10	5.5	14	7	8.1
7	7	8.3	15	6	7.8
8	11	5.5			

a. Determine the regression equation. Interpret the equation. Do more bidders tend to increase or decrease the amount of the winning bid?
b. Estimate the amount of the winning bid if there were seven bidders.

c. A new entrance is to be constructed onto the highway. There are seven bidders on the project. Develop a 95 percent prediction interval for the winning bid.
d. Determine the coefficient of determination. Interpret its value.

52. Mr. William Profit is studying companies going public for the first time. He is particularly interested in the relationship between the size of the offering and the price per share. A sample of 15 companies that recently went public revealed the following information.

Company	Size ($ millions), X	Price per Share ($), Y	Company	Size ($ millions), X	Price per Share ($), Y
1	$9.0	$10.8	9	$160.7	$11.3
2	94.4	11.3	10	96.5	10.6
3	27.3	11.2	11	83.0	10.5
4	179.2	11.1	12	23.5	10.3
5	71.9	11.1	13	58.7	10.7
6	97.9	11.2	14	93.8	11.0
7	93.5	11.0	15	34.4	10.8
8	70.0	10.7			

a. Determine the regression equation.
b. Determine the coefficient of determination. Do you think Mr. Profit should be satisfied with using the size of the offering as the independent variable?

53. Below is information on the price per share and the dividend for a sample of 30 companies.

Company	Price per Share ($)	Dividend ($)	Company	Price per Share ($)	Dividend ($)
1	$20.00	$3.14	16	$57.06	$9.53
2	22.01	3.36	17	57.40	12.60
3	31.39	0.46	18	58.30	10.43
4	33.57	7.99	19	59.51	7.97
5	35.86	0.77	20	60.60	9.19
6	36.12	8.46	21	64.01	16.50
7	36.16	7.62	22	64.66	16.10
8	37.99	8.03	23	64.74	13.76
9	38.85	6.33	24	64.95	10.54
10	39.65	7.96	25	66.43	21.15
11	43.44	8.95	26	68.18	14.30
12	49.08	9.61	27	69.56	24.42
13	53.73	11.11	28	74.90	11.54
14	54.41	13.28	29	77.91	17.65
15	55.10	10.22	30	80.00	17.36

a. Calculate the regression equation using selling price based on the annual dividend. Interpret the slope value.
b. Determine the coefficient of determination. Interpret its value.
c. Determine the coefficient of correlation. Can you conclude that it is greater than 0 using the .05 significance level?

54. A highway employee performed a regression analysis of the relationship between the number of construction work-zone fatalities and the number of unemployed people in a city. The regression equation is shown as Fatalities = 12.7 + 0.000114 (Unemp) and some more of the output is:

Predictor	Coef	SE Coef	T	P
Constant	12.726	8.115	1.57	0.134
Unemp	0.00011386	0.00002896	3.93	0.001

Analysis of Variance

Source	DF	SS	MS	F	P
Regression	1	10354	10354	15.46	0.001
Residual Error	18	12054	670		
Total	19	22408			

a. How many cities were in the sample?
b. Determine the standard error of estimate.
c. Determine the coefficient of determination.
d. Determine the coefficient of correlation.
e. At the .05 significance level does the evidence suggest there is a positive association between fatalities and the number unemployed?

55. Regression analysis relating the current market value in dollars to the size of homes in Greene County has been developed. The computer output follows. The regression equation is shown as the following: Value = −37 186 + 65.0 Size.

Predictor	Coef	SE Coef	T	P	
Constant	−37186	4629	−8.03	0.000	
Size	64.993	3.047	21.33	0.000	
Analysis of Variance					
Source	**DF**	**SS**	**MS**	**F**	**P**
Regression	1	13548662082	13548662082	454.98	0.000
Residual Error	33	9826687392	29778406		
Total	34	14531349474			

a. How many homes were in the sample?
b. Compute the standard error of estimate.
c. Compute the coefficient of determination.
d. Compute the coefficient of correlation.
e. At the .05 significance level does the evidence suggest a positive association between the market value of homes and the size of the home?

56. The Bardi Trucking Company makes deliveries from Manitoba to the Great Lakes region. Zack Bardi, the president, is studying the relationship between the distance a shipment must travel and the length of time, in days, it takes the shipment to arrive at its destination. To investigate, Zack selected a random sample of 20 shipments made last month. The results are as follows.

Distance (km)	Time (days)	Distance (km)	Time (days)
656	5	862	7
853	14	679	5
646	6	835	13
783	11	607	3
610	8	665	8
841	10	647	7
785	9	685	10
639	9	720	8
762	10	652	6
762	9	828	10

a. Draw a scatter diagram. Based on these data, does it appear that there is a relationship between how many kilometres a shipment has to go and the time it takes to arrive at its destination?
b. Determine the coefficient of correlation. Can we conclude there is a positive correlation between distance and time? Use the .05 significance level.
c. Determine and interpret the coefficient of determination.
d. Determine the standard error of the estimate.

57. Super Markets is considering expanding into the Northwest Territories. Luann Miller, the director of planning, must present an analysis of the proposed expansion to the board of directors. As part of her proposal, she needs to include information on the amount people in the region spend per month on grocery items. She would also like to include information on the relationship between the amount spent for grocery items and income. She gathered the following data.

Monthly Amount ($)	Monthly Income ($)	Monthly Amount ($)	Monthly Income ($)
$555	$4388	$913	$6688
489	4558	918	6752
458	4793	710	6837
613	4856	1083	7242
647	4856	937	7263
661	4899	839	7540
662	4899	1030	8009
675	5091	1065	8094
549	5133	1069	8264
606	5304	1064	8392
668	5304	1015	8414
740	5304	1148	8882
592	5346	1125	8925
720	5495	1090	8989
680	5581	1208	9053
540	5730	1217	9138
693	5943	1140	9329
541	5943	1265	9649
673	6156	1206	9862
676	6603	1145	9880

a. Create a scatter diagram.
b. Determine the regression equation. Interpret the slope value.
c. Determine the coefficient of correlation. Interpret your findings.
d. Based on this data, would you recommend the expansion? Explain.

Data Set Exercises

58. Refer to the real estate data, from the south-east area of Edmonton, on the CD-ROM, which reports information on listed homes.

a. Let list price be the dependent variable and size of the home the independent variable. Determine the regression equation. Estimate the list price for a home with an area of 2200 square feet. Determine the 95 percent confidence interval and the 95 percent prediction interval for the list price of a home with 2200 square feet.

b. Let list price be the dependent variable and number of bedrooms the independent variable. Determine the regression equation. Estimate the list price of a house with three bedrooms. Determine the 95 percent confidence interval and the 95 percent prediction interval for a house with three bedrooms.

c. Can you conclude that the independent variables "number of bedrooms" and "list price" are positively correlated and that the size of the home and the list price are also positively correlated? Use the .05 significance level. Report the *p*-value of the test.

59. Refer to the Baseball 2006 data, which reports information on the 2006 Major League Baseball season.

a. Let the games won be the dependent variable and total team salary, in millions of dollars, be the independent variable. Can you conclude that there is a positive association between the two variables? Determine the regression equation and interpret the slope. How many additional wins will an additional $5 million in salary bring?

b. Determine the correlation between games won and ERA, and between games won and team batting average. Which has the stronger correlation? Can we conclude that there is positive correlation between wins and team batting and a negative correlation between wins and ERA? Use the .05 significance level.

c. Assume the number of games won is the dependent variable and attendance the independent variable. Can we conclude that the correlation between these two variables is greater than 0? Use a significance level of .05.

60. Refer to the International data, which reports demographic and economic information on 46 countries.

a. You wish to use the Labour force variable as the independent variable to predict the unemployment rate. Interpret the slope value. Use the appropriate linear regression equation to predict unemployment in the United Arab Emirates.

b. Find the correlation coefficient between the levels of exports and imports. Use the .05 significance level to test whether there is a positive correlation between these two variables.

c. Does there appear to be a relationship between the percentage of the population over 65 and the literacy percentage? Support your answer with statistical evidence. Conduct an appropriate test of hypothesis and interpret the result.

exercises.com

Additional exercises that require you to access information at related Internet sites are available on the CD-ROM included with this text.

Answers to Self-Reviews

12–1 (a) Advertising expense is the independent variable and sales revenue is the dependent variable.

(b)

12–2 (a)

X	Y	XY	X^2	Y^2
2	7	14	4	49
1	3	3	1	9
3	8	24	9	64
4	10	40	16	100
10	28	81	30	222

$$b = \frac{4(81) - (10)(28)}{4(30) - (10)^2} = \frac{324 - 280}{120 - 100} = 2.2.$$

$$a = \frac{28}{4} - 2.2\left(\frac{10}{4}\right) = 7 - 5.5 = 1.5.$$

(b) The slope is 2.2. This indicates that an increase of \$1 thousand in advertising will result in an increase of \$2.2 thousand in sales. The intercept is 1.5. If there was no expenditure for advertising, sales would be \$1.5 thousand.

(c) $Y' = 1.5 + 2.2(3) = 8.1$.

12–3 0.9487, found by:

$$S_e = \sqrt{\frac{\Sigma Y^2 - a(\Sigma Y) - b(\Sigma XY)}{n - 2}} = \sqrt{\frac{222 - 1.5(28) - 2.2(81)}{4 - 2}} = \sqrt{\frac{1.8}{2}} = 0.9487.$$

12–4 6.58 and 9.62, since Y' for an X of 3 is 8.1, found by $Y' = 1.5 + 2.2(3) = 8.1$, then $\bar{X} = 2.5$ and $\Sigma X^2 = 30$ and $\Sigma X = 10$.

t from Appendix F for $4 - 2 = 2$ degrees of freedom at the .10 level is 2.920.

$$Y' \pm tS_e\sqrt{\frac{1}{n} + \frac{(X - \bar{X})^2}{\Sigma(X - \bar{X})^2}}$$

$$= 8.1 \pm 2.920(0.9487)\sqrt{\frac{1}{4} + \frac{(3 - 2.5)^2}{5}}$$

$$= 8.1 \pm 2.920(0.9487)(0.5477)$$

$$= 6.58 \text{ and } 9.62 \text{ (in \$ thousands).}$$

12–5 See the calculations from Self-Review 12–2, part (a).

(a) $r = .96$, found by

$$r = \frac{4(81) - (10)(28)}{\sqrt{[4(30) - (10)^2][4(222) - (28)^2]}} = \frac{44}{\sqrt{2080}} = \frac{44}{45.607017} = .9648.$$

(b) There is a strong correlation between the advertising expense and sales.

(c) $r^2 = .93$, 93 percent of the variation in sales is "explained" by variation in advertising.

12–6 H_0: $\rho \le 0$, H_1: $\rho > 0$. H_0 is rejected if $t > 1.714$.

$$t = \frac{.43\sqrt{25 - 2}}{\sqrt{1 - (.43)^2}} = 2.284.$$

H_0 is rejected. There is a positive correlation between the percent of the vote received and the amount spent on the campaign.

chapter 13

Multiple Regression and Correlation Analysis

LEARNING GOALS

When you have completed this chapter, you will be able to:

1. Describe the relationship between several independent variables and a dependent variable using a *multiple regression equation*.
2. Compute and interpret the *multiple standard error of estimate* and the *coefficient of multiple determination*.
3. Set up and interpret an ANOVA table.
4. Conduct a test of hypothesis to determine whether regression coefficients differ from zero.
5. Conduct a test of hypothesis on each of the regression coefficients.
6. Interpret a correlation matrix.
7. Evaluate the effects of correlated independent variables.
8. Use and understand qualitative independent variables.

Introduction

In Chapter 12 we described the relationship between a pair of interval-level or ratio-level variables. We began the chapter by developing a procedure to determine a linear equation to express the relationship between the two variables. We referred to this as a *line of regression.* This line describes the relationship between the variables. It also describes the overall pattern of a dependent variable (Y) based on a single independent or explanatory variable (X). Next, we studied the coefficient of correlation, which measures the strength of the relationship. A coefficient near plus or minus 1.00 (−.88 or .88, for example) indicates a very strong linear relationship between X and Y. A coefficient near 0 (−.12 or .12, for example) means that the relationship is weak.

In multiple linear correlation and regression we use additional independent variables (denoted X_1, X_2, . . . , and so on) that help us better explain or predict the dependent variable (Y). Almost all of the ideas we saw in simple linear correlation and regression extend to this more general situation. However, the additional independent variables do lead to some new considerations. Multiple regression analysis can be used either as a descriptive or as an inferential technique.

1 Describe the relationship between several independent variables and a dependent variable using a *multiple regression equation*.

Multiple Regression Analysis

The general descriptive form of a multiple linear equation is shown in formula (13–1). We use k to represent the number of independent variables. So, k can be any positive integer.

GENERAL MULTIPLE REGRESSION EQUATION

$$Y' = a + b_1X_1 + b_2X_2 + \cdots + b_kX_k \qquad [13\text{–}1]$$

where:

- a is the y-intercept, the value of Y when all the X-values are zero.
- b_j is the amount by which Y changes when that particular X_j increases by one unit with all other values held constant. The subscript j can assume values between 1 and k, which is the number of independent variables.

In Chapter 12, the regression analysis described and tested the relationship between a dependent variable, Y', and a single independent variable, X. The relationship between Y' and X was graphically portrayed by a line. When there are two independent variables, the regression equation is:

$$Y' = a + b_1X_1 + b_2X_2$$

Because there are two independent variables, this relationship is graphically portrayed as a plane and is shown in Chart 13–1. This chart shows the residuals as the difference between the actual Y and the fitted Y' on the plane. If a multiple regression analysis includes more than two independent variables, we cannot use a graph to illustrate the analysis since graphs are limited to three dimensions.

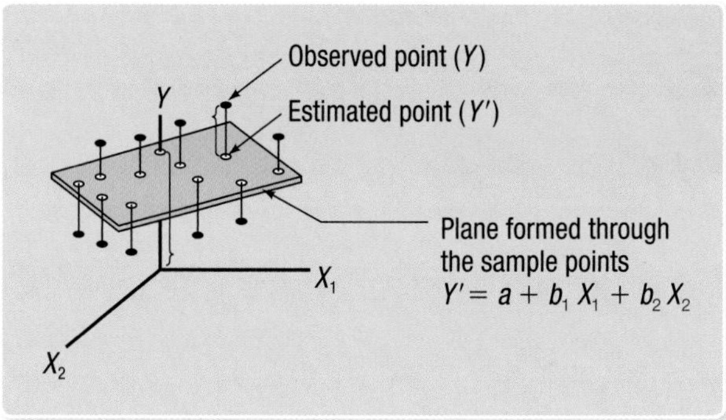

CHART 13–1 Regression Plane with 10 Sample Points

To illustrate the interpretation of the intercept and the two regression coefficients, suppose a vehicle's fuel efficiency is directly related to the octane rating of the gasoline being used (X_1) and inversely related to the mass of the automobile (X_2). Assume that the regression equation, calculated using statistical software, is:

$$Y' = 10.143 + 0.322X_1 - 0.00045X_2$$

The intercept value of 10.143 indicates the regression equation intersects the Y-axis at 10.143 when both X_1 and X_2 are zero. Of course, this does not make any physical sense to own an automobile that has no (zero) mass and to use gasoline with no octane. It is important to keep in mind that a regression equation is not generally used outside the range of the sample values.

The b_1 of 0.322 indicates that for each increase of 1 in the octane rating of the gasoline, the automobile would travel 0.322 km more per litre, *regardless of the mass of the vehicle*. That is, the vehicle's mass is held constant. The b_2 value of -0.00045 reveals that for each increase of one kilogram in the vehicle's mass, the number of kilometres travelled per litre decreases by 0.00045, *regardless of the octane of the gasoline being used*.

As an example, an automobile with 92-octane gasoline in the tank and having a mass of 900 kg would travel an average 39.4 km/L, found by:

$$Y' = a + b_1X_1 + b_2X_2 = 10.143 + 0.322(92) - 0.00045(900) = 39.4$$

The value of 39.4 is in kilometres per litre.

The values for the coefficients in the multiple linear equation are found by using the method of least squares. Recall from the previous chapter that the least squares method makes the sum of the squared differences between the fitted and actual values of Y as small as possible. However, to arrive at a, b_1, and b_2 in the multiple regression equation, the many calculations are very tedious, even using a calculator. As an example, for two independent variables, three equations must be solved simultaneously, namely:

$$\Sigma Y = na + b_1\Sigma X_1 + b_2\Sigma X_2$$
$$\Sigma X_1Y = a\Sigma X_1 + b_1\Sigma X_1^2 + b_2\Sigma X_1X_2$$
$$\Sigma X_2Y = a\Sigma X_2 + b_1\Sigma X_1X_2 + b_2\Sigma X_2^2$$

Because the calculations are so tedious, they are usually performed by a statistical software package, such as **Excel** or MINITAB. Fortunately, the information reported is fairly standard.

We begin the discussion of the multiple regression by describing a situation involving three independent variables.

example

Superior Realty sells homes in Eastern Canada. One of the questions most frequently asked by prospective buyers is: If we purchase this home, how much can we expect to pay to heat it during the winter? The research department at Superior has been asked to develop some guidelines regarding heating costs for single-family homes. Three variables are thought to relate to the heating costs: (1) the mean daily outside temperature, (2) the number of centimetres of insulation in the attic, and (3) the age of the furnace. To investigate, Superior's research department selected a random sample of 20 recently sold homes. They determined the cost to heat the home last January, as well as the January outside temperature in the region, the number of centimetres of insulation in the attic, and the age of the furnace. The sample information is reported in Table 13–1.

TABLE 13–1 Factors in January Heating Cost for a Sample of 20 Homes

Home	Heating Cost ($)	Mean Outside Temperature (°C)	Attic Insulation (cm)	Age of Furnace (years)
1	$250	−8	7.5	6
2	360	−13	10	10
3	165	−9	17.5	3
4	143	−2	15	9
5	192	−7	12.5	6
6	200	−8	12.5	5
7	355	−14	15	7
8	290	−15	22.5	10
9	230	−10	22.5	11
10	120	0	5	5
11	173	−6	30	4
12	205	−10	12.5	1
13	400	−12	12.5	15
14	320	−6	10	7
15	172	−5	20	6
16	272	−5	12.5	8
17	194	−7	17.5	3
18	190	−9	20	11
19	235	−8	22.5	8
20	139	0	17.5	5

The data in Table 13–1 is available on the student CD in both **Excel** and MINITAB formats.

Determine the multiple regression equation. Which variables are the independent variables? Which variable is the dependent variable? Discuss the regression coefficients. What does it indicate that some are positive and some are negative? What is the intercept value? What is the estimated heating cost for a home if the mean outside temperature is −5°C, there are 12.5 cm of insulation in the attic, and the furnace is 10 years old?

solution

Excel output and steps to create the multiple regression output follow. Note that the columns containing the independent variables must be adjacent.

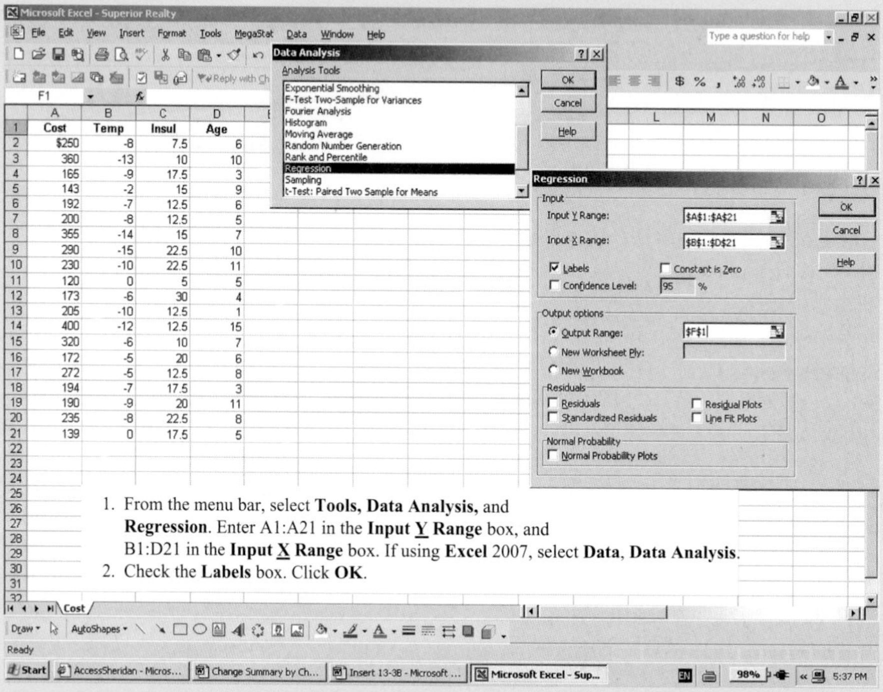

1. From the menu bar, select **Tools, Data Analysis,** and **Regression**. Enter A1:A21 in the **Input Y Range** box, and B1:D21 in the **Input X Range** box. If using **Excel** 2007, select **Data, Data Analysis.**
2. Check the **Labels** box. Click **OK**.

Statistics in Action

Many studies indicate a woman will earn about 70 percent of what a man would for the same work. Researchers have found that about one-third of the difference can be explained by such social factors as differences in education, seniority, and work interruptions. The remaining two-thirds is not explained by these social factors.

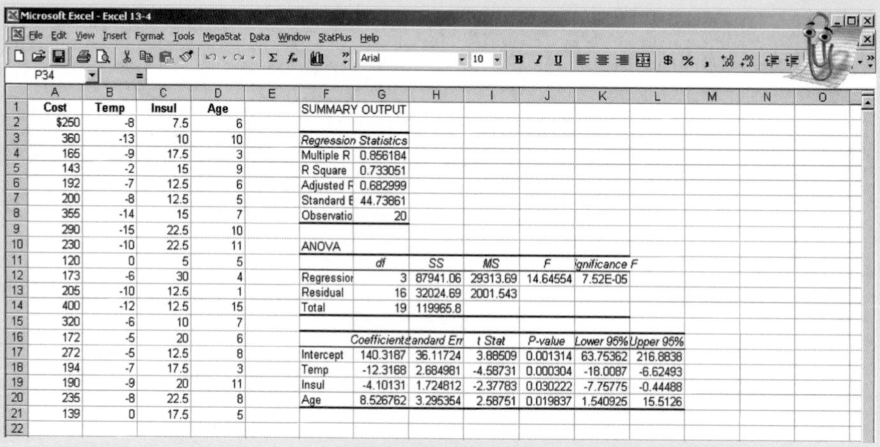

We begin the analysis by defining the dependent and independent variables. The dependent variable is the January heating cost. There are three independent variables:

- The mean outside temperature in January, represented by X_1.
- The number of centimetres of insulation in the attic, represented by X_2.
- The age in years of the furnace, represented by X_3.

Given these definitions, the general form of the multiple regression equation follows. The value Y' is used to estimate the value of Y.

$$Y' = a + b_1X_1 + b_2X_2 + b_3X_3$$

To use the regression equation to predict the January heating cost, we need to know the values of the regression coefficients, b_1, b_2 and b_3. Refer to the above **Excel** output. In this case the multiple regression equation is $Y' = 140.3187 - 12.3168X_1 - 4.10131X_2 + 8.526762X_3$. Note that the software used the variable name or labels associated with each independent variable. We can now estimate or predict the January heating cost for a home if we know the mean outside temperature, the number of centimetres of insulation, and the age of the furnace. For the first example home, the mean outside temperature for the month is −8°C, (X_1), with 7.5 cm of insulation (X_2), and the furnace is 6 years old (X_3). By substituting the values for the independent variables:

$$\mathbf{Y' = 140.3187 - 12.3168(-8) - 4.10131(7.5) + 8.526762(6) = 259.25}$$

The estimated January heating cost is \$259.25.

The regression coefficients and their algebraic signs also provide information about the individual relationships with the January heating cost. The regression coefficient for the mean outside temperature is −12.3168. The coefficient is negative and shows an inverse relationship between heating cost and temperature. This is not surprising. As the outside temperature increases, the cost to heat the home decreases. The numeric value of the regression coefficient provides more information. If we increase the temperature by 1 degree and hold the other two independent variables constant, we can estimate a decrease of \$12.32 in monthly heating cost. So, if the mean temperature in Charlottetown is −3.4°C and it is −4°C in Fredericton, all other things being the same, we expect the heating cost would be \$7.39 less in Charlottetown, found by −12.3168 times the difference in the mean temperature, 0.6.

The variable "attic insulation" also shows an inverse relationship: the more insulation in the attic, the less the cost to heat the home. So, the negative sign for this coefficient is logical. For each additional centimetre of insulation, we expect the cost to heat the home to decline \$4.10 per month, holding the outside temperature and the age of the furnace constant.

The age of furnace variable shows a direct relationship. With an older furnace, the cost to heat the home increases. Specifically, for each additional year old the furnace is, we expect the cost to increase \$8.53 per month.

self-review 13–1

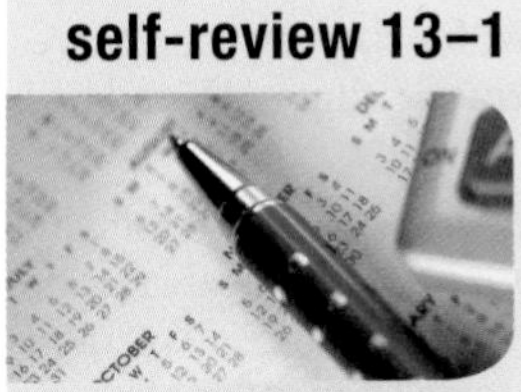

The quality control engineer at Palmer Industries is interested in estimating the tensile strength of steel wire based on its outside diameter and the amount of molybdenum in the steel. As an experiment, she selected 25 pieces of wire, measured the outside diameters, and determined the molybdenum content. Then she measured the tensile strength of each piece. The results of the first four were:

Piece	Tensile Strength, (psi), Y	Outside Diameter (mm), X_1	Amount of Molybdenum (units), X_2
A	11	.3	6
B	9	.2	5
C	16	.4	8
D	12	.3	7

Using a statistical software package, the QC engineer determined the multiple regression equation to be $Y' = -0.5 + 20X_1 + 1X_2$.

(a) Based on the equation, what is the estimated tensile strength of a steel wire having an outside diameter of .35 mm and 6.4 units of molybdenum?

(b) Interpret the value of b_1 in the equation.

Exercises

1. The director of marketing at Reeves Wholesale Products is studying the monthly sales. Three independent variables were selected as estimators of sales: regional population (X_1), per capita income (X_2), and regional unemployment rate (X_3). The regression equation was computed to be (in dollars):

$$Y' = 64\,100 + 0.394X_1 + 9.6X_2 - 11\,600X_3$$

   a. What is the full name of the equation?
   b. Interpret the number 64 100.
   c. What are the estimated monthly sales for a particular region with a population of 796 000, per capita income of \$6940, and an unemployment rate of 6.0 percent? (Use 6.0 in your calculations.)

2. Thompson Photo Works purchased several new, highly sophisticated machines. The production department needed some guidance with respect to qualifications needed by an operator. Is age a factor? Is the length of service as a machine operator important? In order to explore further the factors needed to estimate performance on the new machines, four variables were listed:

   X_1 = Length of time employee was a machinist.
   X_2 = Mechanical aptitude test score.
   X_3 = Prior on-the-job rating.
   X_4 = Age.

   Performance on the new machine is designated Y.

   Thirty machinists were selected at random. Data were collected for each, and their performances on the new machines were recorded. A few results are:

Name	Performance on New Machine, Y	Length of Time as a Machinist, X_1	Mechanical Aptitude Score, X_2	Prior On-the-Job Performance, X_3	Age, X_4
Andy Kosin	112	12	312	121	52
Sue Annis	113	2	380	123	27

   The equation is:

$$Y' = 11.6 + 0.4X_1 + 0.286X_2 + 0.112X_3 + 0.002X_4$$

   a. What is the full designation of the equation?
   b. How many dependent variables are there? Independent variables?
   c. What is the number 0.286 called?
   d. As age increases by one year, how much does estimated performance on the new machine increase?
   e. Carl Knox applied for a job at Photo Works. He has been a machinist for six years, and scored 280 on the mechanical aptitude test. Carl's prior on-the-job performance rating is 97, and he is 35 years old. Estimate Carl's performance on the new machine.

3. A sample of General Mills employees was studied to determine their degree of satisfaction with their present life. A special index, called the index of satisfaction, was used to measure satisfaction. Six factors were studied, namely, age at the time of first marriage (X_1), annual income (X_2), number of children living (X_3), value of all assets (X_4), status of health in the form of an index (X_5), and the average number of social activities per week—such as bowling and dancing (X_6). Suppose the multiple regression equation is:

$$Y' = 16.24 + 0.017X_1 + 0.0028X_2 + 42X_3 + 0.0012X_4 + 0.19X_5 + 26.8X_6$$

   a. What is the estimated index of satisfaction for a person who first married at 18, has an annual income of \$26 500, has three children living, has assets of \$156 000, has an index of health status of 141, and has 2.5 social activities a week on the average?
   b. Which would add more to satisfaction, an additional income of \$10 000 a year or two more social activities a week?

4. Cellulon, a manufacturer of a new type of home insulation, wants to develop guidelines for builders and consumers regarding the effects on natural gas consumption (1) of the thickness of the insulation

in the attic of a home and (2) of the outdoor temperature. In the laboratory they varied the insulation thickness and temperature. A few of the findings are:

Monthly Natural Gas Consumption (cubic feet), Y	Thickness of Insulation (cm), X_1	Outdoor Temperature (°C), X_2
30.3	12.5	4
26.9	30	4
22.1	20	9

Based on the sample results, the regression equation is:

$$Y' = 38.12 - 0.194X_1 - 1.349X_2$$

a. How much natural gas can homeowners expect to use per month if they install 15 cm of insulation and the outdoor temperature is 10°C?

b. What effect would installing 18 cm of insulation instead of 15 have on the monthly natural gas consumption (assuming the outdoor temperature remains at 10°C)?

c. Why are the regression coefficients, b_1 and b_2, negative? Is this logical?

How Well Does the Equation Fit the Data?

Once you have the multiple regression equation, it is natural to ask "how well does the equation fit the data?" In linear regression, discussed in the previous chapter, you used summary statistics such as the standard error of the estimate and the coefficient of determination to describe how effectively a single independent variable explained the variation of the dependent variable. The same procedures, broadened to additional independent variables, are used in multiple regression.

2 Compute and interpret the *multiple standard error of estimate* and the *coefficient of multiple determination.*

Multiple Standard Error of Estimate

We begin with the **multiple standard error of estimate**. Recall that the standard error of estimate is comparable to the standard deviation. The standard deviation uses squared deviations from the mean, $(Y - \bar{Y})^2$, whereas the standard error of estimate utilizes squared deviations from the regression line, $(Y - Y')^2$. To explain the details of the standard error of estimate, refer to the first sampled home in Table 13–1 in the previous example. The actual heating cost for the first observation, Y, is \$295.25; the outside temperature X_1 is −8°C, the depth of insulation X_2, is 7.5 cm, and the age of the furnace X_3, 6 years. The estimated heating cost Y' is found by:

$$Y' = 140.3187 - 12.3168(-8) - 4.10131(7.5) + 8.526762(6) = \$259.25$$

The actual heating cost was \$250, so the residual—which is the difference between the actual value and the estimate value—is $Y - Y' = 250 - 259.25 = -9.25$. This difference of \$9.25 is the random or unexplained error for the first item sampled. Our next step is to square this difference, that is find $(Y - Y')^2 = (250 - 259.25)^2 = (-9.25)^2 = 85.5625$. We repeat these operations for the other 19 observations and total these squared values. This value is the numerator of the multiple standard error of estimate. The denominator is the degrees of freedom, that is $n - (k + 1)$. The formula for the standard error is:

MULTIPLE STANDARD ERROR OF ESTIMATE

$$s_{e \cdot 12 \cdots k} = \sqrt{\frac{\Sigma(Y - Y')^2}{n - k - 1}} \quad [13\text{–}2]$$

where:

Y is the observation.
Y' is the value estimated from the regression equation.

n is the number of observations in the sample.
k is the number of independent variables.

In this example $n = 20$ and $k = 3$ (three independent variables), so the multiple standard error of estimate is:

$$S_{e \cdot 123} = \sqrt{\frac{\Sigma(Y - Y')^2}{n - k - 1}} = \sqrt{\frac{32\,024.69}{20 - 3 - 1}} = 44.74$$

Since we have three independent variables, we identify the multiple standard error as $S_{e \cdot 123}$. The subscripts indicate that three independent variables are being used to estimate Y. This value also appears in the previous **Excel** output labelled as 'Standard Error.'

How do we interpret the 44.74? It is the typical "error" we make when we use this equation to predict the cost. First, the units are the same as the dependent variable, so the standard error in dollars is \$44.74. Second, if the residuals are approximately normally distributed, about 68 percent of them will be within ±\$44.74 and about 95 percent within ±2(\$44.74) = \$89.48. Refer to the second column from the right in Table 13–2, the column headed $(Y - Y')$. Of the 20 residuals reported in this column, 14 are between ±\$44.74 and all are between ±\$89.48, which is very close to the guidelines of 68 percent and 95 percent.

TABLE 13–2 Calculations Needed for the Multiple Standard Error of Estimate

Home	Temperature °C	Insulation (cm)	Age (years)	Actual Cost (\$) Y	Estimated Cost (\$) Y'	Residual (\$) $(Y - Y')$	$(Y - Y')^2$
1	−8	7.5	6	\$250	\$259.25	−\$9.25	85.56
2	−13	10	10	360	344.69	15.31	234.40
3	−9	17.5	3	165	204.98	−39.98	1598.40
4	−2	15	9	143	180.17	−37.17	1381.61
5	−7	12.5	6	192	226.43	−34.43	1185.42
6	−8	12.5	5	200	230.22	−30.22	913.25
7	−14	15	7	355	310.92	44.08	1943.05
8	−15	22.5	10	290	318.06	−28.06	787.36
9	−10	22.5	11	230	265.00	−35	1225.00
10	0	5	5	120	162.45	−42.45	1802.00
11	−6	30	4	173	125.29	47.71	2276.24
12	−10	12.5	1	205	220.75	−15.75	248.06
13	−12	12.5	15	400	364.76	35.24	1241.86
14	−6	10	7	320	232.89	87.11	7588.15
15	−5	20	6	172	171.04	0.96	0.92
16	−5	12.5	8	272	218.85	53.15	2824.92
17	−7	17.5	3	194	180.34	13.66	186.60
18	−9	20	11	190	262.94	−72.94	5320.24
19	−8	22.5	8	235	214.79	20.21	408.44
20	0	17.5	5	139	111.18	27.82	773.95
Total							32 025.45

3 Set up and interpret an ANOVA table.

The ANOVA Table

As mentioned previously, the multiple regression calculations are long. Fortunately, many software systems are available to perform the calculations. Most of them report the results in a standard format. The output from **Excel** that follows is typical. It includes the regression equation, the standard error of estimate, the coefficient of determination, as well as an analysis of variance table. We have already described the meaning of the regression coefficients in the equation $Y' = 140.3187 - 12.3168X_1 - 4.10131X_2 + 8.526762X_3$. We will discuss the meanings of the column headings later.

ANOVA

	df	*SS*	*MS*	*F*	*Significance F*
Regression	3	87941.06	29313.69	14.64554	7.52E-05
Residual	16	32024.69	2001.543		
Total	19	119965.75			

	Coefficients	*Standard Error*	*t Stat*	*P-value*	*Lower 95%*	*Upper 95%*
Intercept	140.3187	36.11724	3.88509	0.001314	63.75362	216.8838
Temp	−12.3168	2.684981	−4.58731	0.000304	−18.0087	−6.62493
Insul	−4.10131	1.724812	−2.37783	0.030222	−7.75775	−0.44488
Age	8.526762	3.295354	2.58751	0.019837	1.540925	15.5126

First, let's focus on the analysis of variance table. It is similar to the ANOVA table described in Chapter 11. In that chapter the variation was divided into two components: variance due to the *treatments* and variance due to random *error*. Here the total variance is also separated into two components: variance explained by **regression**, that is, the independent variables, and the **residual** or **error** variation (unexplained variation). This is the random error due to sampling. There are three categories identified in the first or Source column in the ANOVA table: Regression (explained variation), Residual or Residual Error (unexplained variation) and Total (total variation).

The second column is labelled *df* in the ANOVA table. It is the degrees of freedom. The degrees of freedom in the "Regression" row is the number of independent variables. We let k represent the number of independent variables, so $k = 3$. The degrees of freedom in the "Residual" is $n - (k + 1) = 20 - (3 + 1) = 16$. In this example, there are 20 observations so $n = 20$. The total degrees of freedom is $n - 1 = 20 - 1 = 19$.

The heading "SS" in the third column of the ANOVA table refers to the sum of squares, or the variation.

$$\text{Total variation} = \text{SS total} = \Sigma(Y - \bar{Y})^2 = 119\,965.75$$
$$\text{Residual variation} = \text{SSE} = \Sigma(Y - Y')^2 = 32\,024.69$$
$$\text{Regression variation} = \text{SSR} = \Sigma(Y' - \bar{Y}) = \text{SS total} - \text{SSE}$$
$$= 119\,965.75 - 32\,024.69 = 87\,941.06$$

The column headed "MS", or mean square, is determined by dividing the SS quantity by the matching *df* term. Thus, MSR, the mean square regression, is equal to SSR/k, and MSE, the mean square error, equals SSE/$[n - k - 1]$. The general format of the ANOVA table is:

Source	*df*	SS	MS	*F*
Regression	k	SSR	MSR = SSR/k	MSR/MSE
Error	$n - k - 1$	SSE	MSE = SSE/$[n - k - 1]$	
Total	$n - 1$	SS total		

Each value in the ANOVA table plays an important role in the evaluation and interpretation of a multiple regression equation. Notice, for example, that the standard error of estimate can be very easily computed from the ANOVA table.

$$S_{e\cdot 123} = \sqrt{\text{MSE}} = \sqrt{2001.543} = 44.74$$

Coefficient of Multiple Determination

coefficient of multiple determination The percent of variation in the dependent variable, Y, explained by the set of independent variables, $X_1, X_2, X_3, \ldots X_k$.

Next, let's look at the **coefficient of multiple determination**. Recall from the previous chapter the coefficient of determination is defined as the percent of variation in the dependent variable explained, or accounted for, by the independent variable. In the multiple regression case we extend this definition as follows.

The characteristics of the coefficient of multiple determination are:

1. **It is symbolized by a capital R squared (R^2).** It is written as R^2, as it behaves like the square of a correlation coefficient.
2. **It can range from 0 to 1.** A value near 0 indicates little association between the set of independent variables and the dependent variable. A value near 1 means a strong association.
3. **It cannot assume negative values.** Any number that is squared or raised to the second power cannot be negative.
4. **It is easy to interpret.** Because R^2 is a value between 0 and 1 it is easy to interpret, compare, and understand.

We can calculate the coefficient of determination from the information found in the ANOVA table. We look in the sum of squares column, which is labelled SS in the output, and use the regression sum of squares, SSR, then divide by SS total, the total sum of squares.

COEFFICIENT OF MULTIPLE DETERMINATION $$R^2 = \frac{\text{SSR}}{\text{SS total}} \quad [13\text{–}3]$$

$$R^2 = \frac{\text{SSR}}{\text{SS total}} = \frac{87\,941.06}{119\,965.75} = .733$$

How do we interpret this value? We say the independent variables (outside temperature, amount of insulation, and age of furnace) explain, or account for, 73.3 percent of the variation in heating cost. To put it another way, 26.7 percent of the variation is due to other sources, such as random error or variables not included in the analysis. Using the ANOVA table, 26.7 percent is the error sum of squares divided by the total sum of squares. Knowing that SSR + SSE = SS Total, the following relationship is true.

$$1 - R^2 = 1 - \frac{\text{SSR}}{\text{SS total}} = \frac{\text{SSE}}{\text{SS total}} = \frac{32\,024.69}{119\,965.75} = .267$$

The multiple standard error of estimate may also be found directly from the ANOVA table.

$$S_{e\cdot 123} = \sqrt{\frac{\text{SSE}}{n-k-1}} = \sqrt{\frac{32\,024.69}{20-3-1}} = 44.74$$

Note that the multiple standard error of estimate is also the square root of MS Residual: $\sqrt{2001.543} = 44.74$.

self-review 13–2

Refer to the following ANOVA table.

SOURCE	DF	SS	MS	F
Regression	4	10	2.50	10.0
Error	20	5	0.25	
Total	24	15		

(a) How large was the sample?
(b) How many independent variables are there?
(c) Compute the coefficient of multiple determination. Interpret this value.
(d) Compute the multiple standard error of estimate.

Exercises

5. Refer to the following A NOVA table.

SOURCE	DF	SS	MS	F
Regression	3	21	7.0	2.33
Error	15	45	3.0	
Total	18	66		

a. How large was the sample?
b. How many independent variables are there?
c. Compute the coefficient of multiple determination. Interpret this value.
d. Compute the multiple standard error of estimate.

6. Refer to the following ANOVA table.

SOURCE	DF	SS	MS	F
Regression	5	60	12	1.714
Error	20	140	7	
Total	25	200		

a. How large was the sample?
b. How many independent variables are there?
c. Compute the coefficient of multiple determination. Interpret this value.
d. Compute the multiple standard error of estimate.

Inferences in Multiple Linear Regression

Thus far, multiple regression analysis has been viewed only as a way to describe the relationship between a dependent variable and several independent variables. However, the least squares method also has the ability to draw inferences or generalizations about the relationship for an entire population. Recall that when you create confidence intervals or perform hypothesis tests as part of inferential statistics, you view the data as a random sample taken from some population.

In the multiple regression setting, we assume there is an unknown population regression equation that relates the dependent variable to the k independent variables. This is sometimes called a **model** of the relationship. In symbols, we write:

$$Y' = \alpha + \beta_1 X_1 + \beta_2 X_2 + \cdots + \beta_k X_k$$

This formula is analogous to formula (13–1) except the coefficients are now reported as Greek letters. We use Greek letters to denote *population parameters*. Then under a certain set of assumptions, which will be discussed shortly, the computed values of a and b_j are sample statistics. These sample statistics are point estimates of the corresponding population parameters α and β_j. For example, the sample regression coefficient b_2, is a point-estimate of the population parameter β_2. The sampling distribution of these point estimates follows the normal probability distribution. These sampling distributions are each centred at their respective parameter values. To put it another way, the means of the sampling distributions are equal to the parameter values to be estimated. Thus, by using the properties of the sampling distributions of these statistics, inferences about the population parameters are possible.

Evaluating the Regression Equation

Earlier in the chapter we described an example in which Superior Realty developed, using multiple regression techniques, an equation to express the cost to heat a home during the month of January based on the mean outside temperature, the number of centimetres of attic insulation, and the age of the furnace. The equation seemed reasonable, but we wish to verify that the multiple coefficient of determination is significantly larger than zero, evaluate the regression coefficients to see which are not equal to zero, and verify that the regression assumptions are met.

4 Conduct a test of hypothesis to determine whether regression coefficients differ from zero.

Global Test: Testing the Multiple Regression Model

We can test the ability of the independent variables, $X_1, X_2, \ldots, X_k$, to explain the behaviour of the dependent variable, Y. To put this in question form: Can the dependent variable be estimated without relying on the independent variables? The test used is referred to as the

global test. Basically, it investigates whether it is possible that all the independent variables have zero net regression coefficients. To put it another way, could the amount of explained variation, R^2, occur by chance?

To relate this question to the heating cost example, we will test whether the independent variables (amount of insulation in the attic, mean daily outside temperature, and age of furnace) effectively estimate home heating costs.

Recall that in testing a hypothesis, the first step is to state the null hypothesis and the alternative hypothesis. In the heating cost example, there are three independent variables. Recall that b_1, b_2, and b_3 are sample net regression coefficients. The corresponding coefficients in the population are given the symbols β_1, β_2, and β_3. We now test whether the net regression coefficients in the population are all zero. The null hypothesis is:

$$\boldsymbol{H_0: \beta_1 = \beta_2 = \beta_3 = 0}$$

The alternative hypothesis is:

$$\boldsymbol{H_1}\textbf{: Not all the } \boldsymbol{\beta}\textbf{s are 0.}$$

If the null hypothesis is true, it implies the regression coefficients are all zero and, logically, are of no use in estimating the dependent variable (heating cost). Should that be the case, we would have to search for some other independent variables—or take a different approach—to predict home heating costs.

The second step in testing a hypothesis is to select a level of significance, and the third step is to select a test statistic. To test the null hypothesis that the multiple regression coefficients are all zero, we employ the F distribution introduced in Chapter 11. We will use the .05 level of significance. Recall these characteristics of the F distribution:

Characteristics of the *F* distribution

1. **There is a family of *F* distributions**. Each time the degrees of freedom in either the numerator or denominator changes a new F distribution is created.
2. **It is a continuous distribution**. The distribution can assume an infinite number of values between 0 and positive infinity.
3. **The *F* distribution cannot be negative**. The smallest possible value is 0.
4. **It is positively skewed**. The long tail of the distribution is to the right-hand side. As the number of degrees of freedom increases in both the numerator and the denominator, the distribution approaches the normal probability distribution. That is, the distribution will move toward a symmetric distribution.
5. **It is asymptotic**. As the values of X increase, the F curve will approach the horizontal axis, but will never touch it.

The degrees of freedom for the numerator and the denominator may be found in the ANOVA table. The top number in the column marked "df" is 3, indicating that there are 3 degrees of freedom in the numerator. This value corresponds to the number of independent variables. The middle number in the "df" column (16) indicates that there are 16 degrees of freedom in the denominator. The number 16 is found by $n - k - 1 = 20 - 3 - 1 = 16$.

The critical value of F is found in Appendix G. Using the table for the .05 level, move horizontally to 3 degrees of freedom in the numerator, then down to 16 degrees of freedom in the denominator, and read the critical value. It is 3.24. The region where H_0 is not rejected and the region where H_0 is rejected are shown in the following diagram.

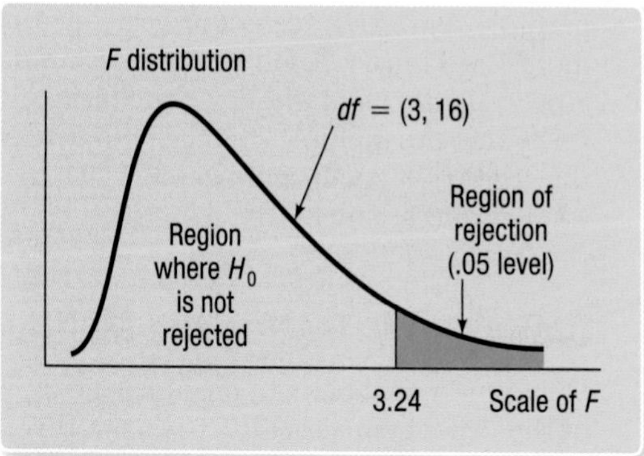

Continuing with the global test, step 4 is to formulate the decision rule: Do not reject the null hypothesis that all the regression coefficients are 0 if the computed value of F is less than or equal to 3.24. If the computed F is greater than 3.24, reject H_0 and accept the alternative hypothesis, H_1.

The value of F is found from the following equation.

GLOBAL TEST

$$F = \frac{\text{MSR}}{\text{MSE}} = \frac{\text{SSR}/k}{\text{SSE}/[n-k-1]} \quad \text{[13–4]}$$

SSR is the sum of the squares "explained by" the regression, SSE is the sum of squares error, n is the number of observations, and k is the number of independent variables. Inserting these values into formula (13–4):

$$F = \frac{\text{SSR}/k}{\text{SSE}/[n-k-1]} = \frac{87\,941.06/3}{32\,024.69/[20-3-1]} = 14.65$$

The computed value of F is 14.65, which is in the rejection region. Step 5 is to make a decision. The null hypothesis that all the multiple regression coefficients are zero is therefore rejected. The calculated value of F and the p-value can be found in the ANOVA table. The F-value is 14.646, the same as we calculated by hand. The p-value, labelled as "*Significant F*" is 7.5177E-05 in scientific notation. The E-05 means that the decimal place should be moved 5 places to the left. When this is done, the value is .000075177. This number is so close to zero that it is quite unlikely that H_0 is true. The null hypothesis is rejected, indicating that not all the regression coefficients are zero. From a practical standpoint, this means that at least one of the independent variables (amount of insulation, etc.) do have the ability to explain the variation in the dependent variable (heating cost). We expected this decision. Logically, the outside temperature, the amount of insulation, and age of the furnace have a great bearing on heating costs. The global test assures us that they do.

5 **Conduct a test of hypothesis on each of the regression coefficients.**

Evaluating Individual Regression Coefficients

So far we have shown that at least one, but not necessarily all, of the regression coefficients are not equal to zero and thus useful for predictions. The next step is to test the independent variables *individually* to determine which regression coefficients may be 0 and which are not.

Why is it important to know if any of the βs equal 0? If a β could equal 0, it implies that this particular independent variable is of no value in explaining any variation in the dependent variable. If there are coefficients for which H_0 cannot be rejected, we may want to eliminate them from the regression equation.

We will now conduct three separate tests of hypothesis—for temperature, for insulation, and for the age of the furnace.

Step 1: Is to state the null and alternative hypothesis.

For temperature:	For insulation:	For furnace age:
$H_0: \beta_1 = 0$	$H_0: \beta_2 = 0$	$H_0: \beta_3 = 0$
$H_1: \beta_1 \neq 0$	$H_1: \beta_2 \neq 0$	$H_1: \beta_3 \neq 0$

Step 2: We will test the hypotheses at the .05 level. The way the alternative hypothesis is stated indicates that the test is two-tailed.

Step 3: The test statistic is the Student t distribution with $n - k - 1$ degrees of freedom. The number of sample observations is n. There are 20 homes in the study, so $n = 20$. The number of independent variables is k, which is 3. Thus, there are $n - k - 1 = 20 - 3 - 1 = 16$ degrees of freedom.

Step 4: The critical value for t is in Appendix F. For a two-tailed test with 16 degrees of freedom using the .05 significance level, H_0 is rejected if t is less than -2.120 or greater than 2.120. The following is part of the **Excel** output from the previous section.

excel

	Coefficients	Standard Error	t Stat	P-value
Intercept	140.3187306	36.11723747	3.88509	0.001314
Temp	−12.31683726	2.684981109	−4.58731	0.000304
Insul	−4.101314862	1.724812351	−2.37783	0.030222
Age	8.526761655	3.295354018	2.58751	0.019837

The column headed "Coefficients" lists the values for the multiple regression equation.

$$Y' = 140.3187 - 12.3168X_1 - 4.10131X_2 + 8.526762X_3$$

Interpreting the term $-12.3168X_1$ in the equation: For each degree the temperature increases, it is expected that the heating cost will decrease about \$12.32, holding the two other variables constant.

The column on the **Excel** output labelled "Standard Error" indicates the standard error of the sample regression coefficient. Recall that Superior Realty selected a sample of 20 homes in Eastern Canada. If it were to select a second sample at random and compute the regression coefficients of that sample, the values would likely be similar. If it repeated the sampling process many times, however, we could design a sampling distribution of these regression coefficients. The column labelled "Standard Error" estimates the variability of these regression coefficients. The sampling distribution of Coefficients/Standard Error follows the t distribution with $n - k - 1$ degrees of freedom. Hence, we are able to test the independent variables individually to determine whether the net regression coefficients differ from zero. The computed t ratio is −4.587 for temperature, −2.378 for insulation, and 2.588 for age. All of the t-values are in the rejection region. Thus, we conclude that the regression coefficients for temperature, insulation, and age are not zero. We can test individual regression coefficients using the t distribution. The formula is:

TESTING INDIVIDUAL REGRESSION COEFFICIENTS $$t = \frac{b_i - 0}{S_{b_i}} \quad [13\text{–}5]$$

The b_i refers to any one of the regression coefficients and S_{b_i} refers to the standard deviation of that distribution of the regression coefficient. We include 0 in the equation because the null hypothesis is $\beta_i = 0$.

To illustrate this formula, refer to the test of the regression coefficient for the independent variable temperature. We let b_1 refer to the regression coefficient. From the computer output it is −12.32. S_{b_i} is the standard deviation of the sampling distribution of the regression coefficient for the independent variable temperature. Again, from the computer output, it is 2.68. Inserting these values in formula (13–5):

$$t = \frac{b_1 - 0}{S_{b_i}} = \frac{-12.32 - 0}{2.68} = -4.59$$

This is the value found in the "t Stat" column of the **Excel** output.

When computer output is available, p-values are commonly used to test the independent variables individually. Given the significance level of $\alpha = .05$, any independent variable with a p-value less than the significance level would cause the null hypothesis to be rejected. In this example, all three independent variables have a significance level less than .05, so the null hypothesis is rejected in each case, and all three independent variables are significant to the regression model.

At this point, we should also develop a strategy for deleting independent variables. In the Superior Realty case, the three independent variables were significant. If an independent variable were found not to be significant, we should drop that variable. Therefore, we delete that variable and rerun the regression equation. However, in some instances, it may not be as clear-cut which variable to delete.

To explain, suppose we developed a multiple regression equation based on five independent variables. We conducted the global test and found that some of the regression coefficients were different from zero. Next, we tested the regression coefficients individually and found that three were significant and two were not. The preferred procedure is to drop the single independent variable with the *smallest absolute t-value* or *largest p-value* and rerun the regression analysis with the four remaining variables. Then, on the new regression equation with four independent variables, conduct the individual tests. If there are still regression coefficients that are not significant, again drop the variable with the smallest absolute *t*-value. To describe the process in another way, we should delete only one variable at a time. Each time we delete a variable, we need to rerun the regression analysis and check the remaining variables.

This process of selecting variables to include in a regression model can be automated, using **Excel**, MegaStat, MINITAB, or other statistical software. Most statistical software includes methods to sequentially remove and/or add independent variables and at the same time provide estimates of the percentage of variation explained (the R-square term). Two of the common methods are **stepwise regression** and **best subset regression.** If need be, you could compute every possible regression between the dependent variable and any subset of the independent variables, but it may take a long time.

Unfortunately, on occasion, the software may work "too hard" to find an equation that fits all the quirks of your particular data set. The resultant equation may not represent the relationship in the population. You will need to use your judgment to choose among the relationships presented. Consider whether the results are logical. They should have a simple interpretation and be consistent with your knowledge of the application under study.

self-review 13–3

The multiple regression and correlation data for the preceding heating cost example were rerun using only the first two significant independent variables—temperature and insulation. (See the following **Excel** output.)

(a) What is the new multiple regression equation? (Temperature is X_1 and insulation X_2.)
(b) What is the coefficient of multiple determination? Interpret.
(c) Are the two independent variables significant in predicting heating costs? Select an appropriate significance level. Interpret your findings.

SUMMARY OUTPUT

Regression Statistics	
Multiple R	0.78825543
R Square	0.621346623
Adjusted R Square	0.576799166
Standard Error	51.69220923
Observations	20

ANOVA

	df	*SS*	*MS*	*F*
Regression	2	74540.31358	37270.15679	13.94797
Residual	17	45425.43642	2672.084495	
Total	19	119965.75		

	Coefficients	*Standard Error*	*t Stat*	*P-value*
Intercept	181.5025101	37.46015524	4.845215108	0.000152
Temp	−14.8098087	2.895691159	−5.114429643	8.63E-05
Insul	−4.145272198	1.992798615	−2.080125993	0.052955

Statistics in Action

In recent years, multiple regression has been used in a variety of legal proceedings. It is particularly useful in cases alleging discrimination by gender or race. As an example, suppose that a woman alleges that Company X's wage rates are unfair to women. To support the claim, the plaintiff produces data showing that, on the average, women earn less than men. In response, Company X argues that its wage rates are based on experience, training, and skill and that its female employees, on the average, are younger and less experienced than the male employees. In fact, the company might further argue that the current situation is actually due to its recent successful efforts to hire more women.

Exercises

7. Refer to the following information:

Predictor	Coef	StDev
Constant	20.00	10.00
X_1	−1.00	0.25
X_2	12.00	8.00
X_3	−15.00	5.00

SOURCE	DF	SS	MS	F
Regression	3	7500.00		
Error	18			
Total	21	10000.0		

a. What is the regression equation?
b. If $X_1 = 4$, $X_2 = 6$, and $X_3 = 8$, what is the value of the independent variable?
c. How large is the sample? How many independent variables are there?
d. Complete the ANOVA table.
e. Conduct a global test of hypothesis, using the .05 significance level. Can you conclude that any of the net regression coefficients are different from zero?
f. Conduct a test of hypothesis on each of the regression coefficients. Could you delete any of the variables?

8. Refer to the following information:

Predictor	Coef	StDev
Constant	−150	90
X_1	2000	500
X_2	−25	30
X_3	5	5
X_4	−300	100
X_5	0.60	0.15

SOURCE	DF	SS	MS	F
Regression	5	1500.0		
Error	15			
Total	20	2000.0		

a. What is the regression equation?
b. If $X_1 = 4$, $X_2 = 6$, $X_3 = 8$, $X_4 = 6$, and $X_5 = 8$, what is the value of the independent variable?
c. How large is the sample? How many independent variables are there?
d. Complete the ANOVA table.
e. Conduct a global test of hypothesis, using the .05 significance level. Can you conclude that any of the net regression coefficients are different from zero?
f. Conduct a test of hypothesis on each of the regression coefficients. Could you delete any of the variables?

Evaluating the Assumptions of Multiple Regression

In the previous section, we described the methods to statistically evaluate the multiple regression equation. The results of the test let us know if at least one of the coefficients was not equal to zero and we described a procedure of evaluating each regression coefficient. We also discussed the decision-making process for including and excluding independent variables in the multiple regression equation.

It is important to know that the validity of the global and individual tests rely on several assumptions. That is, if the assumptions are not true, the results might be biased or misleading. It should be mentioned, however, that in practice strict adherence to the following assumptions is not always possible. However, the statistical techniques discussed in this chapter appear to work effectively even when one or more of the assumptions are violated.

Even if the values in the multiple regression equation are "off" slightly, our estimates using a multiple regression equation will be closer than any that could otherwise be made. Usually the statistical procedures are robust enough to overcome violations of some assumptions.

In Chapter 12 we listed the necessary assumptions for regression when we considered only a single independent variable. The assumptions for multiple regression are similar.

1. **There is a linear relationship.** That is, there is a straight-line relationship between the dependent variable and the set of independent variables.
2. **The variation in the residuals is the same for both large and small values of Y'.** To put it another way, $(Y - Y')$ is unrelated to whether Y' is large or small.
3. **The residuals follow the normal probability distribution.** Recall the residual is the difference between the actual value of Y and the estimated value, Y'. So, the term $(Y - Y')$ is computed for every observation in the data set. These residuals should approximately follow a normal probability distribution. In addition, the mean of the residuals should be 0.
4. **The independent variables should not be correlated.** That is, we would like to select a set of independent variables that are not themselves correlated.
5. **The residuals are independent.** This means that successive observations of the dependent variable are not correlated. This assumption is often violated when time is involved with the sampled observations. Violation of this assumption is called **autocorrelation.**

In this section we present a brief discussion of each of these assumptions. In addition, we provide methods to validate these assumptions and indicate the consequences if these assumptions cannot be met.

Linear Relationship

Let's begin with the linearity assumption. The idea is that the relationship between the set of independent variables and the dependent variable is linear. If we are considering three independent variables, we can visualize this assumption. We can evaluate this assumption with scatter diagrams and residual plots.

Using Scatter Diagrams

The evaluation of a multiple regression equation should always include scatter diagrams that plot the dependent variable against each independent variable. These graphs help us to visualize the relationships and provide some initial information about the direction (positive or negative), linearity, and strength of the relationship. For example, the scatter diagrams for home heating example follow.

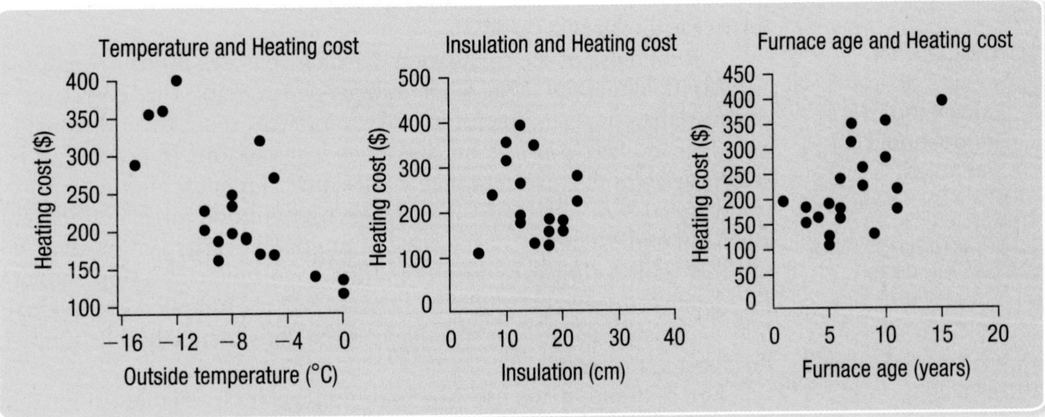

Of the three independent variables, the strongest association is between heating cost and the mean outside temperature. The relationships between cost and temperature and cost and insulation both are inverse. That is, as the independent variable increases, the dependent variable decreases. The relationship between the heating cost and the age of the furnace is direct. As the furnace gets older, it costs more to heat the home.

6 **Interpret a correlation matrix.**

correlation matrix A matrix showing the coefficients of correlation between all pairs of variables.

Correlation Matrix

A **correlation matrix** is also useful in analyzing the factors involved in the cost to heat a home.

The correlation matrix of the Superior Realty example follows. The matrix, which appears at the bottom of the output, was developed using **Excel**. The **Excel** steps are also shown.

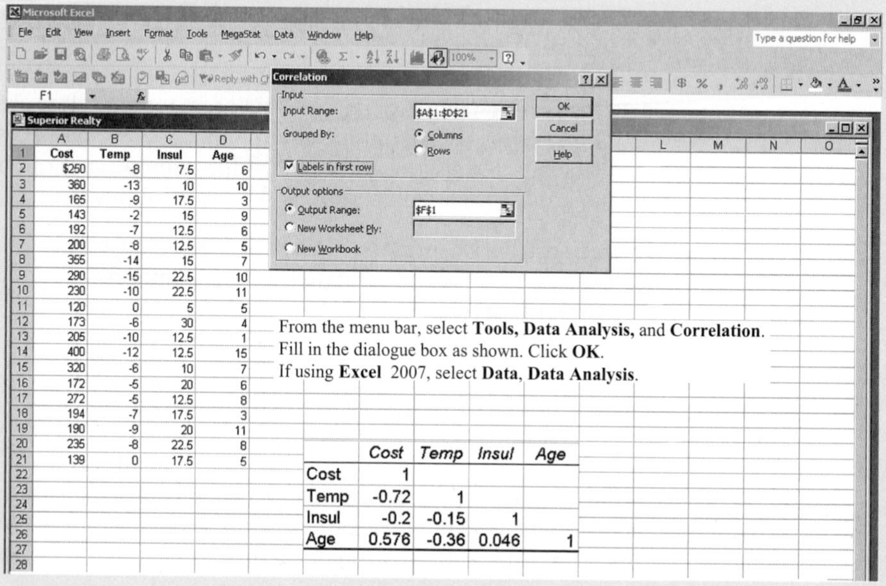

Cost is the dependent variable, Y. We are particularly interested in independent variables that have a strong correlation with the dependent variable. We may wish to develop a simpler multiple regression equation using fewer independent variables and the correlation matrix helps us identify which variables may be relatively more important. As indicated in the output, temperature has the strongest correlation with cost, -0.72. The negative sign indicates the inverse relationship we were expecting. Age has a stronger correlation with cost than insulation and, again as we expected, the correlation between cost and the age of the furnace is direct. It is 0.576.

7 **Evaluate the effects of correlated independent variables.**

multicollinearity Correlation among the independent variables.

A second use of the correlation matrix is to check for **multicollinearity**.

Multicollinearity exists when independent variables are correlated. Correlated independent variables make it difficult to make inferences about the individual regression coefficients and their individual effects on the dependent variable. In practice, it is nearly impossible to select variables that are completely unrelated. To put it another way, it is nearly impossible to create a set of independent variables that are not correlated to some degree. However, a general understanding of the issue of multicollinearity is important. First, we should point out that multicollinearity does not affect a multiple regression equation's ability to predict the dependent variable. However, when we are interested in evaluating the relationship between each independent variable and the dependent variable, multicollinearity may show unexpected results.

For example, if we use two highly correlated variables, high school marks and high school class standing, to predict the GPA of incoming college students (dependent variable), we would expect that both independent variables would be positively related to the dependent variable. However, because the independent variables are highly correlated, one of the independent variables may have an unexpected and inexplicable negative sign. In essence, these two independent variables are redundant in that they explain the same variation in the dependent variable.

A second reason for avoiding correlated independent variables is they may lead to erroneous results in the hypothesis tests for the individual independent variables. This is due to the instability of the standard error of estimate. Several clues that indicate problems with multicollinearity include the following:

1. An independent variable known to be an important predictor ends up having a regression coefficient that is not significant.
2. A regression coefficient that should have a positive sign turns out to be negative, or vice versa.
3. When an independent variable is added or removed, there is a drastic change in the values of the remaining regression coefficients.

In our evaluation of a multiple regression equation, an approach to reducing the effects of multicollinearity is to carefully select the independent variables that are included in the regression equation. A general rule is if the correlation between two independent variables is between −.70 and .70, there is likely not a problem using both of the independent variables.

Analysis of Residuals

Recall that a residual ($Y - Y'$) can be computed using the multiple regression equation for each observation in a data set as is shown in Table 13–3. In Chapter 12, we discussed the idea that the best regression line passed through the centre of the data in a scatter plot. In this case, you would find a good number of the observations above the regression line (these residuals would have a positive sign), and a good number of the observations below the line (these residuals would have a negative sign). Further, the observations would be scattered above and below the line over the entire range of the independent variable.

The same concept is true for multiple regression, but we cannot graphically portray the multiple regression. However, plots of the residuals can help us evaluate the linearity

TABLE 13–3 Summary of Actual Costs, Estimated Costs, and Residuals for Superior Realty Problem

Observation	Actual Cost ($)	Estimated Cost ($)	Residual
1	$250.0	$231.9	18.1
2	360.0	336.9	23.1
3	165.0	215.0	−50.0
4	143.0	149.2	−6.2
5	192.0	207.9	−15.9
6	200.0	218.3	−18.3
7	355.0	333.6	21.4
8	290.0	323.6	−33.6
9	230.0	211.8	18.2
10	120.0	155.6	−35.6
11	173.0	149.8	23.2
12	205.0	298.9	−93.9
13	400.0	319.7	80.3
14	320.0	264.2	55.8
15	172.0	166.7	5.3
16	272.0	247.0	25.0
17	194.0	194.3	−0.3
18	190.0	268.1	−78.1
19	235.0	191.0	44.0
20	139.0	121.6	17.4

of the multiple regression equation. To investigate, the residuals are plotted on the vertical axis against the predictor variable, Y'. The graph below shows the residual plot for the home heating cost example. Notice the following:

- The residuals are plotted on the vertical axis and are centered around zero. There are both positive and negative residuals.
- The residual plot shows a random distribution of positive and negative values across the entire range of the variable plotted on the horizontal axis.
- The points are scattered and there is no obvious pattern, so there is no reason to doubt the linearity assumption.

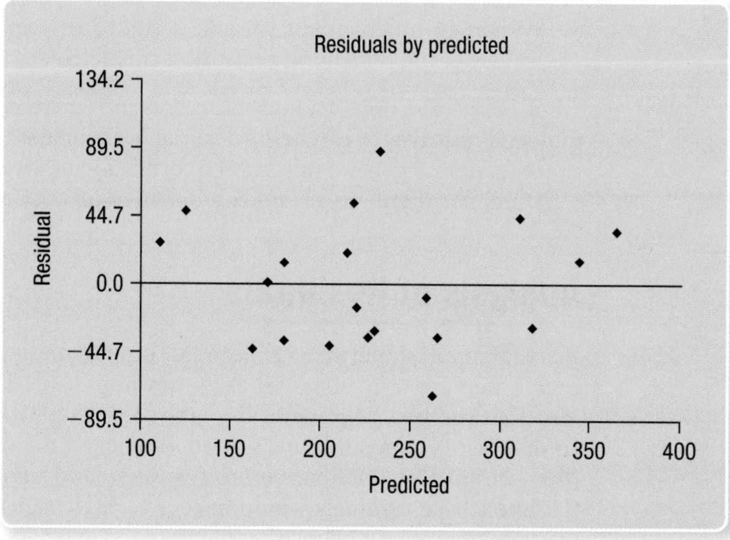

If there is a pattern to the points in the scatter plot, further investigation is necessary. For example, if the graph shows a curvature to the residual plots, the relationship may not be linear.

Variation in Residuals Same for Large and Small *Y′* Values

The second assumption is that the variation about the predicted values is constant regardless of whether the predicted values are large or small. For an example which may violate this assumption, suppose we use the single independent variable, age, to explain the variation in income. We suspect that as age increases so does salary, but it also seems reasonable that as age increases there may be more variation around the regression line. That is, there will likely be more variation in income for a 50-year-old person than for a 35-year-old person. The requirement for constant variation around the regression line is called **homoscedasticity**.

homoscedasticity
The variation around the regression equation is the same for all of the values of the independent variables.

To check for homoscedasticity the residuals are plotted against the fitted values of Y. This is the same graph that we used to evaluate the assumption of linearity. Based on the scatter diagram it is reasonable to conclude that this assumption has not been violated.

Distribution of Residuals

The third assumption evaluates the distribution of the residuals. Ideally, the residuals should follow a normal probability distribution. To evaluate this assumption, we can organize the residuals into a frequency distribution. The histogram of the residuals is shown following on the left side for the home heating cost example. Although it is difficult to show that the residuals follow a normal distribution with only 20 observations, it does appear that the normality assumption is reasonable.

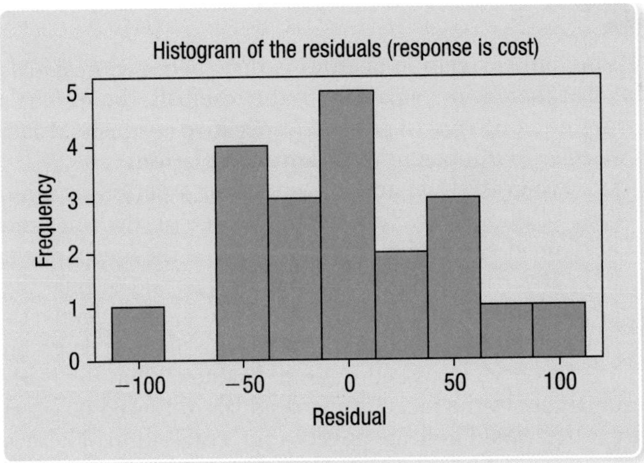

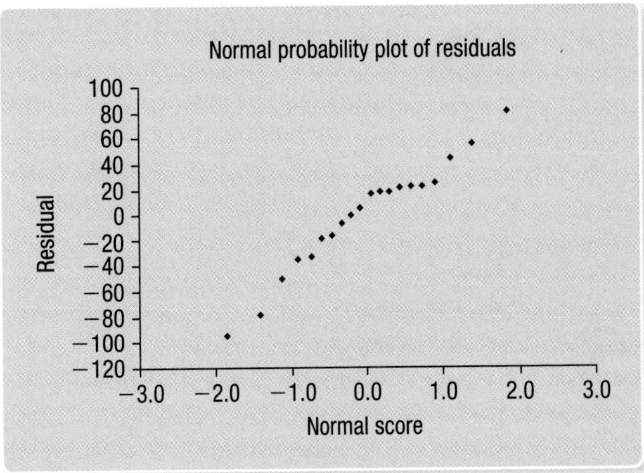

Another graph that helps to evaluate the assumption of normality distributed residuals is called a **normal probability plot**, shown to the right of the histogram above. The normal probability plot supports the assumption of normally distributed residuals if the plotted points are fairly close to a straight line drawn from the lower left to the upper right of the graph.

In this case, both graphs support the assumption that the residuals follow the normal probability distribution. Therefore, the inferences that we made based on the global and individual hypothesis tests are supported with the results of this evaluation.

The following are the MegaStat commands to produce the Normal Probability Plot.

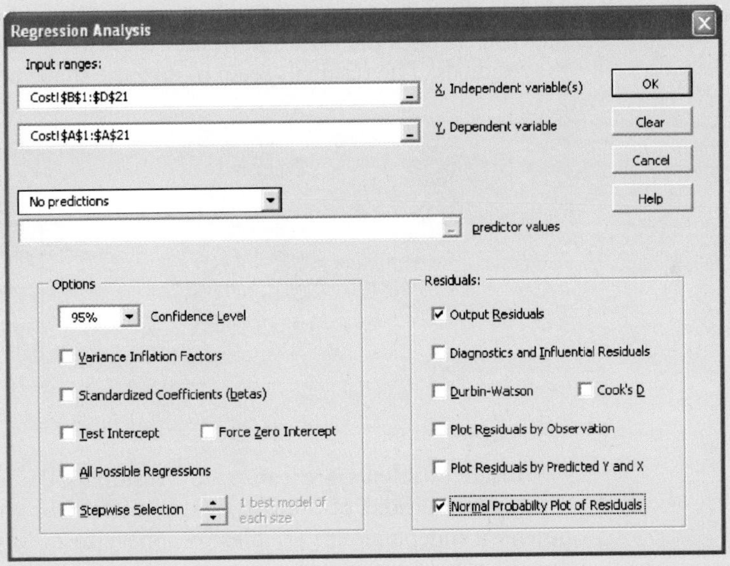

Multicollinearity

Recall that multicollinearity exists when independent variables are highly correlated. From our correlation matrix developed earlier in a previous section, none of the correlations among the independent variables exceed −.70 or .70, so we do not suspect problems with multicollinearity. The largest correlation among the independent variables is −.36, between temperature and age, but it is not large enough to cause a problem. Therefore, our fourth assumption is not violated.

Independent Observations

Our fifth assumption about regression and correlation analysis is that successive residuals should be independent. This means that there is not a pattern to the residuals, the residuals are not highly correlated, and there are not long runs of positive or negative residuals. When successive residuals are correlated we refer to this condition as **autocorrelation.**

Autocorrelation frequently occurs when the data are collected over a period of time. For example, we wish to predict yearly sales of Ages Software Inc., based on the time and the amount spent on advertising. The dependent variable is yearly sales and the independent variables are time and amount spent on advertising. It is likely that for a period of time the actual points will be above the regression plane (remember, there are two independent variables) and then for a period of time the points will be below the regression plane. The graph below shows the residuals plotted on the vertical axis and the fitted values, Y, on the horizontal axis. Note the run of the residuals above the mean of the residuals, followed by a run below the mean. A scatter plot such as this would indicate possible autocorrelation. There is a formal statistical test for autocorrelation, called the Durbin-Watson.

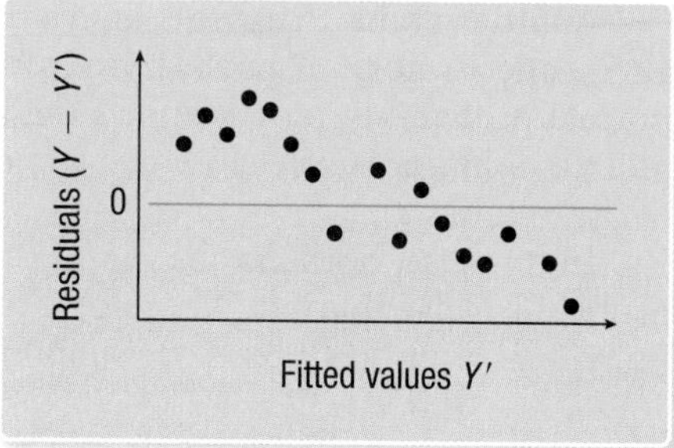

Following are two examples in which the homoscedasticity requirement is not met. Note in the first example, the plot of residuals is funnel-shaped. That is, as the fitted Y values increase, so does the variation in the residuals. In the second example, there is a pattern to the residuals. The residuals seem to take the shape of a polynomial equation.

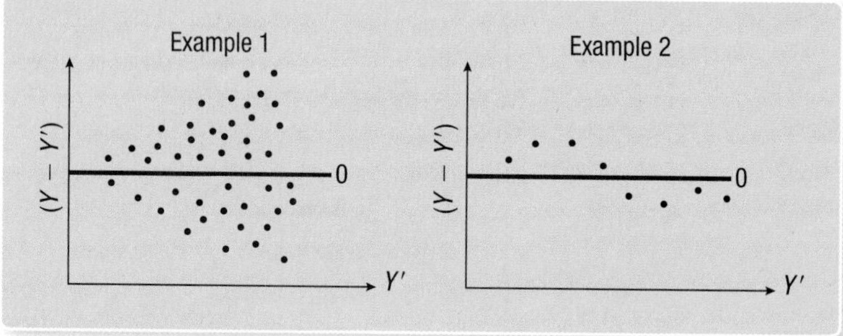

What problems are caused by residuals that fail to show homoscedasticity? The standard deviations of the regression coefficients will be understated (too small), causing potential independent variables to appear to be significant when they may not be. The remedy for this condition is to select other independent variables or to transform some of the variables.

8 Use and understand qualitative independent variables.

Qualitative Independent Variables

dummy variable A variable in which there are only two possible outcomes. For analysis, one of the outcomes is coded a 0 and the other a 1.

In the previous example regarding heating cost, the three independent variables were all quantitative; that is, numerical in nature. Frequently, we wish to use nominal-level variables—such as gender, whether the home has a swimming pool, or whether the sports team was the home or the visiting team—in our analysis. These are called *qualitative variables* because they describe a particular quality, such as male or female. To use a qualitative variable in regression analysis, we use a scheme of **dummy variables** in which one of the two possible conditions is coded 0 and the other 1.

Statistics in Action

In recent years, multiple regression has been used in a variety of legal proceedings. It is particularly useful in cases alleging discrimination by gender or race. As an example, suppose that a woman alleges that Company X's wage rates are unfair to women. To support the claim, the plaintiff produces data showing that, on the average, women earn less than men. In response, Company X argues that its wage rates are based on experience, training, and skill and that its female employees, on the average, are younger and less experienced than the male employees. In fact, the company might further argue that the current situation is actually due to its recent successful efforts to hire more women.

TABLE 13–4 Home Heating Costs, Temperature, Insulation, and Presence of a Garage for a Sample of 20 Homes

Cost, ($) Y	Temperature, X_1	Insulation, X_2	Garage, X_4
$250	−8	7.5	0
360	−13	10	1
165	−9	17.5	0
143	−2	15	0
192	−7	12.5	0
200	−8	12.5	0
355	−14	15	1
290	−15	22.5	1
230	−10	22.5	0
120	0	5	0
173	−6	30	0
205	−10	12.5	1
400	−12	12.5	1
320	−6	10	1
172	−5	20	0
272	−5	12.5	1
194	−7	17.5	0
190	−9	20	1
235	−8	22.5	0
139	0	17.5	0

For example, we might be interested in estimating an executive's salary based on years of job experience and whether he or she graduated from college. "Graduation from college" can take on only one of two conditions: yes or no. Thus, it is considered a qualitative variable.

Suppose in the Superior Realty example that the independent variable "garage" is added. For those homes without an attached garage, 0 is used; for homes with an attached garage, a 1 is used. We will refer to the "garage" variable as X_4. The data from Table 13–4 are entered into an **Excel** worksheet:

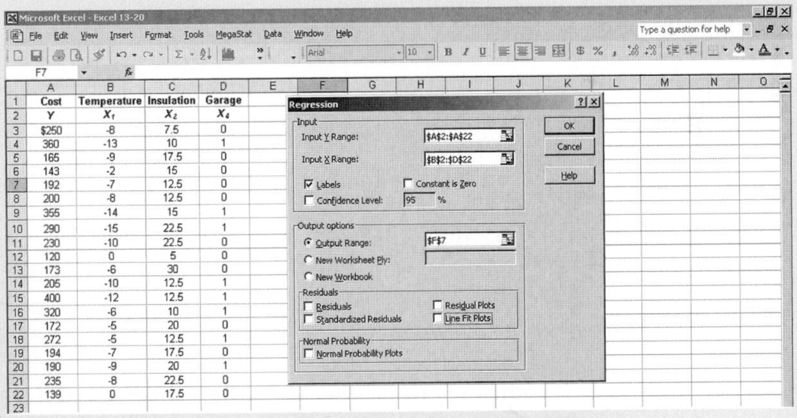

ANOVA

	df	*SS*	*MS*	*F*	*Significance F*
Regression	3	84877.49258	28292.5	12.90118	0.000153788
Residual	16	35088.25742	2193.016		
Total	19	119965.75			

	Coefficients	*Standard Error*	*t Stat*	*P-value*	*Lower 95%*	*Upper 95%*
Intercept	169.2779643	34.40029907	4.920828	0.000154	96.35260445	242.2033
X Variable 1	−10.38547303	3.321815349	−3.12645	0.006509	−17.4274054	−3.34354
X Variable 2	−2.726593417	1.919957358	−1.42013	0.174762	−6.796720275	1.343533
X Variable 4	59.86934928	27.57556556	2.171101	0.045311	1.411774923	118.3269

What is the effect of the variable "garage"? Should it be included in the analysis? To show the effect of the variable, suppose we have two houses exactly alike next to each other in Charlottetown, PEI, one has an attached garage, and the other does not. Both homes have 7.5 cm of insulation, and the mean January temperature in Charlottetown is −3.4°C. For the house without an attached garage, a 0 is substituted for X_4 in the regression equation. The estimated heating cost is $184.13, found by:

$$\begin{aligned} Y' &= 169.28 - 10.39X_1 - 2.73X_2 + 59.87X_4 \\ &= 169.28 - 10.39(-3.4) - 2.73(7.5) + 59.87(0) = 184.13 \end{aligned}$$

For the house with an attached garage, a 1 is substituted for X_4 in the regression equation. The estimated heating cost is $244.00, found by:

$$\begin{aligned} Y' &= 169.28 - 10.39X_1 - 2.73X_2 + 59.87X_4 \\ &= 169.28 - 10.39(-3.4) - 2.73(7.5) + 59.87(1) = 244.0 \end{aligned}$$

The difference between the estimated heating costs is $59.87 ($244.00 − $184.13). Hence, we can expect the cost to heat a house with an attached garage to be $59.87 more than the cost for an equivalent house without a garage.

We have shown the difference between the two types of homes to be $59.87, but is the difference significant? We conduct the following test of hypothesis. Again, we will follow the five-step procedure for testing a hypothesis.

$$\begin{aligned} H_0 &: \beta_4 = 0 \\ H_1 &: \beta_4 \neq 0 \end{aligned}$$

The information necessary to answer this question is on the previous **Excel** output. The regression coefficient for the independent variable Garage is 59.87, the standard deviation of the distribution of sampling distribution is 27.58. We identify this as the fourth independent variable, so we use a subscript of 4. Finally, we insert these values in formula (13–5).

$$t = \frac{b_4 - 0}{s_{b_4}} = \frac{59.87 - 0}{27.58} = 2.17$$

There are three independent variables in the analysis, so there are 16 degrees of freedom ($n - k - 1 = 20 - 3 - 1$). The critical value from Appendix F is 2.120. The decision rule, using a two-tailed test and the .05 significance level, is to reject H_0 if the computed t is to the left of −2.120 or to the right of 2.120. Since the computed value of 2.17 is to the right of 2.120, the null hypothesis is rejected. It is concluded that the regression coefficient is not zero. The independent variable "Garage" should be included in the analysis.

Another way to answer the question is to look at the p-value for the variable. The p-value for "Garage" is 0.045311 as found in the fifth column of the **Excel** output. Since 0.045311 is less than the significance level of .05, the null hypothesis is rejected, and so the variable "Garage" should be included in the analysis.

Is it possible to use a qualitative variable with more than two possible outcomes? Yes, but the coding scheme becomes more complex and will require a series of dummy variables. To explain, suppose a company is studying its sales as they relate to advertising expense by quarter for the last five years. Let sales be the dependent variable and advertising expense be the first independent variable, X_1. To include the qualitative information regarding the quarter, we use three additional independent variables. For the variable X_2, the five observations referring to the first quarter of each of the five years are coded 1 and the other quarters 0. Similarly, for X_3 the five observations referring to the second quarter are coded 1 and the other quarters 0. For X_4 the five observations referring to the third quarter are coded 1 and the other quarters 0. An observation that does not refer to any of the first three quarters must refer to the fourth quarter, so a distinct independent variable referring to this quarter is not necessary.

Exercises

9. Refer to the following correlation matrix:

	Y	X_1	X_2	X_3	X_4
Y	1.000				
X_1	.192	1.000			
X_2	.510	.124	1.000		
X_3	.806	.062	.438	1.000	
X_4	−.819	.650	−.481	−.729	1.00

a. Which independent variable has the strongest correlation with the dependent variable?
b. Suppose you could only use three of the four independent variables in your regression equation to estimate the dependent variable. Based on the correlation matrix above, which would you use? Explain.
c. Is there evidence of multicollinearity? If so, where does it occur?

10. Refer to the following correlation matrix:

	Sales	Advertising ($)	Population	Income
Sales	1.000			
Advertising ($)	.192	1.000		
Population	.510	.124	1.000	
Income	.806	.062	.438	1.000

a. Which independent variable has the strongest correlation with the dependent variable?
b. Suppose you could only use two of Advertising ($), Population, and Income in your regression equation to estimate Sales. Based on the correlation matrix above, which would you use? Explain.
c. Is there evidence of multicollinearity? If so, where does it occur?

11. The speed of a car can be estimated using many factors, three of which are horsepower, the weight of the car, and the age of the car. A study was done on 35 cars and the following correlation matrix was developed from the sample data.

	Speed	H-Power	Weight	Age
Speed	1			
H-Power	.83	1		
Weight	−.197	−.15	1	
Age	.15	.13	.05	1

a. Suppose you could only use horsepower or weight in your regression equation to estimate speed. Based on the correlation matrix above, which would you use? Explain.
b. Weight has an inverse relationship with speed. Does this seem reasonable?
c. Is there evidence of multicollinearity?

12. The selling price of a residence can be estimated using many factors, three of which are the square footage, number of bedrooms and bathrooms, and the location. A study was conducted on 50 homes and the following correlation matrix was developed from the sample data.

	Price	Sq. Ft.	Bath	Bed	Location
Price	1				
Square Feet	.63	1			
No. of Bathrooms	.78	.56	1		
No. of Bedrooms	.84	.66	.88	1	
Location	.85	.24	.09	.08	1

a. Suppose you could only use one of the four independent variables to estimate the selling price. Based on the correlation matrix above, which would you use? Explain.
b. Is there evidence of multicollinearity? If so, how would this affect your regression equation?

Chapter Summary

I. The general form of the multiple regression equation is:

$$Y' = a + b_1X_1 + b_2X_2 + b_3X_3 + \cdots + b_kX_k \qquad [13\text{–}1]$$

where a is the Y-intercept when all Xs are zero, b_i refers to the sample regression coefficients, and X_i refers to the value of the various independent variables.

A. There can be any number of independent variables.

B. The least squares criterion is used to develop the equation.

C. A computer is needed to develop the regression equation.

II. There are two measures of the effectiveness of the regression equation.

A. The multiple standard error of estimate is similar to the standard deviation.
1. It is measured in the same units as the dependent variable.
2. It is based on squared deviations from the regression equation.
3. It ranges from 0 to plus infinity.
4. It is calculated from the following equation,

$$S_{e \cdot 123 \cdots k} = \sqrt{\frac{\Sigma(Y - Y')^2}{n - k - 1}} \text{ also, } = \sqrt{\text{MSE}} \qquad [13\text{–}2]$$

B. The coefficient of determination may range from 0 to 1.
1. It may range from 0 to 1.
2. It is also based on squared deviations from the regression equation.
3. It is found by the following equation,

$$R^2 = \frac{\text{SSR}}{\text{SS total}} \qquad [13\text{–}3]$$

III. The ANOVA table summarizes the multiple regression analysis.

A. It reports the total amount of the variation in the dependent variable and divides this variation into that explained by the set of independent variables and that unexplained.

B. It reports the degrees of freedom associated with the independent variables, the error variation, and the total variation.

III. A correlation matrix shows all possible simple correlation coefficients between pairs of variables.

A. It shows the correlation between each independent variable and the dependent variable.

B. It shows the correlation between each pair of independent variables.

V. A global test is used to investigate whether any of the independent variables have significant regression coefficients.

A. The null hypothesis is: All the regression coefficients are zero.

B. The alternative hypothesis is: At least one regression coefficient is not zero.

C. The test statistic is the F distribution with k (the number of independent variables) degrees of freedom in the numerator and $n - k - 1$ degrees of freedom in the denominator, where n is the sample size.

D. The formula to calculate the value of the test statistic for the global test is:

$$F = \frac{\text{SSR}/k}{\text{SSE}/[n-k-1]} \qquad [13\text{–}4]$$

VI. The test for individual variables determines which independent variables have nonzero regression coefficients.

A. The variables that have zero regression coefficients are usually dropped from the analysis.

B. The test statistic is the t distribution with $n - k - 1$ degrees of freedom.

C. The formula to calculate the value of the test statistic for the individual test is:

$$t = \frac{b_i - 0}{s_{b_i}} \qquad [13\text{–}5]$$

VII. Dummy variables are used to represent qualitative variables and can assume only one of two possible conditions.

VIII. There are five assumptions to use multiple regression analysis.

A. The relationship between the dependent variable and the set of independent variables must be linear.

1. To verify this assumption, develop a scatter diagram and plot the residuals on the vertical axis and the fitted values on the horizontal axis.

2. If the plots appear random, we conclude the relationship is linear.

B. The variation is the same for both large and small values of Y'.

1. Homoscedasticity means the variation is the same for all fitted values of the dependent variable.

2. This condition is checked by developing a scatter diagram with the residuals on the vertical axis.

3. If there is no pattern to the plots—that is, they appear random—the residuals meet the homoscedasicity requirement.

C. The residuals follow the normal probability distribution.

1. This condition is checked by developing a histogram of the residuals to see if they follow a normal distribution.

2. The mean of the distribution of the residuals is 0.

D. The independent variables are not correlated.

1. A correlation matrix will show all possible correlations among independent variables. An indication of difficulty is a correlation larger than .70 or less than −.070.

2. Other indications of correlated independent variables are:

a. When an important predictor variable is found insignificant.

b. When an obvious reversal occurs in signs in one or more of the independent variables.

c. When a variable is removed from the solution, there is a large change in the regression coefficients.

E. Each residual is independent of other residuals.

1. Autocorrelation occurs when successive residuals are correlated.

2. When autocorrelation exists, the value of the standard error will be biased and will return poor results for tests of hypothesis regarding the regression coefficients.

Pronunciation Key

SYMBOL	MEANING	PRONUNCIATION
b_1	Regression coefficient for the first independent variable	*b sub 1*
b_k	Regression coefficient for any independent variable	*b sub k*
$s_{e \cdot 12 \cdots k}$	Multiple standard error of estimate	*s sub e 1,2 . . . k*
R^2	Coefficient of multiple determination	*R squared*

Chapter Exercises

13. A multiple regression equation yields the following partial results.

Source	Sum of Squares	df
Regression	750	4
Error	500	35

a. What is the total sample size?
b. How many independent variables are being considered?
c. Compute the coefficient of determination.
d. Compute the standard error of estimate.
e. Test the hypothesis that none of the regression coefficients is equal to zero. Let $\alpha = .05$.

14. In a multiple regression equation two independent variables are considered, and the sample size is 25. The regression coefficients and the standard errors are as follows.

$$b_1 = 2.676 \qquad s_{b_1} = 0.56$$
$$b_2 = -0.880 \qquad s_{b_2} = 0.71$$

Conduct a test of hypothesis to determine whether either independent variable has a coefficient equal to zero. Would you consider deleting either variable from the regression equation? Use the .05 significance level.

15. The following output was obtained.

Analysis of variance

SOURCE	df	SS	MS
Regression	5	100	20
Error	20	40	2
Total	25	140	

Predictor	Coef	StDev	t-ratio
Constant	3.00	1.50	2.00
X_1	4.00	3.00	1.33
X_2	3.00	0.20	15.00
X_3	0.20	0.05	4.00
X_4	−2.50	1.00	−2.50
X_5	3.00	4.00	0.75

a. What is the sample size?
b. Compute the value of R^2.
c. Compute the multiple standard error of estimate.
d. Conduct a global test of hypothesis to determine whether any of the regression coefficients are significant. Use the .05 significance level.
e. Test the regression coefficients individually. Would you consider omitting any variable(s)? If so, which one(s)? Use the .05 significance level.

16. In a multiple regression equation $k = 5$ and $n = 20$, the MSE value is 5.10, and SST is 519.68. At the .05 significance level, can we conclude that any of the regression coefficients are not equal to 0?

17. The district manager of Jason's, a large discount retail chain, is investigating why certain stores in her region are performing better than others. She believes that three factors are related to total sales: the number of competitors in the region, the population in the surrounding area, and the amount spent on advertising. From her district, consisting of several hundred stores, she selects a random sample of 30 stores. For each store she gathered the following information.

Y = total sales last year (in \$ thousands).
X_1 = number of competitors in the region.
X_2 = population of the region (in millions).
X_3 = advertising expense (in \$ thousands).

The sample data produces the following results.

Analysis of variance			
SOURCE	*df*	*SS*	*MS*
Regression	3	3050.00	1016.67
Error	26	2200.00	84.62
Total	29	5250.00	

Predictor	*Coef*	*StDev*	*t-ratio*
Constant	14.00	7.00	2.00
X_1	−1.00	0.70	−1.43
X_2	30.00	5.20	5.77
X_3	0.20	0.08	2.50

a. What are the estimated sales for the Bryne Store, which has four competitors, a regional population of 0.4 (400 000), and advertising expense of 30 ($30 000)?
b. Compute the R^2 value.
c. Compute the multiple standard error of estimate.
d. Conduct a global test of hypothesis to determine whether any of the regression coefficients are not equal to zero. Use the .05 level of significance.
e. Conduct tests of hypotheses to determine which of the independent variables have significant regression coefficients. Which variables would you consider eliminating? Use the .05 significance level.

18. Mike Wilde is president of the teachers' union for Otsego School District. In preparing for upcoming negotiations, he would like to investigate the salary structure of classroom teachers in the district. He believes there are three factors that affect a teacher's salary: years of experience, a rating of teaching effectiveness given by the principal, and whether the teacher has a master's degree. A random sample of 20 teachers resulted in the following data.

Salary ($ thousands), Y	Years of Experience, X_1	Principal's Rating, X_2	Master's Degree,* X_3
$55.1	8	35	0
57.6	5	43	0
53.3	2	51	1
67.0	15	60	1
62.6	11	73	0
69.0	14	80	1
66.0	9	76	0
60.8	7	54	1
72.6	22	55	1
55.7	3	90	1
49.7	1	30	0
54.6	5	44	0
75.8	23	84	1
70.7	17	76	0
62.4	12	68	1
57.6	14	25	0
65.8	8	90	1
54.7	4	62	0
56.8	2	80	1
66.8	8	72	0

*1 = yes, 0 = no.

a. Develop a correlation matrix. Which independent variable has the strongest correlation with the dependent variable? Does it appear there will be any problems with multicollinearity?
b. Determine the regression equation. What salary would you estimate for a teacher with five years' experience, a rating by the principal of 60, and no master's degree?
c. Conduct a global test of hypothesis to determine whether any of the net regression coefficients differ from zero. Use the .05 significance level.
d. Conduct a test of hypothesis for the individual regression coefficients. Would you consider deleting any of the independent variables? Use the .05 significance level.
e. If your conclusion in part (d) was to delete one or more independent variables, run the regression equation again without those variables.

f. Determine the residuals for the equation of part (e). Plot the residuals by observation to verify that the distribution of the residuals is approximately normal.

g. Plot the residuals computed in part (f) in a scatter diagram with the residuals on the Y-axis and the Y' values on the X-axis. Does the plot reveal any violations of the assumptions of regression?

19. The district sales manager for a major automobile manufacturer is studying car sales. Specifically, he would like to determine what factors affect the number of cars sold at a dealership. To investigate, he randomly selects 12 dealers. From these dealers he obtains the number of cars sold last month, the minutes of radio advertising purchased last month, the number of full-time salespeople employed in the dealership, and whether the dealer is located in the city. The information is as follows:

Cars Sold Last Month, Y	Advertising, X_1	Sales Force, X_2	City, X_3	Cars Sold Last Month, Y	Advertising, X_1	Sales Force, X_2	City, X_3
127	18	10	Yes	161	25	14	Yes
138	15	15	No	180	26	17	Yes
159	22	14	Yes	102	15	7	No
144	23	12	Yes	163	24	16	Yes
139	17	12	No	106	18	10	No
128	16	12	Yes	149	25	11	Yes

a. Develop a correlation matrix. Which independent variable has the strongest correlation with the dependent variable? Does it appear there will be any problems with multicollinearity?

b. Determine the regression equation. How many cars would you expect to be sold by a dealership employing 20 salespeople, purchasing 15 minutes of advertising, and located in a city?

c. Conduct a global test of hypothesis to determine whether any of the net regression coefficients differ from zero. Let $\alpha = .05$.

d. Conduct a test of hypothesis for the individual regression coefficients. Would you consider deleting any of the independent variables? Let $\alpha = .05$.

e. If your conclusion in part (d) was to delete one or more independent variables, run the regression equation again without those variables.

f. Determine the residuals for the equation of part (e). Plot the residuals by observation to verify that the distribution of the residuals is approximately normal.

g. Plot the residuals computed in part (f) in a scatter diagram with the residuals on the Y-axis and the Y' values on the X-axis. Does the plot reveal any violations of the assumptions of regression?

20. Fran's Convenience Marts are located throughout a metropolitan area. Fran, the owner, would like to expand into other communities. As part of her presentation to the local bank, she would like to better understand the factors that make a particular outlet profitable. She must do all the work herself, so she will not be able to study all her outlets. She selects a random sample of 15 marts and record s the average daily sales (Y), the floor space (area), the number of parking spaces, and the median income of families in each region. The sample information is reported below.

Sampled Mart	Daily Sales ($)	Store Area	Parking Spaces	Income ($ thousands)
1	$1840	532	6	$44
2	1746	478	4	51
3	1812	530	7	45
4	1806	508	7	46
5	1792	514	5	44
6	1825	556	6	46
7	1811	541	4	49
8	1803	513	6	52
9	1830	532	5	46
10	1827	537	5	46
11	1764	499	3	48
12	1825	510	8	47
13	1763	490	4	48
14	1846	516	8	45
15	1815	482	7	43

a. Determine the regression equation.
b. What is the value of R^2? Comment on the value.
c. Conduct a global hypothesis test to determine if any of the independent variables are different from zero. Test at a significance level of .05.
d. Conduct individual hypothesis tests to determine if any of the independent variables can be dropped. Test at a significance level of .05.
e. If variables are dropped, recompute the regression equation and R^2.

21. Steve Douglas has been hired as a management trainee by a large brokerage firm. As his first project, he is asked to study the gross profit of firms in the chemical industry. What factors affect profitability in that industry? Steve selects a random sample of 16 firms and obtains data on the number of employees, number of consecutive common stock dividends paid, the total value of inventory at the start of the current year, and the gross profit for each firm. His findings are:

Company	Gross Profit ($ thousands), Y	Number of Employees, X_1	Consecutive Dividends, X_2	Beginning Inventory ($ thousands), X_3
1	$2800	140	12	$1800
2	1300	65	21	320
3	1230	130	42	820
4	1600	115	80	76
5	4500	390	120	3600
6	5700	670	64	8400
7	3150	205	43	508
8	640	40	14	870
9	3400	480	88	5500
10	6700	810	98	9875
11	3700	120	44	6500
12	6440	590	110	9130
13	1280	440	38	1200
14	4160	280	24	890
15	3870	650	60	1200
16	980	150	24	1300

a. Determine the regression equation. The Master Chemical Company employs 220 people, has paid 64 consecutive common stock dividends, and has an inventory valued at $1 500 000 at the start of the year. What is the estimate of the gross profit?
b. Conduct a global test of hypothesis to determine whether any of the net regression coefficients differ from zero. Test at a significance level of .05.
c. Conduct a test of hypothesis for the individual regression coefficients. Would you consider deleting any of the independent variables? Test at a significance level of .05.
d. If your conclusion in part (c) was to delete one or more independent variables, run the regression equation again, deleting those variables.
e. Determine the residuals for the equation of part (d). Plot the residuals by observation to verify that the distribution of the residuals is approximately normal.
f. Plot the residuals computed in part (e) in a scatter diagram with the residuals on the Y-axis and the Y' values on the X-axis. Does the plot reveal any violations of the assumptions of regression?

22. A mortgage department of a large bank is studying its recent loans. Of particular interest is how such factors as the value of the home (in thousands of dollars), education level of the head of the household, age of the head of the household, current monthly mortgage payment (in dollars), and sex of the head of the household (male = 1, female = 0) relate to the family income. Are these variables effective predictors of the income of the household? A random sample of 25 recent loans is obtained.

www.mcgrawhill.ca/olc/lind

Income ($ thousands)	Value ($ thousands)	Years of Education	Age	Mortgage Payment ($)	Sex
$40.3	$190	14	53	$230	1
39.6	121	15	49	370	1
40.8	161	14	44	397	1
40.3	161	14	39	181	1
40.0	179	14	53	378	0
38.1	99	14	46	304	0
40.4	114	15	42	285	1
40.7	202	14	49	551	0
40.8	184	13	37	370	0
37.1	90	14	43	135	0
39.9	181	14	48	332	1
40.4	143	15	54	217	1
38.0	132	14	44	490	0
39.0	127	14	37	220	0
39.5	153	14	50	270	1
40.6	145	14	50	279	1
40.3	174	15	52	329	1
40.1	177	15	47	274	0
41.7	188	15	49	433	1
40.1	153	15	53	333	1
40.6	150	16	58	148	0
40.4	173	13	42	390	1
40.9	163	14	46	142	1
40.1	150	15	50	343	0
38.5	139	14	45	373	0

a. Determine the regression equation.
b. What is the value of R^2? Comment on the value.
c. Conduct a global hypothesis test to determine whether any of the independent variables are different from zero. Test at a significance level of .05.
d. Conduct individual hypothesis tests to determine whether any of the independent variables can be dropped. Test at a significance level of .05.
e. If variables are dropped, recompute the regression equation and R^2.

23. Fred G. Hire is the manager of human resources at St. Luke's Medical Center. As part of his yearly report to the president of the medical center, he is required to present an analysis of the salaried employees. Because there are over 1000 employees, he does not have the staff to gather information on each salaried employee, so he selects a random sample of 30. For each employee, he records monthly salary; service at St. Luke's, in months; sex (1 = male, 0 = female); and whether the employee has a technical or clerical job. Those working technical jobs are coded 1, and those who are clerical 0.

Sampled Employee	Monthly Salary ($)	Length of Service	Age	Sex	Job
1	$1769	93	42	1	0
2	1740	104	33	1	0
3	1941	104	42	1	1
4	2367	126	57	1	1
5	2467	98	30	1	1
6	1640	99	49	1	1
7	1756	94	35	1	0
8	1706	96	46	0	1
9	1767	124	56	0	0
10	1200	73	23	0	1
11	1706	110	67	0	1
12	1985	90	36	0	1
13	1555	104	53	0	0
14	1749	81	29	0	0
15	2056	106	45	1	0

(Continued)

(Continued)

16	1729	113	55	0	1
17	2186	129	46	1	1
18	1858	97	39	0	1
19	1819	101	43	1	1
20	1350	91	35	1	1
21	2030	100	40	1	0
22	2550	123	59	1	0
23	1544	88	30	0	0
24	1766	117	60	1	1
25	1937	107	45	1	1
26	1691	105	32	0	1
27	1623	86	33	0	0
28	1791	131	56	0	1
29	2001	95	30	1	1
30	1874	98	47	1	0

a. Determine the regression equation, using salary as the dependent variable and the other four variables as independent variables.
b. What is the value of R^2? Comment on this value.
c. Conduct a global test of hypothesis to determine whether any of the independent variables are different from 0. Test at a significance level of .05.
d. Conduct an individual test to determine whether any of the independent variables can be dropped. Test at a significance level of .05.
e. Rerun the regression equation, using only the independent variables that are significant. How much more does a man earn per month than a woman? Does it make a difference whether the employee has a technical or a clerical job?

24. Many urban regions have experienced rapid population growth over the last 10 years. It is expected that growth will continue over the next 10 years. This has resulted in many of the large grocery store chains building new stores. The Kelley's Super Grocery Stores Inc. chain is no exception. The director of planning for Kelley's Super Grocery Stores wants to study adding more stores. He believes there are two main factors that indicate the amount families spend on groceries. The first is their income and the other is the number of people in the family. The director gathered the following sample information.

Family	Food ($)	Income ($)	Size
1	$5.04	$73.98	4
2	4.08	54.90	2
3	5.76	94.14	4
4	3.48	52.02	1
5	4.20	65.70	2
6	4.80	53.64	4
7	4.32	79.74	3
8	5.04	68.58	4
9	6.12	165.60	5
10	3.24	64.80	1
11	4.80	138.42	3
12	3.24	125.82	1
13	6.60	77.58	7
14	4.92	171.36	2
15	6.60	82.08	9
16	5.40	141.30	3
17	6.00	36.90	5
18	5.40	56.88	4
19	3.36	71.82	1
20	4.68	69.48	3
21	4.32	54.36	2
22	5.52	87.66	5
23	4.56	38.16	3
24	5.40	43.74	7
25	4.80	48.42	5

Food and income are reported in thousands of dollars per year, and the variable "size" refers to the number of people in the household.

a. Develop a correlation matrix. Do you see any problems with multicollinearity?
b. Determine the regression equation. Discuss the regression equation. How much does an additional family member add to the amount spent on food?
c. What is the value of R^2? Can we conclude that this value is greater than 0?
d. Would you consider deleting either of the independent variables?
e. Plot the residuals by observation. Is there any problem with the normality assumption?
f. Plot the fitted values against the residuals. Does this plot indicate any problems with homoscedasticity?

25. Suppose that the sales manager of a large automotive parts distributor wants to estimate as early as April the total annual sales of a region. On the basis of regional sales, the total sales for the company can also be estimated. If, based on past experience, it is found that the April estimates of annual sales are reasonably accurate, then in future years the April forecast could be used to revise production schedules and maintain the correct inventory at the retail outlets.

Several factors appear to be related to sales, included the number of retail outlets in the region stocking the company's parts, the number of automobiles in the region registered as of April 1, and the total personal income for the first quarter of the year. Five independent variables were finally selected as being the most important (according to the sales manager). Then, the data were gathered for a recent year. The total annual sales for that year for each region were also recorded. Note in the following table that for region 1 there were 1739 retail outlets stocking the company's automotive parts, 9 270 000 (9.27 million) registered automobiles in the region as of April 1 and so on. The sales for that region for that year were \$37 702 000. (\$37.702 million).

Y Annual Sales (\$ millions)
X_1 Number of Retail Outlets
X_2 Number of Automobiles Registered (millions)
X_3 Personal Income (\$ billions)
X_4 Average Age of Automobiles (years)
X_5 Number of Supervisors

Y	X_1	X_2	X_3	X_4	X_5
\$37.702	1739	9.27	\$85.4	3.5	9.0
24.196	1221	5.86	60.7	5.0	5.0
32.055	1846	8.81	68.1	4.4	7.0
3.611	120	3.81	20.2	4.0	5.0
17.625	1096	10.31	33.8	3.5	7.0
45.919	2290	11.62	95.1	4.1	13.0
29.600	1687	8.96	69.3	4.1	15.0
8.114	241	6.28	16.3	5.9	11.0
20.116	649	7.77	34.9	5.5	16.0
12.994	1427	10.92	15.1	4.1	10.0

a. Consider the following correlation matrix. Which single variable has the strongest correlation with the dependent variable? The correlations between the independent variables "outlets" and "income" and between "cars" and "outlets" are fairly strong. What is this condition called? Could this be a problem?

	Y	X_1	X_2	X_3	X_4	X_5
X_1	.899	1.000				
X_2	.605	.775	1.000			
X_3	.964	.825	.409	1.000		
X_4	−.323	−.489	−.447	−.349	1.000	
X_5	.286	.183	.395	.155	.291	1.000

b. The following regression output was obtained using the five independent variables. What is the regression equation? What percent of the variation is explained by the regression equation?

ANOVA table

Source	*SS*	*df*	*MS*	*F*	*p-value*
Regression	1593.8097	5	318.7619	140.36	.0001
Residual	9.0843	4	2.2711		
Total	1602.8940	9			

Regression output

variables	*coefficients*	*std. error*	*t (df = 4)*	*p-value*
Intercept	−19.6715			
X_1	−0.0006	0.0026	−0.238	.8234
X_2	1.7399	0.5530	3.146	.0346
X_3	0.4099	0.0439	9.348	.0007
X_4	2.0357	0.8779	2.319	.0812
X_5	−0.0344	0.1880	−0.183	.8635

c. Conduct a global test of hypothesis to determine whether any of the regression coefficients are not zero. Use the .05 significance level.

d. Conduct a test of hypothesis on each of the independent variables. Would you consider eliminating "outlets" and "supervisors?" Use the .05 significance level.

e. The regression equation has been rerun below with "outlets" and "supervisors" eliminated. Compute the coefficient of determination. How much has R^2 changed from the previous analysis? Which model is the better predictor of Annual Sales?

ANOVA table

Source	*SS*	*df*	*MS*	*F*	*p-value*
Regression	1593.6621	3	531.2207	345.25	4.17E−07
Residual	9.2319	6	1.5387		
Total	1602.8940	9			

Regression output

variables	*coefficients*	*std. error*	*t (df = 6)*	*p-value*
Intercept	−18.9239			
X_2	1.6129	0.1979	8.152	.0002
X_3	0.4003	0.0157	25.517	2.39E − 07
X_4	1.9637	0.5846	3.359	.0152

f. Following is a normal probability plot of residuals from the first model. Does the normality assumption for the residuals seem reasonable?

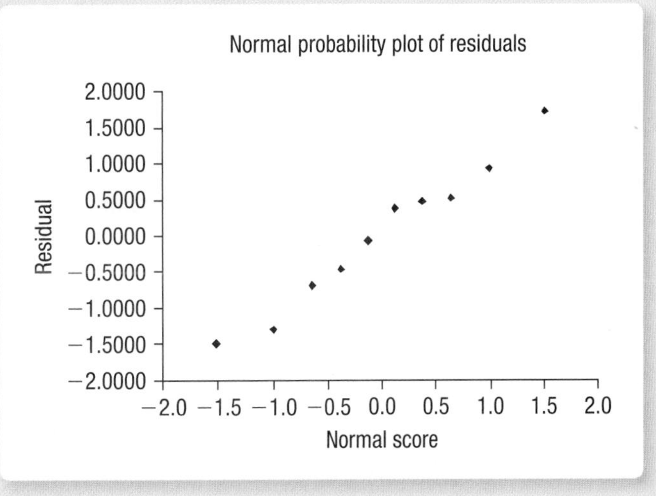

g. Following is a plot of the residuals and the Y' values. Do you see any violation of the assumptions?

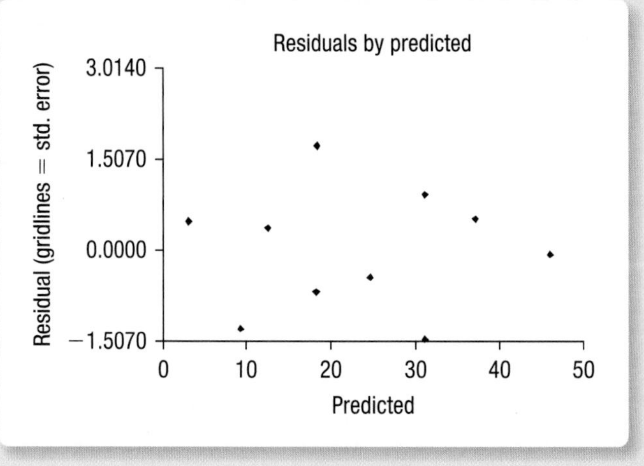

26. The administrator of a new paralegal program at a college wants to estimate a student's GPA (grade point average) in the new program. He thought that high school marks, and the verbal and mathematical scores on the entrance examinations would be good predictors of student GPAs. A study of nine students was done. The data on the nine students are:

Student	HS Marks	Verbal	Math	GPA
1	75	480	410	3.21
2	58	290	270	1.68
3	68	420	410	3.58
4	78	500	600	3.92
5	72	500	490	3.00
6	68	430	460	2.82
7	64	320	490	1.65
8	62	530	480	2.30
9	66	469	440	2.33

a. Consider the following correlation matrix. Which single variable has the strongest correlation with the dependent variable? Some of the correlations between the independent variables are strong. Could this be a problem?

	HS Marks	Verbal	Math	GPA
HS Marks	1.000			
Verbal	.595	1.000		
Math	.639	.599	1.000	
GPA	.857	.616	.487	1.000

b. Consider the following output. Compute the coefficient of multiple determination.

ANOVA table

Source	*SS*	*df*	*MS*	*F*	*p-value*
Regression	3.8967	3	1.2989	5.57	.0474
Residual	1.1664	5	0.2333		
Total	5.0631	8			

c. Conduct a global test of hypothesis from the preceding output. Does it appear that any of the regression coefficients are not equal to zero? Test at a significance level of .05.

d. Conduct a test of hypothesis on each independent variable. Would you consider eliminating the variables verbal or math? Test at a .05 significance level.

Regression output

variables	*coefficients*	*std. error*	*t (df = 5)*	*p-value*
Intercept	−4.6451	1.8812	−2.469	.0566
HS Marks	0.1055	0.0373	2.826	.0368
Verbal	0.0022	0.0027	0.801	.4595
Math	−0.0017	0.0027	−0.625	.5595

e. The analysis has been rerun without the variables Verbal and Math. See the following output. Compute the coefficient of determination. How much has R^2 changed from the previous analysis? Which model is the better predictor of GPA?

ANOVA table

Source	*SS*	*df*	*MS*	*F*	*p-value*
Regression	3.7159	1	3.7159	19.31	.0032
Residual	1.3472	7	0.1925		
Total	5.0631	8			

f. Following is a normal probability plot of residuals from the first model. Does the normality assumption for the residuals seem reasonable?

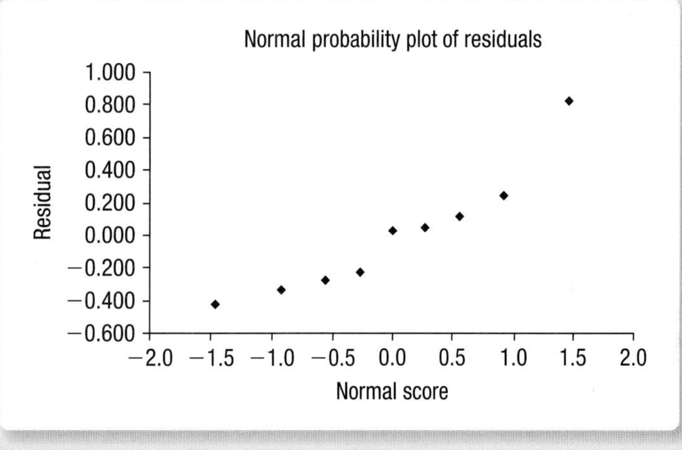

g. Following is a plot of the residuals and the Y' values. Do you see any violation of the assumptions?

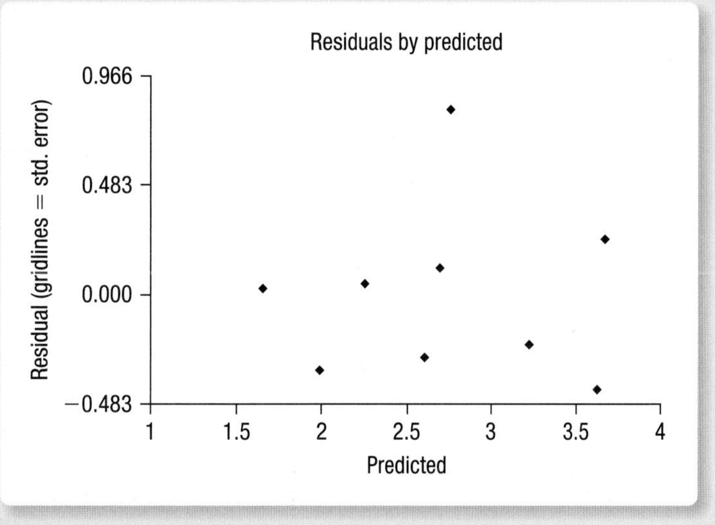

27. How important is GPA in determining the starting salary of recent business school graduates? Does graduating from a business program increase the starting salary? The placement officer at a local college wanted to study these questions. She gathered the following sample information on 15 graduates last spring to investigate these questions.

Student	Salary($)	GPA	Business	Student	Salary($)	GPA	Business
1	$31.5	3.245	0	9	$34.7	3.355	1
2	33	3.278	0	10	32.5	3.08	0
3	34.1	3.52	1	11	31.5	3.025	0
4	35.4	3.74	1	12	32.2	3.146	0
5	34.2	3.52	1	13	34	3.465	1
6	34	3.421	1	14	32.8	3.245	0
7	34.5	3.41	1	15	31.8	3.025	0
8	35	3.63	1				

The salary is reported in $000. The Business column indicates a '1' if the student graduated from a school of business, and a '0' if the student graduated from another program.

a. Develop a correlation matrix. Do you see any problems with multicollinearity?
b. Determine the regression equation. How much does graduating from a college business school add to a starting salary? What is the estimate of the starting salary for a student with a GPA of 3.00 who graduated from a business school?
c. What is the value of the coefficient of determination? What does this value tell us?
d. Would you consider deleting either of the independent variables?
e. Develop a normal probability plot of residuals. Is there any problem with the normality assumption?
f. Plot the fitted values against the residuals. Does this plot indicate any problems with homoscedasticity?

28. An investment advisor is studying the relationship between a common stock's price to earnings (P/E) ratio and factors that she thinks would influence it. She has the following data on the earnings per share (EPS) and the dividend percentage (Yield) for a sample of 20 stocks.

Stock	P/E	EPS($)	Yield	Stock	P/E	EPS($)	Yield
1	20.79	$2.46	1.42	11	1.35	$2.93	2.59
2	3.03	2.69	4.05	12	25.43	2.07	1.04
3	44.46	−0.28	4.16	13	22.14	2.19	3.52
4	41.72	−0.45	1.27	14	24.21	−0.83	1.56
5	18.96	1.60	3.39	15	30.91	2.29	2.23
6	18.42	2.32	3.86	16	35.79	1.64	3.36
7	34.82	0.81	4.56	17	18.99	3.07	1.98
8	30.43	2.13	1.62	18	30.21	1.71	3.07
9	29.97	2.22	5.10	19	32.88	0.35	2.21
10	10.86	1.44	1.17	20	15.19	5.02	3.50

a. Develop a multiple linear regression equation with P/E as the dependent variable.
b. Are either of the two independent variables an effective predictor of P/E?
c. Interpret the regression coefficients.
d. Do any of the stocks look undervalued?
e. Develop a normal probability plot of residuals. Is there any problem with the normality assumption?
f. Plot the fitted values against the residuals. Does this plot indicate any problems with homoscedasticity?
g. Develop a correlation matrix. Do any of the correlations indicate multicollinearity?

29. The president of Blitz Sales Enterprises sells kitchen products through television commercials, often called Infomercials. He gathered data from the last 15 weeks of sales to determine the relationship between sales and the number of infomercials.

Infomercials	Sales ($000)	Infomercials	Sales ($000)
20	$3.2	22	$2.5
15	2.6	15	2.4
25	3.4	25	3.0
10	1.8	16	2.7
18	2.2	12	2.0
18	2.4	20	2.6
15	2.4	25	2.8
12	1.5		

a. Determine the regression equation.
b. Are the sales predictable from the number of commercials? Test at a significance level of .01.
c. Develop a normal probability plot of the residuals.
d. Does the normality assumption seem reasonable?

30. The *Times-Observer* is a daily newspaper in Metro City. Like many city newspapers, the *Times-Observer* is suffering through difficult financial times. The circulation manager is studying other papers in similar cities in Canada and the United States. She is particularly interested in what variables relate to the number of subscriptions to the paper. She is able to obtain the following sample information on 25 newspapers in similar cities. The following notation is used.

Sub: Number of subscriptions (in thousands)
Popul: The metropolitan population (in thousands)
Adv: The advertising budget of the paper (in $ hundreds)
Income: The median family income in the metropolitan area (in $ thousands)

Sub.	Popul.	Adv.($)	Income($)	Sub.	Popul.	Adv.($)	Income($)
37.95	588.9	$13.2	$35.1	38.39	586.5	$15.4	$35.5
37.66	585.3	13.2	34.7	37.29	544.0	11.0	34.9
37.55	566.3	19.8	34.8	39.15	611.1	24.2	35.0
38.78	642.9	17.6	35.1	38.29	643.3	17.6	35.3
37.67	624.2	17.6	34.6	38.09	635.6	19.8	34.8
38.23	603.9	15.4	34.8	37.83	598.9	15.4	35.1
36.90	571.9	11.0	34.7	39.37	657.0	22.0	35.3
38.28	584.3	28.6	35.3	37.81	595.2	15.4	35.1
38.95	605.0	28.6	35.1	37.42	520.0	19.8	35.1
39.27	676.3	17.6	35.6	38.83	629.6	22.0	35.3
38.30	587.4	17.6	34.9	38.33	680.0	24.2	34.7
38.84	576.4	22.0	35.4	40.24	651.2	33.0	35.8
38.14	570.8	17.6	35.0				

a. Determine the regression equation.
b. Conduct a global test of hypothesis to determine whether any of the regression coefficients are not equal to zero. Use a significance level of .05.
c. Conduct a test for the individual coefficients. Would you consider deleting any coefficients?
d. Plot the fitted values against the residuals. Does this plot indicate any problems?
e. Develop a normal probability plot of residuals. Is there any problem with the normality assumption?

Data Set Exercises

31. Refer to the real estate data, from the south-east area of Edmonton on the CD-ROM, which reports information on listed homes. Use the list price of the home as the dependent variable and determine the regression equation with number of bedrooms, number of full bathrooms, size of the house, and style as independent variables.
    - **a.** Write out the regression equation. Discuss each of the variables. For example, are any of the coefficients negative?
    - **b.** Determine the value of R^2. Interpret.
    - **c.** Develop a correlation matrix. Which independent variables have strong or weak correlations with the dependent variable? Do you see any problems with multicollinearity?
    - **d.** Conduct the global test on the set of independent variables. Interpret. Test at a significance level of .05.
    - **e.** Conduct a test of hypothesis on each of the independent variables. Would you consider deleting any of the variables? If so, which ones? Test at a significance level of .05.
    - **f.** Rerun the regression equation until only significant net regression coefficients remain in the analysis. Identify these variables. Test at a significance level of .05.
    - **g.** Develop a normal probability plot of residuals from the final regression equation developed in part (f). Is it reasonable to conclude that the normality assumption has been met?

32. Refer to the Baseball 2006 data, which reports information on the 30 Major League Baseball teams for the 2006 season. Let the number of games won be the dependent variable and the following variables be independent variables: team batting average, number of stolen bases, number of errors committed, team ERA, number of home runs, and whether the team's home field is natural grass or artificial turf.
    - **a.** Write out the regression equation. Discuss each of the variables. For example, are you surprised that the regression coefficient for ERA is negative? How many wins does playing on natural grass for a home field add to or subtract from the total wins for the season?
    - **b.** Determine the value of R^2. Interpret.
    - **c.** Develop a correlation matrix. Which independent variables have strong or weak correlations with the dependent variable? Do you see any problems with multicollinearity?
    - **d.** Conduct a global test on the set of independent variables. Interpret. Test at a significance level of .05.
    - **e.** Conduct a test of hypothesis on each of the independent variables. Would you consider deleting any of the variables? If so, which ones? Test at a significance level of .05.
    - **f.** Rerun the analysis until only significant net regression coefficients remain in the analysis. Identify these variables. Test at a significance level of .05.
    - **g.** Develop a normal probability plot of residuals from the final regression equation developed in part (f). Is it reasonable to conclude that the normality assumption has been met?
    - **h.** Plot the residuals by observation from the final regression equation developed in part (f). Does this plot indicate any problems?

33. Refer to the International data, which reports demographic and economic information on 46 countries. Let unemployment be the dependent variable and percent of the population over 65, life expectancy, and literacy be the independent variables. Note: Remove any rows with an asterisk (unavailable data) before proceeding.
    - **a.** Determine the regression equation using a software package. Write out the regression equation.
    - **b.** What is the value of the coefficient of determination?
    - **c.** Check the independent variables for multicollinearity.
    - **d.** Conduct a global test on the set of independent variables. Test at a significance level of .05.
    - **e.** Test each of the independent variables to determine if they differ from zero. Test at a significance level of .05.
    - **f.** Would you delete any of the independent variables? If so, rerun the regression analysis and report the new equation.
    - **g.** Plot the residuals versus the fitted values from your final regression equation. Is it reasonable to conclude that the residuals follow a normal distribution?

exercises.com

Additional exercises that require you to access information at related Internet sites are available on the CD-ROM included with this text.

Answers to Self-Reviews

13–1 (a) 12.9 psi, found by $Y' = -0.5 + 20(.35) + 1(6.4)$.

(b) The b_1 of 20 indicates that the tensile strength of the wire will increase 20 psi for each increase of 1mm in outside diameter, with the amount of molybdenum held constant. That is, tensile strength will increase 20 psi if there is no change in the amount of molybdenum in the wire.

13–2 (a) $n = 25$.

(b) 4.

(c) $R^2 = \frac{10}{15} = 0.667$.

66.7 percent of the deviation in the Y-variable is accounted for by the four independent variables.

(d) $s_e = \sqrt{\frac{5}{20}} = 0.50$.

13–3 (a) $Y' = 181.5 - 14.81X_1 - 4.15X_2$.

(b) .621. A total of 62. 1 percent of the variation in heating cost is explained by temperature and insulation. Note that using the three independent variables explained 13.3 percent of the variation. This is a significant increase from the 62.1 percent with only two of the independent variables.

(c) H_0: $\beta_1 = \beta_2 = 0$.

H_1: not all βs are 0.

The p-value of temperature is close to zero, and so, temperature is a significant variable. The p-value of insulation is 0.052, which may or may not be considered a significant variable, depending on the significance level chosen.

chapter 14

Chi-Square Applications for Nominal Data

LEARNING GOALS

When you have completed this chapter, you will be able to:

1. Conduct a test of hypothesis comparing an observed *set of frequencies* to an *expected distribution*.
2. List the characteristics of the *chi-square distribution*.
3. Conduct a test of hypothesis to determine whether two classification criteria are related.

Introduction

Chapters 8 through 11 discuss statistical inference for data of interval or ratio scale, such as weights of steel ingots, incomes of graduates, and years of employment. We conduct hypothesis tests about a single population mean, two population means, and three or more population means. For these tests we assume the populations follow the normal probability distribution. However, there are tests available in which no assumption regarding the shape of the population is necessary. These tests are referred to as nonparametric. This means the assumption of a normal population is not necessary.

There are also tests exclusively for data of nominal scale of measurement. Recall from Chapter 1 that nominal data is the "lowest" or most primitive. For this type of measurement, data are classified into categories where there is no natural order. Examples include gender, province of birth, or brand of peanut butter purchased. In this chapter we introduce a new test statistic, the chi-square statistic. We use it for data measured with a nominal scale.

1 Conduct a test of hypothesis comparing an observed *set of frequencies* to an *expected distribution*.

Goodness-of-Fit Test: Equal Expected Frequencies

The goodness-of-fit test is one of the most commonly used statistical tests. The first illustration of this test involves the case in which the expected cell frequencies are equal.

As the full name implies, the purpose of the goodness-of-fit test is to compare an observed distribution to an expected distribution. An example will describe the hypothesis testing situation.

example

Ms. Jan Kilpatrick is the marketing manager for a manufacturer of sports cards. She plans to begin a series of cards with pictures and playing statistics of former Major League Baseball players. One of the problems is the selection of the former players. At the baseball card show at the Keswick Flea Market last weekend, she set up a booth and offered cards of the following six Hall of Fame baseball players: Tom Seaver, Nolan Ryan, Ty Cobb, George Brett, Hank Aaron, and Johnny Bench. At the end of the day she sold a total of 120 cards. The number of cards sold for each old-time player is shown in Table 14–1. Can she conclude the sales are not the same for each player?

TABLE 14–1 Number of Cards Sold for Each Player

Player	Cards Sold
Tom Seaver	13
Nolan Ryan	33
Ty Cobb	14
George Brett	7
Hank Aaron	36
Johnny Bench	17
Total	120

If there is no significant difference in the popularity of the players, we would expect that the observed frequencies (f_0) would be equal—or nearly equal. That is, we would expect to sell as many cards for Tom Seaver as for Nolan Ryan. Thus, any discrepancy in the observed and expected frequencies could be attributed to sampling (chance).

What about the level of measurement in this problem? Notice when a card is sold, the "measurement" of the card is based on the player's name. There is no natural order to the players. Therefore, a nominal level is used to evaluate each observation.

Because there are 120 cards in the sample, we expect that 20 (f_e) cards, i.e., the expected frequency, will fall in each of the six categories. These categories are called **cells**. An examination of the set of observed frequencies in Table 14–2 indicates that the card for George Brett is sold rather infrequently, whereas the cards for Hank Aaron and Nolan Ryan are sold more often. Is the difference in sales due to chance, or can we conclude that there is a preference for the cards of certain players?

TABLE 14–2 Observed and Expected Frequencies for the 120 Cards Sold

Player	Cards Sold, f_o	Expected Number Sold, f_e
Tom Seaver	13	20
Nolan Ryan	33	20
Ty Cobb	14	20
George Brett	7	20
Hank Aaron	36	20
Johnny Bench	17	20
Total	120	120

solution

We will use the same systematic five-step hypothesis testing procedure followed in previous chapters.

Step 1: State the null hypothesis and the alternative hypothesis. The null hypothesis, H_0, is that there is no difference between the set of observed frequencies and the set of expected frequencies; that is, any difference between the two sets of frequencies can be attributed to sampling (chance). The alternative hypothesis, H_1, is that there is a difference between the observed and expected sets of frequencies. If H_0 is rejected and H_1 is accepted, it means that sales are not equally distributed among the six categories (cells).

Step 2: Select the level of significance. We selected the .05 significance level. The probability is .05 that a true null hypothesis will be rejected.

Step 3: Select the test statistic. The test statistic follows a chi-square distribution, designated as χ^2:

CHI-SQUARE TEST STATISTIC

$$\chi^2 = \Sigma\left[\frac{(f_o - f_e)^2}{f_e}\right] \quad [14\text{–}1]$$

with $k - 1$ degrees of freedom, where:

k is the number of categories.
f_o is an observed frequency in a particular category.
f_e is an expected frequency in a particular category.

We will examine the characteristics of the chi-square distribution in more detail shortly.

Step 4: Formulate the decision rule. Recall the decision rule in hypothesis testing requires finding a number that separates the region where we do not reject H_0 from the region of rejection. This number is called the *critical value*. As we will soon see, the chi-square distribution is really a family of distributions. Each distribution has a slightly different shape, depending on the number of degrees of freedom. The number of degrees of freedom in this type of problem is found by $k - 1$, where k is the number of categories. In this particular problem there are six. Since there are six categories, there are 5 degrees of freedom ($k - 1 = 6 - 1$). As noted, a category is called a *cell*, so there are six cells. The critical value for 5 degrees of freedom and the .05 level of significance is found in Appendix B. A portion of that table is shown in Table 14–3. The critical value is 11.070, found by locating 5 degrees of freedom in the left margin and then moving horizontally (to the right) and reading the critical value in the .05 column.

TABLE 14–3 A Portion of the Chi-Square Table

Degrees of Freedom	Right-Tail Area			
df	.10	.05	.02	.01
1	2.706	3.841	5.412	6.635
2	4.605	5.991	7.824	9.210
3	6.251	7.815	9.837	11.345
4	7.779	9.488	11.668	13.277
5	9.236	11.070	13.388	15.086

The decision rule is to reject H_0 if the computed value of chi-square is greater than 11.070. If it is less than or equal to 11.070, do not reject H_0. Chart 14–1 shows the decision rule.

The decision rule indicates that if there are large differences between the observed and expected frequencies, resulting in a computed χ^2 of more than 11.070, the null hypothesis should be rejected. However, if the differences between f_0 and f_e are small, the computed χ^2 value will be 11.070 or less, and the null hypothesis should not be rejected. The reasoning is that such small differences between the observed and expected frequencies are probably due to chance. Remember, the 120 observations are a sample of the population.

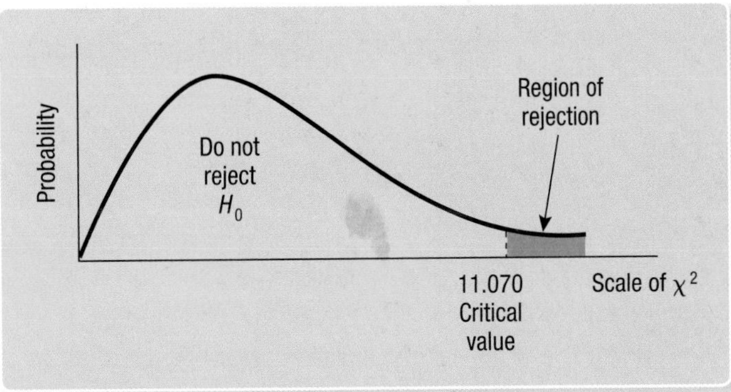

CHART 14–1 Chi-Square Probability Distribution for 5 Degrees of Freedom, Showing the Region of Rejection, .05 Level of Significance

Statistics in Action

For many years, researchers and statisticians believed that all variables were normally distributed. In fact, it was generally assumed to be a universal law. However, Karl Pearson observed that experimental data were not always normally distributed but there was no way to prove his observations were correct. To solve this problem, Pearson discovered the chi-square statistic that basically compares an observed frequency distribution with an assumed normal distribution. His discovery proved that not all variables are normally distributed.

Step 5: Compute the value of chi-square and make a decision. Of the 120 cards sold in the sample, we counted the number of times Tom Seaver and Nolan Ryan, and each of the others were sold. The counts were reported in Table 14–1. The calculations for chi-square follow. (Note again that the expected frequencies are the same for each cell.)

Column 1: Determine the differences between each f_o and f_e. That is, $(f_o - f_e)$. The sum of these differences is zero.

Column 2: Square the difference between each observed and expected frequency. That is, $(f_o - f_e)^2$.

Column 3: Divide the result for each observation by the expected frequency. That is, $\frac{(f_o - f_e)^2}{f_e}$. Finally, sum these values. The result is the value of χ^2, which is 34.40.

Baseball Player	f_o	f_e	(1) $(f_o - f_e)$	(2) $(f_o - f_e)^2$	(3) $\frac{(f_o - f_e)^2}{f_e}$
Tom Seaver	13	20	−7	49	49/20 = 2.45
Nolan Ryan	33	20	13	169	169/20 = 8.45
Ty Cobb	14	20	−6	36	36/20 = 1.80
George Brett	7	20	−13	169	169/20 = 8.45
Hank Aaron	36	20	16	256	256/20 = 12.80
Johnny Bench	17	20	−3	9	9/20 = 0.45
		Must be →	0		χ^2 → 34.40

The computed χ^2 of 34.40 is in the rejection region beyond the critical value of 11.070. The decision, therefore, is to reject H_0 at the .05 level and to accept H_1. The difference between the observed and the expected frequencies is not due to chance. Rather, the differences between f_o and f_e are large enough to be considered significant. The chance of these differences being due to sampling is very small. So we conclude that it is unlikely that card sales are the same among the six players.

The output of MegaStat follows. The computed value of chi-square is 34.40, the same value obtained in our earlier calculations. MegaStat also returns a p-value of 1.98E-06, which is in scientific notation. Rewriting the p-value gives us .00000198, which is very close to zero, and as the p-value is smaller than the significance level of .05, the null hypothesis is rejected.

excel

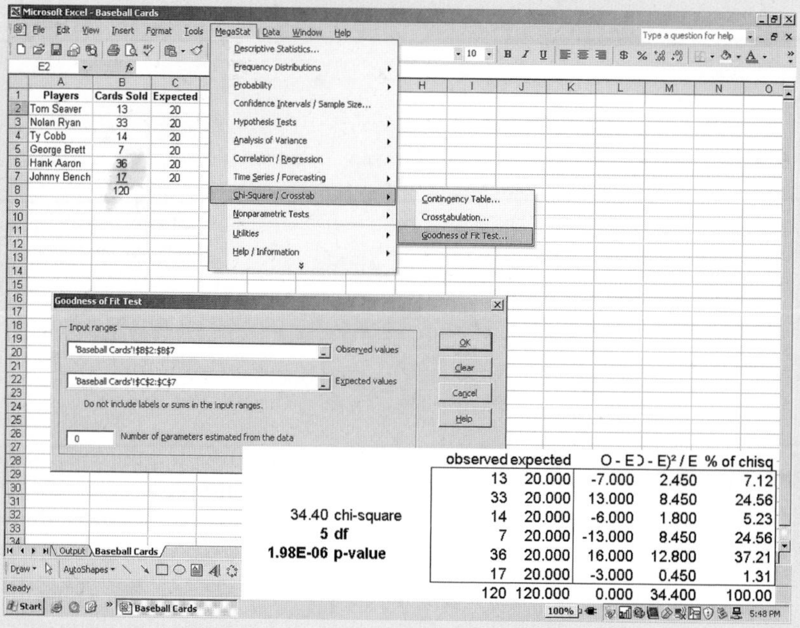

CHIDIST is an **Excel** function that will also return the *p*-value. It is necessary to know the chi-square value and the degrees of freedom to use this function. Enter the values into the dialogue box as follows. The result is 1.98193E-06, which is in scientific notation. Rewriting the *p*-value gives us .00000198, which is very close to zero, and as the *p*-value is smaller than the significance level of .05, the null hypothesis is rejected.

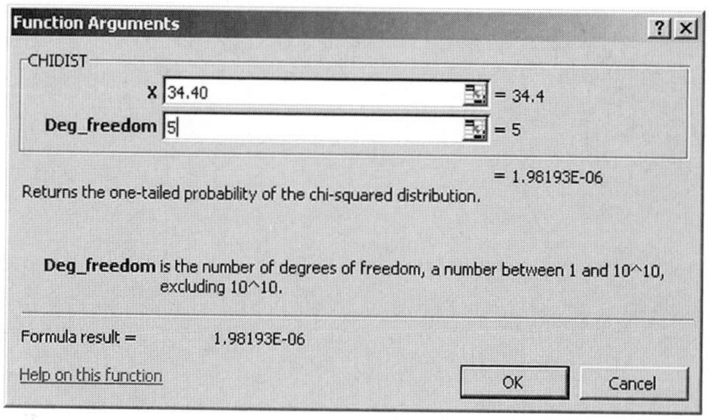

CHIINV is an **Excel** function that will return the Chi-Square table value. It is necessary to know the significance level and the degrees of freedom to use this function. Enter the values into the dialogue box as follows. The result is 11.070, the same value that we obtained from the table.

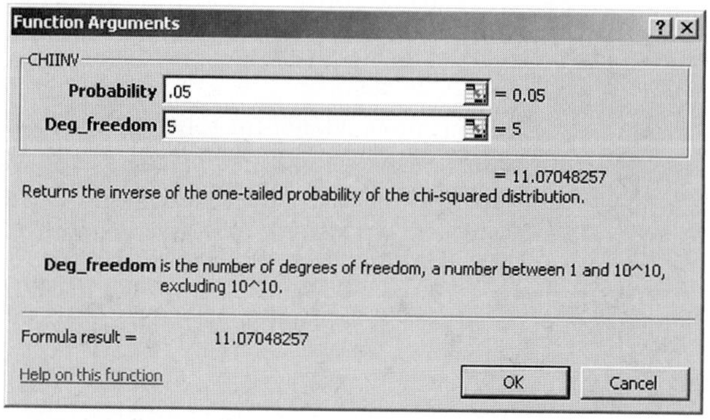

2 **List the characteristics of the *chi-square distribution*.**

The chi-square distribution, which is used as the test statistic in this chapter, has the following characteristics.

1. **Chi-square is never negative.** This is because the difference between f_o and f_e is squared, that is, $(f_o - f_e)^2$.
2. **There is a family of chi-square distributions.** There is a chi-square distribution for 1 degree of freedom, another for 2 degrees of freedom, another for 3 degrees of freedom, and so on. In this type of problem, the number of degrees of freedom is determined by $k - 1$, where k is the number of categories. Therefore, the shape of the chi-square distribution does *not* depend on the size of the sample, but on the number of categories used. For example, if 200 employees of an airline were classified into one of three categories—flight personnel, ground support, and administrative personnel—there would be 2 degrees of freedom $(k - 1 = 3 - 1)$.
3. **The chi-square distribution is positively skewed.** However, as the number of degrees of freedom increases, the distribution begins to approximate a normal distribution. Chart 14–2 shows the distributions for selected degrees of freedom. Notice that for 10 degrees of freedom, the curve is approaching a normal distribution.

Shape of χ^2 distribution approaches normal distribution as *df* becomes larger

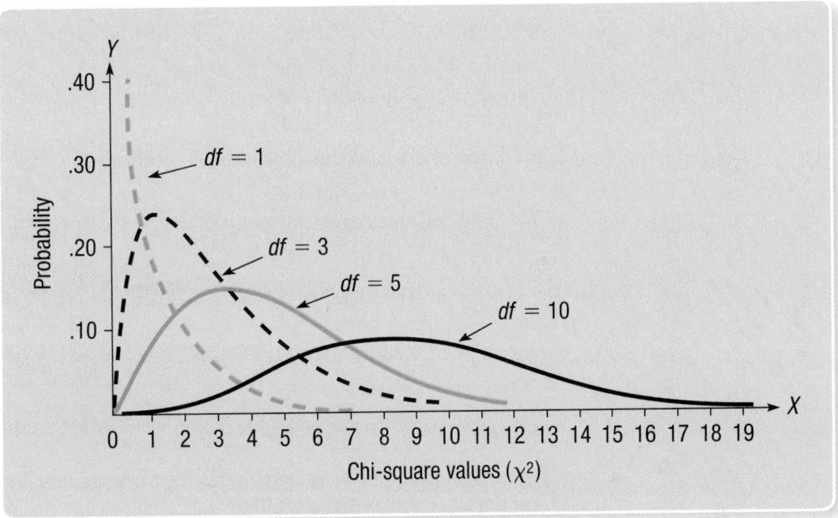

CHART 14–2 Chi-Square Distributions for Selected Degrees of Freedom

self-review 14–1

The human resources director at Georgetown Paper Inc. is concerned about absenteeism among hourly workers. She decides to sample the records to determine whether absenteeism is distributed evenly throughout the six-day workweek. The hypotheses are:

H_0: Absenteeism is evenly distributed throughout the work week.
H_1: Absenteeism is *not* evenly distributed throughout the work week.

The sample results are:

	Number Absent		Number Absent
Monday	12	Thursday	10
Tuesday	9	Friday	9
Wednesday	11	Saturday	9

(a) What are the numbers 12, 9, 11, 10, 9, and 9 called?
(b) How many categories (cells) are there?
(c) What is the *expected* frequency for each day?
(d) How many degrees of freedom are there?
(e) What is the chi-square critical value at the 1 percent significance level?
(f) Compute the χ^2 test statistic.
(g) What is the decision regarding the null hypothesis?
(h) Specifically, what does this indicate to the human resources director?

Exercises

1. In a particular chi-square goodness-of-fit test there are four categories and 200 observations. Use the .05 significance level.
   a. How many degrees of freedom are there?
   b. What is the critical value of chi-square?
2. In a particular chi-square goodness-of-fit test there are six categories and 500 observations. Use the .01 significance level.
   a. How many degrees of freedom are there?
   b. What is the critical value of chi-square?
3. The null hypothesis and the alternative hypothesis are:

   H_0: The cell categories are equal.
   H_1: The cell categories are not equal.

Category	f_o
A	10
B	20
C	30

   a. State the decision rule, using the .05 significance level.
   b. Compute the value of chi-square.
   c. What is your decision regarding H_0?
4. The null hypothesis and the alternative hypothesis are:

   H_0: The cell categories are equal.
   H_1: The cell categories are not equal.

Category	f_o
A	10
B	20
C	30
D	20

   a. State the decision rule, using the .05 significance level.
   b. Compute the value of chi-square.
   c. What is your decision regarding H_0?
5. A six-sided die is rolled 30 times and the numbers 1 through 6 appear as shown in the following frequency distribution. At the .10 significance level, can we conclude that the die is fair?

Outcome	Frequency	Outcome	Frequency
1	3	4	3
2	6	5	9
3	2	6	7

6. The director of golf for the Links Group wishes to study the number of rounds of golf played by members on weekdays. He gathered the following sample information for 520 rounds.

Day	Rounds
Monday	124
Tuesday	74
Wednesday	104
Thursday	98
Friday	120

   At the .05 significance level, is there a difference in the number of rounds played by day of the week?

7. A group of department store buyers viewed a new line of dresses and gave their opinions of them. The results were:

Opinion	Number of Buyers	Opinion	Number of Buyers
Outstanding	47	Good	39
Excellent	45	Fair	35
Very good	40	Undesirable	34

Because the largest number (47) indicated the new line is outstanding, the head designer thinks that this is a mandate to go into mass production of the dresses. The head sweeper (who somehow became involved in this) believes that there is not a clear mandate and claims that the opinions are evenly distributed among the six categories. He further states that the slight differences among the various counts are probably due to chance. Test the null hypothesis that there is no significant difference among the opinions of the buyers. Test at the .01 level of risk. Follow a formal approach; that is, state the null hypothesis, the alternative hypothesis, and so on.

8. The safety director of Honda took samples at random from the file of minor work-related accidents and classified them according to the time the accident took place.

Time	Number of Accidents	Time	Number of Accidents
8 up to 9 a.m.	6	1 up to 2 p.m.	7
9 up to 10 a.m.	6	2 up to 3 p.m.	8
10 up to 11 a.m.	20	3 up to 4 p.m.	19
11 up to 12 p.m.	8	4 up to 5 p.m.	6

Using the goodness-of-fit test and the .01 level of significance, determine whether the accidents are evenly distributed throughout the day. Write a brief explanation of your conclusion.

Goodness-of-Fit Test: Unequal Expected Frequencies

The expected frequencies (f_e) in the previous distribution involving baseball cards were all equal (20). According to the null hypothesis, it was expected that a picture of Tom Seaver would appear 20 times at random, a picture of Johnny Bench would appear 20 times out of 120 trials, and so on. The chi-square test can also be used if the expected frequencies are not equal.

Expected frequencies not equal in this problem

The following example illustrates the case of unequal frequencies and also gives a practical use of chi-square—namely, to find whether a local experience differs from the national experience.

example

The following information reports the number of times senior citizens are admitted to a hospital during a one-year period. Forty percent are not admitted, 30 percent are admitted once, 20 percent are admitted twice, and the remaining 10 percent are admitted three or more times.

A survey of 150 residents of Bartow Estates, a community devoted to active seniors, revealed 55 residents were not admitted during the last year, 50 were admitted to a hospital once, 32 were admitted twice, and the rest of those in the survey were admitted three or more times. Can we conclude the survey at Bartow Estates is consistent with the information suggested by the report? Use the .05 significance level.

solution

We begin by organizing the above information into Table 14–4. Clearly, we cannot compare percentages given in the study to the frequencies reported for the Bartow Estates. However, these percentages can be converted to expected frequencies, f_e. According to the report, 40 percent of the Bartow residents in the survey did not require hospitalization. Thus, if there is no difference between the national experience and those of Bartow Estates, then 40 percent of the 150 seniors surveyed (60 residents) would not have been hospitalized. Further, 30 percent of those surveyed were admitted once (45 residents) would have been admitted once, and so on. The observed frequencies for Bartow residents and the expected frequencies based on the percentages in the national study are given in Table 14–4.

TABLE 14–4 Summary of the Report and of Bartow Estates Residents

Number of Times Admitted	Reported Percent of Total (%)	Number of Bartow Residents (f_o)	Expected Number of Residents (f_e)
0	40%	55	60
1	30	50	45
2	20	32	30
3 or more	10	13	15
Total	100%	150	150

Statistics in Action

Many provincial governments operate lotteries to help fund hospitals, health care and education, and amateur sport among other activities. In many lotteries, numbered balls are mixed and selected randomly from three groups of balls numbered zero through nine. Randomness would predict that the frequency of each number is equal. How would you prove that the selection machine ensured randomness? A chi-square, goodness-of-fit test could be used to prove or disprove randomness.

The null hypothesis and the alternative hypotheses are:

H_0: There is no difference between local and national experience for hospital admissions.

H_1: There is a difference between local and national experience for hospital admissions.

To find the decision rule we use Appendix B. There are four admitting categories, so the degrees of freedom are $df = 4 - 1 = 3$. The critical value is 7.815. Therefore, the decision rule is to reject the null hypothesis if $\chi^2 > 7.815$. The decision rule is portrayed in Chart 14–3.

Now, to compute the chi-square test statistic:

Number of Times Admitted	(f_o)	(f_e)	$f_o - f_e$	$(f_o - f_e)^2/f_e$
0	55	60	−5	0.4167
1	50	45	5	0.5556
2	32	30	2	0.1333
3 or more	13	15	−2	0.2667
Total	150	150	0	1.3723

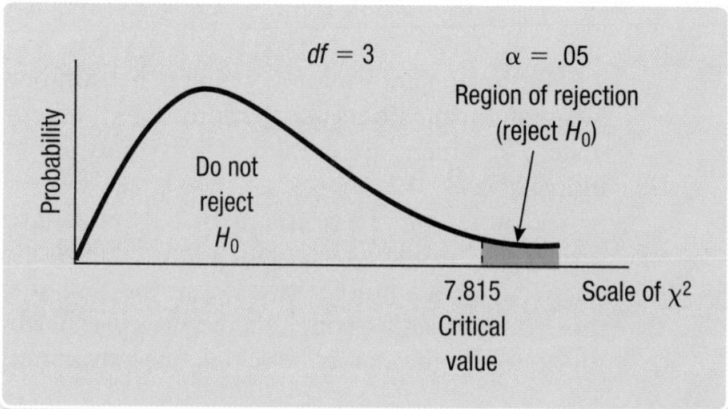

CHART 14–3 Decision Criteria for the Bartow Estates Study

The computed values of χ^2 (1.3723) lies to the left of 7.815. Thus, we cannot reject the null hypothesis. We conclude that there is no evidence of a difference between local and national experience for hospital admissions. MegaStat steps and commands follow.

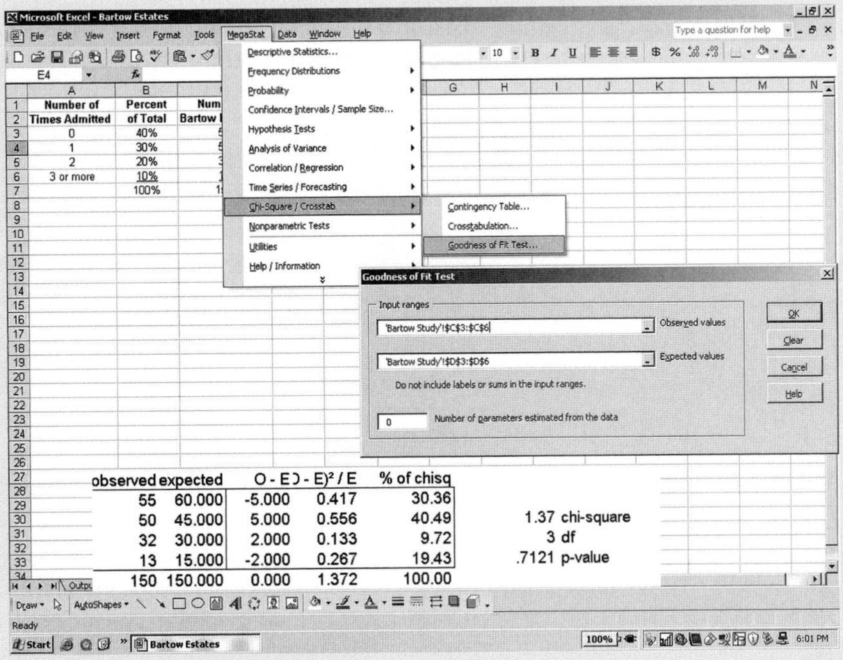

MegaStat returns the chi-square value of 1.37 as expected and a p-value of .7121. As the p-value is greater than the significance level, there is not enough evidence to reject the null hypothesis and we conclude that there is no difference between local and national experience for hospital admissions.

Limitations of Chi-Square

Be careful in applying χ^2 to some problems

If there is an unusually small expected frequency in a cell, chi-square (if applied) might result in an erroneous conclusion. This can happen because f_e appears in the denominator, and dividing by a very small number makes the quotient quite large! Two generally accepted rules regarding small cell frequencies are:

1. **If there are only two cells, the expected frequency in each cell should be 5 or more.** The computation of chi-square would be permissible in the following problem, involving a minimum f_e of 6.

Individual	f_o	f_e
Literate	643	642
Illiterate	7	6

2. **For more than two cells, chi-square should *not* be used if more than 20 percent of the f_e cells have expected frequencies less than 5.** According to this rule, it would not be appropriate to use the goodness-of-fit test on the following data. Three of the seven cells, or 43 percent, have expected frequencies (f_e) of less than 5.

Level of Management	f_o	f_e
Foreman	30	32
Supervisor	110	113
Manager	86	87
Middle management	23	24
Assistant vice president	5	2
Vice president	5	4
Senior vice president	4	1
Total	263	263

To show the reason for the 20 percent policy, we conducted the goodness-of-fit test on the above data on the levels of management. The hypothesis is that the observed and expected frequency distributions are the same. The MegaStat output follows.

Observed	Expected	O − E	(O − E)²/E	% of chisq
30	32.000	−2.000	0.125	0.89
110	113.000	−3.000	0.080	0.57
86	87.000	−1.000	0.011	0.08
23	24.000	−1.000	0.042	0.30
5	2.000	3.000	4.500	32.12
5	4.000	1.000	0.250	1.78
4	1.000	3.000	9.000	64.25
263	263.000	0.000	14.008	100.00

14.01 chi-square
6 *df*
.0295 *p*-value

For this test at the .05 significance level, H_0 is rejected if the computed value of chi-square is greater than 12.592. The computed value is 14.01, with a *p*-value of 0.0295. So we reject the null hypothesis that the observed frequencies represent a random sample from the population of the expected values. Examine the MegaStat output above. More than 98 percent of the computed chi-square value is accounted for by the three vice president categories ([4.500 + 0.250 + 9.000]/14.008 = 0.9815). Logically, too much weight is being given to these categories.

The dilemma can be resolved by combining categories if it is logical to do so. In the above example we combine the three vice-presidential categories, which satisfies the 20 percent rule.

Level of Management	f_o	f_e
Foreman	30	32
Supervisor	110	113
Manager	86	87
Middle management	23	24
Vice president	14	7
Total	263	263

The computed value of chi-square with the revised categories is 7.26. See the following output. This value is less than the critical value of 9.488 for the .05 significance level. The null hypothesis is, therefore, not rejected at the .05 significance level. This indicates there is no significant difference between the observed distribution and the expected distribution.

Observed	Expected	O − E	(O − E)²/E	% of chisq
30	32.000	−2.000	0.125	1.72
110	113.000	−3.000	0.080	1.10
86	87.000	−1.000	0.011	0.16
23	24.000	−1.000	0.042	0.57
14	7.000	7.000	7.000	96.45
263	263.000	0.000	7.258	100.00

7.26 chi-square
4 *df*
.1229 *p*-value

Note that the *p*-value is .1229. As the *p*-value is greater than the significance level, there is not enough evidence to reject the null hypothesis and we conclude that there is no difference between the observed distribution and the expected distribution.

self-review 14–2

Accounts receivable are classified as "current," "late," and "not collectible." Industry figures show that 60 percent of accounts receivable are current, 30 percent are late, and 10 percent are not collectible. Massa and Barr, attorneys in Devon, Alberta, have 500 accounts receivable: 320 are current, 120 are late, and 60 are not collectible. Are these numbers in agreement with the industry distribution? Use the .05 significance level.

Exercises

9. The following hypotheses are given:

H_0: Forty percent of the observations are in category A, 40 percent are in B, and 20 percent are in C.
H_1: The observations are not as described in H_0.

We took a sample of 60, with the following results.

Category	f_o
A	30
B	20
C	10

a. State the decision rule using the .01 significance level.
b. Compute the value of chi-square.
c. What is your decision regarding H_0?

10. The chief of security for a shopping mall in Calgary, Alberta, was directed to study the problem of missing goods. He selected a sample of 100 boxes that had been tampered with and ascertained that for 60 of the boxes, the missing pants, shoes, and so on were attributed to shoplifting. For 30 other boxes employees had stolen the goods, and for the remaining 10 boxes he blamed poor inventory control. In his report to the mall management, can he say that shoplifting is *twice* as likely to be the cause of the loss as compared with either employee theft or poor inventory control and that employee theft and poor inventory control are equally likely? Use the .02 level.

11. A bank credit card department knows from experience that 5 percent of the card holders have had some high school, 15 percent have completed high school, 25 percent have had some college or university, and 55 percent have completed college or university. Of the 500 card holders whose cards have been called in for failure to pay their charges this month, 50 had some high school, 100 had completed high school, 190 had some college or university, and 160 had completed college or university. Can we conclude that the distribution of card holders who do not pay their charges is different from all others? Use the .01 significance level.

12. For many years, TV executives used the guideline that 30 percent of the audience were watching each of the prime-time networks and 10 percent cable stations on a weekday night. A random sample of 500 viewers last Monday night showed that 165 homes were tuned in to the ABC affiliate, 140 to the CBS affiliate, 125 to the NBC affiliate, and the remainder were viewing a cable station. At the .05 significance level, can we conclude that the guideline is still reasonable?

3 Conduct a test of hypothesis to determine whether two classification criteria are related.

Contingency Table Analysis

In Chapter 4 we discussed bivariate data, where we studied the relationship between two variables. We described a contingency table which simultaneously summarizes two nominal scale variables of interest. For example, a sample of students enrolled in the School of Business is classified by gender (male or female) and major (accounting, finance, marketing, or human resources). This classification is based on the nominal scale, because there is no natural order to the classifications.

Also in Chapter 4, we illustrated the relationship between loyalty to a company and length of employment. Are older employees likely to be more or less loyal to the company? We can use a chi-square statistic to formally test for a relationship between two nominal scale variables. To put it another way, is one variable independent of the other? Here are some examples where we are interested in testing whether two variables are related.

- A sample of 100 drivers who were stopped for speeding violations was classified by gender and whether or not they were wearing a seat belt. For this sample, is wearing a seatbelt related to gender?
- The Ford Motor Company operates several assembly plants. One such plant operates three shifts per day, five days per week. The quality control manager wishes to compare the quality level on the three shifts. Vehicles are classified by quality level (acceptable, unacceptable) and shift (day, afternoon, night). Is there a difference in the quality level on the three shifts? That is, is the quality of the product related to the shift when it was manufactured? Or, is the quality of the product independent of the shift on which it was manufactured?
- Does a male released from federal prison make a different adjustment to civilian life if he returns to his hometown or if he goes elsewhere to live? The two variables are adjustment to civilian life and place of residence. Note that both variables are measured at the nominal level. See the following example.

example

Does a male released from federal prison make a different adjustment to civilian life if he returns to his hometown or if he goes elsewhere to live? To put it another way, is there a relationship between adjustment to civilian life and place of residence after release from prison?

solution

As before, the first step in hypothesis testing is to state the null and alternative hypotheses.

H_0: There is no relationship between adjustment to civilian life and where the individual lives after being released from prison.
H_1: There is a relationship between adjustment to civilian life and where the individual lives after being released from prison.

The .01 level of significance will be used to test the hypothesis.

Psychologists interviewed 200 randomly selected former prisoners. Using a series of questions, the psychologists classified the adjustment of each individual to civilian life as outstanding, good, fair, or unsatisfactory. The classifications for the 200 former prisoners were tallied as follows. Joseph Camden, for example, returned to his hometown and has shown outstanding adjustment to civilian life. His case is one of the 27 tallies in the upper left box.

Residence after Release from Prison	Adjustment to Civilian Life			
	Outstanding	Good	Fair	Unsatisfactory
Hometown	𝍸 𝍸 𝍸 𝍸 𝍸 ||	𝍸 𝍸 𝍸 𝍸 𝍸 𝍸 𝍸	𝍸 𝍸 𝍸 𝍸 𝍸 𝍸 |||	𝍸 𝍸 𝍸 𝍸 𝍸
Not hometown	𝍸 𝍸 |||	𝍸 𝍸 𝍸	𝍸 𝍸 𝍸 𝍸 𝍸 ||	𝍸 𝍸 𝍸 𝍸 𝍸

Contingency table consists of count data

The tallies in each box, or *cell*, were counted. The counts are given in the following **contingency table.** (See Table 14–5.) In this case, the psychologists wondered whether adjustment to civilian life is *contingent* on or related to where the prisoner goes after release from prison.

TABLE 14–5 Adjustment to Civilian Life and Place of Residence

Residence after Release from Prison	Adjustment to Civilian Life				
	Outstanding	Good	Fair	Unsatisfactory	Total
Hometown	27	35	33	25	120
Not hometown	13	15	27	25	80
Total	40	50	60	50	200

Once we know how many rows (2) and columns (4) there are in the contingency table, we can determine the critical value and the decision rule. For a chi-square test of significance where two traits are classified in a contingency table, the degrees of freedom are found by:

$$df = (\textbf{number of rows} - 1)(\textbf{number of columns} - 1) = (r - 1)(c - 1)$$

In this problem:

$$df = (r - 1)(c - 1) = (2 - 1)(4 - 1) = 3$$

To find the critical value for 3 degrees of freedom and the .01 level (selected earlier), refer to Appendix B. It is 11.345. The decision rule is to reject the null hypothesis if the computed value of χ^2 is greater than 11.345. The decision rule is portrayed graphically in Chart 14–4.

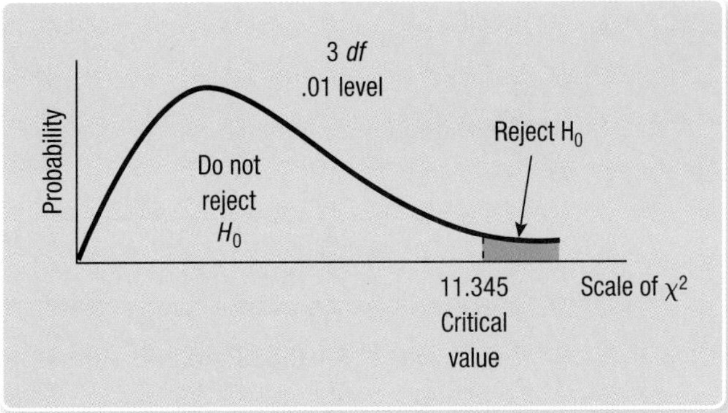

CHART 14–4 Chi-Square Distribution for 3 Degrees of Freedom

Next, we find the computed value of χ^2: The observed frequencies, f_o, are shown in Table 14–5. How are the corresponding expected frequencies, f_e, determined? Note in the "Total" column of Table 14–5 that 120 of the 200 former prisoners (60 percent) returned to their hometowns. *If there were no relationship* between adjustment and residency after release from prison, we would expect 60 percent of the 40 ex-prisoners who made outstanding adjustment to civilian life to reside in their hometowns. Thus, the expected frequency f_e for the upper left cell is $.60 \times 40 = 24$. Likewise, if there were no relationship between adjustment and present residence, we would expect 60 percent of the 50 ex-prisoners (30) who had "good" adjustment to civilian life to reside in their hometowns.

Further, notice that 80 of the 200 ex-prisoners studied (40 percent) did not return to their hometowns to live. Thus, of the 60 considered by the psychologists to have made "fair" adjustment to civilian life, $.40 \times 60$, or 24, would be expected not to return to their hometowns.

The expected frequency for any cell can be determined by

EXPECTED FREQUENCY

$$f_e = \frac{\textbf{(Row total)(Column total)}}{\textbf{Grand total}} \qquad \textbf{[14–2]}$$

Using this formula, the expected frequency for the upper left cell in Table 14–5 is:

$$\textbf{Expected frequency} = \frac{\textbf{(Row total)(Column total)}}{\textbf{Grand total}} = \frac{\textbf{(120)(40)}}{\textbf{200}} = 24$$

The observed frequencies, f_o, and the expected frequencies, f_e, for all of the cells in the contingency table are listed in Table 14–6.

TABLE 14–6 Observed and Expected Frequencies

Residence after Release from Prison	Adjustment to Civilian Life									
	Outstanding		Good		Fair		Unsatisfactory		Total	
	f_o	f_e	f_o	f_e	f_o	f_e	f_o	f_e	f_o	f_e
Hometown	27	24	35	30	33	36	25	30	120	120
Not hometown	13	16	15	20	27	24	25	20	80	80
Total	40	40	50	50	60	60	50	50	200	200

Must be equal (Outstanding totals: 40 and 40)

$\frac{(80)(50)}{200}$ (expected frequency for Not hometown, Good: 20)

Must be equal (Total: 200 and 200)

Recall that the computed value of chi-square using formula (14–1) is found by:

$$\chi^2 = \Sigma\left[\frac{(f_o - f_e)^2}{f_e}\right]$$

Starting with the upper left cell:

$$\begin{aligned}\chi^2 &= \frac{(27-24)^2}{24} + \frac{(35-30)^2}{30} + \frac{(33-36)^2}{36} + \frac{(25-30)^2}{30} \\ &\quad + \frac{(13-16)^2}{16} + \frac{(15-20)^2}{20} + \frac{(27-24)^2}{24} + \frac{(25-20)^2}{20} \\ &= 0.375 + 0.833 + 0.250 + 0.833 + 0.563 + 1.250 + 0.375 + 1.250 \\ &= 5.729\end{aligned}$$

Because the computed value of chi-square (5.729) lies in the region to the left of 11.345, the null hypothesis is not rejected at the .01 level. We conclude there is no evidence of a relationship between adjustment to civilian life and where the prisoner resides after being released from prison. MegaStat steps and commands to produce the output follow.

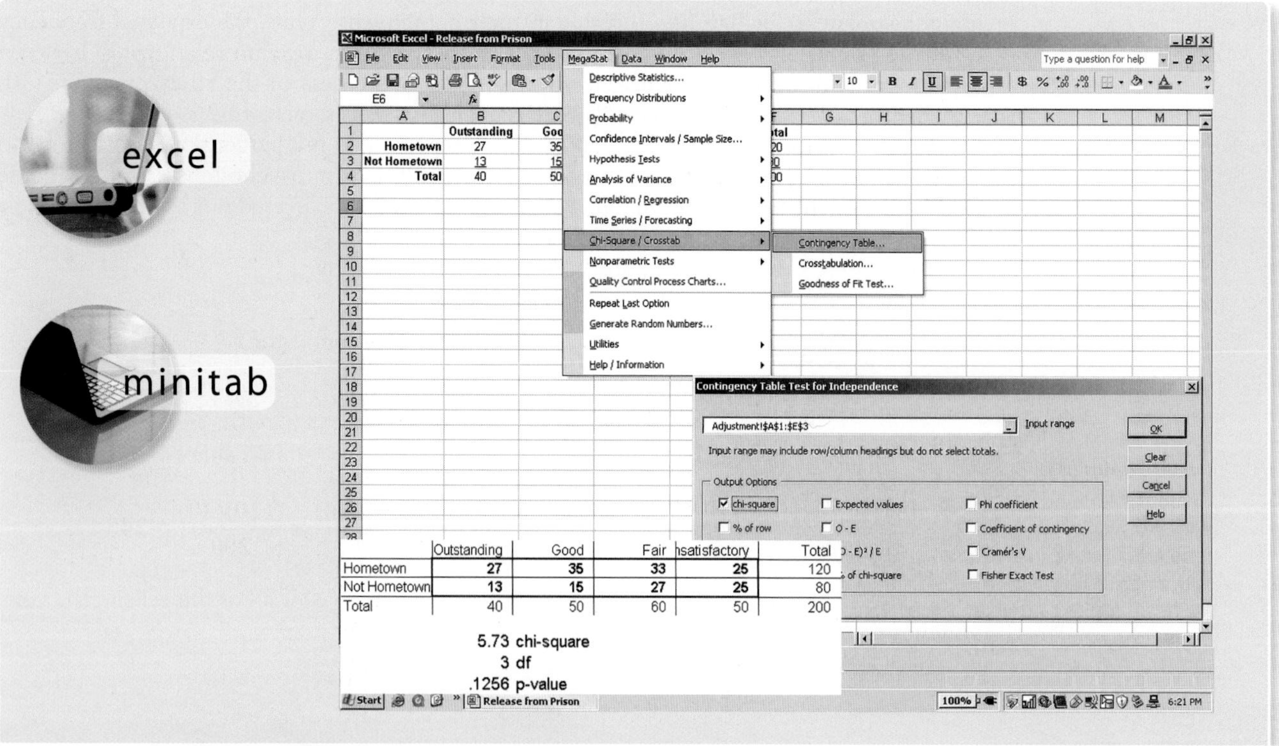

Observe that the value of chi-square is the same as that calculated earlier. MegaStat also reports the p-value as .1256. Therefore, the probability of finding a value of the test statistic as large or larger is .1256 when the null hypothesis is true. Therefore, there is not enough evidence to reject the null hypothesis.

self-review 14–3

At a recent automobile show, a sample of 125 people produced the following results. Use the .05 significance level to determine if there is a relationship between age and model preferred.

Age (in Years)	Sports	SUV	Luxury	Total
Under 30	18	12	10	40
30 to 50	17	15	13	45
Over 50	9	9	22	40
	44	36	45	125

(a) What is the above called?
(b) State the null hypothesis.
(c) Determine the value of chi-square. What is your decision regarding the null hypothesis?
(d) Interpret the results.

Exercises

13. The director of advertising for a large newspaper is studying the relationship between the type of community in which a subscriber resides and the portion of the newspaper he or she reads first. For a sample of readers, she collected the following sample information.

	National News	Sports	Comics
City	170	124	90
Suburb	120	112	100
Rural	130	90	88

At the .05 significance level, can we conclude there is a relationship between the type of community where the person resides and the portion of the paper read first?

14. Four brands of light bulbs are being considered for use in a large manufacturing plant. The director of purchasing asked for samples of 100 from each manufacturer. The numbers of acceptable and unacceptable bulbs from each manufacturer are shown below. At the .05 significance level, is there a difference in the quality of the bulbs?

	Manufacturer			
	A	B	C	D
Unacceptable	12	8	5	11
Acceptable	88	92	95	89
Total	100	100	100	100

15. The quality control department at Food Town Inc. conducts a monthly check on the comparison of scanned prices to posted prices. The chart below summarizes the results of a sample of 500 items last month. Company management would like to know whether there is any relationship between error rates on regular priced items and specially priced items. Use the .01 significance level.

	Regular Price	Advertised Special Price
Undercharge	20	10
Overcharge	15	30
Correct price	200	225

16. The use of cellular phones in automobiles has increased dramatically in the last few years. Of concern to traffic experts, as well as manufacturers of cellular phones, is the effect on accident rates. Is someone who is using a cellular phone more likely to be involved in a traffic accident? What is your conclusion from the following sample information? Use the .05 significance level.

	Had Accident in the Last Year	Did Not Have an Accident in the Last Year
Cellular phone in use	25	300
Cellular phone not in use	50	400

Chapter Summary

I. The characteristics of the chi-square distribution are:

A. The value of chi-square is never negative.

B. The chi-square distribution is positively skewed.

C. There is a family of chi-square distributions.

1. Each time the degrees of freedom change, a new distribution is formed.

2. As the degrees of freedom increase, the distribution approaches a normal distribution.

II. A goodness-of-fit test will show whether an observed set of frequencies could have come from a hypothesized population distribution.

A. The degrees of freedom are $k - 1$, where k is the number of categories.

B. The formula for computing the value of chi-square is

$$\chi^2 = \Sigma\left[\frac{(f_o - f_e)^2}{f_e}\right] \quad [14\text{–}1]$$

III. A contingency table is used to test whether two traits or characteristics are related.

A. Each observation is classified according to two traits.

B. The expected frequency is determined as follows:

$$f_e = \frac{(\text{Row total})(\text{Column total})}{(\text{Grand total})} \quad [14\text{–}2]$$

C. The degrees of freedom are found by:

$$df = (\text{Rows} - 1)(\text{Columns} - 1)$$

D. The usual hypothesis testing procedure is used.

Pronunciation Key

SYMBOL	MEANING	PRONUNCIATION
χ^2	Probability distribution	*ki square*
f_o	Observed frequency	*f sub oh*
f_e	Expected frequency	*f sub e*

Chapter Exercises

17. Vehicles heading west on Front Street may turn right, left, or go straight ahead at Elm Street. The city traffic engineer believes that half of the vehicles will continue straight through the intersection. Of the remaining half, equal proportions will turn right and left. Two hundred vehicles were observed, with the following results. Use the .10 significance level. Can we conclude that the traffic engineer is correct?

	Straight	Right Turn	Left Turn
Frequency	112	48	40

18. The publisher of a sports magazine plans to offer new subscribers one of three gifts: a sweatshirt with the logo of their favourite team, a coffee cup with the logo of their favourite team, or a pair of earrings also with the logo of their favourite team. In a sample of 500 new subscribers, the number selecting each gift is reported below. At the .05 significance level, is there a preference for the gifts or should we conclude that the gifts are equally well liked?

Gift	Frequency
Sweatshirt	183
Coffee cup	175
Earrings	142

19. In a small city there are three commercial television stations, each with its own evening news program from 6:00 to 6:30 p.m. According to a report in this morning's local newspaper, a random sample of 150 viewers last night revealed 53 watched the news on CHIP (channel 5), 64 watched on CHOT (channel 11), and 33 on COLD (channel 13). At the .05 significance level, is there a difference in the proportion of viewers watching the three channels?

20. There are four entrances to a large office building in downtown Halifax. The building maintenance supervisor would like to know if the entrances are equally utilized. To investigate, 400 people were observed entering the building. The number using each entrance is reported below. At the .01 significance level, is there a difference in the use of the four entrances?

Entrance	Frequency
Main Street	140
Broad Street	120
Cherry Street	90
Walnut Street	50
Total	400

21. In order to update her marketing strategies, the owner of a private ski club in Collingwood, Ontario, wants to compare the current geographical distribution of her club members to those of 10 years ago. According to her past records, 21 percent are from New York State, 24 percent from Ontario (excluding the GTA), 35 percent from the GTA, and 20 percent from other areas. Listed below is a breakdown of a sample of 400 current members, randomly selected from all club members.

At the .01 significance level, has the geographical distribution of her club members changed?

Area	Frequency
New York State	68
Ontario (excluding GTA)	104
GTA	155
Other	73
Total	400

22. The Banner Mattress and Furniture Company wishes to study the number of credit applications received per day for the last 300 days. The information is reported on the next page.

Number of Credit Applications	Frequency (Number of Days)
0	50
1	77
2	81
3	48
4	31
5 or more	13

To interpret, there were 50 days on which no credit applications were received, 77 days on which only one application was received, and so on. Would it be reasonable to conclude that the population distribution is Poisson with a mean of 2.0? Use the .05 significance level. *Hint:* To find the expected frequencies use the Poisson distribution with a mean of 2.0. Find the probability of exactly one success given a Poisson distribution with a mean of 2.0. Multiply this probability by 300 to find the expected frequency for the number of days in which there was exactly one application. Determine the expected frequency for the other days in a similar manner.

23. In the early 2000s the Deep Down Mining Company implemented new safety guidelines. Prior to these new guidelines, management expected there to be no accidents in 40 percent of the months, one accident in 30 percent of the months, two accidents in 20 percent of the months, and three accidents in 10 percent of the months. Over the last 10 years, or 120 months, there have been 46 months in which there were no accidents, 40 months in which there was one accident, 22 months in which there were two accidents, and 12 months in which there were 3 accidents. At the .05 significance level, can the management at Deep Down conclude that there has been a change in the monthly accident distribution?

24. A recent study by a large retailer designed to determine whether there was a relationship between the importance a store manager placed on advertising and the size of the store revealed the following sample information:

	Important	Not Important
Small	40	52
Medium	106	47
Large	67	32

What is your conclusion? Use the .05 significance level.

25. Two hundred managers from various levels were randomly selected and interviewed regarding their concern about environmental issues. The response of each person was tallied into one of three categories: no concern, some concern, and great concern. The results were:

Level of Management	No Concern	Some Concern	Great Concern
Top management	15	13	12
Middle management	20	19	21
Supervisor	7	7	6
Group leader	28	21	31

Use the .01 significance level to determine whether there is a relationship between management level and environmental concern.

26. A study regarding the relationship between age and the amount of pressure sales personnel feel in relation to their jobs revealed the following sample information. At the .01 significance level, is there a relationship between job pressure and age?

	Degree of Job Pressure		
Age (years)	Low	Medium	High
Less than 25	20	18	22
25 up to < 40	50	46	44
40 up to < 60	58	63	59
60 and older	34	43	43

27. The claims department at the Wise Insurance Company believes that younger drivers have more accidents and, therefore, should be charged higher insurance rates. Investigating a sample of 1200 Wise policyholders revealed the following breakdown on whether a claim had been filed in the last three years and the age of the policyholder. Is it reasonable to conclude that there is a relationship between the age of the policyholder and whether or not the person filed a claim? Use the .05 significance level.

Age Group	No Claim	Claim
16 up to < 25	170	74
25 up to < 40	240	58
40 up to < 55	400	44
55 or older	190	24
Total	1000	200

28. A sample of employees at a large chemical plant was asked to indicate a preference for one of three pension plans. The results are given in the following table. Does it seem that there is a relationship between the pension plan selected and the job classification of the employees? Use the .01 significance level.

	Pension Plan		
Job Class	Plan A	Plan B	Plan C
Supervisor	10	13	29
Clerical	19	80	19
Labour	81	57	22

29. A recent survey suggested that 55 percent of all adults favoured legislation requiring restaurants to include information on their menus regarding calories, fat, and carbohydrates of the menu items. The same survey indicated that 28 percent of all adult respondents were opposed to such legislation. The remainder of those surveyed were unsure of the need. A sample of 450 young adults revealed 220 favoured the proposed legislation, 158 opposed it, and the remaining 72 were unsure. At the .05 significance level, is it reasonable to conclude the position of young adults regarding adding dietary information to restaurant menus is different from the total population?

30. Is it proper to respond with an email after a job interview thanking the prospective employer for the interview? This question was asked of a sample of 200 human resource professionals and 250 technical personnel who were a part of the interview process. The results are reported below. At the .01 significance level, is it reasonable to conclude that human resource and technical personnel differ on whether an email response is appropriate?

Email response	Human resource	Technical
Very appropriate	35	98
Somewhat appropriate	95	114
Somewhat inappropriate	40	22
Very inappropriate	30	16
Total	200	250

Data Set Exercises

31. Refer to the real estate data, from the south-east area of Edmonton, on the CD-ROM, which reports information on listed homes.

a. Develop a contingency table that shows the style of a home (bungalow, two-storey, bi-level, four level split, or 2½ storey). Is there an association between the variable style and list price? Use under $300 000, $300 000 to under $500 000, $500 000 to under $700 000, and over $700 000 as the list price categories. Use the .05 significance level.

b. Develop a contingency table that shows whether a home has three or fewer bedrooms and list price. Is there an association between the variables three or fewer bedrooms and price? Use under $300 000, $300 000 to under $500 000, $500 000 to under $700 000, and over $700 000 as the list price categories. Use the .05 significance level.

32. Refer to the Baseball 2006 data, which reports information on the 30 Major League Baseball teams for the 2006 season. Set up a variable that divides the teams into two groups, those that had a winning season and those that did not. There are 162 games in the season, so define a winning season as having won 81 or more games. Next, divide the teams into two salary groups. Let the 15 teams with the largest salaries be in one group and the 15 teams with the smallest salaries in the other. At the .05 significance level, is there a relationship between salaries and winning?

33. Refer to the Whitner-2007 file found on the CD-ROM, which reports information on car sales.
a. Develop a contingency table that shows the code and selling price. Is there an association between the variables code and selling price? Use under \$25 000, \$25 000 to under \$30 000, \$30 000 to under \$35 000, and over \$35 000 as the selling price categories. Use the .05 significance level.
b. Develop a contingency table that shows the age of the buyer and the selling price. Is there an association between the age of the buyer and the selling price? Use under \$25 000, \$25 000 to under \$30 000, \$30 000 to under \$35 000, and over \$35 000 as the selling price categories. Use the .05 significance level.

34. Refer to the International data, which reports demographic and economic information on 46 countries.
a. Develop a contingency table that shows G-20 membership versus level of petroleum activity. Is there a significant association at the .05 level of significance between these variables?
b. Group the countries into "young" (percent of population over 65 is less than 10) and "old" (percent of population over 65 is more than 10). Then develop a contingency table between this "age" variable and the level of petroleum activity. At the .05 level of significance, can we conclude these variables are related?

exercises.com

Additional exercises that require you to access information at related Internet sites are available on the CD-ROM included with this text.

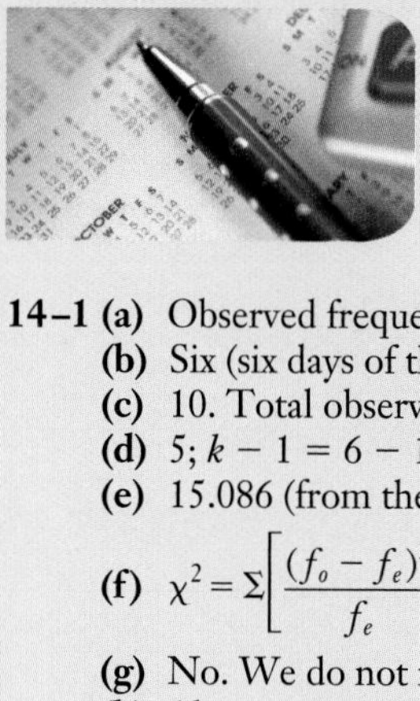

Answers to Self-Reviews

14–1 **(a)** Observed frequencies.
(b) Six (six days of the week).
(c) 10. Total observed frequencies ÷ 6 = 60/6 = 10.
(d) 5; $k - 1 = 6 - 1 = 5$.
(e) 15.086 (from the chi-square table in Appendix B).
(f) $\chi^2 = \Sigma\left[\frac{(f_o - f_e)^2}{f_e}\right] = \frac{(12-10)^2}{10} + \cdots + \frac{(9-10)^2}{10} = 0.8.$
(g) No. We do not reject H_0.
(h) Absenteeism is distributed evenly throughout the week. The observed differences are due to sampling variation.

14–2 H_0: $P_C = .60$, $P_L = .30$, and $P_U = .10$.
H_1: Distribution is not as above.
Reject H_0 if $\chi^2 > 5.991$.

Category	f_o	f_e	$\frac{(f_o - f_e)^2}{f_e}$
Current	320	300	1.33
Late	120	150	6.00
Uncollectible	60	50	2.00
	500	500	9.33

Reject H_0. The accounts receivable data does not reflect the national average.

14–3 **(a)** Contingency table
(b) There is no relationship between age and model preferred.
(c) The value of chi-square is computed from the following table.

	Sports		SUV		Luxury		
Age	f_o	f_e	f_o	f_e	f_o	f_e	**Total**
Under 30	18	14.08	12	11.52	10	14.40	40
30 to 50	17	15.84	15	12.96	13	16.20	45
Over 50	9	14.08	9	11.52	22	14.40	40
	44	44.00	36	36.00	45	45.00	125

$$\chi^2 = \frac{(18-14.08)^2}{14.08} + \frac{(12-11.52)^2}{11.52} + \cdots + \frac{(22-14.40)^2}{14.40}$$
$$= 9.889.$$

The critical value of chi-square is 9.488, so H_0 is rejected.
(d) There is a relationship between age and model preferred.

Appendices

Tables

Data Sets — CD-ROM

Appendix A

Binomial Probability Distribution

n = 1
Probability

x	0.05	0.10	0.20	0.30	0.40	0.50	0.60	0.70	0.80	0.90	0.95
0	0.950	0.900	0.800	0.700	0.600	0.500	0.400	0.300	0.200	0.100	0.050
1	0.050	0.100	0.200	0.300	0.400	0.500	0.600	0.700	0.800	0.900	0.950

n = 2
Probability

x	0.05	0.10	0.20	0.30	0.40	0.50	0.60	0.70	0.80	0.90	0.95
0	0.903	0.810	0.640	0.490	0.360	0.250	0.160	0.090	0.040	0.010	0.003
1	0.095	0.180	0.320	0.420	0.480	0.500	0.480	0.420	0.320	0.180	0.095
2	0.003	0.010	0.040	0.090	0.160	0.250	0.360	0.490	0.640	0.810	0.903

n = 3
Probability

x	0.05	0.10	0.20	0.30	0.40	0.50	0.60	0.70	0.80	0.90	0.95
0	0.857	0.729	0.512	0.343	0.216	0.125	0.064	0.027	0.008	0.001	0.000
1	0.135	0.243	0.384	0.441	0.432	0.375	0.288	0.189	0.096	0.027	0.007
2	0.007	0.027	0.096	0.189	0.288	0.375	0.432	0.441	0.384	0.243	0.135
3	0.000	0.001	0.008	0.027	0.064	0.125	0.216	0.343	0.512	0.729	0.857

n = 4
Probability

x	0.05	0.10	0.20	0.30	0.40	0.50	0.60	0.70	0.80	0.90	0.95
0	0.815	0.656	0.410	0.240	0.130	0.063	0.026	0.008	0.002	0.000	0.000
1	0.171	0.292	0.410	0.412	0.346	0.250	0.154	0.076	0.026	0.004	0.000
2	0.014	0.049	0.154	0.265	0.346	0.375	0.346	0.265	0.154	0.049	0.014
3	0.000	0.004	0.026	0.076	0.154	0.250	0.346	0.412	0.410	0.292	0.171
4	0.000	0.000	0.002	0.008	0.026	0.063	0.130	0.240	0.410	0.656	0.815

n = 5
Probability

x	0.05	0.10	0.20	0.30	0.40	0.50	0.60	0.70	0.80	0.90	0.95
0	0.774	0.590	0.328	0.168	0.078	0.031	0.010	0.002	0.000	0.000	0.000
1	0.204	0.328	0.410	0.360	0.259	0.156	0.077	0.028	0.006	0.000	0.000
2	0.021	0.073	0.205	0.309	0.346	0.313	0.230	0.132	0.051	0.008	0.001
3	0.001	0.008	0.051	0.132	0.230	0.313	0.346	0.309	0.205	0.073	0.021
4	0.000	0.000	0.006	0.028	0.077	0.156	0.259	0.360	0.410	0.328	0.204
5	0.000	0.000	0.000	0.002	0.010	0.031	0.078	0.168	0.328	0.590	0.774

Appendix A

Binomial Probability Distribution *(continued)*

$n = 6$

Probability

x	0.05	0.10	0.20	0.30	0.40	0.50	0.60	0.70	0.80	0.90	0.95
0	0.735	0.531	0.262	0.118	0.047	0.016	0.004	0.001	0.000	0.000	0.000
1	0.232	0.354	0.393	0.303	0.187	0.094	0.037	0.010	0.002	0.000	0.000
2	0.031	0.098	0.246	0.324	0.311	0.234	0.138	0.060	0.015	0.001	0.000
3	0.002	0.015	0.082	0.185	0.276	0.313	0.276	0.185	0.082	0.015	0.002
4	0.000	0.001	0.015	0.060	0.138	0.234	0.311	0.324	0.246	0.098	0.031
5	0.000	0.000	0.002	0.010	0.037	0.094	0.187	0.303	0.393	0.354	0.232
6	0.000	0.000	0.000	0.001	0.004	0.016	0.047	0.118	0.262	0.531	0.735

$n = 7$

Probability

x	0.05	0.10	0.20	0.30	0.40	0.50	0.60	0.70	0.80	0.90	0.95
0	0.698	0.478	0.210	0.082	0.028	0.008	0.002	0.000	0.000	0.000	0.000
1	0.257	0.372	0.367	0.247	0.131	0.055	0.017	0.004	0.000	0.000	0.000
2	0.041	0.124	0.275	0.318	0.261	0.164	0.077	0.025	0.004	0.000	0.000
3	0.004	0.023	0.115	0.227	0.290	0.273	0.194	0.097	0.029	0.003	0.000
4	0.000	0.003	0.029	0.097	0.194	0.273	0.290	0.227	0.115	0.023	0.004
5	0.000	0.000	0.004	0.025	0.077	0.164	0.261	0.318	0.275	0.124	0.041
6	0.000	0.000	0.000	0.004	0.017	0.055	0.131	0.247	0.367	0.372	0.257
7	0.000	0.000	0.000	0.000	0.002	0.008	0.028	0.082	0.210	0.478	0.698

$n = 8$

Probability

x	0.05	0.10	0.20	0.30	0.40	0.50	0.60	0.70	0.80	0.90	0.95
0	0.663	0.430	0.168	0.058	0.017	0.004	0.001	0.000	0.000	0.000	0.000
1	0.279	0.383	0.336	0.198	0.090	0.031	0.008	0.001	0.000	0.000	0.000
2	0.051	0.149	0.294	0.296	0.209	0.109	0.041	0.010	0.001	0.000	0.000
3	0.005	0.033	0.147	0.254	0.279	0.219	0.124	0.047	0.009	0.000	0.000
4	0.000	0.005	0.046	0.136	0.232	0.273	0.232	0.136	0.046	0.005	0.000
5	0.000	0.000	0.009	0.047	0.124	0.219	0.279	0.254	0.147	0.033	0.005
6	0.000	0.000	0.001	0.010	0.041	0.109	0.209	0.296	0.294	0.149	0.051
7	0.000	0.000	0.000	0.001	0.008	0.031	0.090	0.198	0.336	0.383	0.279
8	0.000	0.000	0.000	0.000	0.001	0.004	0.017	0.058	0.168	0.430	0.663

Appendix A

Binomial Probability Distribution *(continued)*

n = 9
Probability

x	0.05	0.10	0.20	0.30	0.40	0.50	0.60	0.70	0.80	0.90	0.95
0	0.630	0.387	0.134	0.040	0.010	0.002	0.000	0.000	0.000	0.000	0.000
1	0.299	0.387	0.302	0.156	0.060	0.018	0.004	0.000	0.000	0.000	0.000
2	0.063	0.172	0.302	0.267	0.161	0.070	0.021	0.004	0.000	0.000	0.000
3	0.008	0.045	0.176	0.267	0.251	0.164	0.074	0.021	0.003	0.000	0.000
4	0.001	0.007	0.066	0.172	0.251	0.246	0.167	0.074	0.017	0.001	0.000
5	0.000	0.001	0.017	0.074	0.167	0.246	0.251	0.172	0.066	0.007	0.001
6	0.000	0.000	0.003	0.021	0.074	0.164	0.251	0.267	0.176	0.045	0.008
7	0.000	0.000	0.000	0.004	0.021	0.070	0.161	0.267	0.302	0.172	0.063
8	0.000	0.000	0.000	0.000	0.004	0.018	0.060	0.156	0.302	0.387	0.299
9	0.000	0.000	0.000	0.000	0.000	0.002	0.010	0.040	0.134	0.387	0.630

n = 10
Probability

x	0.05	0.10	0.20	0.30	0.40	0.50	0.60	0.70	0.80	0.90	0.95
0	0.599	0.349	0.107	0.028	0.006	0.001	0.000	0.000	0.000	0.000	0.000
1	0.315	0.387	0.268	0.121	0.040	0.010	0.002	0.000	0.000	0.000	0.000
2	0.075	0.194	0.302	0.233	0.121	0.044	0.011	0.001	0.000	0.000	0.000
3	0.010	0.057	0.201	0.267	0.215	0.117	0.042	0.009	0.001	0.000	0.000
4	0.001	0.011	0.088	0.200	0.251	0.205	0.111	0.037	0.006	0.000	0.000
5	0.000	0.001	0.026	0.103	0.201	0.246	0.201	0.103	0.026	0.001	0.000
6	0.000	0.000	0.006	0.037	0.111	0.205	0.251	0.200	0.088	0.011	0.001
7	0.000	0.000	0.001	0.009	0.042	0.117	0.215	0.267	0.201	0.057	0.010
8	0.000	0.000	0.000	0.001	0.011	0.044	0.121	0.233	0.302	0.194	0.075
9	0.000	0.000	0.000	0.000	0.002	0.010	0.040	0.121	0.268	0.387	0.315
10	0.000	0.000	0.000	0.000	0.000	0.001	0.006	0.028	0.107	0.349	0.599

n = 11
Probability

x	0.05	0.10	0.20	0.30	0.40	0.50	0.60	0.70	0.80	0.90	0.95
0	0.569	0.314	0.086	0.020	0.004	0.000	0.000	0.000	0.000	0.000	0.000
1	0.329	0.384	0.236	0.093	0.027	0.005	0.001	0.000	0.000	0.000	0.000
2	0.087	0.213	0.295	0.200	0.089	0.027	0.005	0.001	0.000	0.000	0.000
3	0.014	0.071	0.221	0.257	0.177	0.081	0.023	0.004	0.000	0.000	0.000
4	0.001	0.016	0.111	0.220	0.236	0.161	0.070	0.017	0.002	0.000	0.000
5	0.000	0.002	0.039	0.132	0.221	0.226	0.147	0.057	0.010	0.000	0.000
6	0.000	0.000	0.010	0.057	0.147	0.226	0.221	0.132	0.039	0.002	0.000
7	0.000	0.000	0.002	0.017	0.070	0.161	0.236	0.220	0.111	0.016	0.001
8	0.000	0.000	0.000	0.004	0.023	0.081	0.177	0.257	0.221	0.071	0.014
9	0.000	0.000	0.000	0.001	0.005	0.027	0.089	0.200	0.295	0.213	0.087
10	0.000	0.000	0.000	0.000	0.001	0.005	0.027	0.093	0.236	0.384	0.329
11	0.000	0.000	0.000	0.000	0.000	0.000	0.004	0.020	0.086	0.314	0.569

Appendix A

Binomial Probability Distribution *(continued)*

$n = 12$
Probability

x	0.05	0.10	0.20	0.30	0.40	0.50	0.60	0.70	0.80	0.90	0.95
0	0.540	0.282	0.069	0.014	0.002	0.000	0.000	0.000	0.000	0.000	0.000
1	0.341	0.377	0.206	0.071	0.017	0.003	0.000	0.000	0.000	0.000	0.000
2	0.099	0.230	0.283	0.168	0.064	0.016	0.002	0.000	0.000	0.000	0.000
3	0.017	0.085	0.236	0.240	0.142	0.054	0.012	0.001	0.000	0.000	0.000
4	0.002	0.021	0.133	0.231	0.213	0.121	0.042	0.008	0.001	0.000	0.000
5	0.000	0.004	0.053	0.158	0.227	0.193	0.101	0.029	0.003	0.000	0.000
6	0.000	0.000	0.016	0.079	0.177	0.226	0.177	0.079	0.016	0.000	0.000
7	0.000	0.000	0.003	0.029	0.101	0.193	0.227	0.158	0.053	0.004	0.000
8	0.000	0.000	0.001	0.008	0.042	0.121	0.213	0.231	0.133	0.021	0.002
9	0.000	0.000	0.000	0.001	0.012	0.054	0.142	0.240	0.236	0.085	0.017
10	0.000	0.000	0.000	0.000	0.002	0.016	0.064	0.168	0.283	0.230	0.099
11	0.000	0.000	0.000	0.000	0.000	0.003	0.017	0.071	0.206	0.377	0.341
12	0.000	0.000	0.000	0.000	0.000	0.000	0.002	0.014	0.069	0.282	0.540

$n = 13$
Probability

x	0.05	0.10	0.20	0.30	0.40	0.50	0.60	0.70	0.80	0.90	0.95
0	0.513	0.254	0.055	0.010	0.001	0.000	0.000	0.000	0.000	0.000	0.000
1	0.351	0.367	0.179	0.054	0.011	0.002	0.000	0.000	0.000	0.000	0.000
2	0.111	0.245	0.268	0.139	0.045	0.010	0.001	0.000	0.000	0.000	0.000
3	0.021	0.100	0.246	0.218	0.111	0.035	0.006	0.001	0.000	0.000	0.000
4	0.003	0.028	0.154	0.234	0.184	0.087	0.024	0.003	0.000	0.000	0.000
5	0.000	0.006	0.069	0.180	0.221	0.157	0.066	0.014	0.001	0.000	0.000
6	0.000	0.001	0.023	0.103	0.197	0.209	0.131	0.044	0.006	0.000	0.000
7	0.000	0.000	0.006	0.044	0.131	0.209	0.197	0.103	0.023	0.001	0.000
8	0.000	0.000	0.001	0.014	0.066	0.157	0.221	0.180	0.069	0.006	0.000
9	0.000	0.000	0.000	0.003	0.024	0.087	0.184	0.234	0.154	0.028	0.003
10	0.000	0.000	0.000	0.001	0.006	0.035	0.111	0.218	0.246	0.100	0.021
11	0.000	0.000	0.000	0.000	0.001	0.010	0.045	0.139	0.268	0.245	0.111
12	0.000	0.000	0.000	0.000	0.000	0.002	0.011	0.054	0.179	0.367	0.351
13	0.000	0.000	0.000	0.000	0.000	0.000	0.001	0.010	0.055	0.254	0.513

Binomial Probability Distribution *(continued)*

$n = 14$

Probability

x	0.05	0.10	0.20	0.30	0.40	0.50	0.60	0.70	0.80	0.90	0.95
0	0.488	0.229	0.044	0.007	0.001	0.000	0.000	0.000	0.000	0.000	0.000
1	0.359	0.356	0.154	0.041	0.007	0.001	0.000	0.000	0.000	0.000	0.000
2	0.123	0.257	0.250	0.113	0.032	0.006	0.001	0.000	0.000	0.000	0.000
3	0.026	0.114	0.250	0.194	0.085	0.022	0.003	0.000	0.000	0.000	0.000
4	0.004	0.035	0.172	0.229	0.155	0.061	0.014	0.001	0.000	0.000	0.000
5	0.000	0.008	0.086	0.196	0.207	0.122	0.041	0.007	0.000	0.000	0.000
6	0.000	0.001	0.032	0.126	0.207	0.183	0.092	0.023	0.002	0.000	0.000
7	0.000	0.000	0.009	0.062	0.157	0.209	0.157	0.062	0.009	0.000	0.000
8	0.000	0.000	0.002	0.023	0.092	0.183	0.207	0.126	0.032	0.001	0.000
9	0.000	0.000	0.000	0.007	0.041	0.122	0.207	0.196	0.086	0.008	0.000
10	0.000	0.000	0.000	0.001	0.014	0.061	0.155	0.229	0.172	0.035	0.004
11	0.000	0.000	0.000	0.000	0.003	0.022	0.085	0.194	0.250	0.114	0.026
12	0.000	0.000	0.000	0.000	0.001	0.006	0.032	0.113	0.250	0.257	0.123
13	0.000	0.000	0.000	0.000	0.000	0.001	0.007	0.041	0.154	0.356	0.359
14	0.000	0.000	0.000	0.000	0.000	0.000	0.001	0.007	0.044	0.229	0.488

$n = 15$

Probability

x	0.05	0.10	0.20	0.30	0.40	0.50	0.60	0.70	0.80	0.90	0.95
0	0.463	0.206	0.035	0.005	0.000	0.000	0.000	0.000	0.000	0.000	0.000
1	0.366	0.343	0.132	0.031	0.005	0.000	0.000	0.000	0.000	0.000	0.000
2	0.135	0.267	0.231	0.092	0.022	0.003	0.000	0.000	0.000	0.000	0.000
3	0.031	0.129	0.250	0.170	0.063	0.014	0.002	0.000	0.000	0.000	0.000
4	0.005	0.043	0.188	0.219	0.127	0.042	0.007	0.001	0.000	0.000	0.000
5	0.001	0.010	0.103	0.206	0.186	0.092	0.024	0.003	0.000	0.000	0.000
6	0.000	0.002	0.043	0.147	0.207	0.153	0.061	0.012	0.001	0.000	0.000
7	0.000	0.000	0.014	0.081	0.177	0.196	0.118	0.035	0.003	0.000	0.000
8	0.000	0.000	0.003	0.035	0.118	0.196	0.177	0.081	0.014	0.000	0.000
9	0.000	0.000	0.001	0.012	0.061	0.153	0.207	0.147	0.043	0.002	0.000
10	0.000	0.000	0.000	0.003	0.024	0.092	0.186	0.206	0.103	0.010	0.001
11	0.000	0.000	0.000	0.001	0.007	0.042	0.127	0.219	0.188	0.043	0.005
12	0.000	0.000	0.000	0.000	0.002	0.014	0.063	0.170	0.250	0.129	0.031
13	0.000	0.000	0.000	0.000	0.000	0.003	0.022	0.092	0.231	0.267	0.135
14	0.000	0.000	0.000	0.000	0.000	0.000	0.005	0.031	0.132	0.343	0.366
15	0.000	0.000	0.000	0.000	0.000	0.000	0.000	0.005	0.035	0.206	0.463

Appendix A

Binomial Probability Distribution *(continued)*

$n = 16$
Probability

x	0.05	0.10	0.20	0.30	0.40	0.50	0.60	0.70	0.80	0.90	0.95
0	0.440	0.185	0.028	0.003	0.000	0.000	0.000	0.000	0.000	0.000	0.000
1	0.371	0.329	0.113	0.023	0.003	0.000	0.000	0.000	0.000	0.000	0.000
2	0.146	0.275	0.211	0.073	0.015	0.002	0.000	0.000	0.000	0.000	0.000
3	0.036	0.142	0.246	0.146	0.047	0.009	0.001	0.000	0.000	0.000	0.000
4	0.006	0.051	0.200	0.204	0.101	0.028	0.004	0.000	0.000	0.000	0.000
5	0.001	0.014	0.120	0.210	0.162	0.067	0.014	0.001	0.000	0.000	0.000
6	0.000	0.003	0.055	0.165	0.198	0.122	0.039	0.006	0.000	0.000	0.000
7	0.000	0.000	0.020	0.101	0.189	0.175	0.084	0.019	0.001	0.000	0.000
8	0.000	0.000	0.006	0.049	0.142	0.196	0.142	0.049	0.006	0.000	0.000
9	0.000	0.000	0.001	0.019	0.084	0.175	0.189	0.101	0.020	0.000	0.000
10	0.000	0.000	0.000	0.006	0.039	0.122	0.198	0.165	0.055	0.003	0.000
11	0.000	0.000	0.000	0.001	0.014	0.067	0.162	0.210	0.120	0.014	0.001
12	0.000	0.000	0.000	0.000	0.004	0.028	0.101	0.204	0.200	0.051	0.006
13	0.000	0.000	0.000	0.000	0.001	0.009	0.047	0.146	0.246	0.142	0.036
14	0.000	0.000	0.000	0.000	0.000	0.002	0.015	0.073	0.211	0.275	0.146
15	0.000	0.000	0.000	0.000	0.000	0.000	0.003	0.023	0.113	0.329	0.371
16	0.000	0.000	0.000	0.000	0.000	0.000	0.000	0.003	0.028	0.185	0.440

$n = 17$
Probability

x	0.05	0.10	0.20	0.30	0.40	0.50	0.60	0.70	0.80	0.90	0.95
0	0.418	0.167	0.023	0.002	0.000	0.000	0.000	0.000	0.000	0.000	0.000
1	0.374	0.315	0.096	0.017	0.002	0.000	0.000	0.000	0.000	0.000	0.000
2	0.158	0.280	0.191	0.058	0.010	0.001	0.000	0.000	0.000	0.000	0.000
3	0.041	0.156	0.239	0.125	0.034	0.005	0.000	0.000	0.000	0.000	0.000
4	0.008	0.060	0.209	0.187	0.080	0.018	0.002	0.000	0.000	0.000	0.000
5	0.001	0.017	0.136	0.208	0.138	0.047	0.008	0.001	0.000	0.000	0.000
6	0.000	0.004	0.068	0.178	0.184	0.094	0.024	0.003	0.000	0.000	0.000
7	0.000	0.001	0.027	0.120	0.193	0.148	0.057	0.009	0.000	0.000	0.000
8	0.000	0.000	0.008	0.064	0.161	0.185	0.107	0.028	0.002	0.000	0.000
9	0.000	0.000	0.002	0.028	0.107	0.185	0.161	0.064	0.008	0.000	0.000
10	0.000	0.000	0.000	0.009	0.057	0.148	0.193	0.120	0.027	0.001	0.000
11	0.000	0.000	0.000	0.003	0.024	0.094	0.184	0.178	0.068	0.004	0.000
12	0.000	0.000	0.000	0.001	0.008	0.047	0.138	0.208	0.136	0.017	0.001
13	0.000	0.000	0.000	0.000	0.002	0.018	0.080	0.187	0.209	0.060	0.008
14	0.000	0.000	0.000	0.000	0.000	0.005	0.034	0.125	0.239	0.156	0.041
15	0.000	0.000	0.000	0.000	0.000	0.001	0.010	0.058	0.191	0.280	0.158
16	0.000	0.000	0.000	0.000	0.000	0.000	0.002	0.017	0.096	0.315	0.374
17	0.000	0.000	0.000	0.000	0.000	0.000	0.000	0.002	0.023	0.167	0.418

Appendix A

Binomial Probability Distribution *(continued)*

$n = 18$
Probability

x	0.05	0.10	0.20	0.30	0.40	0.50	0.60	0.70	0.80	0.90	0.95
0	0.397	0.150	0.018	0.002	0.000	0.000	0.000	0.000	0.000	0.000	0.000
1	0.376	0.300	0.081	0.013	0.001	0.000	0.000	0.000	0.000	0.000	0.000
2	0.168	0.284	0.172	0.046	0.007	0.001	0.000	0.000	0.000	0.000	0.000
3	0.047	0.168	0.230	0.105	0.025	0.003	0.000	0.000	0.000	0.000	0.000
4	0.009	0.070	0.215	0.168	0.061	0.012	0.001	0.000	0.000	0.000	0.000
5	0.001	0.022	0.151	0.202	0.115	0.033	0.004	0.000	0.000	0.000	0.000
6	0.000	0.005	0.082	0.187	0.166	0.071	0.015	0.001	0.000	0.000	0.000
7	0.000	0.001	0.035	0.138	0.189	0.121	0.037	0.005	0.000	0.000	0.000
8	0.000	0.000	0.012	0.081	0.173	0.167	0.077	0.015	0.001	0.000	0.000
9	0.000	0.000	0.003	0.039	0.128	0.185	0.128	0.039	0.003	0.000	0.000
10	0.000	0.000	0.001	0.015	0.077	0.167	0.173	0.081	0.012	0.000	0.000
11	0.000	0.000	0.000	0.005	0.037	0.121	0.189	0.138	0.035	0.001	0.000
12	0.000	0.000	0.000	0.001	0.015	0.071	0.166	0.187	0.082	0.005	0.000
13	0.000	0.000	0.000	0.000	0.004	0.033	0.115	0.202	0.151	0.022	0.001
14	0.000	0.000	0.000	0.000	0.001	0.012	0.061	0.168	0.215	0.070	0.009
15	0.000	0.000	0.000	0.000	0.000	0.003	0.025	0.105	0.230	0.168	0.047
16	0.000	0.000	0.000	0.000	0.000	0.001	0.007	0.046	0.172	0.284	0.168
17	0.000	0.000	0.000	0.000	0.000	0.000	0.001	0.013	0.081	0.300	0.376
18	0.000	0.000	0.000	0.000	0.000	0.000	0.000	0.002	0.018	0.150	0.397

$n = 19$
Probability

x	0.05	0.10	0.20	0.30	0.40	0.50	0.60	0.70	0.80	0.90	0.95
0	0.377	0.135	0.014	0.001	0.000	0.000	0.000	0.000	0.000	0.000	0.000
1	0.377	0.285	0.068	0.009	0.001	0.000	0.000	0.000	0.000	0.000	0.000
2	0.179	0.285	0.154	0.036	0.005	0.000	0.000	0.000	0.000	0.000	0.000
3	0.053	0.180	0.218	0.087	0.017	0.002	0.000	0.000	0.000	0.000	0.000
4	0.011	0.080	0.218	0.149	0.047	0.007	0.001	0.000	0.000	0.000	0.000
5	0.002	0.027	0.164	0.192	0.093	0.022	0.002	0.000	0.000	0.000	0.000
6	0.000	0.007	0.095	0.192	0.145	0.052	0.008	0.001	0.000	0.000	0.000
7	0.000	0.001	0.044	0.153	0.180	0.096	0.024	0.002	0.000	0.000	0.000
8	0.000	0.000	0.017	0.098	0.180	0.144	0.053	0.008	0.000	0.000	0.000
9	0.000	0.000	0.005	0.051	0.146	0.176	0.098	0.022	0.001	0.000	0.000
10	0.000	0.000	0.001	0.022	0.098	0.176	0.146	0.051	0.005	0.000	0.000
11	0.000	0.000	0.000	0.008	0.053	0.144	0.180	0.098	0.017	0.000	0.000
12	0.000	0.000	0.000	0.002	0.024	0.096	0.180	0.153	0.044	0.001	0.000
13	0.000	0.000	0.000	0.001	0.008	0.052	0.145	0.192	0.095	0.007	0.000
14	0.000	0.000	0.000	0.000	0.002	0.022	0.093	0.192	0.164	0.027	0.002
15	0.000	0.000	0.000	0.000	0.001	0.007	0.047	0.149	0.218	0.080	0.011
16	0.000	0.000	0.000	0.000	0.000	0.002	0.017	0.087	0.218	0.180	0.053
17	0.000	0.000	0.000	0.000	0.000	0.000	0.005	0.036	0.154	0.285	0.179
18	0.000	0.000	0.000	0.000	0.000	0.000	0.001	0.009	0.068	0.285	0.377
19	0.000	0.000	0.000	0.000	0.000	0.000	0.000	0.001	0.014	0.135	0.377

Binomial Probability Distribution *(continued)*

$n = 20$

Probability

x	0.05	0.10	0.20	0.30	0.40	0.50	0.60	0.70	0.80	0.90	0.95
0	0.358	0.122	0.012	0.001	0.000	0.000	0.000	0.000	0.000	0.000	0.000
1	0.377	0.270	0.058	0.007	0.000	0.000	0.000	0.000	0.000	0.000	0.000
2	0.189	0.285	0.137	0.028	0.003	0.000	0.000	0.000	0.000	0.000	0.000
3	0.060	0.190	0.205	0.072	0.012	0.001	0.000	0.000	0.000	0.000	0.000
4	0.013	0.090	0.218	0.130	0.035	0.005	0.000	0.000	0.000	0.000	0.000
5	0.002	0.032	0.175	0.179	0.075	0.015	0.001	0.000	0.000	0.000	0.000
6	0.000	0.009	0.109	0.192	0.124	0.037	0.005	0.000	0.000	0.000	0.000
7	0.000	0.002	0.055	0.164	0.166	0.074	0.015	0.001	0.000	0.000	0.000
8	0.000	0.000	0.022	0.114	0.180	0.120	0.035	0.004	0.000	0.000	0.000
9	0.000	0.000	0.007	0.065	0.160	0.160	0.071	0.012	0.000	0.000	0.000
10	0.000	0.000	0.002	0.031	0.117	0.176	0.117	0.031	0.002	0.000	0.000
11	0.000	0.000	0.000	0.012	0.071	0.160	0.160	0.065	0.007	0.000	0.000
12	0.000	0.000	0.000	0.004	0.035	0.120	0.180	0.114	0.022	0.000	0.000
13	0.000	0.000	0.000	0.001	0.015	0.074	0.166	0.164	0.055	0.002	0.000
14	0.000	0.000	0.000	0.000	0.005	0.037	0.124	0.192	0.109	0.009	0.000
15	0.000	0.000	0.000	0.000	0.001	0.015	0.075	0.179	0.175	0.032	0.002
16	0.000	0.000	0.000	0.000	0.000	0.005	0.035	0.130	0.218	0.090	0.013
17	0.000	0.000	0.000	0.000	0.000	0.001	0.012	0.072	0.205	0.190	0.060
18	0.000	0.000	0.000	0.000	0.000	0.000	0.003	0.028	0.137	0.285	0.189
19	0.000	0.000	0.000	0.000	0.000	0.000	0.000	0.007	0.058	0.270	0.377
20	0.000	0.000	0.000	0.000	0.000	0.000	0.000	0.001	0.012	0.122	0.358

Binomial Probability Distribution *(concluded)*

$n = 25$
Probability

x	0.05	0.10	0.20	0.30	0.40	0.50	0.60	0.70	0.80	0.90	0.95
0	0.277	0.072	0.004	0.000	0.000	0.000	0.000	0.000	0.000	0.000	0.000
1	0.365	0.199	0.024	0.001	0.000	0.000	0.000	0.000	0.000	0.000	0.000
2	0.231	0.266	0.071	0.007	0.000	0.000	0.000	0.000	0.000	0.000	0.000
3	0.093	0.226	0.136	0.024	0.002	0.000	0.000	0.000	0.000	0.000	0.000
4	0.027	0.138	0.187	0.057	0.007	0.000	0.000	0.000	0.000	0.000	0.000
5	0.006	0.065	0.196	0.103	0.020	0.002	0.000	0.000	0.000	0.000	0.000
6	0.001	0.024	0.163	0.147	0.044	0.005	0.000	0.000	0.000	0.000	0.000
7	0.000	0.007	0.111	0.171	0.080	0.014	0.001	0.000	0.000	0.000	0.000
8	0.000	0.002	0.062	0.165	0.120	0.032	0.003	0.000	0.000	0.000	0.000
9	0.000	0.000	0.029	0.134	0.151	0.061	0.009	0.000	0.000	0.000	0.000
10	0.000	0.000	0.012	0.092	0.161	0.097	0.021	0.001	0.000	0.000	0.000
11	0.000	0.000	0.004	0.054	0.147	0.133	0.043	0.004	0.000	0.000	0.000
12	0.000	0.000	0.001	0.027	0.114	0.155	0.076	0.011	0.000	0.000	0.000
13	0.000	0.000	0.000	0.011	0.076	0.155	0.114	0.027	0.001	0.000	0.000
14	0.000	0.000	0.000	0.004	0.043	0.133	0.147	0.054	0.004	0.000	0.000
15	0.000	0.000	0.000	0.001	0.021	0.097	0.161	0.092	0.012	0.000	0.000
16	0.000	0.000	0.000	0.000	0.009	0.061	0.151	0.134	0.029	0.000	0.000
17	0.000	0.000	0.000	0.000	0.003	0.032	0.120	0.165	0.062	0.002	0.000
18	0.000	0.000	0.000	0.000	0.001	0.014	0.080	0.171	0.111	0.007	0.000
19	0.000	0.000	0.000	0.000	0.000	0.005	0.044	0.147	0.163	0.024	0.001
20	0.000	0.000	0.000	0.000	0.000	0.002	0.020	0.103	0.196	0.065	0.006
21	0.000	0.000	0.000	0.000	0.000	0.000	0.007	0.057	0.187	0.138	0.027
22	0.000	0.000	0.000	0.000	0.000	0.000	0.002	0.024	0.136	0.226	0.093
23	0.000	0.000	0.000	0.000	0.000	0.000	0.000	0.007	0.071	0.266	0.231
24	0.000	0.000	0.000	0.000	0.000	0.000	0.000	0.001	0.024	0.199	0.365
25	0.000	0.000	0.000	0.000	0.000	0.000	0.000	0.000	0.004	0.072	0.277

Appendix B

Critical Values of Chi-Square

This table contains the values of χ^2 that correspond to a specific right-tail area and specific number of degrees of freedom.

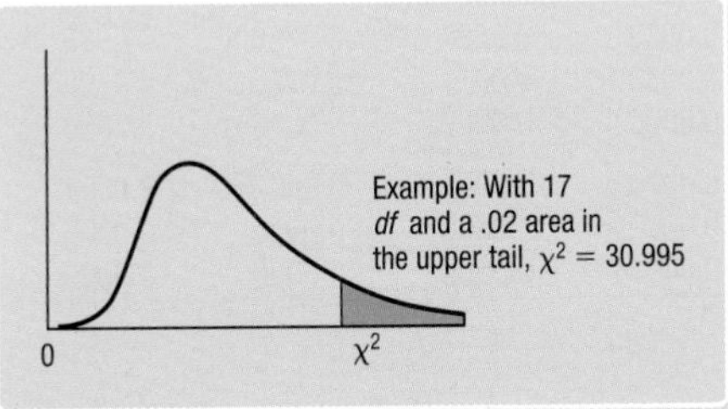

Degrees of Freedom, *df*	Right-Tail Area			
	0.10	0.05	0.02	0.01
1	2.706	3.841	5.412	6.635
2	4.605	5.991	7.824	9.210
3	6.251	7.815	9.837	11.345
4	7.779	9.488	11.668	13.277
5	9.236	11.070	13.388	15.086
6	10.645	12.592	15.033	16.812
7	12.017	14.067	16.622	18.475
8	13.362	15.507	18.168	20.090
9	14.684	16.919	19.679	21.666
10	15.987	18.307	21.161	23.209
11	17.275	19.675	22.618	24.725
12	18.549	21.026	24.054	26.217
13	19.812	22.362	25.472	27.688
14	21.064	23.685	26.873	29.141
15	22.307	24.996	28.259	30.578
16	23.542	26.296	29.633	32.000
17	24.769	27.587	30.995	33.409
18	25.989	28.869	32.346	34.805
19	27.204	30.144	33.687	36.191
20	28.412	31.410	35.020	37.566
21	29.615	32.671	36.343	38.932
22	30.813	33.924	37.659	40.289
23	32.007	35.172	38.968	41.638
24	33.196	36.415	40.270	42.980
25	34.382	37.652	41.566	44.314
26	35.563	38.885	42.856	45.642
27	36.741	40.113	44.140	46.963
28	37.916	41.337	45.419	48.278
29	39.087	42.557	46.693	49.588
30	40.256	43.773	47.962	50.892

Appendix C

Poisson Distribution

	μ								
x	0.1	0.2	0.3	0.4	0.5	0.6	0.7	0.8	0.9
0	0.9048	0.8187	0.7408	0.6703	0.6065	0.5488	0.4966	0.4493	0.4066
1	0.0905	0.1637	0.2222	0.2681	0.3033	0.3293	0.3476	0.3595	0.3659
2	0.0045	0.0164	0.0333	0.0536	0.0758	0.0988	0.1217	0.1438	0.1647
3	0.0002	0.0011	0.0033	0.0072	0.0126	0.0198	0.0284	0.0383	0.0494
4	0.0000	0.0001	0.0003	0.0007	0.0016	0.0030	0.0050	0.0077	0.0111
5	0.0000	0.0000	0.0000	0.0001	0.0002	0.0004	0.0007	0.0012	0.0020
6	0.0000	0.0000	0.0000	0.0000	0.0000	0.0000	0.0001	0.0002	0.0003
7	0.0000	0.0000	0.0000	0.0000	0.0000	0.0000	0.0000	0.0000	0.0000

	μ								
x	1.0	2.0	3.0	4.0	5.0	6.0	7.0	8.0	9.0
0	0.3679	0.1353	0.0498	0.0183	0.0067	0.0025	0.0009	0.0003	0.0001
1	0.3679	0.2707	0.1494	0.0733	0.0337	0.0149	0.0064	0.0027	0.0011
2	0.1839	0.2707	0.2240	0.1465	0.0842	0.0446	0.0223	0.0107	0.0050
3	0.0613	0.1804	0.2240	0.1954	0.1404	0.0892	0.0521	0.0286	0.0150
4	0.0153	0.0902	0.1680	0.1954	0.1755	0.1339	0.0912	0.0573	0.0337
5	0.0031	0.0361	0.1008	0.1563	0.1755	0.1606	0.1277	0.0916	0.0607
6	0.0005	0.0120	0.0504	0.1042	0.1462	0.1606	0.1490	0.1221	0.0911
7	0.0001	0.0034	0.0216	0.0595	0.1044	0.1377	0.1490	0.1396	0.1171
8	0.0000	0.0009	0.0081	0.0298	0.0653	0.1033	0.1304	0.1396	0.1318
9	0.0000	0.0002	0.0027	0.0132	0.0363	0.0688	0.1014	0.1241	0.1318
10	0.0000	0.0000	0.0008	0.0053	0.0181	0.0413	0.0710	0.0993	0.1186
11	0.0000	0.0000	0.0002	0.0019	0.0082	0.0225	0.0452	0.0722	0.0970
12	0.0000	0.0000	0.0001	0.0006	0.0034	0.0113	0.0263	0.0481	0.0728
13	0.0000	0.0000	0.0000	0.0002	0.0013	0.0052	0.0142	0.0296	0.0504
14	0.0000	0.0000	0.0000	0.0001	0.0005	0.0022	0.0071	0.0169	0.0324
15	0.0000	0.0000	0.0000	0.0000	0.0002	0.0009	0.0033	0.0090	0.0194
16	0.0000	0.0000	0.0000	0.0000	0.0000	0.0003	0.0014	0.0045	0.0109
17	0.0000	0.0000	0.0000	0.0000	0.0000	0.0001	0.0006	0.0021	0.0058
18	0.0000	0.0000	0.0000	0.0000	0.0000	0.0000	0.0002	0.0009	0.0029
19	0.0000	0.0000	0.0000	0.0000	0.0000	0.0000	0.0001	0.0004	0.0014
20	0.0000	0.0000	0.0000	0.0000	0.0000	0.0000	0.0000	0.0002	0.0006
21	0.0000	0.0000	0.0000	0.0000	0.0000	0.0000	0.0000	0.0001	0.0003
22	0.0000	0.0000	0.0000	0.0000	0.0000	0.0000	0.0000	0.0000	0.0001

Appendix D

Areas under the Normal Curve

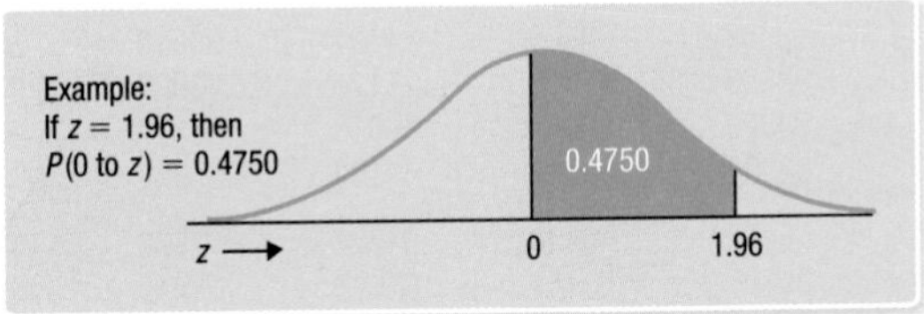

z	0.00	0.01	0.02	0.03	0.04	0.05	0.06	0.07	0.08	0.09
0.0	0.0000	0.0040	0.0080	0.0120	0.0160	0.0199	0.0239	0.0279	0.0319	0.0359
0.1	0.0398	0.0438	0.0478	0.0517	0.0557	0.0596	0.0636	0.0675	0.0714	0.0753
0.2	0.0793	0.0832	0.0871	0.0910	0.0948	0.0987	0.1026	0.1064	0.1103	0.1141
0.3	0.1179	0.1217	0.1255	0.1293	0.1331	0.1368	0.1406	0.1443	0.1480	0.1517
0.4	0.1554	0.1591	0.1628	0.1664	0.1700	0.1736	0.1772	0.1808	0.1844	0.1879
0.5	0.1915	0.1950	0.1985	0.2019	0.2054	0.2088	0.2123	0.2157	0.2190	0.2224
0.6	0.2257	0.2291	0.2324	0.2357	0.2389	0.2422	0.2454	0.2486	0.2517	0.2549
0.7	0.2580	0.2611	0.2642	0.2673	0.2704	0.2734	0.2764	0.2794	0.2823	0.2852
0.8	0.2881	0.2910	0.2939	0.2967	0.2995	0.3023	0.3051	0.3078	0.3106	0.3133
0.9	0.3159	0.3186	0.3212	0.3238	0.3264	0.3289	0.3315	0.3340	0.3365	0.3389
1.0	0.3413	0.3438	0.3461	0.3485	0.3508	0.3531	0.3554	0.3577	0.3599	0.3621
1.1	0.3643	0.3665	0.3686	0.3708	0.3729	0.3749	0.3770	0.3790	0.3810	0.3830
1.2	0.3849	0.3869	0.3888	0.3907	0.3925	0.3944	0.3962	0.3980	0.3997	0.4015
1.3	0.4032	0.4049	0.4066	0.4082	0.4099	0.4115	0.4131	0.4147	0.4162	0.4177
1.4	0.4192	0.4207	0.4222	0.4236	0.4251	0.4265	0.4279	0.4292	0.4306	0.4319
1.5	0.4332	0.4345	0.4357	0.4370	0.4382	0.4394	0.4406	0.4418	0.4429	0.4441
1.6	0.4452	0.4463	0.4474	0.4484	0.4495	0.4505	0.4515	0.4525	0.4535	0.4545
1.7	0.4554	0.4564	0.4573	0.4582	0.4591	0.4599	0.4608	0.4616	0.4625	0.4633
1.8	0.4641	0.4649	0.4656	0.4664	0.4671	0.4678	0.4686	0.4693	0.4699	0.4706
1.9	0.4713	0.4719	0.4726	0.4732	0.4738	0.4744	0.4750	0.4756	0.4761	0.4767
2.0	0.4772	0.4778	0.4783	0.4788	0.4793	0.4798	0.4803	0.4808	0.4812	0.4817
2.1	0.4821	0.4826	0.4830	0.4834	0.4838	0.4842	0.4846	0.4850	0.4854	0.4857
2.2	0.4861	0.4864	0.4868	0.4871	0.4875	0.4878	0.4881	0.4884	0.4887	0.4890
2.3	0.4893	0.4896	0.4898	0.4901	0.4904	0.4906	0.4909	0.4911	0.4913	0.4916
2.4	0.4918	0.4920	0.4922	0.4925	0.4927	0.4929	0.4931	0.4932	0.4934	0.4936
2.5	0.4938	0.4940	0.4941	0.4943	0.4945	0.4946	0.4948	0.4949	0.4951	0.4952
2.6	0.4953	0.4955	0.4956	0.4957	0.4959	0.4960	0.4961	0.4962	0.4963	0.4964
2.7	0.4965	0.4966	0.4967	0.4968	0.4969	0.4970	0.4971	0.4972	0.4973	0.4974
2.8	0.4974	0.4975	0.4976	0.4977	0.4977	0.4978	0.4979	0.4979	0.4980	0.4981
2.9	0.4981	0.4982	0.4982	0.4983	0.4984	0.4984	0.4985	0.4985	0.4986	0.4986
3.0	0.4987	0.4987	0.4987	0.4988	0.4988	0.4989	0.4989	0.4989	0.4990	0.4990

Appendix E

Table of Random Numbers

02711	08182	75997	79866	58095	83319	80295	79741	74599	84379
94873	90935	31684	63952	09865	14491	99518	93394	34691	14985
54921	78680	06635	98689	17306	25170	65928	87709	30533	89736
77640	97636	37397	93379	56454	59818	45827	74164	71666	46977
61545	00835	93251	87203	36759	49197	85967	01704	19634	21898
17147	19519	22497	16857	42426	84822	92598	49186	88247	39967
13748	04742	92460	85801	53444	65626	58710	55406	17173	69776
87455	14813	50373	28037	91182	32786	65261	11173	34376	36408
08999	57409	91185	10200	61411	23392	47797	56377	71635	08601
78804	81333	53809	32471	46034	36306	22498	19239	85428	55721
82173	26921	28472	98958	07960	66124	89731	95069	18625	92405
97594	25168	89178	68190	05043	17407	48201	83917	11413	72920
73881	67176	93504	42636	38233	16154	96451	57925	29667	30859
46071	22912	90326	42453	88108	72064	58601	32357	90610	32921
44492	19686	12495	93135	95185	77799	52441	88272	22024	80631
31864	72170	37722	55794	14636	05148	54505	50113	21119	25228
51574	90692	43339	65689	76539	27909	05467	21727	51141	72949
35350	76132	92925	92124	92634	35681	43690	89136	35599	84138
46943	36502	01172	46045	46991	33804	80006	35542	61056	75666
22665	87226	33304	57975	03985	21566	65796	72915	81466	89205
39437	97957	11838	10433	21564	51570	73558	27495	34533	57808
77082	47784	40098	97962	89845	28392	78187	06112	08169	11261
24544	25649	43370	28007	06779	72402	62632	53956	24709	06978
27503	15558	37738	24849	70722	71859	83736	06016	94397	12529
24590	24545	06435	52758	45685	90151	46516	49644	92686	84870
48155	86226	40359	28723	15364	69125	12609	57171	86857	31702
20226	53752	90648	24362	83314	00014	19207	69413	97016	86290
70178	73444	38790	53626	93780	18629	68766	24371	74639	30782
10169	41465	51935	05711	09799	79077	88159	33437	68519	03040
81084	03701	28598	70013	63794	53169	97054	60303	23259	96196
69202	20777	21727	81511	51887	16175	53746	46516	70339	62727
80561	95787	89426	93325	86412	57479	54194	52153	19197	81877
08199	26703	95128	48599	09333	12584	24374	31232	61782	44032
98883	28220	39358	53720	80161	83371	15181	11131	12219	55920
84568	69286	76054	21615	80883	36797	82845	39139	90900	18172
04269	35173	95745	53893	86022	77722	52498	84193	22448	22571
10538	13124	36099	13140	37706	44562	57179	44693	67877	01549
77843	24955	25900	63843	95029	93859	93634	20205	66294	41218
12034	94636	49455	76362	83532	31062	69903	91186	65768	55949
10524	72829	47641	93315	80875	28090	97728	52560	34937	79548
68935	76632	46984	61772	92786	22651	07086	89754	44143	97687
89450	65665	29190	43709	11172	34481	95977	47535	25658	73898
90696	20451	24211	97310	60446	73530	62865	96574	13829	72226
49006	32047	93086	00112	20470	17136	28255	86328	07293	38809
74591	87025	52368	59416	34417	70557	86746	55809	53628	12000
06315	17012	77103	00968	07235	10728	42189	33292	51487	64443
62386	09184	62092	46617	99419	64230	95034	85481	07857	42510
86848	82122	04028	36959	87827	12813	08627	80699	13345	51695
65643	69480	46598	04501	40403	91408	32343	48130	49303	90689
11084	46534	78957	77353	39578	77868	22970	84349	09184	70603

Appendix F

Student's *t* Distribution

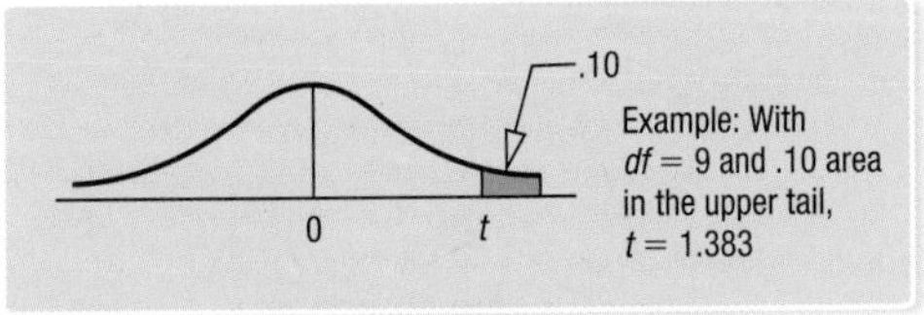

	Confidence Intervals					
	80%	90%	95%	98%	99%	99.9%
	Level of Significance for One-Tailed Test					
df	0.100	0.050	0.025	0.010	0.005	0.0005
	Level of Significance for Two-Tailed Test					
	0.20	0.10	0.05	0.02	0.01	0.001
1	3.078	6.314	12.706	31.821	63.657	636.619
2	1.886	2.920	4.303	6.965	9.925	31.599
3	1.638	2.353	3.182	4.541	5.841	12.924
4	1.533	2.132	2.776	3.747	4.604	8.610
5	1.476	2.015	2.571	3.365	4.032	6.869
6	1.440	1.943	2.447	3.143	3.707	5.959
7	1.415	1.895	2.365	2.998	3.499	5.408
8	1.397	1.860	2.306	2.896	3.355	5.041
9	1.383	1.833	2.262	2.821	3.250	4.781
10	1.372	1.812	2.228	2.764	3.169	4.587
11	1.363	1.796	2.201	2.718	3.106	4.437
12	1.356	1.782	2.179	2.681	3.055	4.318
13	1.350	1.771	2.160	2.650	3.012	4.221
14	1.345	1.761	2.145	2.624	2.977	4.140
15	1.341	1.753	2.131	2.602	2.947	4.073
16	1.337	1.746	2.120	2.583	2.921	4.015
17	1.333	1.740	2.110	2.567	2.898	3.965
18	1.330	1.734	2.101	2.552	2.878	3.922
19	1.328	1.729	2.093	2.539	2.861	3.883
20	1.325	1.725	2.086	2.528	2.845	3.850
21	1.323	1.721	2.080	2.518	2.831	3.819
22	1.321	1.717	2.074	2.508	2.819	3.792
23	1.319	1.714	2.069	2.500	2.807	3.768
24	1.318	1.711	2.064	2.492	2.797	3.745
25	1.316	1.708	2.060	2.485	2.787	3.725
26	1.315	1.706	2.056	2.479	2.779	3.707
27	1.314	1.703	2.052	2.473	2.771	3.690
28	1.313	1.701	2.048	2.467	2.763	3.674
29	1.311	1.699	2.045	2.462	2.756	3.659
30	1.310	1.697	2.042	2.457	2.750	3.646
40	1.303	1.684	2.021	2.423	2.704	3.551
60	1.296	1.671	2.000	2.390	2.660	3.460
120	1.289	1.658	1.980	2.358	2.617	3.373
∞	1.282	1.645	1.960	2.326	2.576	3.291

Appendix G

Critical Values of the *F* Distribution at a 5 Percent Level of Significance

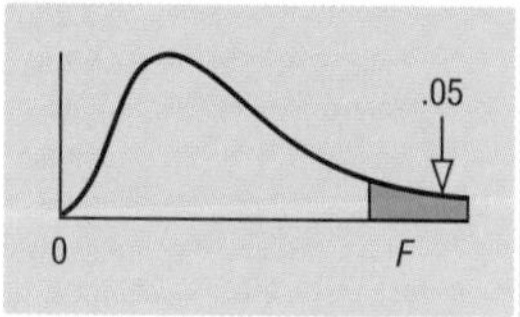

	Degrees of Freedom for the Numerator															
Degrees of Freedom for the Denominator	1	2	3	4	5	6	7	8	9	10	12	15	20	24	30	40
1	161	200	216	225	230	234	237	239	241	242	244	246	248	249	250	251
2	18.5	19.0	19.2	19.2	19.3	19.3	19.4	19.4	19.4	19.4	19.4	19.4	19.4	19.5	19.5	19.5
3	10.1	9.55	9.28	9.12	9.01	8.94	8.89	8.85	8.81	8.79	8.74	8.70	8.66	8.64	8.62	8.59
4	7.71	6.94	6.59	6.39	6.26	6.16	6.09	6.04	6.00	5.96	5.91	5.86	5.80	5.77	5.75	5.72
5	6.61	5.79	5.41	5.19	5.05	4.95	4.88	4.82	4.77	4.74	4.68	4.62	4.56	4.53	4.50	4.46
6	5.99	5.14	4.76	4.53	4.39	4.28	4.21	4.15	4.10	4.06	4.00	3.94	3.87	3.84	3.81	3.77
7	5.59	4.74	4.35	4.12	3.97	3.87	3.79	3.73	3.68	3.64	3.57	3.51	3.44	3.41	3.38	3.34
8	5.32	4.46	4.07	3.84	3.69	3.58	3.50	3.44	3.39	3.35	3.28	3.22	3.15	3.12	3.08	3.04
9	5.12	4.26	3.86	3.63	3.48	3.37	3.29	3.23	3.18	3.14	3.07	3.01	2.94	2.90	2.86	2.83
10	4.96	4.10	3.71	3.48	3.33	3.22	3.14	3.07	3.02	2.98	2.91	2.85	2.77	2.74	2.70	2.66
11	4.84	3.98	3.59	3.36	3.20	3.09	3.01	2.95	2.90	2.85	2.79	2.72	2.65	2.61	2.57	2.53
12	4.75	3.89	3.49	3.26	3.11	3.00	2.91	2.85	2.80	2.75	2.69	2.62	2.54	2.51	2.47	2.43
13	4.67	3.81	3.41	3.18	3.03	2.92	2.83	2.77	2.71	2.67	2.60	2.53	2.46	2.42	2.38	2.34
14	4.60	3.74	3.34	3.11	2.96	2.85	2.76	2.70	2.65	2.60	2.53	2.46	2.39	2.35	2.31	2.27
15	4.54	3.68	3.29	3.06	2.90	2.79	2.71	2.64	2.59	2.54	2.48	2.40	2.33	2.29	2.25	2.20
16	4.49	3.63	3.24	3.01	2.85	2.74	2.66	2.59	2.54	2.49	2.42	2.35	2.28	2.24	2.19	2.15
17	4.45	3.59	3.20	2.96	2.81	2.70	2.61	2.55	2.49	2.45	2.38	2.31	2.23	2.19	2.15	2.10
18	4.41	3.55	3.16	2.93	2.77	2.66	2.58	2.51	2.46	2.41	2.34	2.27	2.19	2.15	2.11	2.06
19	4.38	3.52	3.13	2.90	2.74	2.63	2.54	2.48	2.42	2.38	2.31	2.23	2.16	2.11	2.07	2.03
20	4.35	3.49	3.10	2.87	2.71	2.60	2.51	2.45	2.39	2.35	2.28	2.20	2.12	2.08	2.04	1.99
21	4.32	3.47	3.07	2.84	2.68	2.57	2.49	2.42	2.37	2.32	2.25	2.18	2.10	2.05	2.01	1.96
22	4.30	3.44	3.05	2.82	2.66	2.55	2.46	2.40	2.34	2.30	2.23	2.15	2.07	2.03	1.98	1.94
23	4.28	3.42	3.03	2.80	2.64	2.53	2.44	2.37	2.32	2.27	2.20	2.13	2.05	2.01	1.96	1.91
24	4.26	3.40	3.01	2.78	2.62	2.51	2.42	2.36	2.30	2.25	2.18	2.11	2.03	1.98	1.94	1.89
25	4.24	3.39	2.99	2.76	2.60	2.49	2.40	2.34	2.28	2.24	2.16	2.09	2.01	1.96	1.92	1.87
30	4.17	3.32	2.92	2.69	2.53	2.42	2.33	2.27	2.21	2.16	2.09	2.01	1.93	1.89	1.84	1.79
40	4.08	3.23	2.84	2.61	2.45	2.34	2.25	2.18	2.12	2.08	2.00	1.92	1.84	1.79	1.74	1.69
60	4.00	3.15	2.76	2.53	2.37	2.25	2.17	2.10	2.04	1.99	1.92	1.84	1.75	1.70	1.65	1.59
120	3.92	3.07	2.68	2.45	2.29	2.18	2.09	2.02	1.96	1.91	1.83	1.75	1.66	1.61	1.55	1.50
∞	3.84	3.00	2.60	2.37	2.21	2.10	2.01	1.94	1.88	1.83	1.75	1.67	1.57	1.52	1.46	1.39

Appendix G

Critical Values of the *F* Distribution at a 1 Percent Level of Significance

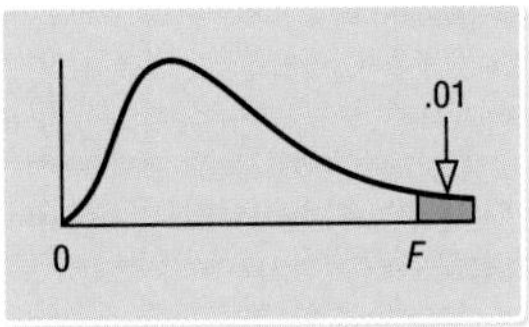

Degrees of Freedom for the Denominator	Degrees of Freedom for the Numerator: 1	2	3	4	5	6	7	8	9	10	12	15	20	24	30	40
1	4052	5000	5403	5625	5764	5859	5928	5981	6022	6056	6106	6157	6209	6235	6261	6287
2	98.5	99.0	99.2	99.2	99.3	99.3	99.4	99.4	99.4	99.4	99.4	99.4	99.4	99.5	99.5	99.5
3	34.1	30.8	29.5	28.7	28.2	27.9	27.7	27.5	27.3	27.2	27.1	26.9	26.7	26.6	26.5	26.4
4	21.2	18.0	16.7	16.0	15.5	15.2	15.0	14.8	14.7	14.5	14.4	14.2	14.0	13.9	13.8	13.7
5	16.3	13.3	12.1	11.4	11.0	10.7	10.5	10.3	10.2	10.1	9.89	9.72	9.55	9.47	9.38	9.29
6	13.7	10.9	9.78	9.15	8.75	8.47	8.26	8.10	7.98	7.87	7.72	7.56	7.40	7.31	7.23	7.14
7	12.2	9.55	8.45	7.85	7.46	7.19	6.99	6.84	6.72	6.62	6.47	6.31	6.16	6.07	5.99	5.91
8	11.3	8.65	7.59	7.01	6.63	6.37	6.18	6.03	5.91	5.81	5.67	5.52	5.36	5.28	5.20	5.12
9	10.6	8.02	6.99	6.42	6.06	5.80	5.61	5.47	5.35	5.26	5.11	4.96	4.81	4.73	4.65	4.57
10	10.0	7.56	6.55	5.99	5.64	5.39	5.20	5.06	4.94	4.85	4.71	4.56	4.41	4.33	4.25	4.17
11	9.65	7.21	6.22	5.67	5.32	5.07	4.89	4.74	4.63	4.54	4.40	4.25	4.10	4.02	3.94	3.86
12	9.33	6.93	5.95	5.41	5.06	4.82	4.64	4.50	4.39	4.30	4.16	4.01	3.86	3.78	3.70	3.62
13	9.07	6.70	5.74	5.21	4.86	4.62	4.44	4.30	4.19	4.10	3.96	3.82	3.66	3.59	3.51	3.43
14	8.86	6.51	5.56	5.04	4.69	4.46	4.28	4.14	4.03	3.94	3.80	3.66	3.51	3.43	3.35	3.27
15	8.68	6.36	5.42	4.89	4.56	4.32	4.14	4.00	3.89	3.80	3.67	3.52	3.37	3.29	3.21	3.13
16	8.53	6.23	5.29	4.77	4.44	4.20	4.03	3.89	3.78	3.69	3.55	3.41	3.26	3.18	3.10	3.02
17	8.40	6.11	5.18	4.67	4.34	4.10	3.93	3.79	3.68	3.59	3.46	3.31	3.16	3.08	3.00	2.92
18	8.29	6.01	5.09	4.58	4.25	4.01	3.84	3.71	3.60	3.51	3.37	3.23	3.08	3.00	2.92	2.84
19	8.18	5.93	5.01	4.50	4.17	3.94	3.77	3.63	3.52	3.43	3.30	3.15	3.00	2.92	2.84	2.76
20	8.10	5.85	4.94	4.43	4.10	3.87	3.70	3.56	3.46	3.37	3.23	3.09	2.94	2.86	2.78	2.69
21	8.02	5.78	4.87	4.37	4.04	3.81	3.64	3.51	3.40	3.31	3.17	3.03	2.88	2.80	2.72	2.64
22	7.95	5.72	4.82	4.31	3.99	3.76	3.59	3.45	3.35	3.26	3.12	2.98	2.83	2.75	2.67	2.58
23	7.88	5.66	4.76	4.26	3.94	3.71	3.54	3.41	3.30	3.21	3.07	2.93	2.78	2.70	2.62	2.54
24	7.82	5.61	4.72	4.22	3.90	3.67	3.50	3.36	3.26	3.17	3.03	2.89	2.74	2.66	2.58	2.49
25	7.77	5.57	4.68	4.18	3.85	3.63	3.46	3.32	3.22	3.13	2.99	2.85	2.70	2.62	2.54	2.45
30	7.56	5.39	4.51	4.02	3.70	3.47	3.30	3.17	3.07	2.98	2.84	2.70	2.55	2.47	2.39	2.30
40	7.31	5.18	4.31	3.83	3.51	3.29	3.12	2.99	2.89	2.80	2.66	2.52	2.37	2.29	2.20	2.11
60	7.08	4.98	4.13	3.65	3.34	3.12	2.95	2.82	2.72	2.63	2.50	2.35	2.20	2.12	2.03	1.94
120	6.85	4.79	3.95	3.48	3.17	2.96	2.79	2.66	2.56	2.47	2.34	2.19	2.03	1.95	1.86	1.76
∞	6.63	4.61	3.78	3.32	3.02	2.80	2.64	2.51	2.41	2.32	2.18	2.04	1.88	1.79	1.70	1.59

Appendix H

MegaStat Quick Reference Guide

What Is MegaStat?

MegaStat is an **Excel** add-in that performs statistical analysis within an **Excel** workbook. After it is installed, it appears on the **Excel** menu and works like **Edit, View,** or any of the other **Excel** options. MegaStat contains options to perform most of the calculations described in an introductory business statistics course.

When you click on **MegaStat** its main menu appears. Most of the options contain submenus. If the menu item is followed by periods, i.e., ". . . ," clicking on that item will display a dialogue box. If the menu item contains the symbol " ▶" additional submenu items are available. Below is the screen if you select **MegaStat** and then **Probability.**

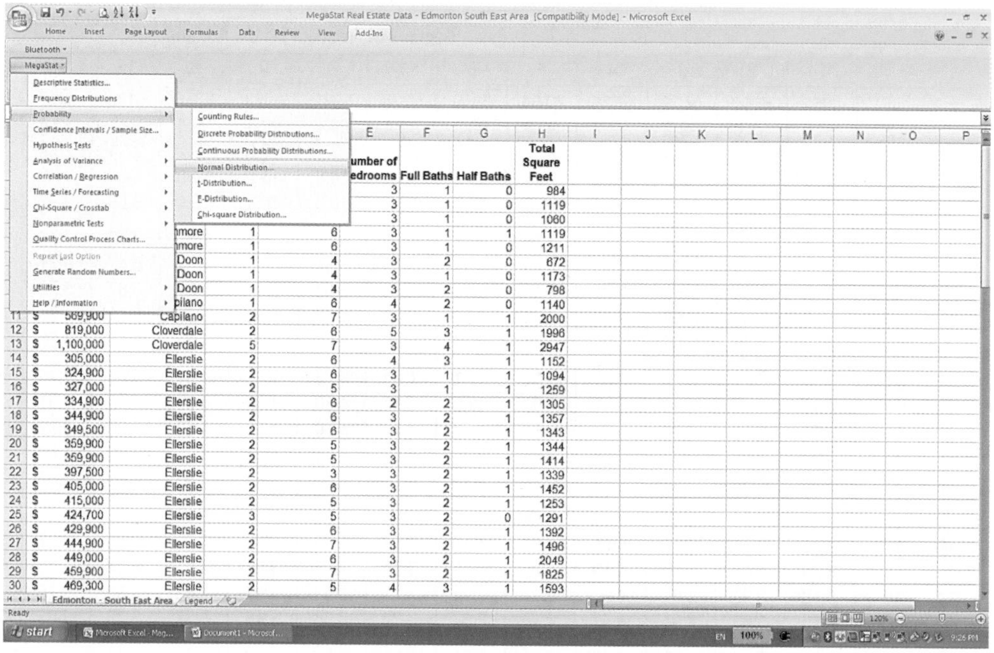

How MegaStat Works

Most MegaStat input is from dialogue boxes. For example, if you selected **MegaStat, Frequency Distributions,** and **Quantitative** you will see the following dialogue box. The dialogue boxes allow you to specify the data cells for the procedure and to specify options. All dialogue boxes have a **Help** button that will provide more information about the procedure. When the required information has been provided, click **OK** to perform the procedure.

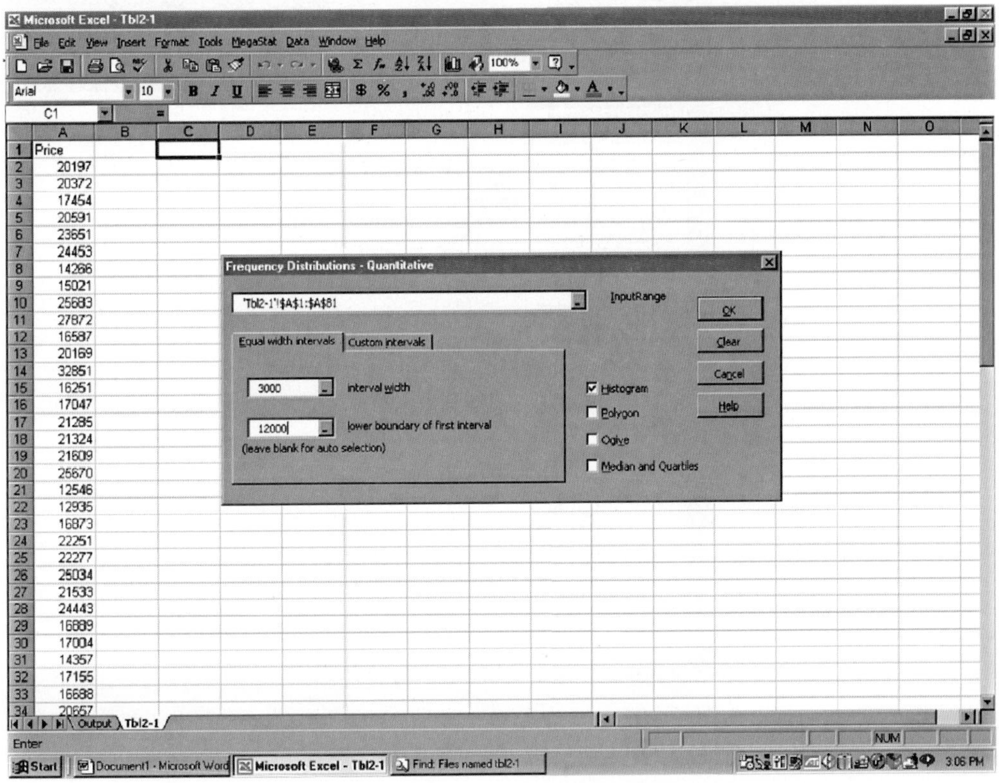

Most dialogue boxes require you to specify the data for the procedure. This can be done in one of several ways:

1. Pointing and dragging with the mouse. This is the easiest and most common method.
2. Typing the name of the named data range.
3. Typing the range address.
4. Using **Ctrl, Shift,** and **Arrow** keystroke combinations.

For most procedures, the first cell in each input range is the label. If the first cell in a range is text, it is considered a label; if it is a numeric value, it is considered data.

MegaStat Output

MegaStat output is placed in a worksheet titled "Output." If there is an existing Output sheet, the new output is placed at the end. The MegaStat output is in the standard **Excel** format, so you may insert, modify, or delete any cells. You can copy all or part of the output to another worksheet or to a word processing application.

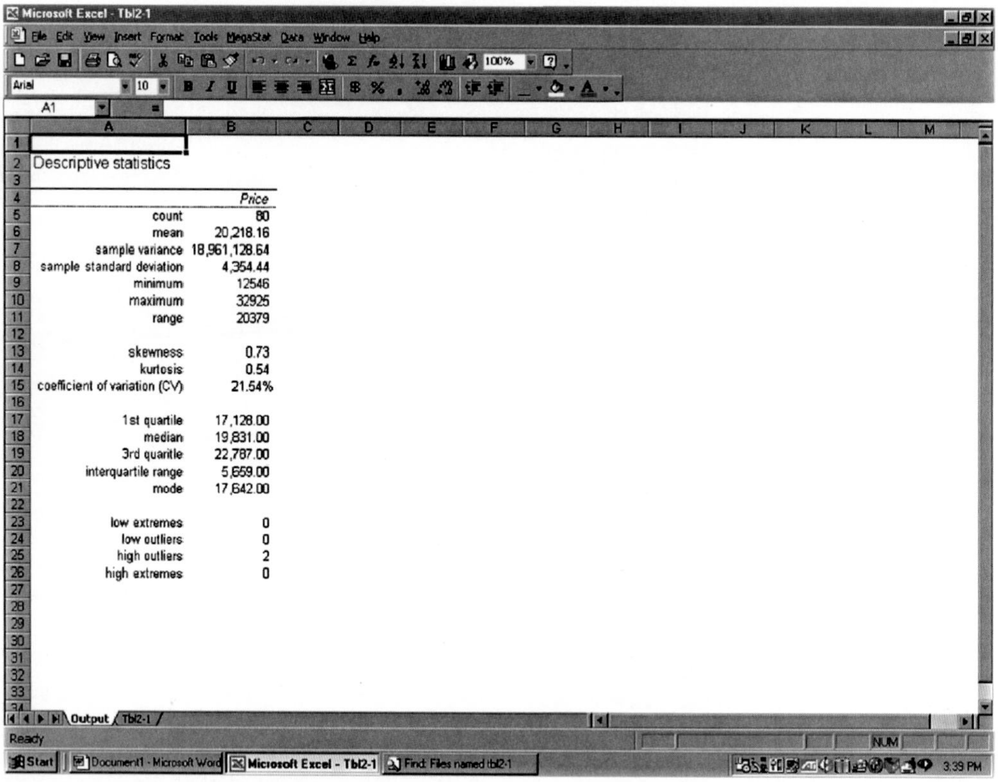

Help Is Always Available

Most of the dialogue boxes are self-explanatory, but if you need more information, click on **Help** and browse the Help contents.

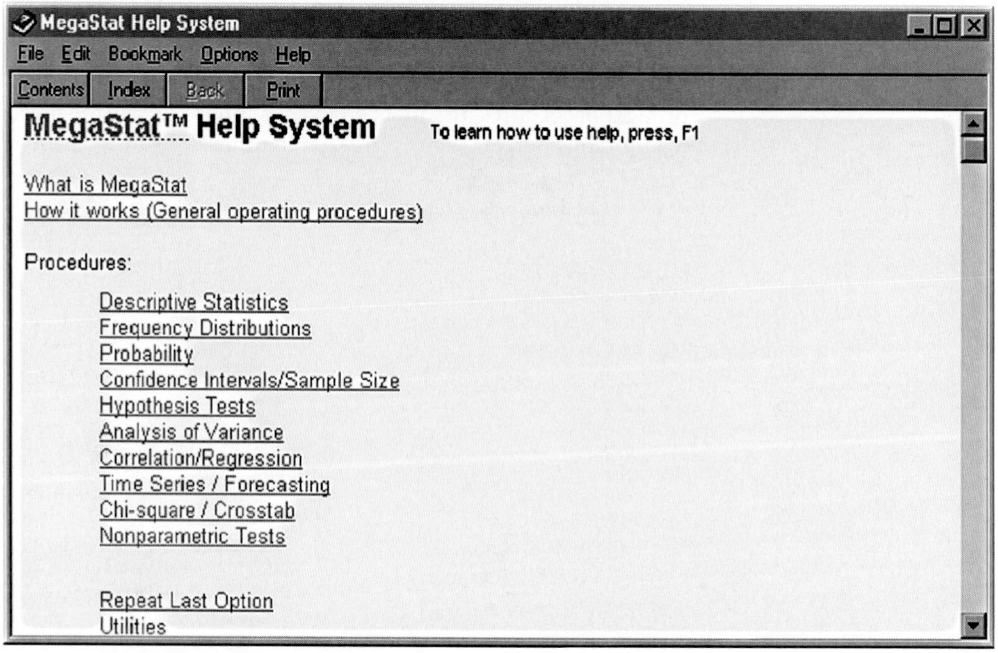

Answers

to Odd-Numbered Chapter Exercises

Chapter 1

1. a. Interval. f. Ratio.
   b. Ratio. g. Nominal.
   c. Ratio. h. Ordinal.
   d. Nominal. i. Nominal.
   e. Ordinal. j. Ratio.
3. Answers will vary.
5. Qualitative data are not numerical, whereas quantitative data are numerical. Examples will vary by student.
7. Nominal, ordinal, interval, and ratio. Examples will vary.
9. a. Continuous, quantitative, ratio.
   b. Discrete, qualitative, nominal.
   c. Discrete, quantitative, ratio.
   d. Discrete, qualitative, nominal.
   e. Continuous, quantitative, interval.
   f. Continuous, quantitative, interval.
   g. Discrete, qualitative, ordinal.
   h. Discrete, qualitative, ordinal.
   i. Discrete, quantitative, ratio.
11. Based on these sample findings, we can infer that 270/300, or 90 percent, of the executives would move.
13. a. 2006 total sales = 1 000 772; 2007 total sales = 942 973 total sales declined about 6 percent from 2006 to 2007.
    b. General Motors and Ford experienced losses of 17 and 19 percent, respectively. Meanwhile, Toyota gained 9.5 percent and Nissan about 9 percent. So, it would appear that there has been a significant shift within the market from domestic to foreign manufacturers.
15. See the CD-ROM.
17. See the CD-ROM.

Chapter 2

1. Maxwell Heating & Air Conditioning far exceeds the other corporations in sales. Mancell Electric & Plumbing and Mizelle Roofing & Sheet Metal are the two corporations with the least amount of fourth quarter sales.

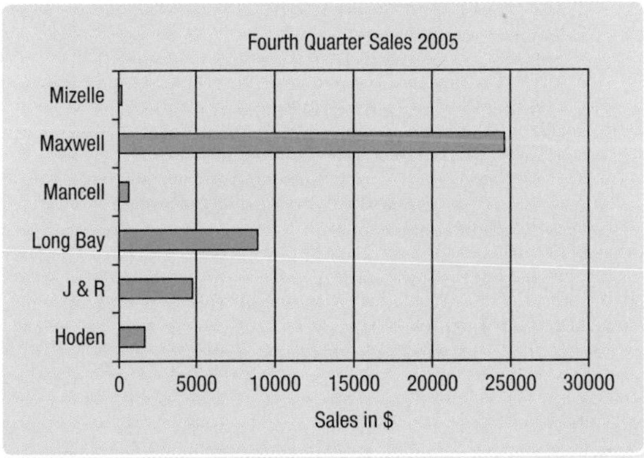

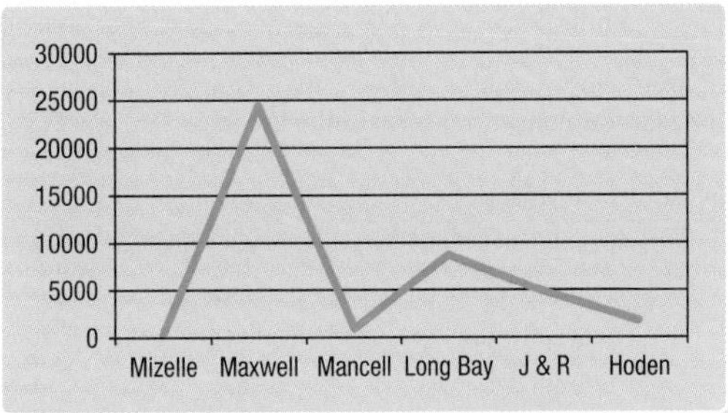

Maxwell has the highest sales, and Mizelle the lowest. The bar chart reflects the differences to a greater degree.

3. There are four classes: winter, spring, summer, and fall. The relative frequencies are 0.1, 0.3, 0.4, and 0.2, respectively.
5. a.

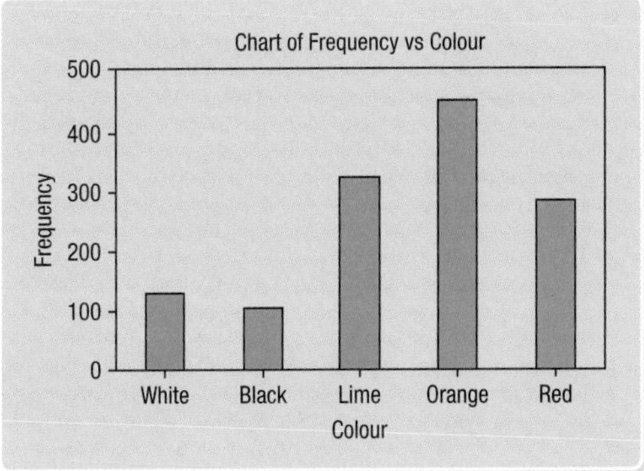

b.

Type	Number	Relative Frequencies
Bright white	130	0.10
Metallic black	104	0.08
Magnetic lime	325	0.25
Tangerine orange	455	0.35
Fusion red	286	0.22
Total	1300	1.00

c.

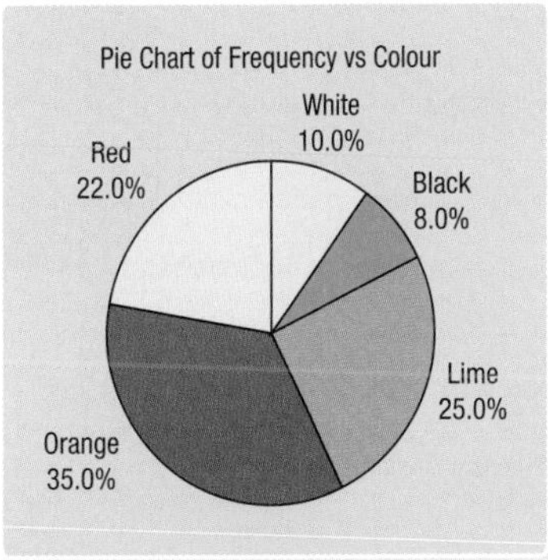

7. $2^5 = 32, 2^6 = 64$. Therefore, 6 classes.
9. $2^7 = 128, 2^8 = 256$. Suggests 8 classes.

$$i \geq \frac{567 - 235}{8} = 41.5.$$ Use interval of 45.

11. **a.** $2^4 = 16$. Suggests 5 classes.

b. $i \geq \frac{31-25}{5} = 1.2$. Use interval of 1.5.

c. 24.

d.

Patients	f	Relative frequency
24.0 to under 25.5	2	0.125
25.5 to under 27.0	4	0.250
27.0 to under 28.5	8	0.500
28.5 to under 30.0	0	0.000
30.0 to under 31.5	2	0.125
Total	16	1.000

e. The largest concentration is in the 27 up to 28.5 class (8).

13. **a.**

Number of Shoppers	f
0 to under 3	9
3 to under 6	21
6 to under 9	13
9 to under 12	4
12 to under 15	3
15 to under 18	1
Total	51

b. The largest group of shoppers (21) shop at Food Queen 3, 4, or 5 times during a month. Some customers visit the store only 1 time during the month, but others shop as many as 15 times.

c.

Number of Visits	Percent of Total
0 to under 3	17.65
3 to under 6	41.18
6 to under 9	25.49
9 to under 12	7.84
12 to under 15	5.88
15 to under 18	1.96
Total	100.00

15. **a.** Histogram.

b. 100.

c. 5.

d. 28.

e. 0.28.

f. 12.5.

g. 13.

17. **a.** 50.

b. 1.5 thousand miles, or 1500 miles.

c. Using lower limits on the X-axis:

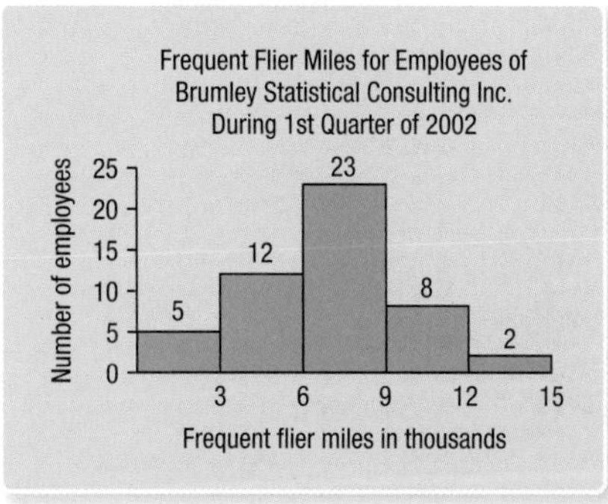

d. 1.5, 5.

e.

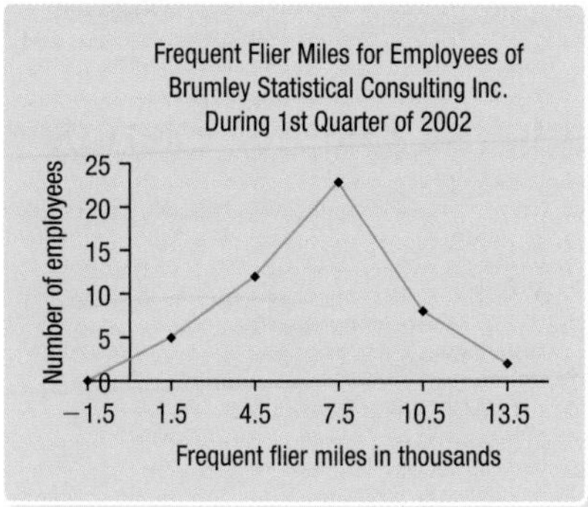

f. Most between 6000–9000, even spread on both sides.

19. **a.** 40.

b. 5.

c. 11 or 12.

d. About \$18/hr.

e. About \$9/hr.

f. About 75 percent.

21. **a.** 5.

b.

Frequent Flier Miles	f	Cumulative Frequency Less-than	More-than
0 to under 3	5	5	50
3 to under 6	12	17	45
6 to under 9	23	40	33
9 to under 12	8	48	10
12 to under 15	2	50	2

c.

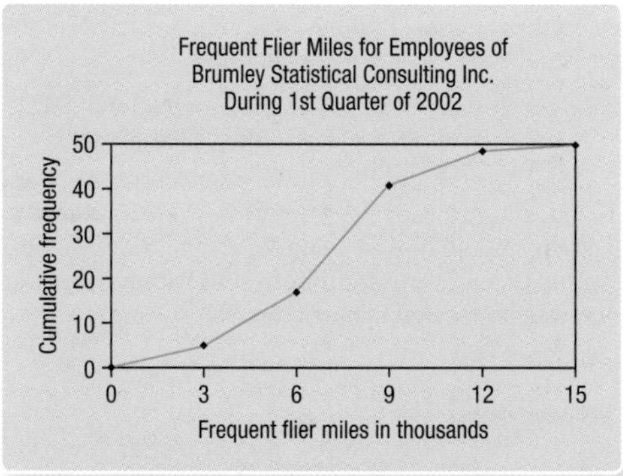

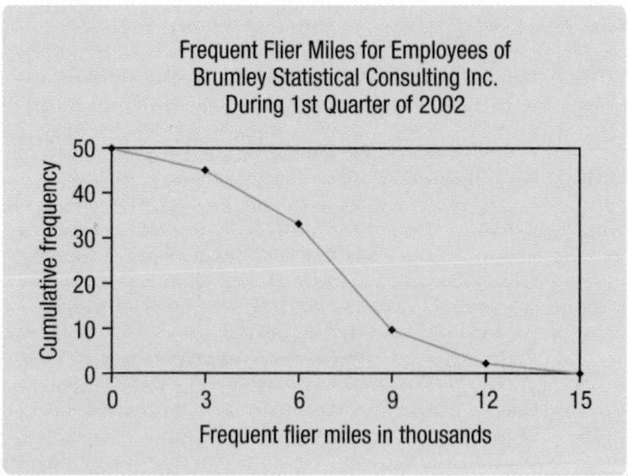

d. About 8500 miles.

e. About 7500 miles.

23. a. 621 to 629.
b. 5.
c. 621, 623, 623, 627, 629.

25. a. 25.
b. 1.
c. 38, 106.
d. 60, 61, 63, 63, 65, 65, 69.
e. No values.
f. 9.
g. 9.
h. 76.
i. 16.

27.

Stem	Leaves
0	5
1	28
2	
3	0024789
4	12366
5	2

There were a total of 16 calls studied. The number of calls ranged from 5 to 52 received. Typical was 30–39 calls, smallest was 5, largest was 52.

29. a. Qualitative variables are ordinarily a nominal level of measurement, but some are ordinal. Quantitative variables are commonly of interval or ratio level or measurement.
b. Yes, both types depict samples and populations.

31. $2^6 = 64$ and $2^7 = 128$. Suggest 7 classes.

33. a. 5, because $2^4 = 16 < 25$ and $2^5 = 32 > 25$.
b. $i \geq \frac{48-16}{5} = 6.4$. Use interval of 7.
c. 15.
d.

Class		Frequency
15 to under 22	|||	3
22 to under 29	~~||||~~ |||	8
29 to under 36	~~||||~~ ||	7
36 to under 43	~~||||~~	5
43 to under 50	||	2
Total		25

e. The values are clustered between 22 and 36.

35. a. 70.
b. 1.
c. 0, 145.
d. 30, 30, 32, 39.
e. 24.
f. 21.
g. 77.5.
h. 25.

37. a. 56.
b. 10 (found by 60 − 50).
c. 55.
d. 17.

39. a. \$36.60, found by (\$265 − \$82)/5.
b. Approx. \$40.
c.

\$80 to under \$120	8
120 to under 160	19
160 to under 200	10
200 to under 240	6
240 to under 280	1
Total	44

d. The purchases ranged from a low of about \$80 to a high of about \$280. The concentration is in the \$120 to under \$160 class.

41.

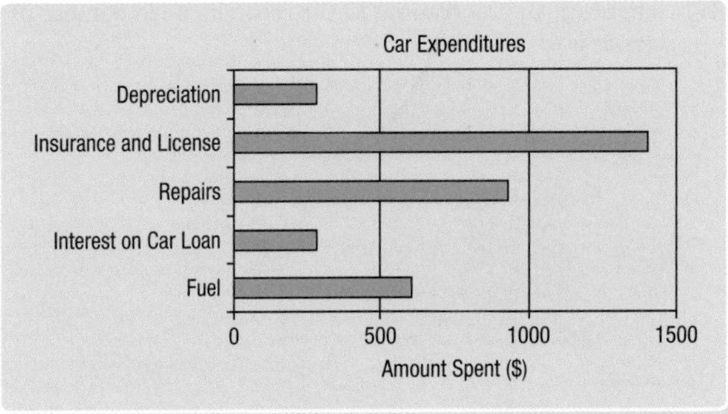

A pie chart is also acceptable. From the graph we can see that insurance and license fees are the highest expense at close to \$1500 per year.

43. a. Since $2^6 = 64 < 70 < 128 = 2^7$, 7 classes are recommended. The interval should be at least (1002.2 − 3.3)/7 = 142.7. Use 150 as a convenient value.
b. There could be several answers for the interpretation.

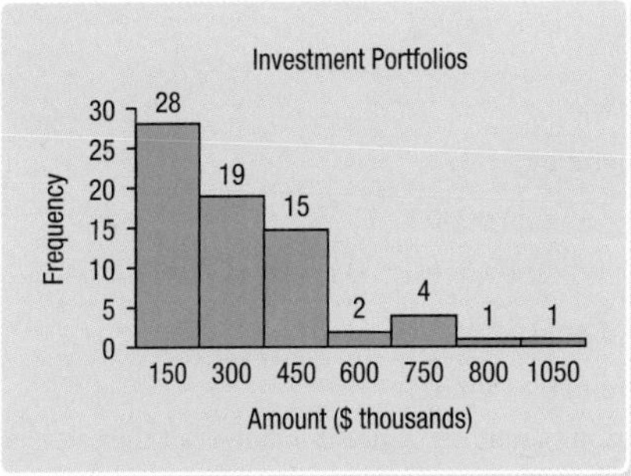

45.

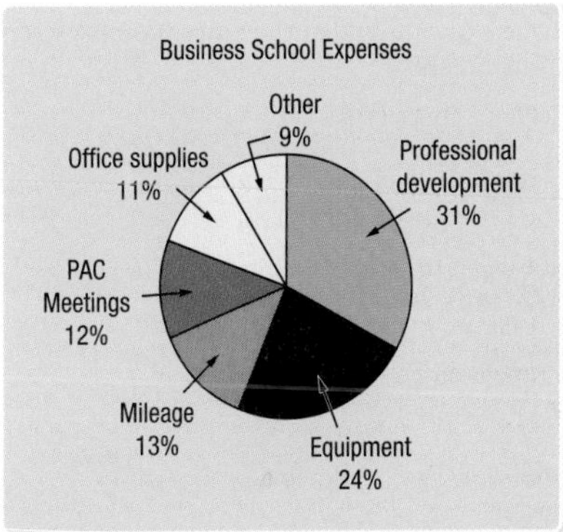

Professional development is the largest expense.

47. 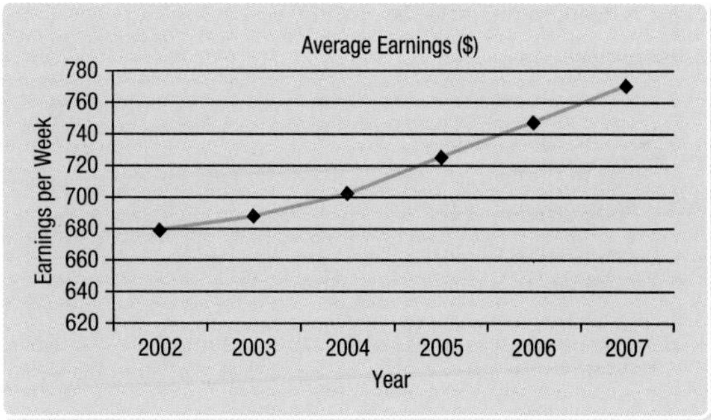

49. There are 50 observations so the recommended number of classes is 6.

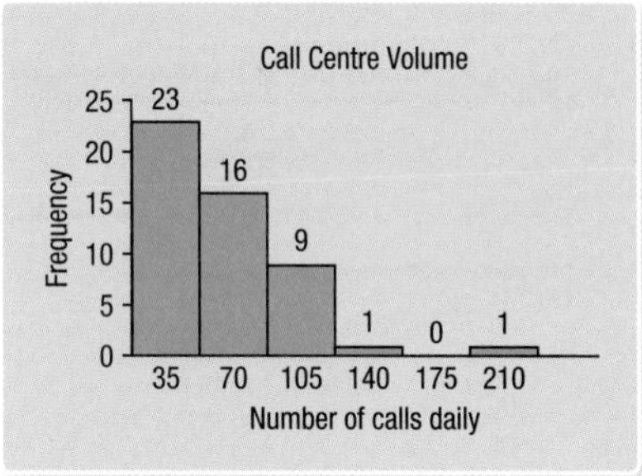

Twenty-nine of the 50 days, or 58 percent, have fewer than 40 calls waiting. There are three days that have more than 100 calls waiting.

51. Earnings for both sexes have increased at approximately the same rate over the 12-year period, but average earnings for men are consistently higher than average earnings for women.

53. See the CD-ROM.

Chapter 3

1. $\mu = 5.4$, found by 27/5.

3. a. $\bar{X} = 7.0$, found by 28/4.
   b. $(5 - 7) + (9 - 7) + (4 - 7) + (10 - 7) = 0$.

5. $\bar{X} = 14.58$, found by 43.74/3.

7. a. 15.4, found by 154/10.
   b. Population parameter, since it includes all the salespeople at Midtown Ford.

9. a. $54.55, found by $1091/20.
   b. A sample statistic—assuming that the power company serves more than 20 customers.

11. Yes, $162 900 found by 30($5430).

13. $22.91, found by $\dfrac{300(\$20) + 400(\$25) + 400(\$23)}{300 + 400 + 400}$.

15. $23.00, found by ($800 + $1000 + $2800)/200.

17. a. No mode.
   b. The given value would be the mode.
   c. 3 and 4; bimodal.

19. Median = 5, Mode = 5.

21. a. Median = (62.8 + 62.9)/2 = 62.85.
   b. Mode = 62.8 & 64.3 (bimodal).

23. Mean = 58.82; median = 58.00; mode = 58.00. All three measures are nearly identical.

25. a. 6.72, found by 80.6/12.
   b. 6.6 is both the median and the mode.
   c. Positively skewed.

27. 12.8 percentage increase, found by $\sqrt[5]{(1.08)(1.12)(1.14)(1.26)(1.05)} = 1.128$.

29. 12.28 percentage increase, found by $\sqrt[5]{(1.094)(1.138)(1.117)(1.119)(1.147)} = 1.1228$.

31. 1.01 percent, found by $\sqrt[35]{\dfrac{31\,241\,030}{21\,961\,999}} - 1$.

33. 10.76 percent, found by $\sqrt[5]{\dfrac{70}{42}} - 1$.

35. a. 7, found by 10 − 3.
   b. 6, found by 30/5.
   c. 2.4, found by 12/5.
   d. The difference between the highest number sold (10) and the smallest number sold (3) is 7. On average, the number of service reps on duty deviates by 2.4 from the mean of 6.

37. a. 30, found by 54 − 24.
   b. 38, found by 380/10.
   c. 7.2, found by 72/10.
   d. The difference of 54 and 24 is 30. On average, the number of minutes required to install a door deviates 7.2 minutes from the mean of 38 minutes.

39. British Columbia: median = 34; mean = 33.1; mode = 34; and range = 32.
Manitoba: median = 25; mean = 24.5; mode = 25; and range = 19.
In BC, there was a greater average preference for the pizza than in Manitoba; however, BC also had a greater dispersion in preference.

41. a. 5.
   b. 4.4, found by
$$\frac{(8-5)^2 - (3-5)^2 + (7-5)^2 + (3-5)^2 + (4-5)^2}{5}.$$

43. a. $2.77.
   b. 1.26, found by
$$\frac{(2.68-2.77)^2 + (1.03-2.77)^2 + (2.26-2.77)^2 + (4.30-2.77)^2 + (3.58-2.77)^2}{5}.$$

45. a. Range: 7.3, found by 11.6 − 4.3. Arithmetic mean: 6.94, found by 34.7/5. Variance: 6.5944, found by 32.972/5. Standard deviation: 2.568, found by $\sqrt{6.5944}$.
   b. Dennis has a higher mean return (11.76 > 6.94). However, Dennis has greater spread in its returns on equity (16.89 > 6.59).

47. a. $\bar{X} = 4$.
$$s^2 = \frac{(7-4)^2 + \cdots + (3-4)^2}{5-1} = 5.5.$$
   b. $$s^2 = \frac{102 - \dfrac{(20)^2}{5}}{5-1} = 5.50.$$
   c. $s = 2.3452$.

49. a. $\bar{X} = 38$.
$$s^2 = \frac{(28-38)^2 + \cdots + (42-38)^2}{10-1} = 82.6667.$$
   b. $$s^2 = \frac{15\,194 - (390)^2}{10-1} = 82.6667.$$
   c. $s = 9.0921$.

51. **a.** $\bar{X} = 95.1.$

$$s^2 = \frac{(101-95.1)^2 + (97-95.1)^2 + \cdots + (88-95.1)^2}{10-1} = 123.66.$$

b. $$s^2 = \sqrt{\frac{91553 - \frac{(951)^2}{10}}{10-1}} = 123.66.$$

c. 11.12.

53. 69.1 percent.

55. **a.** About 95 percent.
b. 47.5 percent, 2.5 percent.

57. 8.06 percent, found by (0.25/3.10)(100).

59. **a.** Because the two series are in different units of measurement.
b. P.E. ratio is 36.73 percent. ROI is 52 percent. Less spread in the P.E. ratios.

61. **a.** The mean is 30.8, found by 154/5. The median is 31.0, and the standard deviation is 3.96, found by

$$\sqrt{\frac{4806 - \frac{154^2}{5}}{4}}.$$

b. −0.15, found by $\frac{3(30.8-31.0)}{3.96}$.

63. **a.** The mean is 21.93, found by 328.9/15. The median is 15.8, and the standard deviation is 21.18, found by

$$\sqrt{\frac{13\,494.67 - \frac{328.9^2}{15}}{14}}.$$

b. 0.868, found by [3(21.93 − 15.8)]/21.18.

65. Median = 53, found by $(11+1)(\frac{1}{2})$; therefore, 6th value in from lowest.
$Q_1 = 49$, found by $(11+1)(\frac{1}{4})$; therefore, 3rd value in from lowest.
$Q_3 = 55$, found by $(11+1)(\frac{3}{4})$; therefore, 9th value in from lowest.

67. **a.** $Q_1 = 33.25$, $Q_3 = 50.25$.
b. $D_2 = 27.8$, $D_8 = 52.6$.
c. $P_{67} = 47$.

69. **a.** 350.
b. $Q_1 = 175$, $Q_3 = 930$.
c. 930 − 175 = 755.
d. Less than 0, or more than about 2060.
e. There are no outliers.
f. The distribution is positively skewed.

71. The distribution is somewhat positively skewed. Note that the line above 15.5 is longer than below 7.8.

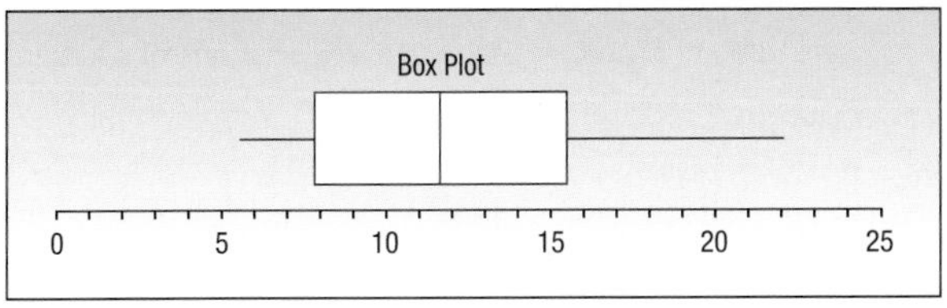

73. Because the exact values in a frequency distribution are not known, the midpoint is used for every member of that class.

75.

Class	f	M	fM	fM^2
\$20 to under \$30	7	25	175	4375
30 to under 40	12	35	420	14 700
40 to under 50	21	45	945	42 525
50 to under 60	18	55	990	54 450
60 to under 70	12	65	780	50 700
Total	70		3310	166 750

$$\bar{X} = \frac{3310}{70} = 47.2857.$$

$$s = \sqrt{\frac{166\,750 - \frac{(3310)^2}{70}}{70-1}} = 12.18.$$

and median $= 40 + \frac{\frac{70}{2} - 19}{21}(10) = 47.6.$

77.

Amount	f	M	fM	fM^2
\$20 to under \$30	1	25	25	625
30 to under 40	15	35	525	18 375
40 to under 50	22	45	990	44 550
50 to under 60	8	55	440	24 200
60 to under 70	4	65	260	16 900
Total	50		2240	104 650

$$\bar{X} = \frac{2240}{50} = 44.8.$$

$$s = \sqrt{\frac{104\,650 - \frac{(2240)^2}{50}}{50-1}} = 9.37.$$

and median $= 40 + \frac{\frac{50}{2} - 16}{22}(10) = 44.1.$

79. **a.** Mean = 5, found by (6 + 4 + 3 + 7 + 5)/5.
Median is 5, found by ordering the values and selecting the middle value.
b. Population, because all partners were included.
c. $\Sigma(X - \mu) = (6-5) + (4-5) + (3-5) + (7-5) + (5-5) = 0.$

81. $\bar{X} = \frac{545}{16} = 34.06.$
Median = 37.50.

83. The Communications industry has older workers than the Retail Trade. Production workers have the most age difference.

85. $$\bar{X}_W = \frac{\$5.00(270) + \$6.50(300) + \$8.00(100)}{270 + 300 + 100} = \$6.12.$$

87. $$\bar{X}_w = \frac{[15\,300(4.5) + 10\,400(3.0) + 150\,600(10.2)]}{176\,300}$$
= 9.28 percent.

89.

Wage (X)	Freq (f)	fX	fX^2
\$13.00	20	260	3380
15.50	12	186	2883
18.00	8	144	2592
Totals:	40	590	8855

Mean = 590/40 = 14.75. Variance $= \frac{8855 - \frac{(590)^2}{40}}{40} = 3.8125.$

Standard deviation = 1.95.

91. **a.** 55, found by 72 − 17.
b. 14.4, found by 144/10, where $\bar{X} = 43.2$.

c. 17.6245.

d. $1 - \frac{1}{4} = 0.75 = 75$ percent.

e. $43.2 + 2(17.6245) = 78.45$.
$43.2 - 2(17.6245) = 7.95$.

93. a. Population.

b. 183.47.

c. 94.92 percent. A lot of variability compared to the mean.

95. $Q_1 = 44.25$, $Q_3 = 68.5$, and the median is 55.50. The distribution is approximately symmetric. The box plot is as follows.

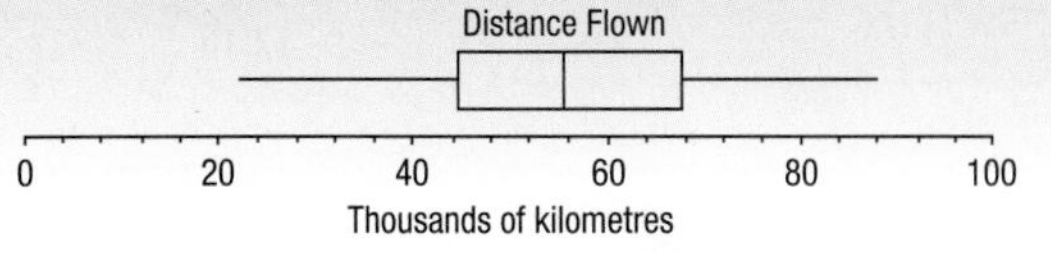

The above results are found using MINITAB.

97. The distribution is positively skewed. The first quartile is approx. \$20 and the third quartile is approx. \$90. There is one outlier located at approx. \$255. The median is about \$50.

99. a. $\bar{X} = \dfrac{857.90}{50} = 17.158$, median = 16.35.

b. $s = \sqrt{\dfrac{20\,206.73 - \dfrac{(857.90)^2}{50}}{50 - 1}} = 10.58$.

c. $17.158 \pm (2)(10.58) = -4.002, 38.318$.

d. $CV = \dfrac{10.58}{17.158}(100) = 61.66$ percent.

e. $sk = \dfrac{3(17.158 - 16.35)}{10.58} = 0.23$.

f. $L_{25} = (50 + 1)\dfrac{25}{100} = 12.75$. $Q_1 = 7.825$ (Excel: 8.075).
$L_{75} = (50 + 1)\dfrac{75}{100} = 38.25$. $Q_3 = 27.400$ (Excel: 27.025).

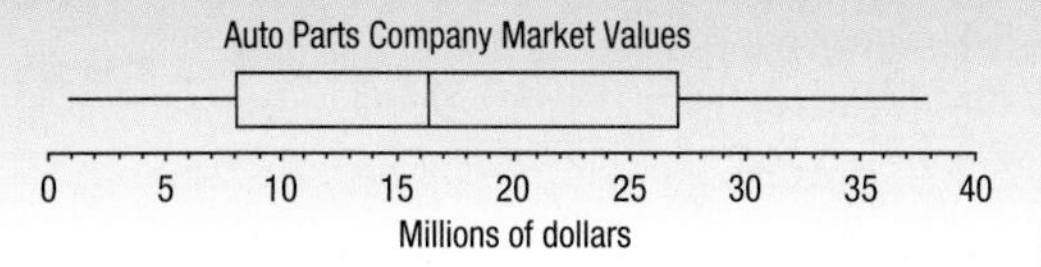

g. The distribution is nearly symmetrical. The mean is 17.158, the median is 16.35, and the standard deviation is 10.58. About 75 percent of the companies have a value less than 27.4, and 25 percent have a value less than 7.825.

101. a. The mean is 173.77 hours, found by 2259/13. The median is 195 hours.

$s = 101.47$ hours, found by $\sqrt{\dfrac{526\,391 - \dfrac{2259^2}{13}}{13}}$.

b. $CV = 58.4$ percent, found by $\dfrac{101.47}{173.77}(100)$.

Coefficient of skewness is −0.697; slight negative skewness.

c. $L_{45} = 14 \times 0.45 = 6.3$. So the 45th percentile is $192 + 0.3(195 - 192) = 192.9$.

$L_{82} = 14 \times 0.82 = 11.48$. So the 82nd percentile is $260 + 0.48(295 - 260) = 276.8$.

d.

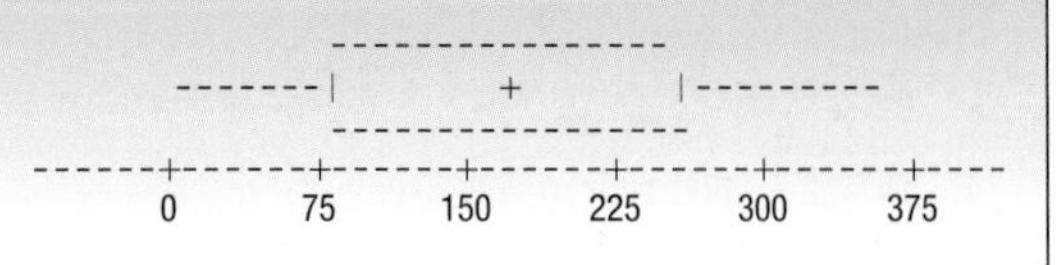

There is a slight negative skewness visible, but no outliers.

103. Mean is 13, found by 910/70. The median is 12.96 km.

$$s = \sqrt{\frac{13\,637.50 - \dfrac{(910)^2}{70}}{69}} = 5.118.$$

105. Mean = 6.24; mode = 7; IQR = 7 − 5 = 2; standard deviation = 1.70.

107. See the CD-ROM.

109. See the CD-ROM.

Chapter 4

1.

	Person	
Outcome	**1**	**2**
1	A	A
2	A	F
3	F	A
4	F	F

3. a. .176, found by $\dfrac{6}{34}$.

b. Empirical.

5. a. Empirical.

b. Classical.

c. Classical.

d. Subjective.

7. a. The survey of 40 people about environmental issues.

b. 26 or more respond yes, for example.

c. 10/40 = .25.

d. Empirical.

e. The events are probably not equally likely, but they are mutually exclusive.

9. a. Answers will vary, here are some possibilities: 1234, 1243, 1245, 9999.

b. $(1/10)^4$.

c. Classical.

11. a. 78 960 960.

b. 840, found by (7)(6)(5)(4). That is 7!/3!

c. 10, found by 5!/3!2!

13. 210, found by (10)(9)(8)(7)/(4)(3)(2).

15. 120, found by 5!

17. 10 897 286 400 found by
$_{15}P_{10} = 15 \times 14 \times 13 \times 12 \times 11 \times 10 \times 9 \times 8 \times 7 \times 6$.

19. $P(A \text{ or } B) = P(A) + P(B) = .30 + .20 = .50$
$P(\text{neither}) = 1 - .50 = .50$.

21. a. 102/200 = .51.

b. .49 found by (1 − .51) or by 61/200 + 37/200 = .305 + .185. Special rule of addition.

23. $P(\text{above } C) = .25 + .50 = .75$.

25. $P(A \text{ or } B) = P(A) + P(B) - P(A \text{ and } B)$
$= .20 + .30 - .15 = .35$.

27. When two events are mutually exclusive, it means that if one occurs the other event cannot occur. Therefore, the probability of their joint occurrence is zero.

29. a. 0.20.

b. 0.30.

c. No, because a store could have both.

d. Joint probability.
e. 0.90, found by 1.0 − 0.10.

31. $P(A \text{ and } B) = P(A) \times P(B \mid A) = .40 \times .30 = .12$.

33. .90, found by (.80 + .60) − .5.
.10, found by (1 − .90).

35. **a.** $P(A_1) = 3/10 = .30$.
b. $P(B_1 \mid A_2) = 1/3 = .33$.
c. $P(B_2 \text{ and } A_3) = 1/10 = .10$.

37. **a.** A contingency table.
b. .27, found by 300/500 × 135/300.
c. The tree diagram would appear as:

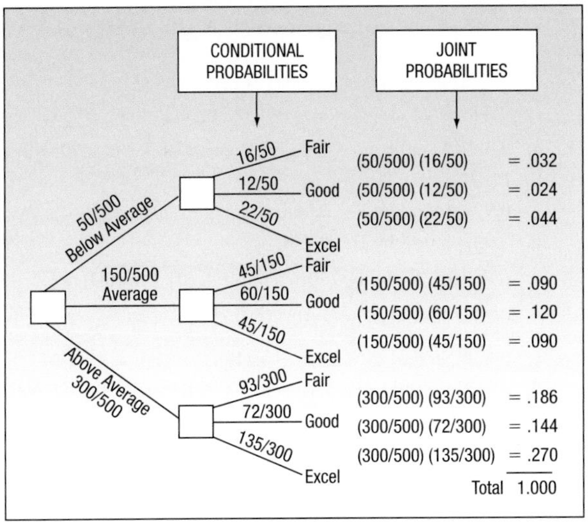

39. Probability the first presentation wins = 3/5 = .60. Probability the second presentation wins = 2/5 (3/4) = .30.
Probability the third presentation wins = (2/5)(1/4)(3/3) = .10.

41. **a.** Nominal.
b. 32/200 = 16 percent.
c. 85/200 = 42.5 percent.
d. Yes, as 32 percent of men ordered dessert compared to 15 percent of women.

43. **a.** 106/659 = 16.1 percent.
b. 143/659 = 21.7 percent.
c. 12/659 = 1.8 percent.
d. 233/659 + 233/659 − 87/659 = 57.5 percent.
d. 40/161 = 24.8 percent.

45. **a.** Asking teenagers to compare their reactions to a newly developed soft drink.
b. Answers will vary. One possibility is more than half of the respondents like it.

47. Subjective.

49. **a.** The likelihood an event will occur, assuming that another event has already occurred.
b. The collection of one or more outcomes of an experiment.
c. A measure of the likelihood that two or more events will happen concurrently.

51. 26 × 10 × 26 × 10 × 26 × 10 = 17 576 000 ways.

53. C(52, 7) = 133 784 560 ways.

55. $P(15, 6)$ = 3 603 600 ways.

57. **a.** .8145, found by $(.95)^4$.
b. Special rule of multiplication.
c. $P(A \text{ and } B \text{ and } C \text{ and } D) = P(A) \times P(B) \times P(C) \times P(D)$.

59. **a.** .08, found by .80 × .10.
b.

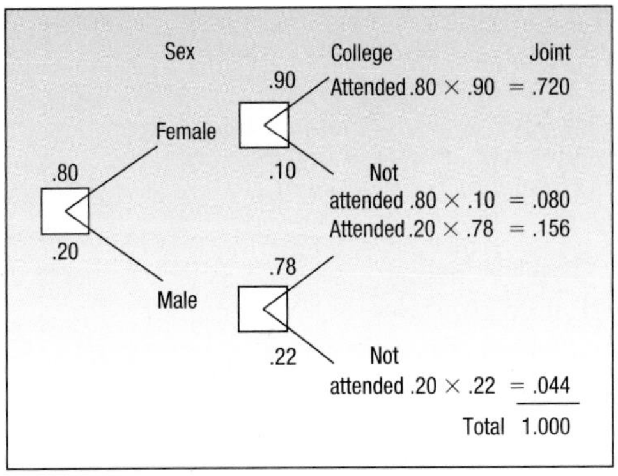

c. Yes, because all the possible outcomes are shown on the tree diagram.

61. **a.** 0.57, found by 57/100.
b. 0.97, found by (57/100) + (40/100).
c. Yes, because an employee cannot be both.
d. 0.03, found by 1 − 0.97.

63. **a.** 0.4096, found by $(0.8)^4$.
b. 0.0016, found by $(0.2)^4$.
c. 0.9984, found by 1 − 0.0016.

65. **a.** 0.9039, found by $(0.98)^5$.
b. 0.0961, found by 1 − 0.9039.

67. **a.** 0.0333, found by (4/10)(3/9)(2/8).
b. 0.1667, found by (6/10)(5/9)(4/8).
c. 0.8333, found by 1 − 0.1667.
d. Dependent.

69. **a.** 0.3818, found by (9/12)(8/11)(7/10).
b. 0.6182, found by 1 − 0.3818.

71. C(20,4)C(15,3) = (4845)(455) = 2 204 475 ways.

73. C(30,4)C(20,4) + C(30,5)C(20,3) + C(30,6)C(20,2) + C(30,7)C(20,1) + C(30,8)C(20,0) = 454 620 240 ways.

75. **a.** 0.30, found by 6/20.
b. 0.45, found by (6 + 7 − 4)/20.
c. 0.5714, found by 4/7.
d. 0.0789, found by (6/20)(5/19).

77. **a.** P(P or D) = 1/10 + 1/50 = .10 + .02 = .12.
b. P(No) = (49/50)(9/10) = .882.
c. P(No on 3) = $(.882)^3$ = .686.
d. P(at least one prize) = 1 − .686 = .314.

79. Yes. 256 is found by 2^8.

81. 0.9744, found by $1 - (0.40)^4$.

83. **a.** 0.185, found by (0.15)(0.95) + (0.05)(0.85).
b. 0.0075, found by (0.15)(0.05).

85. **a.** $P(\text{F and} > 60) = .25$, found by solving with the general rule of multiplication:
$P(\text{F}) \cdot P(>60 \mid \text{F}) = (.5)(.5)$.
b. 0.
c. 0.3333, found by 1/3.

87. 26^4 = 456 976.

89. 3 628 800 matches are possible. So, the probability is 1 out of 3 628 800.

91. .99(.98) = .9702.

93. See the CD-ROM.

Chapter 5

1. $\mu = 1.3, \sigma^2 = .81$, found by:
$\mu = 0(.20) + 1(.40) + 2(.30) + 3(.10) = 1.3.$
$\sigma^2 = (0 - 1.3)^2(.2) + (1 - 1.3)^2(.4) + (2 - 1.3)^2(.3) + (3 - 1.3)^2(.1) = .81.$

3. a. The middle one.
b. (1) 0.3 = 30 percent.
(2) 0.3 = 30 percent.
(3) 0.9 = 90 percent.
c. $\mu = 5(0.1) + 10(0.2) + 15(0.3) + 20(0.4) = 15.$
$\sigma^2 = (5 - 15)^2(0.1) + (10 - 15)^2(0.2) + (15 - 15)^2(0.2) + (20 - 15)^2(0.4) = 25.$
$\sigma = 5.$

5. a.

Number of Calls	Probability
0	0.16
1	0.20
2	0.44
3	0.18
4	0.02

b. Discrete.
c. 1.7, found by 0.16(0) + 0.20(1) + 0.44(2) + 0.18(3) + 0.02(4).
d. 1.005, found by

$$\sqrt{0.16(0-1.7)^2+0.20(1-1.7)^2+0.44(2-1.7)^2+0.18(3-1.7)^2+0.02(4-1.7)^2}.$$

7. a. .20.
b. .55.
c. .95.
d. $\mu = 0(.45) + 10(.30) + 100(.20) + 500(.05) = 48.0.$
$\sigma^2 = (0 - 48)^2(.45) + (10 - 48)^2(.3) + (100 - 48)^2(.2) + (500 - 48)^2(.05) = 12\ 226.$
$\sigma = 110.57$, found by $\sqrt{12\ 226}$.

9. a. 21, found by 0.50(10) + 0.40(25) + 0.08(50) + 0.02(100).
b. 16.09, found by

$$\sqrt{0.50(10-21)^2+0.40(25-21)^2+0.08(50-21)^2+0.02(100-21)^2}.$$

11. a. $P(2) = \frac{4!}{2!(4-2)!}(.25)^2(.75)^{4-2} = .2109.$
b. $P(3) = \frac{4!}{3!(4-3)!}(.25)^3(.75)^{4-3} = .0469.$
c. $P(2) + P(3) + P(4) = 0.2109 + 0.0469 + 0.0039 = 0.2617.$
d. $P(0) + P(1) + P(2) = 0.3164 + 0.4219 + 0.2109 = 0.9492.$

13. a.

X	$P(X)$
0	.064
1	.288
2	.432
3	.216

b. $\mu = 1.8.$
$\sigma^2 = 0.72.$
$\sigma = \sqrt{0.72} = 0.8485.$

15. a. 0.2668, found by $P(2) = \frac{9!}{(9-2)!2!}(.3)^2(.7)^7.$
b. 0.1715, found by $P(4) = \frac{9!}{(9-4)!4!}(.3)^4(.7)^5.$
c. 0.0404, found by $P(0) = \frac{9!}{(9-0)!0!}(.3)^0(.7)^9.$

17. a. 0.2824, found by $P(0) = \frac{12!}{(12-0)!0!}(.10)^0(.9)^{12}.$
b. 0.3765, found by $P(1) = \frac{12!}{(12-1)!1!}(.10)^1(.9)^{11}.$
c. 0.2301, found by $P(2) = \frac{12!}{(12-2)!2!}(.10)^2(.9)^{10}.$
d. $P(0) + P(1) + P(2) = 0.2824 + 0.3765 + 0.2301 = 0.8890.$
e. $\mu = 1.2$, found by 12(0.10).
$\sigma = 1.0392$, found by $\sqrt{1.08}$.

19. a. 0.1858, found by $\frac{15!}{2!13!}(0.23)^2(0.77)^{13}.$
b. 0.1416, found by $\frac{15!}{5!10!}(0.23)^5(0.77)^{10}.$
c. 3.45, found by (0.23)(15).

21. a. 0.296, found by using Appendix A with n of 8, p of 0.30, and x of 2.
b. $P(x \le 2) = 0.058 + 0.198 + 0.296 = 0.552.$
c. 0.448, found by $P(x \ge 3) = 1 - P(x \le 2) = 1 - 0.552.$

23. a. 0.387, found from Appendix A with n of 9, p of 0.90, and x of 9.
b. $P(x < 5) = 0.001.$
c. 0.992, found by 1 − 0.008.
d. 0.947, found by 1 − 0.053.

25. a. $\mu = 10.5$, found by 15(0.7) and $\sigma = \sqrt{15(0.7)(0.3)} = 1.7748.$
b. 0.2061, found by $\frac{15!}{10!5!}(0.7)^{10}(0.3)^5.$
c. 0.4247, found by 0.2061 + 0.2186.
d. 0.5154, found by 0.2186 + 0.1700 + 0.0916 + 0.0305 + 0.0047.

27. $P(2) = \frac{[{}_6C_2][{}_4C_1]}{{}_{10}C_3} = \frac{15(4)}{120} = .50.$

29. $P(0) = \frac{[{}_7C_2][{}_3C_0]}{[{}_{10}C_2]} = \frac{21(1)}{45} = .4667.$

31. $P(2) = \frac{[{}_9C_3][{}_6C_2]}{[{}_{15}C_5]} = \frac{84(15)}{3003} = .4196.$

33. a. 0.6703.
b. 0.3297.

35. a. 0.0613.
b. 0.0803.

37. $\mu = 6.$
$P(X \ge 5) = .7149 = 1 - (0.0025 + 0.0149 + 0.0446 + 0.0892 + 0.1339).$

39. A random variable is a quantitative or qualitative outcome that results from a chance experiment. A probability distribution also includes the likelihood of each possible outcome.

41. The binomial distribution is a discrete probability distribution for which there are only two possible outcomes. A second important part is that data collected are a result of counts. Additionally, one trial is independent from the next, and the chance for success remains the same from one trial to the next.

43. $\mu = 0(.1) + 1(.2) + 2(.3) + 3(.4) = 2.00.$
$\sigma^2 = (0-2)^2(.1) + \cdots + (3-2)^2(.40) = 1.0.$
$\sigma = 1.$

45. $\mu = 0(.4) + 1(.2) + 2(.2) + 3(.1) + 4(.1) = 1.3.$
$\sigma^2 = (0-1.30)^2(.4) + \cdots + (4-1.30)^2(.1) = 1.81.$
$\sigma = 1.3454.$

47. $\mu = 13.2$, found by $12(.25) + 13(.4) + 14(.25) + 15(.1) = 3.0 + 5.2 + 3.5 + 1.5.$
$\sigma^2 = 0.86$, found by $0.36 + 0.016 + 0.16 + 0.324.$
$\sigma = \sqrt{0.86} = 0.9274.$

49. a. Discrete.
b. Continuous.

c. Discrete.
d. Discrete.
e. Continuous.

51. a. 6, found by 0.4 × 15.
b. 0.0245, found by $\frac{15!}{10!5!}(0.4)^{10}(0.6)^{5}$.
c. 0.0338, found by 0.0245 + 0.0074 + 0.0016 + 0.0003 + 0.0000.
d. 0.4032, found by 0.0005 + 0.0047 + 0.0219 + 0.0634 + 0.1268 + 0.1859.

53. a. $\mu = 20(0.075) = 1.5$.
$\sigma = \sqrt{20(0.075)(0.925)} = 1.1779$.
b. 0.2103, found by $\frac{20!}{0!20!}(0.075)^{0}(0.925)^{20}$.
c. 0.7897, found by 1 − 0.2103.

55. a. 0.1311, found by $\frac{16!}{4!12!}(0.15)^{4}(0.85)^{12}$.
b. 2.4, found by (0.15)(16).
c. 0.2100, found by 1 − 0.0743 − 0.2097 − 0.2775 − 0.2285.

57. a.

0	0.0002
1	0.0019
2	0.0116
3	0.0418
4	0.1020
5	0.1768
6	0.2234
7	0.2075
8	0.1405
9	0.0676
10	0.0220
11	0.0043
12	0.0004

b. $\mu = 12(0.52) = 6.24$.
$\sigma = \sqrt{12(0.52)(0.48)} = 1.7307$.
c. 0.1768.
d. 0.3343, found by 0.0002 + 0.0019 + 0.0116 + 0.0418 + 0.1020 + 0.1768.

59. a. 0.0498.
b. 0.7746, found by $(1 - 0.0498)^5$.

61. $\mu = 4.0$, from Appendix C.
a. 0.0183.
b. 0.1954.
c. 0.6289.
d. 0.5665.

63. a. 0.00005, found by $\frac{(18.4)e^{-18.4}}{4!}$.
b. Almost 0, found by $\frac{(18.4)e^{-18.4}}{0!}$.
c. 0.38489, found by 1 − 0.61511.

65. $P(0) = 0.98246$ and $P(2) = 0.00015$.

67. Let $\mu = np = 155(1/3709) = 0.042$.
$P(5) = \frac{0.042^5 e^{-0.042}}{5!} = 0.000000001$.
Very unlikely!

69. See the CD-ROM.

Chapter 6

1. a. 490 and 510, found by 500 ± 1(10).
b. 480 and 520, found by 500 ± 2(10).
c. 470 and 530, found by 500 ± 3(10).

3. a. 68.26 percent.
b. 95.44 percent.
c. 99.7 percent.

5. $Z_{Rob} = \frac{\$50\,000 - \$60\,000}{\$5000} = -2.00$

$Z_{Rachel} = \frac{\$50\,000 - \$35\,000}{\$8000} = 1.875$

Adjusting for their industries, Rob is well below average and Rachel well above.

7. a. .8413; .1587.
b. .1056; .8944.
c. .9977; .0023.
d. .0094; .9906.

9. a. 1.25, found by $z = \frac{25 - 20}{4.0} = 1.25$.
b. 0.3944 = 39.44 percent, found in Appendix D.
c. 0.3085 = 30.85 percent, found by $z = \frac{18 - 20}{4.0} = -0.5$.
Find 0.1915 in Appendix D for $z = -0.5$. Then, 0.5000 − 0.1915 = 0.3085.

11. a. 0.3413, found by $z = \frac{\$20 - \$16.50}{\$3.50} = 1.00$. Then, find 0.3413 in Appendix D for $z = 1$.
b. 0.1587, found by 0.5000 − 0.3413 = 0.1587.
c. 0.3336, found by $z = \frac{\$15.00 - \$16.50}{\$3.50} = -0.43$.
Find 0.1664 in Appendix D, for $z = -0.43$, then 0.5000 − 0.1664 = 0.3336.

13. a. 0.8276: First find $z = -1.5$, found by (44 − 50)/4 and $z = 1.25 = (55 - 50)/4$. The area between −1.5 and 0 is 0.4332 and the area between 0 and 1.25 is 0.3944, both from Appendix D. Then, adding the two areas, we find that 0.4332 + 0.3944 = 0.8276.
b. 0.1056, found by 0.5000 − 0.3994, where $z = 1.25$.
c. 0.2029: Recall that the area for $z = 1.25$ is 0.3944, and the area for $z = 0.5$, found by (52 − 50)/4, is 0.1915. Then subtract 0.3944 − 0.1915 and find 0.2029.

15. a. 0.1525, found by subtracting 0.4938 − 0.3413, which are the areas associated with z values of 2.5 and 1.00, respectively.
b. 0.0062, found by 0.5000 − 0.4938.
c. 0.9710, found by recalling that the area of the z-value of 2.5 is 0.4938. Then find $z = -2.00$, found by (205 − 225)/10. Thus, 0.4938 + 0.4772 = 0.9710.

17. a. 0.0764, found by $z = (20 - 15)/3.5 = 1.43$, then 0.5000 − 0.4236 = 0.0764.
b. 0.9236, found by 0.5000 + 0.4236, where $z = 1.43$.
c. 0.1185, found by $z = (12 - 15)/3.5 = -0.86$. The area under the curve is 0.3051, then $z = (10 - 15)/3.5 = -1.43$. The area is 0.4236. Finally, 0.4236 − 0.3051 = 0.1185.

19. $X = 56.58$, found by adding 0.5000 (the area left of the mean) and then finding a z-value that forces 45 percent of the data to fall inside the curve. Solving for X: $1.645 = (X - 50)/4 = 56.58$.

21. 200.7; find a z-value where 0.4900 of area is between 0 and z. That value is $z = 2.33$, then solve for X: $(X - 200)/0.3$ so $X = 200.7$.

23. \$1630, found by \$2100 − 1.88(\$250).

25. a. $\mu = np = 50(0.25) = 12.5$.
$\sigma^2 = np(1 - p) = 12.5(1 - 0.25) = 9.375$.
$\sigma = \sqrt{9.375} = 3.0619$.
b. 0.2578, found by (14.5 − 12.5)/3.0619 = 0.65. The area is 0.2422. Then, 0.5000 − 0.2422 = 0.2578.
c. 0.2578, found by (10.5 − 12.5)/3.0619 = −0.65. The area is 0.2422. Then, 0.5000 − 0.2422 = 0.2578.

27. **a.** 0.0192, found by 0.5000 − 0.4808.
b. 0.0694, found by 0.5000 − 0.4306.
c. 0.0502, found by 0.0694 − 0.0192.

29. **a.** Yes. (1) There are two mutually exclusive outcomes: overweight and not overweight. (2) It is the result of counting the number of successes (overweight members). (3) Each trial is independent. (4) The probability of 0.30 remains the same for each trial.
b. 0.0084, found by
$\mu = 500(0.30) = 150.$
$\sigma^2 = 500(0.30)(0.70) = 105.$
$\sigma = \sqrt{105} = 10.24695.$
$$z = \frac{X - \mu}{\sigma} = \frac{174.5 - 150}{10.24695} = 2.39.$$
The area under the curve for 2.39 is 0.4916. Then, 0.5000 − 0.4916 = 0.0084.
c. 0.8461, found by $z = \dfrac{139.5 - 150}{10.24695} = -1.02.$
The area between 139.5 and 150 is 0.3461. Adding 0.3461 + 0.5000 = 0.8461.

31. **a.** .9406 and .0594.
b. .9664 and .0336.
c. .2177 and .7823.
d. .0071 and .9929.

33. **a.** −0.71.
b. 0.2611 + 0.4686 = .7297 = 72.9 percent.
c. 0.2611 + 0.5 = .7611 = 76.11 percent.
d. 0.4251 + 0.5 = .9251 = 92.51 percent.
e. 0.0749 + 0.2389 = 0.3138 = 31.38 percent.
f. $0.84 = (X - 50)/7; X = 55.88.$

35. **a.** −0.4 for net sales, found by (170 − 180)/25. 2.92 for employees, found by (1850 − 1500)/120.
b. Net sales are 0.4 standard deviations below the mean. Employees is 2.92 standard deviations above the mean.
c. 65.54 percent of the aluminum fabricators have greater net sales compared with Clarion, found by 0.1554 + 0.5000. Only 0.18 percent have more employees than Clarion, found by 0.5000 − 0.4982.

37. **a.** Almost 0.5000, because $z = \dfrac{30 - 490}{90} = -5.11.$
b. 0.2514, found by 0.5000 − 0.2486.
c. 0.6374, found by 0.2486 + 0.3888.
d. 0.3450, found by 0.3888 − 0.0438.

39. **a.** 0.3015, found by 0.5000 − 0.1985.
b. 0.2579, found by 0.4564 − 0.1985.
c. 0.0011 = .11 percent, found by 0.5000 − 0.4989.
d. $1818, found by $1280 + 1.28($420).

41. **a.** 0.0026, found by 0.5000 − 0.4974.
b. 0.1129, found by 0.4772 − 0.3643.
c. 0.8617, found by 0.4974 + 0.3643.

43. About 4099 units, found by solving for X. $1.645 = (X - 4000)/60.$

45. **a.** 15.39 percent, found by (8 − 10.3)/2.25 = −1.02, then, 0.5000 − 0.3461 = 0.1539.
b. 17.31 percent, found by:
$z = (12 - 10.3)/2.25 = 0.76.$ Area is 0.2764.
$z = (14 - 10.3)/2.25 = 1.64.$ Area is 0.4495.
The area between 12 and 14 is 0.1731, found by 0.4495 − 0.2764.
c. Yes, but it is rather remote. Reasoning: On 99.73 percent of the days, returns are between 3.55 and 17.03, found by 10.3 ± 3(2.25). Thus, the chance of less than 3.55 returns is rather remote.

47. **a.** (30 − 26.3)/4.5 = 0.82. Then, 0.2939 + 0.5000 = 0.7939.
b. (18 − 20.7)/5.1 = −0.53. Then, 0.2019 + 0.5000 = 0.7019.
c. 36.8 hrs; 32.6 hrs.

49. **a.** (37 − 39.5)/1.5 = −1.67. Then, 0.4525 + 0.5 = 0.9575.
b. (41.5 − 39.5)/1.5 = 1.33. Then, 0.4082 + 0.5 = 0.9082.
c. (36 − 39.5)/1.5 = −2.33. Then, 0.4901 − 0.4525 = 0.0376.
d. 0.0099 + 0.0475 = 0.0574.

51. **a.** 0.9678, found by:
$\mu = 60(0.64) = 38.4.$
$\sigma^2 = 60(0.64)(0.36) = 13.824.$
$\sigma = \sqrt{13.824} = 3.72.$
Then, (31.5 − 38.4)/3.72 = −1.85, for which the area is 0.4678. Then, 0.5000 + 0.4678 = 0.9678.
b. 0.0853, found by (43.5 − 38.4)/3.72 = 1.37, for which the area is 0.4147. Then, 0.5000 − 0.4147 = 0.0853.
c. 0.8084, found by 0.4441 + 0.3643.
d. 0.0348, found by 0.4495 − 0.4147.

53. 0.0968, found by:
$\mu = 50(0.40) = 20.$
$\sigma^2 = 50(0.40)(0.60) = 12.$
$\sigma = \sqrt{12} = 3.4641.$
$z = (24.5 - 20)/3.4641 = 1.30.$
The area is 0.4032. Then, for 25 or more, 0.5000 − 0.4032 = 0.0968.

55. **a.** $1.645 = (45 - \mu)/5. \quad \mu = 36.78.$
b. $1.645 = (45 - \mu)/10. \quad \mu = 28.55.$
c. $z = (30 - 28.5)/10 = 0.15$, then, 0.5000 + 0.0596 = 0.5596.

57. **a.** $\dfrac{2 - 3.1}{0.3} = -3.67. \quad \dfrac{3 - 3.1}{0.3} = -0.33.$
0.3707, found by 0.5000 − 0.1293.
b. Almost 0.
c. 0.0228, found by 0.5000 − 0.4772; leads to 228 students, found by 10 000(0.0228).
d. 3.484, found by 3.1 + 1.28(0.3).

59. **a.** 21.19 percent found by $z = (3 - 3.1)/0.125 = -0.80$; so, 0.5000 − 0.2881 = 0.2119.
b. Increase the mean. $z = (3-3.15)/0.125 = -1.2$; probability is 0.5000 − 0.3849 = 0.1151. Reduce the standard deviation. $z = (3 - 3.1)/0.1 = -1.0$; the probability = 0.500 − 0.3413 = 0.1587.
Increasing the mean is better because a smaller percent of the hams will be below the limit.

61. **a.** $z = (100 - 85)/8 = 1.88$, so, 0.5000 − 0.4699 = 0.0301= 3.01 percent.
b. Let $z = 0.67$, so, $0.67 = (X - 85)/8$ and $X = 90.36$, set mileage at 90 360.
c. $z = (72 - 85)/8 = -1.63$, so, 0.5000 − 0.4484 = 0.0516 = 5.16 percent.

63. $\dfrac{470 - \mu}{\sigma} = 0.25. \quad \dfrac{500 - \mu}{\sigma} = 1.28.$
$\sigma = 29.126$ and $\mu = 462.719.$

65. $\mu = 150(0.15) = 22.5. \quad \sigma = \sqrt{150(0.15)(0.85)} = 4.3732.$
$z = (30.5 - 22.5)/4.3732 = 1.83.$
$P(z > 1.83) = 0.5000 - 0.4664 = 0.0336.$

67. See the CD-ROM.

Chapter 7

1. a. 303 Louisiana Av, 5155 S. Main, 3501 Monroe St, 2652 W. Central.
   b. Answers will vary.
   c. 630 Dixie Hwy, 835 S. McCord Rd, 4624 Woodville Rd.
   d. Answers will vary.
3. Systematic random sampling.
5. a.

Sample	Values	Sum	Mean
1	12, 12	24	12
2	12, 14	26	13
3	12, 16	28	14
4	12, 14	26	13
5	12, 16	28	14
6	14, 16	30	15

   b. $\mu_{\bar{X}} = (12 + 13 + 14 + 13 + 14 + 15)/6 = 13.5.$
   $\mu = (12 + 12 + 14 + 16)/4 = 13.5.$
   c. More dispersion with population data compared to the sample means. The sample means vary from 12 to 15, whereas the population varies from 12 to 16.
7. a.

Sample	Values	Sum	Mean
1	12, 12, 14	38	12.67
2	12, 12, 15	39	13.00
3	12, 12, 20	44	14.67
4	14, 15, 20	49	16.33
5	12, 14, 15	41	13.67
6	12, 14, 15	41	13.67
7	12, 15, 20	47	15.67
8	12, 15, 20	47	15.67
9	12, 14, 20	46	15.33
10	12, 14, 20	46	15.33

   b. $\mu_{\bar{X}} = \dfrac{(12.67 + \cdots + 15.33 + 15.33)}{10} = 14.6.$
   $\mu = (12 + 12 + 14 + 15 + 20)/5 = 14.6.$
   c. The dispersion of the population is greater than that of the sample means. The sample means vary from 12.67 to 16.33, whereas the population varies from 12 to 20.
9. a. 20, found by ${}_6C_3$.
   b.

Sample	Cases	Sum	Mean
Ruud, Austin, Sass	3, 6, 3	12	4.00
Ruud, Sass, Palmer	3, 3, 3	9	3.00
.	.	.	.
.	.	.	.
.	.	.	.
Sass, Palmer, Schueller	3, 3, 1	7	2.33

   c. $\mu_{\bar{X}} = \dfrac{53.33}{20} = 2.667.$
   $\mu = (3 + 6 + 3 + 3 + 1 + 0)/6 = 2.667.$ They are equal.
   d.

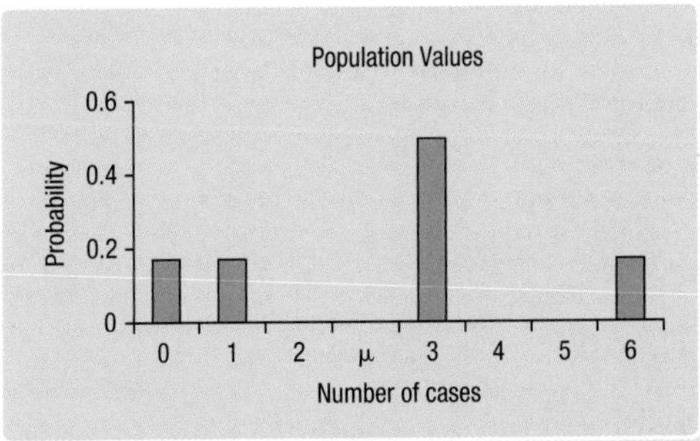

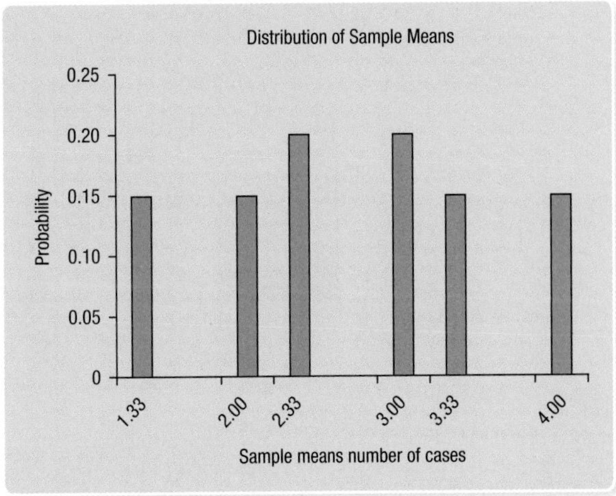

Sample Mean	Number of Means	Probability
1.33	3	0.1500
2.00	3	0.1500
2.33	5	0.2500
3.00	3	0.1500
3.33	3	0.1500
4.00	3	0.1500
Total	20	1.0000

The population has more dispersion than the sample means. The sample means vary from 1.33 to 4.0. The population varies from 0 to 6.

11. a.

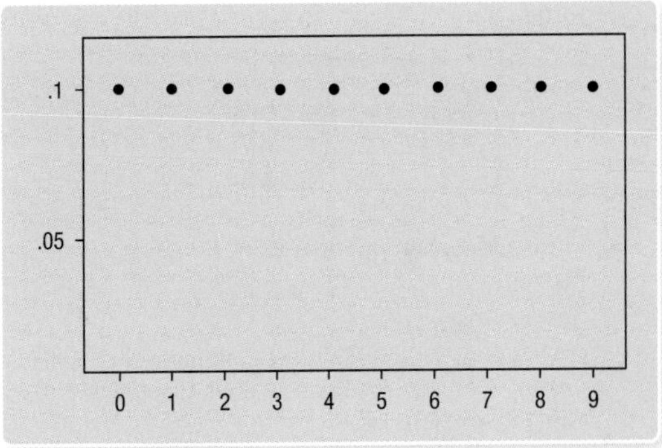

$$\mu = \frac{0 + 1 + \cdots + 9}{10} = 4.5$$

   b.

Sample	Sum	$\bar{X}$
1	11	2.2
2	31	6.2
3	21	4.2
4	24	4.8
5	21	4.2
6	20	4.0
7	23	4.6
8	29	5.8
9	35	7.0
10	27	5.4

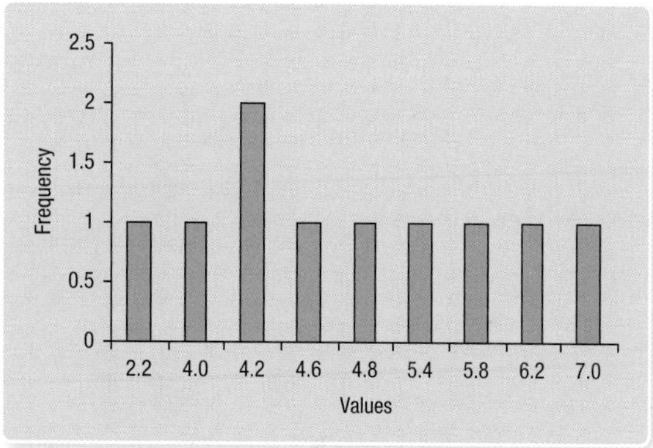

The mean of the 10 sample means is 4.84, which is close to the population mean of 4.5. The sample means range from 2.2 to 7.0, whereas the population values range from 0 to 9. From the above graph, the sample means tend to cluster between 4 and 5.

13. **a.** Answers will vary.
b. Answers will vary.
c. The sample distribution should be more bell-shaped.

15. **a.** $z = \dfrac{63 - 60}{12/\sqrt{9}} = 0.75.$
$P = .2266$, found by $.5000 - .2734$.
b. $z = \dfrac{56 - 60}{12/\sqrt{9}} = -1.00.$
$P = .1587$, found by $.5000 - .3413$.
c. $P = .6147$, found by $.3413 + .2734$.

17. $z = \dfrac{950 - 1200}{250/\sqrt{50}} = -7.07$. So, probability is very close to 1, or virtually certain.

19. $\sqrt{\dfrac{.45(1 - .45)}{200}} = 0.035178.$

21. $z = (.06 - .02)/\sqrt{\dfrac{.02(1 - .02)}{50}} = 2.02$; then, $0.5 - .4783 = 0.0217$.

23. $z = (.80 - .75)/\sqrt{\dfrac{.75(1 - .75)}{300}} = 2$; then, $0.5 + .4772 = 0.9772$.

25. **a.** Formal Man, Summit Stationers, Bootleggers, Leather Ltd, Petries.
b. Answers may vary.
c. GAP, Frederick's of Hollywood, Summit Stationers, M Studios, Leather Ltd., Things Remembered, County Seat, Coach House Gifts, Regis Hairstylists.

27. The difference between a sample statistic and the population parameter. Yes, the difference could be zero. The sample mean and the population parameter are equal.

29. Use of either a proportional or nonproportional stratified random sample would be appropriate. For example, suppose the number of banks in the Southwest were as follows:

Assets	Number	Percent of Total
\$500 million and more	20	2.0
\$100 to under \$500 million	324	32.4
Less than \$100 million	656	65.6
Total	1000	100.0

For a proportional stratified sample, if the sample size is 100, then 2 banks with assets of \$500 million would be selected, 32 medium-size banks, and 66 small banks. For a nonproportional sample, 10 or even all 20 large banks could be selected and fewer medium- and small-size banks and the sample results weighted by the appropriate percents of the total.

31. **a.** We selected 60, 104, 75, 72, and 48. Answers will vary.
b. We selected the third observation. So, the sample consists of 75, 72, 68, 82, 48. Answers will vary.
c. Use a stratified random sample.

33. **a.** 15, found by ${}_6C_2$.
b.

Sample	Value	Sum	Mean
1	79, 64	143	71.5
2	79, 84	163	81.5
.	.	.	.
.	.	.	.
.	.	.	.
15	92, 77	169	84.5
Total			1195.0

c. $\mu_{\bar{X}} = 79.67$, found by 1195/15.
$\mu = 79.67$, found by 478/6.
They are equal.
d. No. The student is not graded on all available information. He/she is as likely to get a lower grade based on the sample as a higher grade. Dropping a lower grade is preferable.

35. **a.** 10, found by ${}_5C_2$.
b.

Number of Shutdowns	Mean	Number of Shutdowns	Mean
4, 3	3.5	3, 3	3.0
4, 5	4.5	3, 2	2.5
4, 3	3.5	5, 3	4.0
4, 2	3.0	5, 2	3.5
3, 5	4.0	3, 2	2.5

Sample Mean	Frequency	Probability
2.5	2	0.20
3.0	2	0.20
3.5	3	0.30
4.0	2	0.20
4.5	1	0.10
Total	10	1.00

c. $\mu_{\bar{X}} = (3.5 + 4.5 + \cdots + 2.5)/10 = 3.4.$
$\mu = (4 + 3 + 5 + 3 + 2)/5 = 3.4.$
The two means are equal.
d. The population values are relatively uniform in shape. The distribution of sample means tends toward normality.

37. **a.** The sampling distribution will be normal.
b. $\sigma_{\bar{X}} = \dfrac{5.5}{\sqrt{25}} = 1.1.$
c. $z = \dfrac{36 - 35}{5.5/\sqrt{25}} = 0.91.$
$P = 0.1814$, found by $0.5000 - 0.3186$.
d. $z = \dfrac{34.5 - 35}{5.5/\sqrt{25}} = -0.45.$
$P = 0.6736$, found by $0.5000 + 0.1736$.
e. 0.4922, found by $0.3186 + 0.1736$.

39. $z = \dfrac{\$335 - \$350}{\$45/\sqrt{40}} = -2.11.$
$P = 0.9826$, found by $0.5000 + 0.4826$.

41. $z = \dfrac{31.5 - 30.6}{2.5/\sqrt{60}} = 2.79$. So, probability is 0.9974, found by $0.5000 + 0.4974$.

43. Between 2679 and 2721, found by $2700 \pm 1.96(68/\sqrt{40})$.

45. $z = \frac{900 - 947}{205/\sqrt{60}} = -1.78.$
$P = 0.0375$, found by $0.5000 - 0.4625$.

47. $z = \frac{(73 - 69)}{12.5/\sqrt{50}} = 2.26.$
Area = 0.0119, 1.19 percent, found by $0.5 - 0.4881$.

49. $z = (.3 - .25)/\sqrt{\frac{.25(1-.25)}{200}} = 1.63$; then, $0.5 + 0.4484 = 0.9484$.

51. a. $z = (.85 - .90)/\sqrt{\frac{.90(1-.90)}{300}} = -2.892$; then, $0.5 + 0.4981 = 0.9981$.
b. $z = (.92 - .90)/\sqrt{\frac{.90(1-.90)}{300}} = 1.15$; then, $0.5 - 0.3749 = 0.1251$.
c. $0.4981 + 0.1251 = 0.6232$.

53. See the CD-ROM.

Chapter 8

1. 51.314 and 58.686, found by $55 \pm 2.58(10/\sqrt{49})$.

3. a. 1.581, found by $\sigma_{\bar{X}} = 5/\sqrt{10}$.
b. The population is normally distributed and the population variance is known.
c. 16.901 and 23.099, found by 20 ± 3.099.

5. a. 0.95, found by $4.75/\sqrt{25}$.
b. 14.64 to 19.06, found by $16.85 \pm 2.33(4.75/\sqrt{25})$.
c. Decrease.

7. a. \$20. It is our best estimate of the population mean.
b. \$18.60 and \$21.40, found by $\$20 \pm 1.96(\$5/\sqrt{49})$. About 95 percent of the intervals similarly constructed will include the population mean.

9. a. 40 litres.
b. 36.675 and 43.325, found by $40 \pm 2.58(10/\sqrt{60})$.
c. If 100 such intervals were determined, the population mean would be included in about 99 intervals.

11. a. 2.201.
b. 1.729.
c. 3.499.

13. a. 5.8697, found by $26.25/\sqrt{20}$.
b. 64.85 to 85.15, found by $75 \pm 1.729(5.8697)$.
c. Increase.

15. a. The population mean is unknown, but the best estimate is 20, the sample mean.
b. Use the t distribution as the population standard deviation is unknown. However, we must assume that the population is normally distributed.
c. 2.093.
d. Between 19.06 and 20.94, found by $20 \pm 2.093(2/\sqrt{20})$.
e. Neither value is reasonable, because they are not inside the interval.

17. Between 95.39 and 101.81, found by $98.6 \pm 1.833(5.54/\sqrt{10})$.

19. a. 0.375, found by 75/200.
b. 0.342, found by $\sqrt{\frac{(.375)(1-.375)}{200}} = .0342$.
c. 0.319 to 0.431, found by $.375 \pm 1.645(.0342)$.
d. If 200 such intervals were determined, the population proportion would be included in about 180 intervals.

21. a. 0.8, found by 80/100.
b. 0.04, found by $\sqrt{\frac{0.8(1-0.8)}{100}}$.
c. Between 0.72 and 0.88, found by $0.8 \pm 1.96\left(\sqrt{\frac{0.8(1-0.8)}{100}}\right)$.
d. We are reasonably sure the population proportion is between 72 and 88 percent.

23. a. 0.625, found by 250/400.
b. 0.0242, found by $\sqrt{\frac{.625(1-.625)}{400}}$.
c. Between 0.563 and 0.687, found by $0.625 \pm 2.58\left(\sqrt{\frac{0.625(1-0.625)}{400}}\right)$.
d. We are reasonably sure the population proportion is between 56 and 69 percent.

25. 33.465 and 36.535, found by $35 \pm 1.96\left(\frac{5}{\sqrt{36}}\right)\sqrt{\frac{300-36}{300-1}}$.

27. 1.689 up to 2.031, found by $1.86 \pm 2.58\left(\frac{0.50}{\sqrt{50}}\right)\sqrt{\frac{400-50}{400-1}}$.

29. 0.019 to 0.114, found by
$.066667 \pm 1.645\sqrt{\frac{.667(1-.667)}{75}} \cdot \sqrt{\frac{500-75}{500-1}}$. Since 10/75 = .13, it would not be reasonable as .13 is not in the CI.

31. 97, found by $n = \left[\frac{1.96 \times 10}{2}\right]^2 = 96.04$.

33. 196, found by $n = .15(.85)\left(\frac{1.96}{.05}\right)^2 = 195.9216$.

35. 554, found by $n = \left(\frac{1.96 \times 3}{0.25}\right)^2 = 553.19$.

37. a. 577, found by $n = .60(.40)\left(\frac{1.96}{.04}\right)^2 = 576.24$.
b. 601, found by $n = .50(.50)\left(\frac{1.96}{.04}\right)^2 = 600.25$.

39. 6.13 years to 6.87 years, found by $6.5 \pm 1.989(1.7/\sqrt{85})$.

41. a. Between \$1.27 to \$1.33, found by $1.30 \pm 2.680(0.07/\sqrt{50})$.
b. \$1.40 is not reasonable because it is outside of the confidence interval.

43. a. Between 7.22 and 8.78, found by $8 \pm 1.685(3/\sqrt{40})$.
b. 9 is not reasonable because it is outside of the confidence interval.

45. a. 65.5 up to 71.7 hours, found by $68.6 \pm 2.680(8.2/\sqrt{50})$.
b. The value suggested by the manager is included in the confidence interval. Therefore, it is reasonable.
c. Changing the confidence level to 95 percent would reduce the width of the interval. The value of 2.680 would change to 2.010.

47. 62, found by $n = \left(\frac{1.96 \times 16}{4}\right)^2 = 61.5$.

49. Between \$13 734 up to \$15 028, found by $\$14\,381 \pm 1.711(\$1892/\sqrt{25})$. 15 000 is reasonable because it is inside of the confidence interval.

51. a. \$62.583, found by \$751/12.
b. Between \$60.54 and \$64.63, found by $62.583 \pm 1.796(3.94/\sqrt{12})$.
c. \$60 is not reasonable, because it is outside of the confidence interval.

53. **a.** 89.4667, found by 1342/15.
b. Between 84.99 and 93.94, found by $89.4667 \pm 2.145(8.08/\sqrt{15})$.
c. Yes, because even the lower limit of the confidence interval is above 80.

55. Between .647 and .753, found by $0.7 \pm 2.58\left(\sqrt{\frac{0.7(1-0.7)}{500}}\right)$.
Yes, because even the lower limit of the confidence interval is above .500.

57. \$52.56 and \$55.44, found by
$$\$54.00 \pm 1.96\left(\frac{\$4.50}{\sqrt{35}}\right)\left(\sqrt{\frac{(500-35)}{500-1}}\right).$$

59. 369, found by $n = 0.60(1 - 0.60)[1.96/0.05]^2$.

61. 97, found by $[(1.96 \times 500)/100]^2$.

63. **a.** 708.13, rounded up to 709, found by $0.21(1 - 0.21)[1.96/0.03]^2$.
b. 1068, found by $0.50(0.50)(1.96/0.03)^2$.

65. Between .573 and .653, found by
$$0.613 \pm 2.58\left(\sqrt{\frac{0.613(1-0.613)}{1000}}\right).$$
Yes, because even the lower limit of the confidence interval is above .500.

67. Between 12.69 and 14.11, found by $13.4 \pm 1.96(6.8/\sqrt{352})$.

69. See the CD-ROM.

71. See the CD-ROM.

Chapter 9

1. **a.** $H_0 = 2; H_1 \neq 2$.
b. $H_0 \geq 40; H_1 < 40$.
c. $H_0 \leq 1750; H_1 > 1750$.
d. $H_0 = 3.25; H_1 \neq 3.25$.

3. **a.** Two-tailed.
b. Reject H_0 and accept H_1 when z does not fall in the region from −1.96 and 1.96.
c. −1.2, found by $z = (49 - 50)/(5/\sqrt{36}) = -1.2$.
d. Not enough evidence to reject H_0 and conclude the mean is not different from 50.
e. $p = 0.2302$, found by 2(0.5000 − 0.3849). A 23.02 percent chance of finding a z-value this large when H_0 is true.

5. **a.** One-tailed.
b. Reject H_0 and accept H_1 when $z > 1.645$.
c. 1.2, found by $z = (21 - 20)/(5/\sqrt{36}) = 1.2$.
d. Not enough evidence to reject H_0 at the .05 significance level.
e. $p = .1151$, found by .5000 − .3849. An 11.51 percent chance of finding a z-value this large or larger.

7. **a.** H_0: $\mu = 96\,600$; H_1: $\mu \neq 96\,600$.
b. Reject H_0 if $z < -1.96$ or $z > 1.96$.
c. −0.69, found by: $z = \frac{95\,795 - 96\,600}{(8050/\sqrt{48})}$.
d. There is not enough evidence to reject H_0 at the .05 significance level.
e. $p = .4902$, found by 2(.5000 − .2549). Crosset's experience is not different from that claimed by the manufacturer. If H_0 is true, the probability of finding a value more extreme than this is .4902.

9. **a.** H_0: $\mu \geq 6.8$; H_1: $\mu < 6.8$.
b. Reject H_0 if $z < -2.33$.
c. −7.2, found by $z = \frac{6.2 - 6.8}{(0.5/\sqrt{36})}$.
d. Reject H_0 at a significance level of .01.
e. The p-value is almost zero; the mean number of DVDs watched is less than 6.8 per month. If H_0 is true, there is virtually no chance of getting a statistic this small.

11. **a.** Reject H_0 when $t > 1.833$.
b. $t = \frac{12 - 10}{(3/\sqrt{10})} = 2.108$.
c. Reject H_0. The mean is greater than 10.

13. H_0: $\mu \leq 40$; H_1: $\mu > 40$. Choose a significance level of .05. Reject H_0 if $t > 1.703$.
$$t = \frac{42 - 40}{(2.1/\sqrt{28})} = 5.040$$
Reject H_0 and conclude that the mean number of calls is greater than 40 per week.

15. H_0: $\mu \leq 35\,600$; H_1: $\mu > 35\,600$.
Reject H_0 if $t > 1.740$.
$$t = \frac{37\,675 - 35\,600}{(2415/\sqrt{18})} = 3.645.$$
Reject H_0 and conclude that the claim is true.

17. **a.** Reject H_0 if $t < -3.747$.
b. $\bar{X} = 17$ and $s = \sqrt{\frac{1495 - (85)^2/5}{5-1}} = 3.536$.
$$t = \frac{17 - 20}{(3.536/\sqrt{5})} = -1.90.$$
c. There is not enough evidence to reject H_0. We cannot conclude the population mean is less than 20.
d. Between .05 and .10, about .065. (By computer, the p-value = 0.0653.)

19. H_0: $\mu \leq 4.35$; H_1: $\mu > 4.35$.
Reject H_0 if $t > 2.821$.
$$t = \frac{4.368 - 4.35}{(0.0339/\sqrt{10})} = 1.68.$$
Do not reject H_0. The additive did not increase the mean mass of the puppies. The p-value is between .10 and .05. (Using a computer, the p-value = .0639)

21. H_0: $\mu \leq 4.0$; H_1: $\mu > 4.0$.
Reject H_0 if $t > 1.796$.
$$t = \frac{4.50 - 4.0}{(2.68/\sqrt{12})} = .65.$$
Do not reject H_0. The mean number of kilometres travelled has not been shown to be greater than 4.0. The p-value is greater than .10. (Using a computer, the p-value = 0.2657)

23. **a.** H_0 is rejected if $z > 1.645$.
b. 1.09, found by $z = (.75 - .70)/\sqrt{(.70 \times .30)/100}$.
c. H_0 is not rejected.

25. **a.** H_0: $p \leq .52$; H_1: $p > .52$.
b. H_0 is rejected if $z > 2.33$.
c. 1.62, found by $z = (.5667 - .52)/\sqrt{(0.52 \times 0.48)/300}$.
d. H_0 is not rejected. We cannot conclude that the proportion of men driving on Highway 400 is larger than .52.

27. **a.** H_0: $p \geq .90$; H_1: $p < .90$.
b. H_0 is rejected if $z < -2.33$.
c. −2.67, found by $z = (.82 - .90)/\sqrt{(.90 \times .10)/100}$.
d. H_0 is rejected. Fewer than 90 percent of the customers received their orders in less than 10 minutes.

29. H_0: $\mu \geq 10$; H_1: $\mu < 10$.
Reject H_0 if $z < -1.645$.

$$z = \frac{9.0 - 10.0}{2.8/\sqrt{50}} = -2.53.$$

Reject H_0. The mean weight loss is less than 10 pounds. The p-value $= 0.5000 - 0.4943 = 0.0057$

31. H_0: $\mu \geq 7$; H_1: $\mu < 7$.
Reject H_0 if $t < -1.6765$ at the 5% significance level.

$$t = \frac{(6.8 - 7)}{0.9/\sqrt{50}} = -1.57.$$

The p-value is .0613, so at a significance level of .05, do not reject the null hypothesis. University students sleep no less than the typical adult male.

33. H_0: $\mu = \$60\,000$; H_1: $\mu \neq \$60\,000$.
Reject H_0 if $z < 1.645$ or $z > 1.645$.

$$z = \frac{62500 - 60000}{6000/\sqrt{120}} = 4.56.$$

Reject H_0. We can conclude that the mean salary is not \$60 000. The p-value is very close to zero. The confidence interval is from \$61 599 to \$63 401. As \$60 000 falls outside of the confidence interval, the hypothesized mean is rejected.

35. H_0: $\mu \leq 1.25$; H_1: $\mu > 1.25$.
Reject H_0 if $t > 1.691$.

$$z = \frac{1.27 - 1.25}{0.05/\sqrt{35}} = 2.37.$$

Reject H_0. The mean price of gasoline is greater than \$1.25. The p-value = .0119 (by computer).

37. H_0: $p \leq 0.60$; H_1: $p > 0.60$.
H_0 is rejected if $z > 2.33$.

$$z = \frac{0.70 - 0.60}{\sqrt{(0.60 \times 0.40)/200}} = 2.89.$$

H_0 is rejected. Ms. Dennis is correct. More than 60 percent of the accounts are more than 3 months old.

39. H_0: $p \leq 0.44$; H_1: $p > 0.44$.
H_0 is rejected if $z > 1.645$.

$$z = \frac{0.48 - 0.44}{\sqrt{(0.44 \times 0.56)/1000}} = 2.55.$$

H_0 is rejected. We conclude that there has been an increase in the proportion of people wanting to go to Europe.

41. H_0: $p \leq 0.20$; H_1: $p > 0.20$.
H_0 is rejected if $z > 2.33$.

$$z = \frac{(56/200) - 0.20}{\sqrt{(0.20 \times 0.80)/200}} = 2.83.$$

H_0 is rejected. More than 20 percent of the owners move during a particular year. The p-value $= .5000 - .4977 = 0.0023$.

43. H_0: $\mu \leq 42$; H_1: $\mu > 42$.
Reject H_0 if $t > 1.796$.

$$t = \frac{51 - 42}{8/\sqrt{12}} = 3.90.$$

Reject H_0. The mean time for delivery is more than 42 days. The p-value is less than .005. Using a computer, the p-value $= 0.0012$.

45. H_0: $\mu = 1.92$; H_1: $\mu \neq 1.92$.
Reject H_0 if $t < -2.201$ or $t > 2.201$.

$\bar{X} = 2.087$ $\quad s_d = 0.4048.$

$$t = \frac{2.087 - 1.92}{0.4048/\sqrt{12}} = 1.429.$$

Do not reject H_0. There is not a difference in the mean amount of water consumed at the college surveyed and the national average. The confidence interval is from 1.82944 to 2.34389. The hypothesized mean falls in the confidence interval, and so H_0 is not rejected.

47. H_0: $\mu \geq 6$; H_1: $\mu < 6$.
Reject H_0 if $t < -2.998$ [assuming the population is normally distributed].

$$t = \frac{5.6375 - 6}{0.6346/\sqrt{8}} = -1.62.$$

Do not reject H_0. The mean rate could be 6.0 percent. The p-value is .075.

49. H_0: $\mu \geq 6.5$; H_1: $\mu < 6.5$.
Reject H_0 if $t < -2.178$.
$\bar{X} = 5.1667$. $\quad s = 3.1575$.

$$t = \frac{5.1667 - 6.5}{3.1575/\sqrt{12}} = -1.463.$$

Do not reject H_0. The mean number is not less than 6.5.

51. H_0: $\mu = 0$; H_1: $\mu \neq 0$.
Reject H_0 if $t < -2.110$ or $t > 2.110$.
$\bar{X} = -0.2322$. $\quad s = 0.3120$.

$$t = \frac{-0.2322 - 0}{0.3120/\sqrt{18}} = -3.158.$$

Reject H_0. The mean gain or loss does not equal 0. The p-value is less than .01, but greater than .001. So, the probability of no time gain or loss is very small. Using a computer, the p-value $= 0.0057$, and as this is less than the significance level, the null hypothesis is rejected.

53. H_0: $\mu \geq 8$; H_1: $\mu < 8$.
Reject H_0 if $t < -1.714$.

$$t = \frac{7.5 - 8}{3.2/\sqrt{24}} = -.77.$$

Do not reject the null hypothesis. The time is not less.

55. H_0: $p = 0.50$; H_1: $p \neq 0.50$.
Reject H_0 if z is not between -1.96 and 1.96.

$$z = \frac{0.482 - 0.500}{\sqrt{(0.5)(0.5)/1002}} = -1.14.$$

Do not reject the null hypothesis. There is not enough evidence to indicate that the results have changed.

57. See the CD-ROM.

59. See the CD-ROM.

Chapter 10

1. **a.** Two-tailed test.

b. Reject H_0 if $z < -2.05$ or $z > 2.05$.

c. $$z = \frac{102 - 99}{\sqrt{\dfrac{5^2}{40} + \dfrac{6^2}{50}}} = 2.59.$$

d. Reject H_0.

e. p-value $= 0.0096$, found by $2(.5000 - .4952)$.

3. **Step 1** H_0: $\mu_1 - \mu_2 \geq 0$. $\quad H_1$: $\mu_1 - \mu_2 < 0$.

Step 2 The .05 significance level was chosen.

Step 3 Reject H_0 if $z < -1.645$.

Step 4 -0.83, found by:

$$z = \frac{3.5 - 3.7}{\sqrt{\dfrac{(1.05)^2}{40} + \dfrac{(1.3)^2}{55}}} = -0.83.$$

Step 5 There is not enough evidence to reject H_0. Babies using the Gibbs brand did not gain less weight. The p-value is 0.2033, found by (.5 − .2967).

5. Two-tailed test, because we are trying to show that a difference exists between the two means.
Reject H_0 if $z < -2.58$ or $z > 2.58$.

$$z = \frac{31.4 - 34.9}{\sqrt{\frac{(5.1)^2}{32} + \frac{(6.7)^2}{49}}} = -2.66.$$

Reject H_0 at the .01 level. There is a difference in the mean turnover rate. The p-value = 2(.5000 − .4961) = 0.0078. The p-value is < the significance level; therefore, reject H_0.

7. **a.** H_0 is rejected if $z > 1.645$.
b. .64, found by $p_c = \dfrac{70 + 90}{100 + 150}$.
c. 1.61, found by

$$z = \frac{0.70 - 0.60}{\sqrt{[(0.64 \times 0.36)/100] + [(0.64 \times 0.36)/150]}}.$$

d. There is not enough evidence to reject H_0.
e. The p-value is 0.0537, found by (.5 − .4463). Since the p-value > the significance level, there is not enough evidence to reject the null hypothesis.

9. **a.** $H_0: p_1 - p_2 = 0. \quad H_1: p_1 - p_2 \neq 0.$
b. H_0 is rejected if $z < -1.96$ or $z > 1.96$.
c. $p_c = \dfrac{24 + 40}{400 + 400} = .08.$
d. −2.09, found by

$$z = \frac{0.06 - 0.10}{\sqrt{[(0.08 \times 0.92)/400] + [(0.08 \times 0.92)/400]}}.$$

e. H_0 is rejected. The proportion infested is not the same in the two fields. The p-value = 2(.5 − .4817) = 0.0366. The p-value is < than the significance level, and therefore, H_0 is rejected.

11. $H_0: p_d - p_r \leq 0. \quad H_1: p_d - p_r > 0.$
H_0 is rejected if $z > 2.05$.

$$p_c = \frac{168 + 200}{800 + 1000} = .2044.$$

$$z = \frac{0.21 - 0.20}{\sqrt{\frac{(0.2044)(0.7956)}{800} + \frac{(0.2044)(0.7956)}{1000}}} = 0.52.$$

There is not enough evidence to reject H_0. There is no difference in the proportion of Conservatives and Liberals who favour lowering the standards. The p-value = .5 − .1985 = 0.3015. The p-value is > than the significance level, and therefore, there is not enough evidence to reject H_0.

13. **a.** Reject H_0 if $t > 2.120$ or $t < -2.120$, $df = 10 + 8 - 2 = 16$.
b. $s_p^2 = \dfrac{(10-1)(4)^2 + (8-1)(5)^2}{10 + 8 - 2} = 19.9375.$
c. $t = \dfrac{23 - 26}{\sqrt{19.9375\left(\frac{1}{10} + \frac{1}{8}\right)}} = -1.416.$
d. There is not enough evidence to reject H_0.
e. The p-value is greater than .10 and less than .20. The actual p-value = 0.1758.

15. $H_0: \mu_1 - \mu_2 \leq 0. \quad H_1: \mu_1 - \mu_2 > 0. \quad df = 9 + 7 - 2 = 14.$
Reject H_0 if $t > 2.624$.

$$s_p^2 = \frac{(7-1)(6.88)^2 + (9-1)(9.49)^2}{7 + 9 - 2} = 71.749.$$

$$t = \frac{79 - 78}{\sqrt{71.749\left(\frac{1}{7} + \frac{1}{9}\right)}} = 0.234.$$

There is not enough evidence to reject H_0. The mean grade of women is not higher than that of men. The p-value = 0.4090, which is > than the significance level and supports the decision.

17. $H_0: \mu_s - \mu_a \leq 0. \quad H_1: \mu_s - \mu_a > 0. \quad df = 6 + 7 - 2 = 11.$
Reject H_0 if $t > 1.363$.

$$s_p^2 = \frac{(6-1)(12.2)^2 + (7-1)(15.8)^2}{6 + 7 - 2} = 203.82.$$

$$t = \frac{141.5 - 130.3}{\sqrt{203.82\left(\frac{1}{6} + \frac{1}{7}\right)}} = 1.536.$$

Reject H_0. The mean daily expenses are greater for the sales staff. The p-value is between .05 and .10, which is < than the significance level, and so H_0 is rejected.

19. **a.** Reject H_0 if $t > 2.353$.
b. $\bar{d} = \dfrac{4}{4} = 1.00. \quad s_d = \sqrt{\dfrac{38 - 4^2/4}{3}} = 3.367.$
c. $t = \dfrac{1.00}{3.367/\sqrt{4}} = .59.$
d. There is not enough evidence to reject H_0. There is no difference in defective parts produced on the day or afternoon shift.

21. $H_0: \mu_d \leq 0. \quad H_1: \mu_d > 0.$
$\bar{d} = 25.917.$
$s_d = 40.791.$
Reject H_0 if $t > 1.796$

$$t = \frac{25.917}{40.791/\sqrt{12}} = 2.20.$$

Reject H_0. The incentive plan resulted in an increase in daily income. The p-value is about 0.025, which is < than the significance level, and so reject H_0.

23. $H_0: \mu_1 - \mu_2 = 0. \quad H_1: \mu_1 - \mu_2 \neq 0.$
Reject H_0 if $t < -2.645$ or $t > 2.645$.

$$s_p^2 = \frac{(35-1)(4.48)^2 + (40-1)(3.86)^2}{35 + 40 - 2} = 17.31.$$

$$t = \frac{24.51 - 22.69}{\sqrt{17.31\left(\frac{1}{35} + \frac{1}{40}\right)}} = 1.87.$$

There is not enough evidence to reject the null hypothesis. There is no difference in the means. The p-value is 0.0627, which is > than the significance level, and confirms that there is not enough evidence to reject H_0.

25. $H_0: \mu_1 - \mu_2 = 0. \quad H_1: \mu_1 - \mu_2 \neq 0.$
Reject H_0 if $z < -2.58$ or $z > 2.58$.

$$z = \frac{36.2 - 37.0}{\sqrt{\frac{(1.14)^2}{35} + \frac{(1.30)^2}{40}}} = -2.84.$$

Reject H_0. There is a difference in the useful life of the two brands of paint. The p-value is 0.0046, found by 2(.5000 − .4977). Since the p-value is < than the significance level, H_0 is rejected.

27. $H_0: \mu_1 - \mu_2 = 0$. $H_1: \mu_1 - \mu_2 \neq 0$.
Reject H_0 if $z < -1.96$ or $z > 1.96$.

$$z = \frac{4.77 - 5.02}{\sqrt{\frac{(1.05)^2}{40} + \frac{(1.23)^2}{50}}} = -1.04$$

There is not enough evidence to reject H_0. There is no difference in the mean number of calls. The p-value is .2984, found by 2(.5000 − .3508), which is > than the significance level, and so, there is not enough evidence to reject H_0.

29. $H_0: p_1 - p_2 \leq 0$. $H_1: p_1 - p_2 > 0$.
Reject H_0 if $z > 1.645$.

$$p_c = \frac{180 + 261}{200 + 300} = .882$$

$$z = \frac{0.90 - 0.87}{\sqrt{\frac{0.882(0.118)}{200} + \frac{0.882(0.118)}{300}}} = 1.019$$

There is not enough evidence to reject H_0. There is no difference in the proportions that found relief in the new and the old drugs. The p-value is .5 − .3461 = 0.1539, which is > than the significance level, and confirms that there is not enough evidence to reject H_0.

31. $H_0: p_1 - p_2 \leq 0$. $H_1: p_1 - p_2 > 0$.
If $z > 2.33$, reject H_0.

$$p_c = \frac{990 + 970}{1500 + 1600} = .63$$

$$z = \frac{.6600 - .60625}{\sqrt{\frac{.63(.37)}{1500} + \frac{.63(.37)}{1600}}} = 3.10$$

Reject the null hypothesis. We can conclude the proportion of men who believe the division is fair is greater. The p-value is virtually zero.

33. $H_0: \mu_n - \mu_s = 0$. $H_1: \mu_n - \mu_s \neq 0$.
Reject H_0 if $t < -2.086$ or $t > 2.086$.

$$s_p^2 = \frac{(10-1)(10.5)^2 + (12-1)(14.25)^2}{10 + 12 - 2} = 161.2969$$

$$t = \frac{83.55 - 78.8}{\sqrt{161.2969\left(\frac{1}{10} + \frac{1}{12}\right)}} = .874$$

There is not enough evidence to reject H_0. There is no difference in the mean number of hamburgers sold at the two locations. The p-value is > than .20, which is > than the significance level, and so the decision is supported. (Computer p-value = 0.3928.)

35. $H_0: \mu_1 - \mu_2 \leq 0$. $H_1: \mu_1 - \mu_2 > 0$.
Reject H_0 if $t > 1.665$.

$$s_p^2 = \frac{(35-1)(4.2)^2 + (45-1)(3.9)^2}{35 + 45 - 2} = 16.27.$$

$$t = \frac{18 - 15.5}{\sqrt{16.27\left(\frac{1}{35} + \frac{1}{40}\right)}} = 2.72.$$

Reject H_0. Software issues take longer on average. The p-value is .0037, which is smaller than the significance level, and confirms that the null hypothesis should be rejected.

37. $H_0: \mu_1 - \mu_2 = 0$. $H_1: \mu_1 - \mu_2 \neq 0$.
Reject H_0 if $t > 2.819$ or $t < -2.819$.

$$s_p^2 = \frac{(10-1)(2.33)^2 + (14-1)(2.55)^2}{10 + 14 - 2} = 6.06.$$

$$t = \frac{15.87 - 18.29}{\sqrt{6.06\left(\frac{1}{10} + \frac{1}{14}\right)}} = -2.374.$$

There is not enough evidence to reject H_0. There is no difference in the mean amount purchased. The p-value is between .05 and .02, which is > than the significance level, and so supports the decision not to reject H_0.

39. $H_0: \mu_1 - \mu_2 \leq 0$. $H_1: \mu_1 - \mu_2 > 0$.
Reject H_0 if $t > 2.567$.

$$s_p^2 = \frac{(8-1)(2.2638)^2 + (11-1)(2.4606)^2}{8 + 11 - 2} = 5.672.$$

$$t = \frac{10.375 - 5.636}{\sqrt{5.672\left(\frac{1}{8} + \frac{1}{11}\right)}} = 4.28.$$

Reject H_0. The mean number of transactions by the young adults is more than for the senior citizens.

41. $H_0: \mu_1 - \mu_2 \leq 0$. $H_1: \mu_1 - \mu_2 > 0$.
Reject H_0 if $t > 2.650$.

$\bar{X}_1 = 125.125$. $s_1 = 15.094$.
$\bar{X}_2 = 117.714$. $s_2 = 19.914$.

$$s_p^2 = \frac{(8-1)(15.094)^2 + (7-1)(19.914)^2}{8 + 7 - 2} = 305.708.$$

$$t = \frac{125.125 - 117.714}{\sqrt{305.708\left(\frac{1}{8} + \frac{1}{7}\right)}} = .819.$$

There is not enough evidence to reject H_0. There is no increase in the mean number sold at the regular price and the mean number sold at the reduced price.

43. $H_0: \mu_d \leq 0$. $H_1: \mu_d > 0$.
Reject H_0 if $t > 1.895$.

$\bar{d} = 1.75$. $s_d = 2.9155$.

$$t = \frac{1.75}{2.9155/\sqrt{8}} = 1.698.$$

There is not enough evidence to reject H_0. There is no difference in the mean number of absences. The p-value is greater than .05 but less than .10.

45. $H_0: \mu_1 - \mu_2 = 0$. $H_1: \mu_1 - \mu_2 \neq 0$.
If t is not between −2.024 and 2.024, reject H_0.

$$s_p^2 = \frac{(15-1)(40000)^2 + (25-1)(30000)^2}{15 + 25 - 2} = 1{,}157{,}894{,}737$$

$$t = \frac{150000 - 180000}{\sqrt{1{,}157{,}894{,}737\left(\frac{1}{15} + \frac{1}{25}\right)}} = -2.70$$

Reject the null hypothesis. The population means are different. The p-value is almost zero.

47. $H_0: \mu_d \leq 0$. $H_1: \mu_d > 0$.
Reject H_0 if $t > 1.895$.

$\bar{d} = 3.11$. $s_d = 2.91$.

$$t = \frac{3.11}{2.91/\sqrt{8}} = 3.02.$$

Reject H_0. The mean contamination rate is lower. The p-value is 0.0096.

49. See the CD-ROM.

51. See the CD-ROM.

Chapter 11

1. 9.01, from Appendix G.

3. Reject H_0 if F is greater than 10.5, where there are 7 degrees of freedom in the numerator and 5 in the denominator. Computed $F = 2.04$, found by:

$$F = \frac{s_1^2}{s_2^2} = \frac{(10)^2}{(7)^2} = 2.04.$$

There is not enough evidence to reject H_0. There is no difference in the variations of the two populations.

5. $H_0: \sigma_1^2 - \sigma_2^2 = 0. \quad H_1: \sigma_1^2 - \sigma_2^2 \neq 0.$
Reject H_0 when $F > 3.10$.
Computed $F = 1.44$, found by:

$$F = \frac{(12)^2}{(10)^2} = 1.44.$$

There is not enough evidence to reject H_0. There is no difference in the variations of the two populations.

7. **a.** $H_0: \mu_1 = \mu_2 = \mu_3$. H_1: Treatment means are not all the same.
b. Reject H_0 if $F > 4.26$.
c. 62.17, 12.75, 74.92.
d.

Source	SS	*df*	MS	F
Treatment	62.17	2	31.08	21.94
Error	12.75	9	1.42	
Total	74.92	11		

e. Reject H_0. The treatment means are not all the same.

9. $H_0: \mu_1 = \mu_2 = \mu_3$. H_1: Treatment means are not all the same.
Reject H_0 if $F > 4.26$.

Source	SS	*df*	MS	F
Treatment	276.50	2	138.25	14.18
Error	87.75	9	9.75	
Total	364.75	11		

Reject H_0. The treatment means are not all the same.

11. **a.** $H_0: \mu_1 = \mu_2 = \mu_3$. H_1: Not all means are the same.
b. Reject H_0 if $F > 4.26$.
c. SST = 107.20, SSE = 9.47, SS total = 116.67.
d.

Source	SS	*df*	MS	F
Treatment	107.20	2	53.600	50.96
Error	9.47	9	1.052	
Total	116.67	11		

e. Since 50.96 is greater than 4.26, H_0 is rejected. At least one of the means differs.
f. $(\bar{X}_1 - \bar{X}_2) \pm t\sqrt{\text{MSE}(1/n_1 + 1/n_2)}$.
$= (9.667 - 2.20) \pm 2.262\sqrt{1.052(1/3 + 1/5)}$
$= 7.467 \pm 1.69$
$= [5.777, 9.157]$.
Yes, we can conclude that treatments 1 and 2 have different means.

13. $H_0: \mu_1 = \mu_2 = \mu_3 = \mu_4$. H_1: Not all means are equal. H_0 is rejected if F is greater than 3.71. Because 2.36 is less than 3.71, there is not enough evidence to reject H_0. There is no difference in the mean number of weeks.

15. $H_0: \sigma_1^2 - \sigma_2^2 \leq 0; H_1: \sigma_1^2 - \sigma_2^2 > 0; df_2 = 18 - 1 = 17.$
H_0 is rejected if $F > 3.16$.

$$F = \frac{(45\,600)^2}{(21\,330)^2} = 4.57.$$

Reject H_0. There is more variation in the selling price of waterfront homes.

17. Sharkey: $n = 7$. $s_s = 14.79$.
White: $n = 8$. $s_w = 22.95$.
$H_0: \sigma_w^2 - \sigma_s^2 \leq 0; H_1: \sigma_w^2 - \sigma_s^2 > 0; df_w = 8 - 1 = 7.$
Reject H_0 if $F > 8.26$.

$$F = \frac{(22.95)^2}{(14.79)^2} = 2.41.$$

There is not enough evidence to reject H_0. There is no difference in the variation of the weekly sales.

19. **a.** $H_0: \mu_1 = \mu_2 = \mu_3 = \mu_4$.
H_1: Treatment means are not all equal.
b. $\alpha = .05$. Reject H_0 if $F > 3.10$.
c.

Source	SS	*df*	MS	F
Treatment	50	4 − 1 = 3	50/3	$\frac{50/3}{10} = 1.67$
Error	200	24 − 4 = 20	10	
Total	250	24 − 1 = 23		

d. Do not reject H_0. There is not a difference in the treatment means.

21. $H_0: \mu_1 = \mu_2 = \mu_3$. H_1: Not all treatment means are equal.
H_0 is rejected if $F > 3.89$.

Source	SS	*df*	MS	F
Treatment	63.33	2	31.667	13.38
Error	28.40	12	2.367	
Total	91.73	14		

H_0 is rejected. There is a difference in the treatment means.

23. $H_0: \mu_1 = \mu_2 = \mu_3 = \mu_4$. H_1: Not all means are equal. H_0 is rejected if $F > 3.10$.

Source	SS	*df*	MS	F
Factor	87.79	3	29.26	9.12
Error	64.17	20	3.21	
Total	151.96	23		

Because computed F of 9.12 is greater than 3.10, the null hypothesis of no difference is rejected at the .05 level.

25. **a.** $H_0: \mu_1 = \mu_2$. $H_1: \mu_1 \neq \mu_2$. Critical value of $F = 4.75$.

Source	SS	*df*	MS	F
Treatment	219.43	1	219.43	23.10
Error	114.00	12	9.5	
Total	333.43	13		

b. $$t = \frac{19 - 27}{\sqrt{9.5\left(\frac{1}{6} + \frac{1}{8}\right)}} = -4.81.$$

Then $t^2 = F$. That is $(-4.81)^2 \simeq 23.10$ (actually 23.14; difference is due to rounding).
c. H_0 is rejected. There is a difference in the mean scores.

27. $H_0: \mu_A = \mu_B = \mu_C = \mu_D$. H_1: Treatment means are not equal.
Reject H_0 if $F > 3.49$. The computed value of F is 9.61.
Reject H_0 and conclude the treatment means differ.

29. **a.** $H_0: \mu_A = \mu_B = \mu_C$. H_1: Treatment means are not equal.
Reject H_0 if $F > 6.36$. The computed value of F is 11.33, so H_0 is rejected. There is a difference in the mean production of the three lines.

b. Line B vs. Line C

$$(43.333 - 41.500) \pm 2.947\sqrt{.544\left(\frac{1}{6}+\frac{1}{6}\right)}.$$

$= 1.833 \pm 1.255.$ This pair differs.

31. H_0: $\mu_1 = \mu_2 = \mu_3 = \mu_4 = \mu_5 = \mu_6$. H_1: The treatment means are not equal. Reject H_0 if $F > 2.37$.

Source	SS	*df*	MS	*F*
Treatment	0.03478	5	0.006956	3.86
Error	0.10439	58	0.001800	
Total	0.13917	63		

H_0 is rejected. There is a difference in the mean weight of the colours.

33. See the CD-ROM.

35. See the CD-ROM.

Chapter 12

1. a.

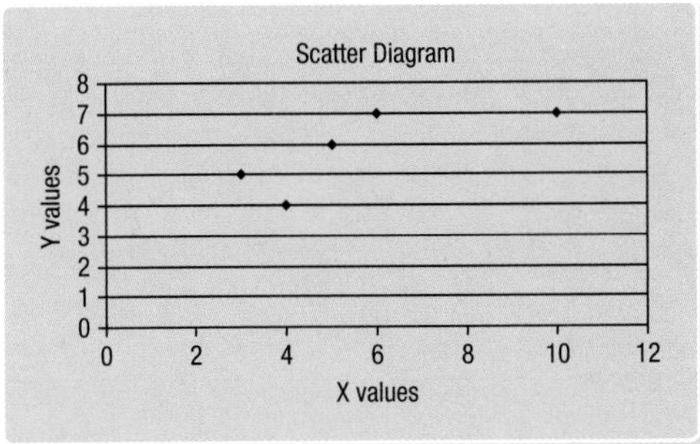

b. $Y' = 3.7671 + 0.3630X$.

$$b = \frac{5(173) - (28)(29)}{5(186) - (28)^2} = 0.3630. \qquad a = \frac{29}{5} - (0.363)\frac{28}{5} = 3.7671.$$

c. 6.3081, found by $Y' = 3.7671 + 0.3630(7)$.

3. a.

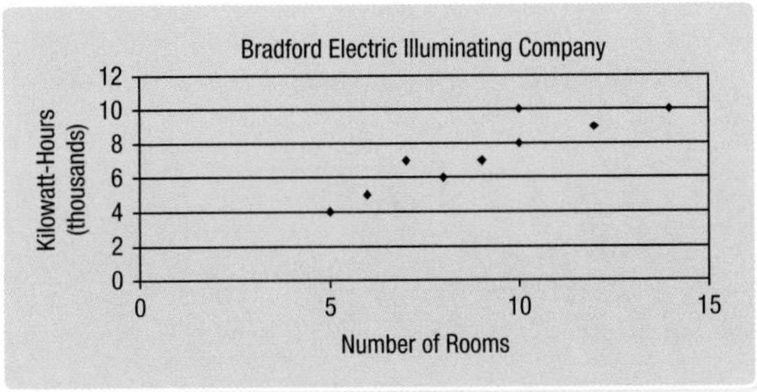

b. $$b = \frac{10(718) - (91)(74)}{10(895) - (91)^2} = \frac{446}{669} = 0.667. \qquad a = \frac{74}{10} - (0.667)\frac{91}{10} = 1.333.$$

c. $Y' = 1.333 + 0.667(6) = 5.335$.

5. a.

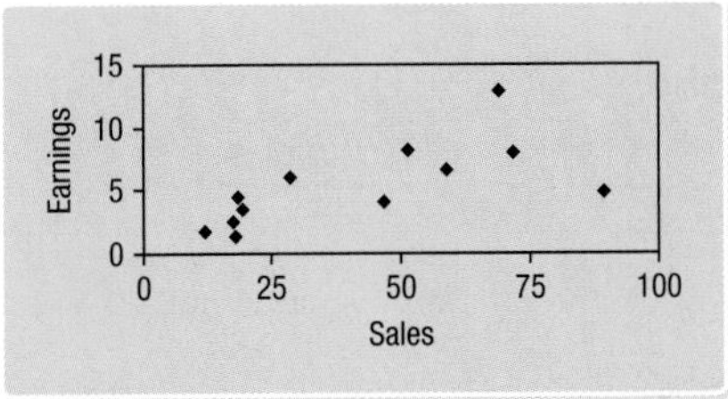

b. $$b = \frac{12(3306.35) - (501.1)(64.1)}{5(28{,}459) - (501.1)^2} = 0.0836. \qquad a = \frac{64.1}{12} - (0.0836)\frac{501.10}{12} = 1.8507.$$

c. $Y' = 1.8517 + 0.0836(50.0) = 6.0307$ ($ thousands).

Note: calculator or computer values may be slightly different due to rounding.

7. a. Police is the independent variable, and crime is the dependent variable.

b.

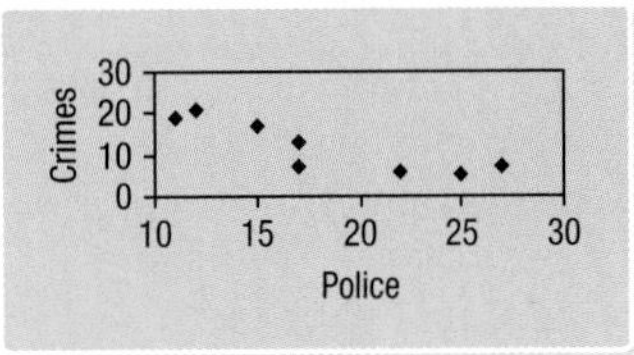

c. Inverse relationship. As the number of police increase, crime decreases.

9. a. 0.993, found by $\sqrt{\dfrac{175 - 3.767(29) - 0.363(173)}{5-2}}$.

b. $Y' \pm 0.993$.

11. a. 0.898, found by $\sqrt{\dfrac{584 - 1.333(74) - 0.667(718)}{10-2}}$.

b. $Y' \pm 1.796$.

13. 3.379, found by $\sqrt{\dfrac{1419 - 29.3877(95) - (-0.9596)(1502)}{8-2}}$.

15. a. $6.308 \pm (3.182)(0.993)\sqrt{0.2 + \dfrac{(7-5.6)^2}{186-(784/5)}} = 6.308 \pm 1.633$

$= [4.675, 7.941]$.

b. $6.308 \pm (3.182)(0.933)\sqrt{1 + 1/5 + 0.0671} = [2.751, 9.865]$.

17. a. 4.495, 6.171.

b. 3.440, 7.226.

19. $\Sigma X = 28$, $\Sigma Y = 29$, $\Sigma X^2 = 186$, $\Sigma XY = 173$, $\Sigma Y^2 = 175$.

$$r = \frac{5(173) - (28)(29)}{\sqrt{[5(186) - (28)^2][5(175) - (29)^2]}} = .75.$$

The .75 coefficient indicates a rather strong positive correlation between X and Y. The coefficient of determination is .5625, found by $(.75)^2$. More than 56 percent of the variation in Y is accounted for by X.

21. a. $n = 5$. $\Sigma X = 20$. $\Sigma Y = 85$. $\Sigma X^2 = 90$. $\Sigma XY = 376$. $\Sigma Y^2 = 1419$.

$$r = \frac{5(376) - (20)(85)}{\sqrt{[5(90) - (20)^2][5(1595) - (85)^2]}} = .9295.$$

b. $r^2 = (.9295)^2 = .864$.

c. The .9295 indicates a very strong positive relationship between X and Y. The coefficient of determination is 0.864. X accounts for about 86.4 percent of the variation in Y.

23. a. $n = 8$. $\Sigma X = 146$. $\Sigma Y = 95$. $\Sigma X^2 = 2906$. $\Sigma XY = 1502$. $\Sigma Y^2 = 1419$.

$$r = \frac{8(1502) - (146)(95)}{\sqrt{[8(2906) - (146)^2][8(1419) - (95)^2]}} = -.874.$$

b. .76, found by $(-.874)^2$.

c. $-.874$ indicates a strong inverse relationship. As the number of police increase, the crime decreases. The coefficient of determination is .76. X accounts for about 76 percent of the variation in Y.

25. Reject H_0 if $t > 1.812$.

$$t = \frac{.32\sqrt{12-2}}{\sqrt{1-(.32)^2}} = 1.07.$$

Do not reject H_0.

27. H_0: $\rho \geq 0$. H_1: $\rho < 0$. Reject H_0 if $t < -2.552$, $df = 18$.

$$t = \frac{-.78\sqrt{20-2}}{\sqrt{1-(-.78)^2}} = -5.288.$$

Reject H_0. There is a negative correlation between litres sold and the pump price.

29. H_0: $\rho \leq 0$. H_1: $\rho > 0$. Reject H_0 if $t > 2.650$, $df = 13$.

$$t = \frac{.667\sqrt{15-2}}{\sqrt{1-(.667)^2}} = 3.23.$$

Reject H_0. There is a positive correlation between passengers and cost.

31. $$r = \frac{(5)(340)-(50)(30)}{\sqrt{[(5)(600)-(50)^2][(5)(200)-(30)^2]}} = .8944.$$

Then, $(.8944)^2 = .80$, the coefficient of determination.

33. **a.** $r^2 = 1000/1500 = .667$.

b. .82, found by $\sqrt{.667}$.

c. 6.20, found by $s_e = \sqrt{\dfrac{500}{15-2}}$.

35. H_0: $\rho \leq 0$. H_1: $\rho > 0$. Reject H_0 if $t > 1.714$.

$$t = \frac{.94\sqrt{25-2}}{\sqrt{1-(.94)^2}} = 13.213.$$

Reject H_0. We have failed to show a positive correlation between passengers and weight of luggage.

37. H_0: $\rho \leq 0$. H_1: $\rho > 0$. Reject H_0 if $t > 2.764$.

$$t = \frac{.47\sqrt{12-2}}{\sqrt{1-(.47)^2}} = 1.684.$$

Do not reject H_0. There is not a positive correlation between engine size and performance. The p-value is greater than .05, but less than .10.

39. H_0: $\rho \geq 0$. H_1: $\rho < 0$. Reject H_0 if $t < -1.701$, $df = 28$.

$$t = \frac{-.45\sqrt{30-2}}{\sqrt{1-.2025}} = -2.67.$$

Reject H_0. There is a negative correlation between the selling price and the number of kilometres driven.

41. **a.**

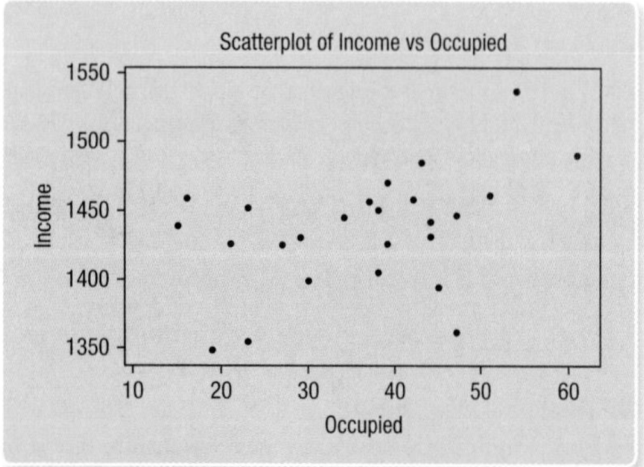

Revenue increases slightly as the number of occupied rooms increases.

b. Pearson correlation of Income and Occupied = .423.

c. H_0: $\rho \leq 0$. H_1: $\rho > 0$. Reject H_0 if $t > 1.319$, $df = 23$.

$$t = \frac{.423\sqrt{25-2}}{\sqrt{1-(.423)^2}} = 2.24.$$

Reject H_0. There is a positive correlation between revenue and occupied rooms.

d. 17.9 percent, found by $(.423)^2$. The variation in revenue is explained by variation in occupied rooms.

43. **a.** No, the coefficient is $-.5170$, which indicates a negative relationship between the variables.

b. $3119.4256/3960 = 78.77$ percent.

c. $r = \sqrt{0.77877} = -.8824$; strong, negative.

d. $Y' = -.5170(10) + 51.0218 = 45.85$; 46 units; yes, this is reasonable.

45. **a.** $r = .589$.

b. $r^2 = (.589)^2 = .3469$.

c. H_0: $\rho \leq 0$. H_1: $\rho > 0$. Reject H_0 if $t > 1.860$.

$$t = \frac{.589\sqrt{10-2}}{\sqrt{1-(.589)^2}} = 2.062.$$

H_0 is rejected. There is a positive association between family size and the amount spent on food.

47. **a.**

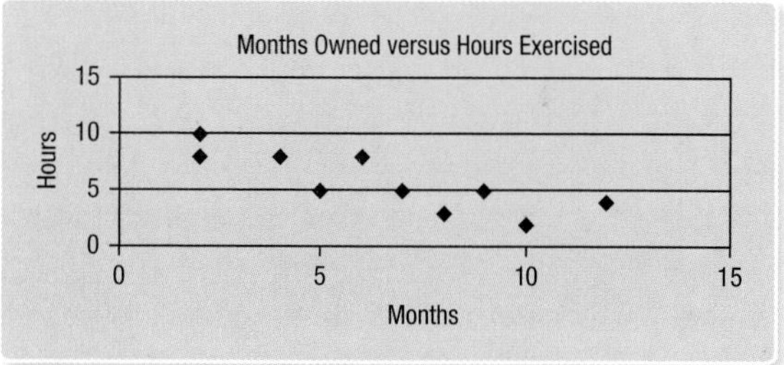

There is an inverse relationship between the variables. As the months owned increase, the number of hours exercised decreases.

b. $$r = \frac{10(313)-(65)(58)}{\sqrt{[10(523)-(65)^2][10(396)-(58)^2]}} = -.827.$$

c. H_0: $\rho \geq 0$. H_1: $\rho < 0$. Reject H_0 if $t < -2.896$.

$$t = \frac{-.827\sqrt{10-2}}{\sqrt{1-(.827)^2}} = -4.16.$$

Reject H_0. There is a negative association between months owned and hours exercised.

49. **a.**

Source	SS	*df*	MS	*F*
Regression	50	1	50	2.5556
Error	450	23	19.5652	
Total	500	24		

b. $n = 25$.

c. $s_e = \sqrt{19.5652} = 4.4233$.

d. $r^2 = \dfrac{50}{100} = .10$.

51. **a.** $n = 15$. $\Sigma X = 107$. $\Sigma X^2 = 837$. $\Sigma Y = 118.6$. $\Sigma Y^2 = 969.92$. $\Sigma XY = 811.60$. $s_{y \cdot x} = 1.114$.

$$b = \frac{15(811.60)-(107)(118.6)}{15(837.0)-(107)^2} = -0.4667.$$

$$a = \frac{118.6}{15} - (-0.4667)\left(\frac{107}{15}\right) = 11.2358.$$

More bidders decrease winning bid.

b. $Y' = 11.2358 - 0.4667(7.0) = 7.9689$.

c. $7.9689 \pm (2.160)(1.114)\sqrt{1+\frac{1}{15}+\frac{(7-7.1333)^2}{837-\frac{(107)^2}{15}}}$

$= 7.9689 \pm 2.4854$

$= [5.4835, 10.4543]$.

d. $r^2 = .499$. Nearly 50 percent of the variation in the amount of the bid is explained by the number of bidders.

53. a. $b = \frac{30(18{,}924) - (320.33)(1575.6)}{30(4292.5) - (320.33)^2} = 2.41.$

$a = \frac{1575.6}{30} - 2.41\left(\frac{320.33}{30}\right) = 26.8.$

The regression equation is: Price = 26.8 + 2.41 dividend. For each additional dollar of dividend, the price increases by \$2.41.

b. $r^2 = \frac{5057.6}{7682.7} = .658.$ Thus, 65.8 percent of the variation in price is explained by the dividend.

c. $r = \sqrt{.658} = .811.$ H_0: $\rho \le 0$. H_1: $\rho > 0$.

At the 5% level, reject H_0 when $t > 1.701$.

$$t = \frac{.811\sqrt{30-2}}{\sqrt{1-(.811)^2}} = 7.34.$$

Thus, H_0 is rejected. The population correlation is positive.

55. a. 35.

b. 5456.96, found by the square root of MSE (mean square error) ($\sqrt{29{,}778{,}406}$).

c. $r^2 = \frac{13\,548\,662\,082}{14\,531\,349\,474} = .932.$

d. $r = \sqrt{.932} = .966.$

e. H_0: $\rho \le 0$. H_1: $\rho > 0$. Reject H_0 if $t > 1.692$.

$$t = \frac{.966\sqrt{35-2}}{\sqrt{1-(.966)^2}} = 21.46.$$

Reject H_0. There is a positive association between market value and size of the home.

57. a.

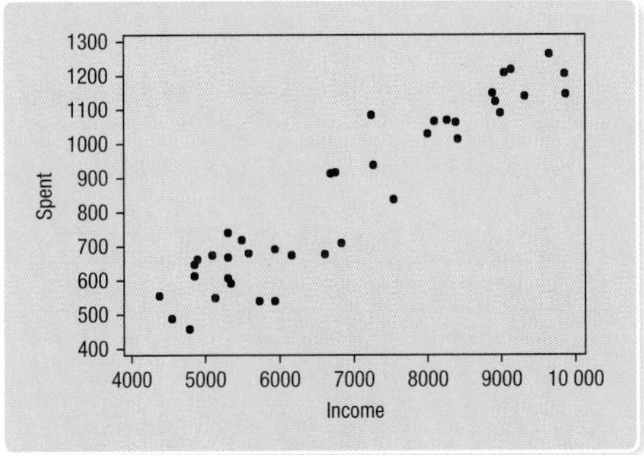

b. $b = \frac{40(245\,795\,835) - (273\,387)(33\,625)}{40(1\,987\,875\,615) - (273\,387)^2} = 0.13388.$

$a = \frac{33\,625}{40} - 0.13388\left(\frac{273\,387}{40}\right) = -74.4.$

The regression equation is Spent = −74.4 + 0.134Income. For each additional dollar of income, \$0.134 more is spent on groceries.

c. $r = \frac{40(245\,795\,835) - (273\,387)(33\,625)}{\sqrt{[40(1\,987\,875\,615) - (273\,387)^2][40(30\,662\,885) - (33\,625)^2]}}$

$= .945.$

H_0: $\rho \le 0$. H_1: $\rho > 0$. At the .05 level, reject H_0 when $t > 1.686$.

$$t = \frac{.945\sqrt{40-2}}{\sqrt{1-(.945)^2}} = 17.8.$$

Thus, H_0 is rejected. The population correlation is positive.

d. We know that there is a strong, positive association between income and groceries; however, other factors such as location and growth in the area need to be considered.

59. See the CD-ROM.

Chapter 13

1. a. Multiple regression equation.

b. The Y-intercept.

c. $Y' = 64\,100 + 0.394(796\,000) + 9.6(6940) - 11\,600(6.0) = \$374\,748$.

3. a. 497.736, found by

$Y' = 16.24 + 0.017(18) + 0.0028(26\,500) + 42(3) + 0.0012(156\,000) + 0.19(141) + 26.8(2.5)$.

b. Two more social activities. Income added only 28 to the index; social activities added 53.6.

5. a. 19.

b. 3.

c. .318, found by 21/66. 31.8 percent of the variation in the Y-variable is explained.

d. 1.732, found by $\sqrt{\frac{45}{[19-(3+1)]}}$.

7. a. $Y' = 20 - X_1 + 12X_2 - 15X_3$.

b. $Y' = 20 - (4) + 12(6) - 15(8) = -32$.

c. $n = 22$; 3 independent variables.

d.

Source	SS	df	MS	F
Regression	7500.0	3	2500	18
Error	2500.0	18	138.89	
Total	10 000.0	21		

e. H_0: $\beta_1 = \beta_2 = \beta_3 = 0$. H_1: Not all βs are 0. Reject H_0 if $F = 18.0$.

Reject H_0. Not all net regression coefficients equal zero.

f.

For X_1:	For X_2:	For X_3:
H_0: $\beta_1 = 0$.	H_0: $\beta_2 = 0$.	H_0: $\beta_3 = 0$.
H_1: $\beta_1 \ne 0$.	H_1: $\beta_2 \ne 0$.	H_1: $\beta_3 \ne 0$.
$t = -4.00$.	$t = 1.50$.	$t = -3.00$.

Reject H_0 if $t > 2.101$ or $t < -2.101$.

Delete variable 2, keep 1 and 3.

9. a. X_4 at −.819 had the strongest correlation with the dependent variable.

b. X_2, X_3, and X_4 have the strongest correlation with the dependent variable.

c. Yes, between X_3 and X_4.

11. a. Horsepower is the most highly correlated with speed at .83.

b. It is reasonable, as the weight of a car would probably slow it down.

c. No, none of the independent variables is highly correlated with each other.

13. a. $n = 40$.

b. 4.

c. $R^2 = \frac{750}{1250} = .60.$

d. $S_{y \cdot 1234} = \sqrt{500/35} = 3.7796.$

e. H_0: $\beta_1 = \beta_2 = \beta_3 = \beta_4 = 0$.
H_1: Not all the βs equal zero.
H_0 is rejected if $F > 2.65$.

$$F = \frac{750/4}{500/35} = 13.125.$$

H_0 is rejected. At least one β_i does not equal zero.

15. a. $n = 26$.

b. $R^2 = 100/140 = .7143$.

c. 1.4142, found by $\sqrt{2}$.

d. H_0: $\beta_1 = \beta_2 = \beta_3 = \beta_4 = \beta_5 = 0$.
H_1: Not all the βs are 0.
H_0 is rejected if $F > 2.71$.
Computed $F = 10.0$. Reject H_0. At least one regression coefficient is not zero.

e. H_0 is rejected in each case if $t < -2.086$ or $t > 2.086$. X_1 and X_5 should be dropped. ($X_1 = 1.33$, do not reject; $X_2 = 15$, reject; $X_3 = 4$, reject; $X_4 = -2.5$, reject; $X_5 = .75$, do not reject).

17. a. \$28 000.

b. $R^2 = \frac{\text{SSR}}{\text{SS total}} = \frac{3050}{5250} = .5809$.

c. 9.199, found by $\sqrt{84.62}$.

d. H_0 is rejected if $F > 2.975$.

$$\text{Computed } F = \frac{1016.67}{84.62} = 12.01.$$

H_0 is rejected. At least one regression coefficient is not zero.

e. If computed t is to the left of -2.056 or to the right of 2.056, the null hypothesis in each of these cases is rejected. Computed t for X_2 and X_3 exceed the critical value. Thus, "population" and "advertising expenses" should be retained and "number of competitors," X_1, dropped.

19. a. The correlation matrix is:

	cars	*adv*	*sales*
adv	.808		
sales	.872	.537	
city	.639	.713	.389

Size of sales force (.872) has the strongest correlation with cars sold. Fairly strong relationship between location of dealership and advertising (.713). Could be a problem.

b. The regression equation is:
$Y' = 31.1328 + 2.1516adv + 5.0140sales + 5.6651city$.
$Y' = 31.1328 + 2.1516(15) + 5.0140(20) + 5.6651(1) = 169.352$.

c. H_0: $\beta_1 = \beta_2 = \beta_3 = 0$. H_1: Not all βs are 0. Reject H_0 if computed $F > 4.07$.

Analysis of Variance

Source	SS	*df*	MS
Regression	5504.4	3	1834.8
Error	420.2	8	52.5
Total	5924.7	11	

$F = 1834.8/52.5 = 34.95$.
Reject H_0. At least one regression coefficient is not 0.

d. H_0 is rejected in all cases if $t < -2.306$ or if $t > 2.306$. Advertising and sales force should be retained, city dropped. (Note that dropping city removes the problem with multicollinearity.)

Predictor	Coef	StDev	*t*-ratio	*P*
Constant	31.13	13.40	2.32	0.049
adv	2.1516	0.8049	2.67	0.028
sales	5.0140	0.9105	5.51	0.000
city	5.665	6.332	0.89	0.397

e. The new output is $Y' = 2.30 + 2.6187adv + 5.0233sales$

Predictor	Coef	StDev	*t*-ratio
Constant	25.30	11.57	2.19
adv	2.6187	0.6057	4.32
sales	5.0233	0.9003	5.58

Analysis of Variance

Source	SS	*df*	MS
Regression	5462.4	2	2731.2
Error	462.3	9	51.4
Total	5924.7	11	

f.

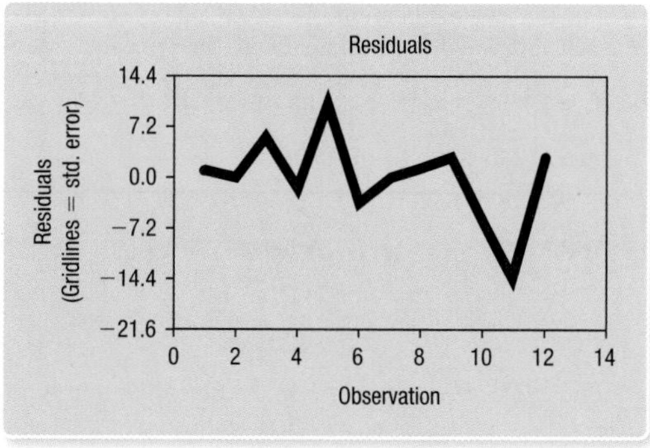

The normality assumption is reasonable.

g.

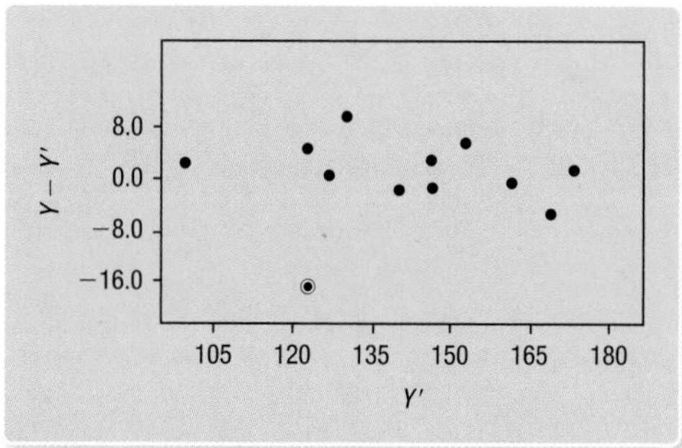

For this small sample, the residual plot is acceptable.

21. a. The regression equation is:
$Y' = 965.3 + 2.865X_1 + 6.75X_2 + 0.2873X_3$.
$Y' = \$2\,458\,780$.

b.

Analysis of Variance

Source	SS	*df*	MS
Regression	45 510 092	3	15 170 032
Error	12 215 892	12	1 017 991
Total	57 725 984	15	

$$F = \frac{15\,170\,032}{1\,017\,991} = 14.902.$$

H_0 is rejected because computed F of 14.902 is greater than the critical value of 3.49. At least one of the regression coefficients is not zero.

c. H_0: $\beta_1 = 0$. H_0: $\beta_2 = 0$. H_0: $\beta_3 = 0$.
H_1: $\beta_1 \neq 0$. H_1: $\beta_2 \neq 0$. H_1: $\beta_3 \neq 0$.
The H_0s are rejected if $t < -2.179$ or $t > 2.179$. $X_1 = 1.810$, do not reject; $X_2 = .657$, do not reject; $X_3 = 2.586$, reject. Both workers and dividends are not significant variables. Inventory is significant. Delete dividends and rerun the regression equation.

d. The regression equation (if we used X_1 and X_3).
$Y' = 1134.8 + 3.258X_1 + 0.3099X_3$.

Predictor	Coef	StDev	*t*-ratio
Constant	1134.8	418.6	2.71
Workers	3.258	1.434	2.27
Inv	0.3099	0.1033	3.00

Analysis of Variance

Source	SS	*df*	MS	*F*
Regression	45 070 624	2	22 535 312	23.15
Error	12 655 356	13	973 489	
Total	57 725 968	15		

e.

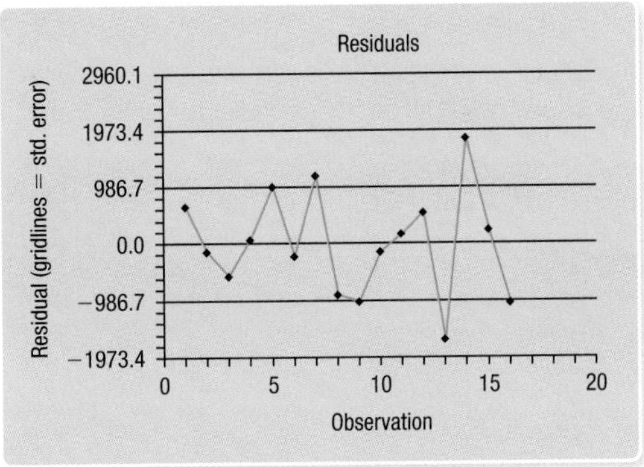

The normality assumption is reasonable.

f.

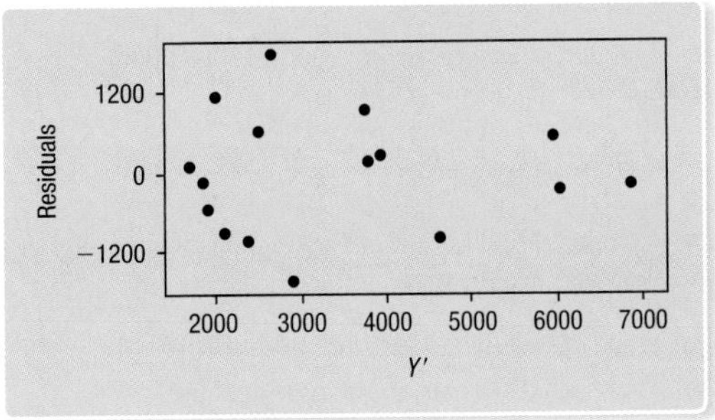

23. The computer output is:

Predictor	Coef	Stdev	t-ratio	p
Constant	651.9	345.3	1.89	0.071
Service	13.422	5.125	2.62	0.015
Age	26.710	6.349	21.06	0.301
Gender	205.65	90.27	2.28	0.032
Job	233.45	89.55	20.37	0.712

Analysis of Variance

SOURCE	DF	SS	MS	F	p
Regression	4	1066830	266708	4.77	0.005
Error	25	1398651	55946		
Total	29	2465481			

a. $Y' = 651.9 + 13.422X_1 - 6.710X_2 + 205.65X_3 - 33.45X_4$.

b. $R^2 = .433$, which is somewhat low for this type of study.

c. H_0: $\beta_1 = \beta_2 = \beta_3 = \beta_4 = 0$. H_1: not all βs equal zero.
Reject H_0 if $F > 2.76$.

$$F = \frac{1066\,830/4}{1398\,651/25} = 4.77.$$

H_0 is rejected. Not all the β_is equal 0.

d. Using the .05 significance level, reject the hypothesis that the regression coefficient is 0 if $t < -2.060$ or $t > 2.060$. Service and gender should remain in the analyses, age and job should be dropped.

e. Following is the computer output using the independent variables service and gender.

Predictor	Coef	Stdev	t-ratio	p
Constant	784.2	316.8	2.48	0.020
Service	9.021	3.106	2.90	0.007
Gender	224.41	87.35	2.57	0.016

Analysis of Variance

SOURCE	SS	DF	MS	F	p
Regression	998779	2	499389	9.19	0.001
Error	1466703	27	54322		
Total	2465481	29			

A man earns \$224 more per month than a woman. The difference between technical and clerical jobs is not significant.

25. a. The strongest relationship is between sales and income (.964). A problem could occur if both "outlets" and "income" (.825) and "cars" and "outlets" (.775) are part of the final solution (.775). This is called multicollinearity.

b. $Y = -19.6715 - .0006(\text{outlets}) + 1.7399(\text{cars}) + .4099(\text{income}) + 2.0357(\text{age}) - .0344(\text{supervisor})$;

$$R^2 = \frac{1593.81}{1602.89} = .9943.$$

c. H_0 is rejected. At least one regression coefficient is not zero. The computed value of F is 140.36. Critical value = 6.26; therefore, reject the null hypothesis. (Note that the p-value = 0.0001, which is less than the significance level, and supports the decision to reject the null hypothesis.)

d. Delete "outlets" and "supervisors". Critical values are −2.776 and 2.776. Note that "age" is also insignificant.

e. $R^2 = \dfrac{1593.66}{1602.89} = .9942$. There was little change in the coefficient of determination. Note that age is now a significant variable.

f. The normality assumption seems reasonable since the graph is fairly linear.

g. There appears to be no violation of homoscedasticity.

27. a.

	Salary	*GPA*	*Business*
Salary	1.000		
GPA	.902	1.000	
Business	.911	.851	1.000

Yes; multicollinearity occurs between GPA and Business (.851).

b. $Y' = 23.4474 + 2.7748\text{GPA} + 1.3071$ Business.
As GPA increases by one point, salary increases by \$2775. The average business school graduate makes \$1307 more than a corresponding non-business graduate. Estimated salary is \$33 079; found by \$23 447 + 2775(3.00) + 1307(1).

c. $R^2 = \dfrac{21.182}{23.857} = .888$ so, 88.8 percent of the variation in the Y-variable is explained or accounted for.

d. Since the p-values are less than .05, there is no need to delete variables.

Predictor	*Coef*	*SE Coef*	*T*	*P*
Constant	23.447	3.490	6.72	0.000
GPA	2.775	1.107	2.51	0.028
Business	1.3071	0.4660	2.80	0.016

e. The residuals appear normally distributed.

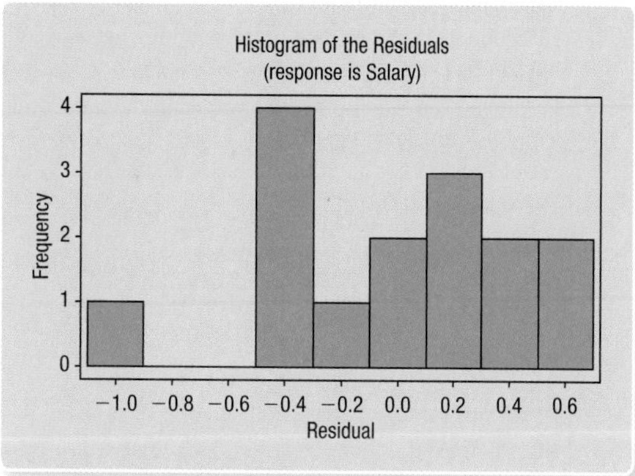

f. The variance is the same as we moved from small values to large. So, there is no homoscedasticity problem.

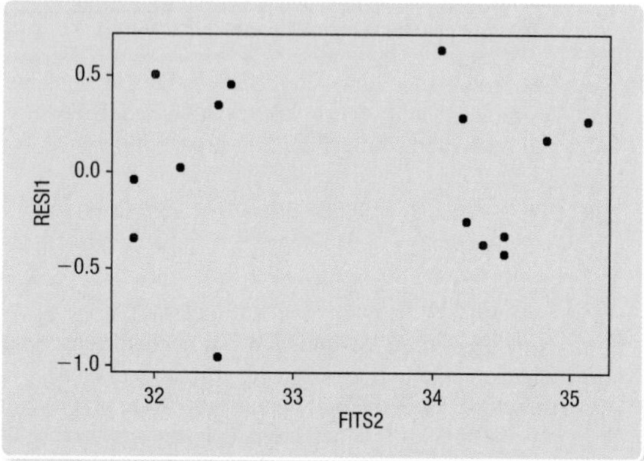

29. a. The regression equation is Sales = 1.02 + 0.0829Infomercials

Predictor	Coef	SE Coef	T	P
Constant	1.0188	0.3105	3.28	0.006
Infomercials	0.08291	0.01680	4.94	0.000

S = 0.308675 R-sq = 65.2% R-sq(adj) = 62.5%

Analysis of Variance

Source	SS	DF	MS	F	P
Regression	2.3214	1	2.3214	24.36	0.000
Residual Error	1.2386	13	0.0953		
Total	3.5600	14			

The global test on F demonstrates there is a substantial connection between sales and the number of commercials.

b.

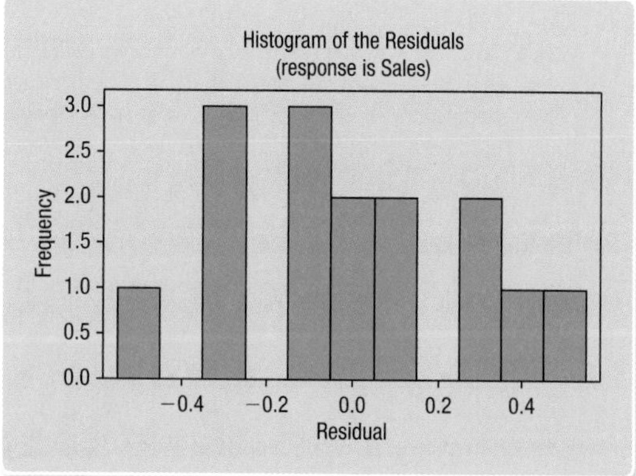

c.

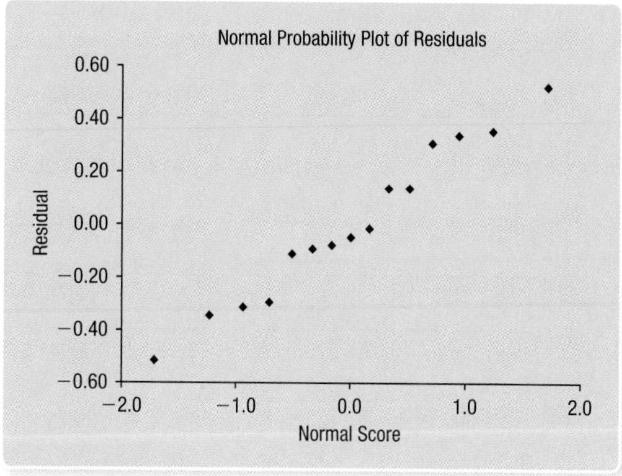

d. The residuals appear to be fairly normally distributed.

31. See the CD-ROM.

33. See the CD-ROM.

Chapter 14

1. a. 3.

b. 7.815.

3. a. Reject H_0 if $\chi^2 > 5.991$.

b. $\chi^2 = \dfrac{(10-20)^2}{20} + \dfrac{(20-20)^2}{20} + \dfrac{(30-20)^2}{20} = 10.0.$

c. Reject H_0. The proportions are not equal.

5. H_0: The outcomes are the same; H_1: The outcomes are not the same. Reject H_0 if $\chi^2 > 9.236$.

$$\chi^2 = \frac{(3-5)^2}{5} + \cdots + \frac{(7-5)^2}{5} = 7.60.$$

Do not reject H_0. There is not enough evidence to reject H_0 that the outcomes are the same.

7. H_0: There is no difference in the proportions.

H_1: There is a difference in the proportions.

Reject H_0 if $\chi^2 > 15.086$.

$$\chi^2 = \frac{(47-40)^2}{40} + \cdots + \frac{(34-40)^2}{40} = 3.400.$$

Do not reject H_0. There is no difference in the proportions.

9. a. Reject H_0 if $\chi^2 > 9.210$.

b. $\chi^2 = \dfrac{(30-24)^2}{24} + \dfrac{(20-24)^2}{12} + \dfrac{(10-12)^2}{12} = 2.50.$

c. Do not reject H_0.

11. H_0: Proportions are as stated; H_1: Proportions are not as stated. Reject H_0 if $\chi^2 > 11.345$.

$$\chi^2 = \frac{(50-25)^2}{25} + \cdots + \frac{(160-275)^2}{275} = 115.22.$$

Reject H_0. The proportions are not as stated.

13. H_0: There is no relationship between community size and section read. H_1: There is a relationship. Reject H_0 if $\chi^2 > 9.488$.

$$\chi^2 = \frac{(170-157.50)^2}{157.50} + \cdots + \frac{(88-83.62)^2}{83.62} = 7.340.$$

Do not reject H_0. There is no relationship between community size and section read.

15. H_0: No relationship between error rates and item type. H_1: There is a relationship between error rates and item type. Reject H_0 if $\chi^2 > 9.21$.

$$\chi^2 = \frac{(20 - 14.1)^2}{14.1} + \cdots + \frac{(225 - 225.25)^2}{255.25} = 8.033.$$

Do not reject H_0. There is not a relationship between error rates and item type.

17. H_0: $p_s = 0.50, p_r = p_e = 0.25$.
H_1: Distribution is not as given above.
$df = 2$. Reject H_0 if $\chi^2 > 4.605$.

Turn	f_o	f_e	$f_o - f_e$	$(f_o - f_e)^2/f_e$
Straight	112	100	12	1.44
Right	48	50	−2	0.08
Left	40	50	−10	2.00
Total	200	200		3.52

H_0 is not rejected. The proportions are as given in the null hypothesis.

19. H_0: There is no preference with respect to TV stations.
H_1: There is a preference with respect to TV stations.
$df = 3 - 1 = 2$. H_0 is rejected if $\chi^2 > 5.991$.

TV Station	f_o	f_e	$f_o - f_e$	$(f_o - f_e)^2$	$(f_o - f_e)^2/f_e$
WNAE	53	50	3	9	0.18
WRRN	64	50	14	196	3.92
WSPD	33	50	−17	289	5.78
Total	150	150	0		9.88

H_0 is rejected. There is a preference for TV stations.

21. H_0: $p_n = 0.21$, $p_m = 0.24$, $p_s = 0.35$, $p_w = 0.20$.
H_1: The distribution is not as given.
Reject H_0 if $\chi^2 > 11.345$.

Area	f_o	f_e	$f_o - f_e$	$(f_o - f_e)^2/f_e$
New York State	68	84	−16	3.0476
Midwest	104	96	8	0.6667
South	155	140	15	1.6071
West	73	80	−7	0.6125
Total	400	400	0	5.9339

There is not enough evidence to reject H_0. The geographical distribution of her club members has not changed.

23. H_0: $p_0 = 0.40, p_1 = 0.30, p_2 = 0.20, p_3 = 0.10$.
H_1: The proportions are not as given. Reject H_0 if $\chi^2 > 7.815$.

Accidents	f_o	f_e	$(f_o - f_e)^2/f_e$
0	46	48	0.083
1	40	36	0.444
2	22	24	0.167
3	12	12	0.000
Total	120		0.694

Do not reject H_0. Evidence does not show a change in the accident distribution.

25. H_0: Levels of management and concern regarding the environment are not related. H_1: Levels of management and concern regarding the environment are related.
Reject H_0 if $\chi^2 > 16.812$.

$$\chi^2 = \frac{(15 - 14)^2}{14} + \cdots + \frac{(31 - 28)^2}{28} = 1.550.$$

Do not reject H_0. Levels of management and environmental concern are not related.

27. H_0: Whether a claim is filed and age are not related.
H_1: Whether a claim is filed and age are related.
Reject H_0 if $\chi^2 > 7.815$.

$$\chi^2 = \frac{(170 - 203.33)^2}{203.33} + \cdots + \frac{(24 - 35.67)^2}{35.67} = 53.639.$$

Reject H_0. Age is related to whether a claim is filed.

29. H_0: $p_0 = 0.55, p_1 = 0.28, p_2 = 0.17$.
H_1: The proportions are not as given.
Reject H_0 if $\chi^2 > 5.991$.

Applications	f_o	f_e	$(f_o - f_e)^2/f_e$
0	220	247.5	3.056
1	158	126	8.127
2	72	76.5	0.265
Total	450		11.448

Reject H_0. Young adults differ from the general population.

31. See the CD-ROM.

33. See the CD-ROM.

Photo Credits

Chapter 1: © SuperStock

Chapter 2: Ryan McVay/Getty Images

Chapter 3: © Digital Vision/Punchstock

Chapter 4: PhotoLink/Getty Images

Chapter 5: Royalty Free/Corbis

Chapter 6: Walter Hodges/Photodisc/Getty Images

Chapter 7: Cocoon

Chapter 8: Royalty Free/Corbis

Chapter 9: Royalty Free/Corbis

Chapter 10: Digital Vision/Punchstock

Chapter 11: Image reprinted with permission from ViewSonic Corporation

Chapter 12: Steve Mason/Getty Images

Chapter 13: Keith Brofsky/Getty Images

Chapter 14: Photo Courtesy of Victoria's Secret

Chapter 15: PhotoLink/Getty Images

Chapter 16: © Goodshoot/PunchStock

Chapter 17: © PhotoDisc/Getty Images

Index

G

H

Q

R

S